Rev (Halperin) JSL Dec 64

G B B Hunter

RETRACING ELEMENTARY MATHEMATICS

A series of mathematics texts under the editorship of Carl B. Allendoerfer

MODERN MATHEMATICS: AN INTRODUCTION by Samuel I. Altwerger

BASIC MATHEMATICS REVIEW: TEXT AND WORKBOOK by James A. Cooley

GEOMETRY, ALGEBRA, AND TRIGONOMETRY BY VECTOR METHODS by Arthur H. Copeland, Sr.

FUNDAMENTALS OF COLLEGE ALGEBRA by William H. Durfee

THEORY AND SOLUTION OF ORDINARY DIFFERENTIAL EQUATIONS by Donald Greenspan

RETRACING ELEMENTARY MATHEMATICS by Leon Henkin, W. Norman Smith, Verne J. Varineau, and Michael J. Walsh

INTRODUCTION TO MATHEMATICAL STATISTICS by Robert V. Hogg and Allen T. Craig

APPLIED BOOLEAN ALGEBRA: AN ELEMENTARY INTRODUCTION by Franz E. Hohn

METHODS IN ANALYSIS by Jack Indritz

ARITHMETIC: AN INTRODUCTION TO MATHEMATICS by L. Clark Lay

STATISTICAL THEORY by B. W. Lindgren

ELEMENTS OF ABSTRACT ALGEBRA by John T. Moore

Retracing Elementary Mathematics

▶ LEON HENKIN
University of California, Berkeley

▶ W. NORMAN SMITH
University of Wyoming

▶ VERNE J. VARINEAU
University of Wyoming

▶ MICHAEL J. WALSH
General Dynamics/Electronics, San Diego

THE MACMILLAN COMPANY–NEW YORK
Macmillan New York, London
A Division of The Crowell-Collier Publishing Company

First Printing

Library of Congress catalog card number: 62-7986

The Macmillan Company, New York
Brett-Macmillan Ltd., Galt, Ontario

Printed in the United States of America

DESIGNED BY HERMANN STROHBACH

TO OUR

FIFTEEN CHILDREN

Preface

In recent years, under the impact of various social, scientific, and technological forces, there has been a widening and intensified awareness of the important role played by mathematics in contemporary culture. Mathematics functions not only as a computational tool, where its power has been increased many fold by utilization of electronic devices, but even more importantly as a means of furnishing abstract conceptual and deductive systems which serve to coalesce and resolve a host of diverse problems, both practical and theoretical.

Although an appreciation of the broadened role of mathematics is widespread, a first hand acquaintance with the revolutionary changes in mathematical content and approach, which have been fashioned by modern research, have been hitherto reserved for the trained mathematician who devoted many years to technical study; to most laymen these details have remained a complete mystery.

The realization of the immensity of the gap between traditional and contemporary mathematical outlook has naturally led to an increased concern with the kind of mathematics which is, or should be, taught in the schools—from the elementary grades through the colleges—and with the nature of the preparation of those teachers who are entrusted with this vital educational task. In the United States this concern has manifested itself in several ways, among which has been the organization by the National Science Foundation of a series of Summer Institutes for Teachers of Mathematics, conducted at universities throughout the country. Institutes are designed to expose teachers of mathematics from the high schools and colleges to some of the new ideas that have been developed by creative mathematicians.

This book is the outcome of our experiences in teaching and directing three such institutes held at the University of Wyoming. The material of the book is an elaboration of the content of a course of lectures, entitled "Foundations of Mathematics," which was developed by Professor Henkin especially for these institutes.

The warm reception accorded this course by the participants in these institutes emboldened us to seek a wider audience for its ideas by fashioning them into a book. Originally, we intended only to appeal to mathematics teachers, both those in service and in training; but as the book began to develop it became clear that most of its content would be of interest to a much broader audience. Indeed, our detailed and explicit treatment of the material makes the work accessible to almost all undergraduate students of mathematics, and even to the attentive layman with an interest in this subject. And the variety of topics covered permits use of the book, either as text or supplementary reading, with a variety of courses.

As regards *treatment*, we have been at pains to presuppose neither extensive mathematical knowledge nor that elusive "mathematical maturity" which serves to remove so many books from the realm of common understanding. However, we have found no way to obviate the need for concentrated attention and inquiring reflection, and the reader who is unprepared to bestow these is likely to find little of profit here.

As regards *content*, the book deals principally with a development of the system of real numbers from the modern deductive point of view. Starting with an axiomatic treatment of the theory of positive integers, based on a variant of the Peano postulates, successive extensions are constructed so as to obtain zero, the negative integers, the rational numbers, certain irrationals, and finally all real numbers. Each of these successive extensions is motivated by formulating certain natural problems which are shown to be uniquely solved by the given constructions. In this development, many of the concepts of modern abstract algebra are naturally introduced and employed, both to focus attention on the essential features of the constructions and proofs, and to indicate the general scope to which the theorems are applicable. The underlying principles of set theory and logic are stressed throughout the book, and there are separate chapters that sketch an axiomatic theory of each of these subjects. In the case of set theory, we have illuminated the material by following the historical development wherein an inconsistent system is studied first and later modified.

Used as a college text, there is enough material for a one-year course of the type commonly given under a title such as "Foundations of Mathematics," or "Fundamental Concepts of Mathematics." For a one-semester course, or for a teacher's institute or in-service offering, there are various ways in which selections of the book's material may be made. (In this connection the instructor may find the following "Note to the Reader" of some help.)

To the individual reader, whether he be student, teacher, or layman, we express our hope that sufficient material will be found to clarify the deductive nature of mathematics, to indicate the subtlety and precision of mathematical vocabulary, and to convey an appreciation of the polished beauty of a rigorous proof.

We would like to acknowledge the important contributions made to the production of this book by the understanding assistance of Mr. A. H. McLeod of the staff of The Macmillan Company, the heroic and devoted efforts of our typists, Miss Laura E. Hill and Mrs. Ruth Lahti, and the suggestions of the many teachers and students upon whom several tentative versions of this material were tried. Professor Henkin wishes, too, to record his appreciation to Dartmouth College, which he served as Visiting Professor of Mathematics during 1960–61; a generously conceived teaching schedule at Dartmouth greatly facilitated a substantial portion of the writing of this book. Finally, we wish to express our grateful admiration for the patient forbearance of our wives—for any author whose family is still intact when his book is finished must indeed be wedded to an angel.

LEON HENKIN, *Berkeley, California*
W. NORMAN SMITH, *Laramie, Wyoming*
VERNE J. VARINEAU, *Laramie, Wyoming*
MICHAEL J. WALSH, *San Diego, California*

A Note to the Reader

The authors would not presume to address this note to the student using this book as a text in a class, but the individual reader who has to struggle along without the help of a teacher deserves all the comfort and encouragement the authors can muster. To such individual readers go our best wishes, along with the suggestions in this note.

These recommendations to the reader are properly a part of the preface, but the authors, well aware that the reading audience of a preface may consist largely of reviewers and proofreaders, prefer to place this advice in a separate section where its chances of being seen are somewhat enhanced.

Even the mathematical novice will find much of *Retracing Elementary Mathematics* quite straightforward. This does not mean, however, that it can be skimmed like a novel. After all, in a novel the reader must keep in mind only a small number of facts: the names of the principal characters (a hardship only in certain Russian novels), a few familiar relationships existing between them (usually based upon their sex), perhaps a smattering of geographic data, and one or two interesting situations in which the characters are involved. The reader soon learns to erase from his mind such trivia as the color of the heroine's hair or the sound of the surf as it breaks on some rockbound coast. In a mathematical treatise, on the other hand, there are many facts which must be noted (and correspondingly fewer trivia which can be safely ignored) if the book is to be read as something other than meaningless gibberish.

Let us be more specific. In *Retracing Elementary Mathematics* the reader will find definitions of unfamiliar terms, as well as unfamiliar definitions of familiar terms. It is essential that these definitions be read carefully and referred to frequently until the terms become a well-understood part of the reader's vocabulary.

The question of the proofs of theorems in a book of this kind is always a troublesome one. For those who delight in following the details of a demonstration, step-by-step proofs, such as those given for most of the theorems, will be welcome. On the other hand, many readers in attempting to wade through a long and subtle proof may lose sight of the structure of the proof itself, not to mention the position of the theorem in the developing theme of the book. It is with these people in mind that we have attempted to make the proofs easier to follow by indicating the key steps of each proof by a double pointer, and the other major steps by a single pointer. The basic structure, or backbone, of the proof may be ascertained by reading only the statements with double pointers. The steps with pointers and double pointers, taken together, give a complete skeleton outline of the proof. The unmarked statements merely fill in details, or justify major steps.

Every reader should find it a rewarding experience to examine at least a few of the proofs in detail, and we certainly hope that many readers will make a step-by-step study of a good number of the proofs. The reader should realize clearly that this cannot be accomplished in a matter of minutes. On the contrary, in the case of some of the longer proofs it may be necessary for the average reader to spend several hours on a careful analysis of the steps, and the reasoning behind each one, in order to appreciate fully the points involved. If, however, the reader finds himself getting lost in the details, the authors suggest that, rather than abandon the book at this point, the reader content himself with a survey of the structure of the proof—or perhaps omit the proof entirely. Certainly very few readers will wish to give concentrated study to all of the proofs—and indeed this is quite unnecessary for an understanding of the material.

One final word about the proofs. The authors are well aware that the amount of detail given will be boring to the trained mathematician. To him, our apologies.

Certain sections of *Retracing Elementary Mathematics* are relatively more important than others, insofar as the principal purposes of the book are concerned. Accordingly, the authors venture to suggest a reading guide.

Chapter I, Introductory Notions, might well receive a rather cursory first reading, then serve as a reference to which the reader can turn frequently as he reencounters the concepts described there in later chapters.

The sections on the axiomatic development of the positive integers and models of axiomatic systems, contained in Chapters II, III, and IV, are basic to the book and should be read with considerable care—bearing in mind that the proofs should not be allowed to distract the reader from the development of the concepts. Many of the proofs, though, should be studied in detail so that the reader learns to recognize a complete, rigorous deductive argument.

Chapter V, which deals with the rather specialized topics of least common multiples, greatest common divisors, and primes, can be omitted entirely without harming the continuity of the book.

The reader should study the definitions (in Chapter VI) concerning finite sequences and general sums and products, but the proofs of the theorems might well be omitted on the first reading.

Chapter VII, on applied arithmetic and counting, may be omitted entirely, but the average reader will probably find the definitions and the statements of the theorems of interest. The proofs in this chapter are rather difficult and are relatively heavily laden with notions of set theory, so that it is probably advisable for most readers to omit them.

The first part of Chapter VIII, in which the number system is extended from the positive integers to the natural numbers, should be studied carefully, as it is a prototype for successive extensions of the number system which are made in later chapters. The section on Arabic Numerals, which makes up the final part of the chapter, is not necessary for later work, but most readers will probably find it of interest to observe the complexity of a rigorous treatment of numerals and to compare it with their grade-school experience with these concepts.

Chapters IX and X, on Set Theory and Logic respectively, are designed for those readers who have become curious about these topics from encountering them in intuitive fashion in earlier chapters. Others can proceed directly to Chapter XI where the development of the number system is continued.

The last four chapters, in which the number system is progressively extended to include negative integers, rationals, certain irrationals, and finally all real numbers, should present no special difficulties to the reader who has studied the earlier chapters with some care.

The reader who wishes to concentrate only on the development of the real number system can do so by reading Chapters II, IV, VIII, XI, XII, and XIV in order. The chapters on set theory and logic, IX and X, can be studied quite independently of the material preceding them. Most of the remaining material can be read independently if the reader will substitute his intuitive knowledge of numbers for the detailed references given to theorems proved in earlier chapters.

To conclude this Note we call attention to the exercises placed at the end of each section. There is no better way to develop insight into the material of this book than by working at these problems. (To those desiring more challenging work we recommend the starred problems.) In order to obtain further problems the reader has only to seek his own proofs for theorems stated in the text, before looking at the proofs which are given. And indeed this is an excellent procedure which will lead to a fuller appreciation of the way in which proofs are found and of the form in which the published proofs are given.

Contents

I

Introductory Notions

1. The Two Components of Mathematics

Mathematics today is the result of the confluence of two great streams of thought. On the one hand there is the long-standing interest people have had in *computation*, the manipulation of mathematical symbols according to prescribed rules so as to obtain numerical answers to given problems. On the other hand there is the traditional concern with *discovering the logical connections* between mathematical statements. Historically, the principal impulse to develop the art of computation originated in the Asian civilizations; it entered Western culture via the nomadic Arab peoples who brought us that superb computational instrument, the system of decimal notation. By contrast, the preoccupation with logical interrelations was a typical characteristic of Greek mathematicians; it is exemplified by Euclid's systematization of the propositions of geometry, or by the Pythagorean school's investigations into certain of the properties of whole numbers.

In modern, creative mathematics, which is very actively pursued by research workers in almost every country, these two lines of thought are richly intertwined. Yet in our entire elementary mathematical education, from first grade through most college courses in calculus and differential equations, the preponderant emphasis is on computation, with only an isolated course in geometry to call attention to the importance of logical deduction for mathematics. How can we account for this imbalance in our teaching between the two components of mathematical thought? It seems to us that the explanation must be combined from several sources.

For one thing, computation is so obviously *useful* in applications of mathematics to commerce, engineering, and other fields that its value hardly need be argued in a society so pragmatically oriented as ours. By contrast, the concern of Greek mathematicians with proofs seems to have been typical of a patrician leisure class, originating largely in speculative intellectual curiosity and to all appearances quite lacking in "practical" employment. For although it is true that proofs sometimes enable us to establish the truth of propositions previously in doubt, in the case of Euclid's work almost all the individual theorems of geometry were known separately beforehand, so that the proofs merely demonstrated the logical relation between the theorems and the axioms rather than furnished new geometric information which could be applied in such practical arts as surveying.

A second contributory factor has been the impression that "reasoning" is innately more difficult than "reckoning," so that its teaching is postponed until the simpler process has been learned and assimilated—and until the less able students have been eliminated from the institutionalized process of education

Finally, it seems to us that the composition of our present-day mathematical curriculum must be explained partly on the basis of the inertial tendency of all institutions to resist and lag behind change. The mathematical ideas we teach today, from grade school through second-year college, are substantially those which had been formulated by the middle of the seventeenth century and were of central interest at that time. The revitalization of the axiomatic method in mathematics is less than one hundred years old, and it simply takes longer than that for new ideas to sift down into our school teaching.

Are the factors which explain the content of our present curriculum valid reasons for maintaining it unchanged? It is not our purpose to argue this question. But there is one point to which we should like to call attention. Mathematical research in recent decades has made it abundantly clear that the deductive method in mathematics is of the greatest importance in applications of mathematics to other disciplines. In part this is so because computational methods have become so sophisticated and specialized that deductions of a very deep kind are needed to establish these methods' validity and to determine under what conditions they may appropriately be employed. But in even greater part, the practicality of the deductive method derives from one of its features which the Greek originators failed entirely to appreciate, namely, that it provides a method for developing a single mathematical theory applicable to a great many diverse domains. Problems of biology, economics, and linguistics, for example, as well as from fields where the application of mathematics is more traditional, can now be treated uniformly within the framework of a single mathematical theory. How this is accomplished will become clear in the sequel when we consider the concept of models of an axiomatic theory.

What we propose to do here is retrace the subject matter of elementary mathematics, beginning with the arithmetic of whole numbers and continuing through algebra, showing how the concepts of elementary mathematics may be treated by the deductive techniques of modern mathematics. The computational aspects of the subject, which form the content of the school curriculum, will, of course, be omitted in this treatment.

EXERCISES

1. Recall the statements of three theorems in geometry whose proofs you have seen. (It is not necessary to recall the proofs.)

2. Recall the statements of three theorems from algebra whose proofs you have seen.

3. Which subject seemed more logical to you when you were a student, elementary algebra or elementary geometry? Why?

2. *Some Words about Logic*

To establish the truth of a given sentence there are two general procedures which may be followed. Either establish the truth of the sentence *directly*, by an investigation into the circumstances described by the sentence, or *infer* the truth of the sentence from some other sentence or sentences already known to be true. We shall be mainly concerned with the latter procedure which is called *deductive inference* or, sometimes, *logical deduction*.

This relation of implication which connects a sentence P with certain other sentences Q_1, Q_2, $\cdots$ in such a way that a knowledge of the truth of the latter sentences serves as a guarantee of the truth of sentence P, is of fundamental importance in every branch of science, for it provides a method of organizing the separate facts of the science into a coherent structure, or theory. In physics, for example, instead of merely amassing a tremendous catalogue of independently observed physical facts, we are able to describe a small number of general principles—the fundamental laws or axioms of physics—from which the detailed phenomena may be deduced. It is worth noticing that in the case of physical theory, while we often know the truth of the implied sentence, since this describes a simple fact we can observe directly, the truth of the fundamental laws is never known with certainty, since these are of a general nature and always subject to rejection on the basis of new evidence.

In mathematics, too, we deal with many facts. For instance, the equations $1 + 2 = 3$, $8 + 9 = 17$, $197 + 348 = 545$ express three among the unlimited number of facts making up the addition table—and the entire table contains only the simplest kind of facts of arithmetic. If we are asked to determine the truth or falsity of an equation of this simple kind—say $4 + 3 = 9$—we can do so by a direct investigation involving a counting process, and naturally for this particular example the process will indicate that the equation is false. In principle we can also use a direct process of counting to decide whether the equation $111 + 222 = 333$ is true; but this would be extremely tedious and of course we have a much more practical method; namely, we may *infer* that the equation is true from the knowledge that $1 + 2 = 3$ together with certain general principles of arithmetic the application of which we all learn in grade school. If we were asked to *formulate* these general principles explicitly we might find it a little difficult, and if we were asked to *justify* these principles most of us would be quite at loss; for this is a topic certainly not dealt with in grade school and one which is generally investigated only by mathematicians. Nevertheless, the ideas which underlie this subject, when properly approached, are not at all difficult to understand, and we shall treat them extensively in what follows.

As indicated, the relation of *implication* which binds sentences together will play a central role in our development of elementary mathematics. This relation, as well as the notion of *proof*—the means by which we establish an implication—constitutes the principal subject matter of the study of *logic*. It might seem reasonable, therefore, to preface our development of arithmetic by a thorough discussion and description of the principles of logic on which the theory of arithmetic is based. Nevertheless, we shall follow another procedure which may at first appear quixotic; we shall postpone our discussion of logic until *after* we have examined arithmetic.

The reason for thus putting the horse behind the cart is a pedagogical one: the subject of logic, being more abstract than that of arithmetic, is more difficult to grasp at first. Psychologically, the mind finds it easier to understand the definitions which pick out the laws of logic if it has first had the opportunity to perceive these laws at work in the construction of arithmetical proofs. The individual learns by practice to recognize intuitively when a law of logic has been correctly applied, just as a child learns intuitively how to construct a sentence long before he begins the study of grammar where the rules of sentence-formation are explicitly formulated.

The fact that the order in which subjects may best be learned is in general different from the order appropriate to the logical connections between these subjects is only a particular manifestation of the more general fact that logical sequences are very different from psychological processes. When we say that a person thinks logically, we are being misleading; what we mean is that the person is able to formulate a logical pattern of inference from premises to conclusions. The thought processes which lead to this formulation, however, very rarely follow the elegant pattern which emerges in the final demonstration. On the contrary, the process of obtaining a mathematical proof is frequently a mixture of shrewd guesses, backward looks, and considerations of the type "If I could prove this, then I could get that." It is only after the structure of the proof finally appears that the mathematician puts it into a polished, logical pattern. The reader will be given ample opportunity to observe this, as we shall ask him to look for various proofs in the sequel. In addition, we shall try to point out the natural way to look for some of the proofs we give for our theorems.

Although we are not going to formulate principles of logic at this time, we do wish to make several remarks which should help in the process of learning to recognize intuitively when such principles are correctly applied. As we shall see, the question of whether one sentence is implied by certain others is closely bound up with the way in which certain key words appear in these sentences. The words which will be of especial importance in this connection are the following: *not, and, or, if . . . then, if and only if, is (equal to), any, each, all, every, there is, exists, some, such that.*

The use of these key words in ordinary discourse may appear to be so familiar to the reader that any discussion of them is unnecessary. Yet their mathematical use, with the occasional restricted meanings mathematicians find it imperative to impose in certain cases, is worthy of comment. It may be, also, that the reader will discover certain subtleties in the nonmathematical use of these terms of which he has been only subconsciously aware.

1. The word "is" is put to a great many uses in the English language—perhaps because it is so short! For example, when we assert "The Empire State Building is the tallest building in the world," we use the word "is" to assert that the Empire State Building and the tallest building in the world are one and the same object. On the other hand, if I tell you "My house is green," I am not saying that my house and greenness are the same object, but rather that the object which is my house possesses the property of being green. In mathematics we use the equality sign "=" for the first meaning of the word "is". Thus it would be mathematically proper to say "The Empire State Building = the tallest building in the world." In general, *the equality sign is placed between two expressions to indicate that these expressions are names or descriptions of one and the same object.* From this logical meaning of the equality sign we may establish at once various rules for using it. For example, whatever expressions A and B may be, if we know that "$A = B$" is true then we may infer that "$B = A$" is true, for if "A" and "B" denote the same object, of course we can conclude that the expressions "B" and "A" denote the same object. In the same way, if we know that $A = B$ and $B = C$ it follows that $A = C$. Again, if x, y, z are numbers such that $x = y$, then we may infer at once that $x + z = y + z$. For then both "$x + z$" and "$y + z$" denote the number obtained by adding z to that number which is denoted by "x" as well as by "y". For example, if we consider the numbers $\sin \pi/2$ and $\cos 0$, we have $\sin \pi/2 = \cos 0$ since both are 1. Hence, we can conclude that $\sin \pi/2 + z = \cos 0 + z$ since both represent the number $1 + z$. More generally: if $x = y$, if we perform *any* operation on x, and if we perform the *same* operation on y, then the results of these operations will be equal. And all of these rules are based on the logical meaning of equality. To indicate that x and y are *not* the same object (i.e., to assert that they are distinct), we write "$x \neq y$".

2. The word "and" may be placed between any two sentences to form a new sentence. If P and Q are any sentences, the compound sentence "P and Q" is called the *conjunction* of P and Q. Thus if P is the sentence "It is raining" and Q the sentence "The sun is shining," the conjunction of P and Q is "It is raining and the sun is shining".

What can be said about the truth of a conjunction? If both P and Q are true, then "P and Q" is considered a true statement; in any other case the conjunction is false. Thus when a sixty-year old violinist says "I am thirty-nine and I play the violin," this is a false statement, even though one of the conjuncts of the conjunction is true. Similarly, his statement "I am thirty-nine and I can't play the violin," is a false statement.

3. The word "or" may be put between two sentences to form a new sentence; if P and Q are the sentences with which we start, the resulting compound sentence "P or Q" is called the *disjunction* of P and Q. Sometimes we put the word "either" before the disjunction, but from the viewpoint of logic and mathematics this does not change the meaning of the disjunction in any way. In ordinary English the use of "or" in a disjunction may have one of two different senses, depending on the context. Sometimes we assert "P or Q" to mean that one or the other of the sentences P and Q is true, but not both; we call this the *exclusive* use of "or". For example, a child who is told he may have either a football or a baseball glove is implicitly given to understand that he may not choose both. On other occasions the meaning we intend by the use of the disjunction "P or Q" is that at least one of the sentences P and Q is true, and possibly both. This is the *inclusive* use of "or." The statement "Good football players are big or good football players are fast" is an example of the use of "or" in the inclusive sense, as any football coach will attest.

This ambiguous use of "or" cannot be tolerated in a discipline where precise meanings are mandatory, such as law or mathematics. The lawyer resolves the difficulty by inventing a new term for the inclusive "or"—the "and/or" of legal documents. The mathematician adopts a convention—he agrees always to use the word "or" with just one of its meanings, namely, its inclusive sense. Thus the mathematical statement "Either y or z is a root of the equation $x^2 - 2x = 0$" admits the possibility (but not the necessity) that both y and z may be roots, hence we get a true sentence if we take y to be 0 and z to be 1, as well as if we choose y to be 0 and z to be 2. If we wish to express the exclusive sense of "or" in mathematics we always add the phrase "but not both" after the disjunction. However, a word of caution is in order in connection with this rule. If we are dealing with a whole number x, for example, we might well have occasion to remark "Either x is an even number or x is an odd number"; and the reader may object that this is an exclusive disjunction since x cannot be both an even number and an odd number. Nevertheless, the objection is not justified. The point is that the meaning of "or" in this sentence is the inclusive meaning that x is even or odd *or possibly both;* the fact that x cannot be both even and odd is not expressed by this sentence as it stands but is a separately known fact which requires another sentence to state.

4. The word "not" may be placed before any sentence P to form a new sentence, "not-P", called the *negation* of P. Thus if P is the sentence "It is raining", the sentences "Not- it is raining", or "It is false that it is raining", or, more elegantly, "It is not raining", are various ways of expressing the negation of P. When P is true, not-P is false, and when P is false, not-P is true. If the sentence "It is raining" is true, the negation "It is not raining" is false, while if the statement "It is raining" is false, the negation "It is not raining" is true. Since "not-P" is a sentence, it is, of course, perfectly possible to form its negation, "not-not-P". This is not the same sentence as P, although the meaning of P and not-not-P are closely connected. In particular, it is evident that if the statement P is true, "not-not-P" is also true, and if P is false then so is not-not-P.

When P is a simple declarative sentence the meaning of not-P is clear. For a compound sentence, the meaning of its negation may not be immediately evident. For example, what is the meaning of the negation of the sentence "It is raining and the sun is shining"? Which one of the following sentences has the same meaning as the negation of this conjunction?

(a) "It is not raining and the sun is not shining."
(b) "It is raining and the sun is not shining."
(c) "It is not raining and the sun is shining."
(d) "Either it is not raining or the sun is not shining."

The answer is (d), but if your off-hand guess was one of the others, you have plenty of company. The original statement asserts two things: (1) that it is raining, and (2) that the sun is shining. To deny that both of these are true is equivalent to affirming that at least one of them is false.

This is not the place to consider a list of compound sentences and their negations, but perhaps this one example will indicate that the sentence "not-P" may offer some advantages over its more elegant English form.

5. The words "if . . . then" are also used to combine two sentences, P and Q, into a new sentence. The resulting compound sentence "If P then Q" is called the *conditional* of P and Q. P is called the *antecedent* of the conditional and Q is known as the *consequent*. Sometimes the expression "P implies Q" is used in place of the equivalent "If P then Q".

In ordinary discourse, as in mathematics, we use a conditional sentence "If P then Q" to tie the truth of Q to that of P so that *when we know that "If P then Q" is a true statement and we know that P is true then we may conclude* *that Q also is true*. Consider the familiar theorem from plane geometry, "If two sides of a triangle are equal, then the angles opposite these sides are equal", which we accept as a true conditional statement. If we observe that for a particular triangle the antecedent "two sides of the triangle are equal" is true, the consequent "the angles opposite these sides are equal" follows logically.

Notice then that *whenever the conditional "if P then Q" holds in a case where we know Q to be false, we may conclude that P is false;* for if P were true the conditional would tell us that Q was true, contrary to what we know about Q. For example, suppose that a teacher should tell his student, "If your final examination grade is over 90 you will receive an A in this course," and suppose the student subsequently receives a grade of B. Clearly we can properly infer that his final examination grade was not over 90. Similarly, reconsider the theorem "If two sides of a triangle are equal, then the angles opposite these sides are equal." If we know that two angles of a certain triangle are unequal we may infer that the sides opposite these angles are also unequal.

Ordinarily, if we know P to be false we would not use a conditional sentence of the form "If P then Q." However, in mathematics we sometimes have occasion to do so. For example, consider the sentence "Every whole number which is a multiple of 4 is also a multiple of 2". For reasons which will become clear in the sequel, we sometimes wish to express the same idea by a sentence having a slightly different form, namely, "For every whole number x, if x is a multiple of 4 then x is a multiple of 2". Now a moment's reflection will show that the proposition expressed by these two (equivalent) sentences is certainly correct. Hence the phrase "if x is a multiple of 4 then x is a multiple of 2", since it holds for *all* numbers x, must be true when we replace "x" by any particular number. Thus we get, as special cases, that the following conditional sentences must be true: "If 3 is a multiple of 4 then 3 is a multiple of 2", and "If 6 is a multiple of 4 then 6 is a multiple of 2". These two examples illustrate the principle that in mathematical usage *a conditional sentence "If P then Q" is always true when the antecedent, P, is false*— irrespective of whether the consequent, Q, is true or false.

From the above discussion we see that the conditional "If P then Q" holds whenever Q is true, regardless of the truth or falsity of P. Hence, the knowledge that the conditional "If P then Q" holds and also that Q is true does *not* allow us to conclude anything about the truth of P.

If we start with sentences P and Q we can form two conditionals from them: "If P then Q" and "If Q then P", and each of these is called the *converse* of the other. If a conditional is true its converse may be either true or false, depending on the particular P and Q. However, the conditionals "If P then Q" and "If not-Q then not-P" are *not* converses of one another but are two equivalent ways of expressing the same idea.

6. The phrase "if and only if" occurs frequently in the formulation of mathematical theorems. If we use it to combine two sentences, P and Q, into a single sentence, the compound sentence which results, "P if and only if Q", is called the *biconditional* of P and Q. As indicated by the form of this compound sentence it is equivalent to the conjunction "(P if Q) and (P only if Q)"; so let us examine each of these conjuncts. "P if Q" is simply a somewhat literary way of saying "If Q then P". The other conjunct, "P only if Q", means that P is false *unless* Q is true, so that if P is true then Q must also be true; i.e., "P only if Q" simply means the same as "If P then Q". Thus we see that the biconditional "P if and only if Q" has the same meaning as the conjunction "(If Q then P) and (if P then Q)". Often when we wish to prove a biconditional "P if and only if Q", we first prove the conditional "If P then Q" and then separately prove its converse "If Q then P". It is essential to prove both parts in order to establish the biconditional. For example, in geometry in order to establish the theorem "A point is equidistant from two distinct points A and B if and only if it is on the perpendicular bisector of the line segment from A to B", we must show two things. First, we must prove that if a point is equidistant from A and B it is on the perpendicular bisector; and then we must show that if a point is on the perpendicular bisector, it is equidistant from A and B.

7. Before discussing the words "each", "all", "any", and "every" we introduce a new concept. In mathematics and also in logic, the letter "x" which appears in such statements as "x is an even integer" is called a *variable*. The intent in using such a variable is that the names of elements from a certain preassigned collection may be inserted in place of the letter x so as to make sentences which are then either true or false; i.e., the variable merely acts as a place holder (or blank space) for which certain names may be inserted. For the statement "x is an even integer", suppose that our collection is the set of all whole numbers. In that case we may replace "x" by the name of any whole number, obtaining, for example, "1 is an even integer" (which is a false sentence), or "2 is an even integer" (which is a true sentence). Sometimes we will specify the collection of objects whose names may be substituted for a given variable, but often it will be assumed that the reader can recognize the collection from the context. The collection of elements whose names may be inserted for the variable is called the *range* of the variable.

The words "any", "each", "all", and "every" are used interchangeably in mathematics in order to make *general statements*. They are usually combined with a letter serving as a variable, and the combination of one of these words with a variable, as in the phrases "for every x", "for each T", etc., is called a *universal quantifier*. For example, instead of saying "January has more than 20 days and February has more than 20 days and . . . and December has more than 20 days" we would ordinarily make the general statement "Every month has more than 20 days", or "All months have more than 20 days", or "Each month has more than 20 days". In mathematical terminology we could express the same idea by writing "For every x, if x is a month then x has more than 20 days", or "For all months y, y has more than 20 days". If we have previously agreed that the letters "b" or "$\mathcal{J}$" shall serve as variables whose range consists of the twelve months of the year, then we may simply write "For each b, b has more than 20 days", "For all $\mathcal{J}$, $\mathcal{J}$ has more than 20 days", "For any $\mathcal{J}$, $\mathcal{J}$ has more than 20 days".

Although the words "any", "each", "all", and "every" have exactly the same meaning as one another when used as part of a universal quantifier to form a general statement, there is a related but different use of the word "any" not shared by the other three words. Suppose that we wish to prove some general statement about numbers—say the statement that for all numbers x, $x + 3 = 3 + x$. Our method of proof often consists in *choosing* a number x in an arbitrary way, and then reasoning about this chosen x until we show that it satisfies the required condition—in this case that $x + 3 = 3 + x$. We can then reach the desired conclusion by applying a law of logic which permits us to conclude that all numbers have a certain property if we know that an arbitrarily selected number has the property. When we wish to indicate that we are choosing a number x in an arbitrary way we usually say "Let x be any number". In this context the word "any" cannot be replaced by any of the words "all", "each", or "every".

8. Just as we use a variable as part of a universal quantifier to make general statements, so we use a variable as part of an *existential quantifier* in order to form statements asserting existence. The typical forms of an existential quantifier involving the variable "x" will be "There is an x such that", or "There exists an x such that", or "For some x"—the three forms being used in a completely interchangeable way. For example, knowing that Venus is a planet, we may truthfully assert "There is an x such that x is a planet and the English name of x begins with '*V*'," or "There exists a planet x whose English name begins with '*V*'," or "For some x, x is a planet and the English name of x begins with '*V*'." Often we can assert an existential statement even when we do not know the identity of the individual whose existence is asserted. For example, a host at a party who suddenly notices one of his art treasures missing might shout "There's a thief in this room!" If he were a mathematician he could express the same idea by asserting "There exists an x such that x is in this room and x is a thief"; and he might be correct even though he did not know just which of his guests was the guilty one. In mathematics, for example, there is a theorem which asserts that if $p(x)$ is a polynomial of odd degree with real coefficients, then there exists a real number x such that $p(x) = 0$. The theorem makes no assertion

as to *which* number is a root of the equation $p(x) = 0$, nor does its proof show how to find such a number.

There is a close connection between universal and existential quantifiers. For example, to deny the statement "For all numbers x, if x is a prime number then x is an odd number" (i.e., to deny that all prime numbers are odd), we assert "There exists an x such that x is a prime number and x is not an odd number" (i.e., we assert that some prime number is not odd). Similarly, to deny the statement "There is a book x such that x is inexpensive" we assert the statement "For every book x, x is expensive".

EXERCISES

1. Comment on the truth of statements of the form "If P then Q", where

(a) P is true, Q is true,
(b) P is true, Q is false,
(c) P is false, Q is true,
(d) P is false, Q is false.

Make up examples illustrating these various possibilities.

2. Given that the statement "If P then Q" is true, what can be said about the truth of

(a) Q, given that (1) P is true, (2) P is false?
(b) P, given that (1) Q is true, (2) Q is false?

Make up examples.

3. Give the converse of the following statements. (Neither the given statements nor their converses are necessarily true.)

(a) If the sides of a triangle are equal, the angles are equal.
(b) If $x = 2$, then x is a solution of the equation $x^2 - 2x = 0$.
(c) The diagonals of a rectangle bisect each other.
(d) All Boy Scouts are courteous (i.e., if x is any Boy Scout, then x is courteous).
(e) Skiing is dangerous.
(f) If x is not a solution of the equation $3x - 12 = 0$, then x is not 4.
(g) If x is a solution of the equation $3x - 12 = 0$, then x is not 5.

4. Consider the theorem: "If $x = \frac{b}{a}$ and $a \neq 0$, then x is a solution of the equation $ax - b = 0$." Are the following three lines a proof of this theorem?

(1) $ax - b = 0$;   given.
(2) $ax = b$;   add b to both sides of (1).
(3) $x = \frac{b}{a}$;   since a is given $\neq 0$, divide both sides of (2) by a.

Justify your answer.

5. Other words in addition to the key words of logic which we have discussed often appear in mathematics and in ordinary discourse. Some of these are "neither . . . nor", "but", "whenever", and "otherwise". However, these may be translated in terms of the key words. Rewrite the following in terms of the words "not", "and", "or", "if . . . then".

(a) Neither P nor Q.
(b) P but not Q.
(c) Q whenever P.
(d) P otherwise Q.
(e) P if Q.

6. If P is the sentence "I like spinach", a mathematician might write "Not, I like spinach" for "not-P". Or he might write "It is not the case that I like spinach" or the more literary equivalent "I do not like spinach". Smooth literary negations of sentences are not always immediately evident. Negate the following by means other than merely prefacing the sentences with the word "not" or the words "it is not the case that":

(a) Mathematics is easy.
(b) Some books are interesting.
(c) All grass is green.
(d) If P then Q.

3. *Some Words about the Theory of Sets*

As we have indicated, every mathematical theory rests upon logic because the theorems of the subject are derived by means of the laws of logic. It happens that besides logical concepts there are certain other mathematical concepts which are so basic and pervasive that they enter into the formulation of every other branch of mathematics; these concepts themselves form the subject of a very abstract mathematical science known as the *theory of sets.* The reader will notice that we have already used the notion of set in our discussion of the word "variable." If our aim were to give a strictly logical development of elementary mathematics we would first have to study the laws of logic, then the theory of sets, and only afterward would we be ready to treat arithmetic, say, or geometry. But those same pedagogical and psychological considerations which impelled us to postpone the explicit study of logic are operative in the case of set theory; because of the high degree of abstractness of the subject it is much easier to understand its concepts and principles if one first encounters them on an intuitive basis as they are employed in some more familiar discipline. Accordingly we shall content ourselves with giving at this point only an informal account of the most important ideas of the theory of sets, and shall reserve until a later point a fuller discussion of some of the subtleties connected with this subject.

1. We use the word "set" interchangeably with the words "class" and "collection". Any set is associated with certain objects called the *members*

or *elements* of the set. We use a form of the Greek letter "ϵ" (epsilon) to denote the relation of membership; thus the formula "$x \epsilon G$" means that G is a set and that x is one of the objects which is an element of G. We sometimes say x *belongs to* G or x *is in* G. For example, "Washington ϵ the class of all presidents of the United States", and "1 ϵ the class of all numbers equal to their own square". (The latter is true because $1 = 1^2$.)

The use of "ϵ" just described is closely connected with one of the uses of the word "is" which we mentioned in item 4 of the preceding section. At that time we considered the sentence "My house is green", in which "is" is used to indicate that a certain object (my house) possesses a certain property (being green). Now connected with any property there is a certain set, namely the set whose members are all and only those objects which possess the given property. For example, connected with the property of being green there is the set of all green things. And now we see that the sentence "My house is green" has essentially the same meaning as "My house ϵ the class of all green things".

While a property always has a class connected with it, the property is not the same thing as the class—for two different properties may be connected with the same class. For instance, the property of being a featherless biped, referring as it does to the nature of skin and the number of legs, is quite different from the property of being a speaking animal—for the latter refers to the production of vocal sounds. However, from the mathematical point of view the class of featherless bipeds is the same as the class of speaking animals, for the objects which are the members of one of these classes are precisely the same objects which are the members of the other. (Strictly speaking we are inaccurate here, since some parrots may be said to speak, though they are not featherless, while some featherless bipeds may be mute. But let us pretend that these exceptions do not exist, for the sake of a useful example.)

As we have indicated above, mathematicians use the word "set" in such a way that if G and H are sets which have exactly the same objects as members, then we say that G is the same set as H. This principle is known as the *Principle of Extensionality for Sets*. In more technical language we can formulate this principle as follows: If G and H are sets such that for every object x we have $x \epsilon G$ if and only if $x \epsilon H$, then $G = H$.

When we use a property to indicate a set connected with it, we generally describe the set with the aid of a variable. For example, the set of all those numbers which have the property of being equal to their own square would usually be described as "the set of all numbers x such that $x = x^2$".

While we often describe a set by means of a property, it is important to bear in mind that it is not at all necessary for the elements of a set to have anything in common (other than being members of that set). Indeed, the mathematician conceives that any objects whatever can be brought together as the elements of a set. For example, there is a set whose elements are the authors of this book, the solar system, the number $\sqrt{2}$, and nothing else.

Suppose that G and H are sets. It may happen that every object which is an element of G is also an element of H. In that case we say that G is a *subset* of H and indicate the fact by the notation $G \subseteq H$. In technical language: $G \subseteq H$ if and only if for every object x, if $x \in G$ then also $x \in H$. Notice that G may be a subset of H whether or not there are additional elements in H which are not in G. If there are no such additional elements then $G = H$, and thus G is a subset of itself.

Suppose that G and H are sets and that each is a subset of the other; that is, we have both $G \subseteq H$ and $H \subseteq G$. Can this really occur? It certainly can, for as noted above every set is a subset of itself, and hence if G and H are the same set then we have both $G \subseteq H$ and $H \subseteq G$. Actually, this is the *only* circumstance in which both relations can occur. For if we ever have sets G and H such that $G \subseteq H$ and $H \subseteq G$, we see by the definition of "subset" that every element of G will be an element of H and also that every element of H will be an element of G. That is, the sets G and H must have exactly the same objects as members. Hence we may apply the principle of extentionality and infer that $G = H$.

A set which has exactly two different objects is called a *pair*. If x and y are distinct objects (i.e., if $x \neq y$), we refer to the pair whose elements are x and y by the notation "$\{x, y\}$". In using this notation we inevitably have to write one of the letters "x" and "y" before the other; but the reader should keep in mind there is no fixed order in which the elements of the set must be considered. This last fact may be expressed by the equation $\{x, y\} = \{y, x\}$ and may be established with the aid of the principle of extensionality.

A set may have only one element, in which case it is called a *unit set*, or a *singleton*. The unit set whose only element is the object x is denoted "$\{x\}$". Notice that the unit set is not to be confused with, or identified with, its element. For example, we clearly have {Dag Hammarskjold} $\neq$ Dag Hammarskjold, for the former is a set and the latter is a man.

Mathematicians also find it convenient to consider sets which have no members whatever, for much the same reason that it is convenient to have a number zero. Indeed, the two notions are closely related, for the number of elements in a set which has no elements is precisely zero. A set of this kind we call an *empty set*. Actually there is only one empty set, for if G and H are any empty sets we have $G \subseteq H$ (since every element of G is an element of H) and $H \subseteq G$, and so as noted above we must have $G = H$. We denote the empty set by the Scandinavian letter "$\varnothing$", pronounced "uh."

EXERCISES

1. Let us use the following definitions: A = Mr. Abercrombie; B = Mr. Bullfinch; a = Mr. Abercrombie's apple tree; and b = Mr. Bullfinch's bulldog. What is meant by the following:

(**a**) $\{A, B, a\}$?
(**b**) $\{b\}$?
(**c**) b ?
(**d**) $\{b, \{b\}\}$?
(**e**) Is $\{A, A, B\} = \{A, B\}$?

2. Give an example of sets A, B, C so that $A \subseteq B$ and $B \subseteq C$. Is $A \subseteq C$? Prove that this is always the case (i.e., for any sets A, B, C satisfying the hypotheses).

3. Explain why $\{\varnothing\}$ is not the same set as the empty set, $\varnothing$.

4. Let $A = \{a, b, c\}$ and $B = \{a, b, c, A\}$. Show that we have both (**a**) $A \subseteq B$ and (**b**) $A \in B$. Give other examples to show that we can have $A \subseteq B$ but not $A \in B$; or $A \in B$ but not $A \subseteq B$; or neither $A \subseteq B$ nor $A \in B$.

5. Let $A = \{a, b, c\}$ and $C = \{a, b, c, \{A\}\}$. (**a**) Is $A \subseteq C$? (**b**) Is $A \in C$?

6. Let A be the set of all those whole numbers x such that $x > 0$ and also $x < 0$. Let B be the set of all those whole numbers x such that $x \geq 0$ and also $x \leq 0$. Let C be the set of all those whole numbers x such that either $x \geq 0$ or $x \leq 0$. Which of these sets is the set of all whole numbers? The empty set? The set $\{0\}$?

4. Relations

We shall next consider briefly the concept of relation, or more precisely, *binary relation*. There are relations other than binary ones, but since we will not be concerned with them in our early work we will drop the adjective "binary" and refer simply to relations.

We have already used one special relation, the *equals* relation. When we say that $x = y$ we are affirming that a particular relationship exists between the pair of objects x and y. Another example of a relation is the *less than* relation, denoted by $<$, which is associated, let us say, with whole numbers. This relation holds for the pair of numbers 2, 5, since $2 < 5$. It does not hold for the pair of numbers 5, 2, since 5 is not less than 2. Nor does it hold for the pair of numbers 7, 7.

To take a nonmathematical example, we might consider the relation *is a brother of*, which is associated with people. If the statement "Joe is a brother of Jane" is true, and if Jane is a girl, it would not be true that "Jane is a brother of Joe."

From these illustrations the essential features of the concept of (binary) relation becomes clear: A relation is associated with a certain set of objects and is said to hold between certain pairs of these objects in a given order.

The set of all objects which make up the pairs with which the relation is associated is called the *field* of the relation; sometimes this is explicitly described, but more often it is tacitly assumed. For example, in speaking of the relation *is a brother of* we tacitly assume that the field is the set of people, while in the case of the relation $<$ the field is assumed to consist of numbers. Still, if we wish to be precise about a relation we should specify the elements of its field; for example, in the case of $<$ we should state whether we mean the field to be only the whole numbers, or the fractions, or all real numbers.

When we speak of a pair of objects for which we wish to distinguish one of the elements as first and the other as second we shall call it an *ordered pair*. If x and y are objects we wish to consider in the order x first and y second we shall denote this ordered pair of objects by $\langle x, y \rangle$. Thus the ordered pairs $\langle 2, 5 \rangle$ and $\langle 5, 2 \rangle$ are not the same, even though each is made up of the numbers 2 and 5. The reader should note that an ordered pair is not simply a set with two elements. The set $\{2, 5\}$ is the same as the set $\{5, 2\}$, but $\langle 2, 5 \rangle$ is different from $\langle 5, 2 \rangle$. More generally, $\{a, b\} = \{b, a\}$ since each set contains the same two elements, a and b, but $\langle a, b \rangle = \langle c, d \rangle$ if and only if $a = c$ and $b = d$.

We shall use the following notation: If a relation R holds for an ordered pair $\langle x, y \rangle$, we write $x \; R \; y$. Thus, if R is the relation *is a brother of*, and if x is Joe and y is Jane, we can symbolize our earlier example by asserting that $x \; R \; y$ but *not* $y \; R \; x$. The fact that R does not hold for the ordered pair $\langle y, x \rangle$ is sometimes symbolized $y \not R \; x$.

Certain kinds of relations are especially important in mathematics. Here we wish to call attention to relations called *reflexive*, *symmetric*, or *transitive*.

If a relation R has the property that $x \; R \; x$ for *every* object x in its field, then R is said to be a *reflexive* relation. The *equals* relation is reflexive, since $x = x$ for every x. The relation *is an even number which is not greater than*, however, is not reflexive, for while it holds for certain pairs $\langle x, x \rangle$, such as $\langle 4, 4 \rangle$, it does not hold for every pair $\langle x, x \rangle$. (E.g., it does not hold for $\langle 5, 5 \rangle$.) The relation *is a brother of* is certainly not reflexive, since it holds for no pair $\langle x, x \rangle$; no one is his own brother.

A relation R is said to be *symmetric* if, whenever R holds for an ordered pair $\langle x, y \rangle$, it also holds for $\langle y, x \rangle$. The *equals* relation is symmetric, for if $x = y$ then $y = x$ (i.e., if x is the same object as y, then of course y is the same object as x). Another example of a symmetric relation is the relation *in the same room as*. If Abercrombie is in the same room as Fitch, then certainly Fitch is in the same room as Abercrombie. On the other hand the *less than* relation is not symmetric, since it is true that $2 < 5$ but not that $5 < 2$.

If the relation R has the property that whenever $x \; R \; y$ and $y \; R \; z$ we also have $x \; R \; z$, the relation is said to be *transitive*. The *equals* relation and the relation *in the same room as* are both transitive. (If Abercrombie is in the same room as Fitch, and Fitch is in the same room as Fenner, then Abercrombie

is in the same room as Fenner.) The relation *stands next in line to* is an example of a nontransitive relation, for if Abercrombie stands next in line to Fitch, and Fitch stands next in line to Fenner, then Abercrombie does not stand next in line to Fenner. (Note that this relation is symmetric, however.) Another relation which is not transitive is the relation *wins at tennis from*. Unlike the case of the relation *stands next in line to*, this relation often holds for three ordered pairs $\langle x, y\rangle$, $\langle y, z\rangle$, $\langle x, z\rangle$. But sometimes it may happen that the relation holds for $\langle x, y\rangle$ and $\langle y, z\rangle$ but not for $\langle x, z\rangle$, and these cases show that the relation is not transitive.

We have a *Principle of Extensionality for Relations* similar to the principle of extensionality for sets. It reads as follows: If R and S are relations which hold for exactly the same ordered pairs of objects, then $R = S$. Hence in mathematics a relation is completely determined by the ordered pairs of objects for which it holds. In technical language we can express the principle of extensionality for relations as follows: Whenever R and S are relations such that for all ordered pairs $\langle x, y\rangle$ we have $x\, R\, y$ if and only if $x\, S\, y$, then $R = S$. For a rather trivial example, let R be the relation *holds more quarts than*, and S the relation *holds more pints than*, both over the field of pots. Clearly $R = S$. As another example, let R be the relation $<$ for whole numbers, and let S be the relation which holds for an ordered pair $\langle x, y\rangle$ of whole numbers only in case there is a positive number z for which $x + z = y$. A moment's reflection should convince the reader that both these relations hold for exactly the same ordered pairs of numbers. Hence, by the Principle of Extensionality, R and S are the same relation.

EXERCISES

1. Which of the following relations is reflexive? Symmetric? Transitive?

- **(a)** *taller than* (for the set of all men on the University of Wyoming basketball squad).
- **(b)** *belongs to the same club as* (for the set of all students at Saratoga High School).
- **(c)** *less than or equal to* (for the set of all whole numbers).
- **(d)** *is a subset of* (for the set of sets of whole numbers).

2. **(a)** Find a relation which is reflexive and symmetric but not transitive.

- **(b)** Find a relation which is reflexive and transitive but not symmetric.
- **(c)** Find a relation which is symmetric and transitive but not reflexive. (*Warning*: There is essentially only one such relation, and it is a relation of a very special kind.)

3. Let A be the set of all positive rational numbers (i.e., fractions); let S be the binary relation on A such that $x\, S\, y$ if and only if for some $z \in A$, $x + z = y$; and let R be the binary relation on A such that $x\, R\, y$ if and only if for some $z \in A$ such that $z > 1$, $xz = y$.

Show that $S = R$.

4. Let B be the set of all positive whole numbers and let S and R be defined as in problem 3, but with A replaced by B in the definitions.

(a) Show that $S \neq R$ in this case.
(b) Show that if $x\ R\ y$ then $x\ S\ y$.

5. Let C be the set of all rational numbers (i.e., fractions); let S be the binary relation on C such that $x\ S\ y$ if and only if for some $z \in C$ such that $z > 0$, $x + z = y$; and let R be the binary relation on C such that $x\ R\ y$ if and only if for some $z \in C$ such that $z > 1$, $xz = y$.

Show $S \neq R$. Exhibit an ordered pair $\langle x, y\rangle$ for which $x\ S\ y$ but not $x\ R\ y$ and also an ordered pair $\langle z, w\rangle$ for which $z\ R\ w$ but not $z\ S\ w$.

5. *Functions*

The reader has undoubtedly encountered the notion of *function* and has some familiarity with it. Intuitively speaking, a function may be described as an abstract operation which acts on certain objects (called *arguments* of the function), the result of any such action being a new object (called the *value* of the function for the given argument).

For example, consider the operation which acts on each page of this book and produces the first symbol on the first line of that page. This is one example of a function. Functions with which we are more familiar are those which operate on numbers and produce numbers. Such a function, for example, is the function which operates on each real number x and produces the real number x^2.

If f is a function and if x is an object on which f may act, then the object which results from acting on x with f is denoted by fx. (Frequently one finds the notation $f(x)$ rather than fx employed, but we shall resort to the use of parentheses only where necessary to avoid ambiguity.)

If f is any function, then by the *domain of* f we mean the set of all objects x on which f may act; that is, the domain is the set of all arguments of the function. In our first example of a function above, the domain of the function is the set of all pages in this book, while in our second example it is the set of all real numbers.

Just as in the case of sets and of relations, we have a *Principle of Extensionality for Functions*. This may be formulated as follows: If f and g are any functions which have the same domain, and if for each element x of this domain we have $fx = gx$, then $f = g$. Intuitively speaking, the content of this statement may be expressed by saying that there is nothing more to a function than the things on which it acts and the objects it produces when it acts on these things.

If f is a function then the set of all objects produced by action of f on the different elements in its domain is called the *range* (*range of values*) *of* f. In mathematical terminology we may say that for any object y, y belongs to the range of f if and only if there is an x in the domain of f such that $y = fx$. Referring to the examples of functions given above, we have as the range of the first function the collection of all symbols which occur at the beginning of the first line of a page of this book, while the range of the second function is the set of all nonnegative real numbers.

If f is a function, if A is the domain of f, and if B is the range of f, then we say that f *maps A onto B*. If C is any set which includes the range B (i.e., such that $B \subseteq C$), then we say that f *maps A into C*. Note then, that when we say the function f maps A *onto* B we mean that (**i**) A is the domain of f, (**ii**) for every x in this domain fx is in B, and (**iii**) there are no other elements in B except these elements fx. When we say the function f maps A *into* C we mean that (**i**) A is the domain of f and (**ii**) for every x in this domain fx is in C; but we leave open the question whether there are elements in C other than these objects fx.

In our example of the function f which acts on each real number x and produces the real number x^2 (so that for each real number x we have $fx = x^2$), we may say that f maps the set of real numbers onto the set of nonnegative real numbers; and we may also say that f maps the set of real numbers into the set of real numbers. Note that it would also be correct to say that f maps the set of real numbers into the set of nonnegative real numbers.

Now let A and B be any sets and let f be a function which maps A into B.

1. We say f is a *constant mapping* if and only if for all x, y in A we have $fx = fy$ (that is, f gives the same value to every element in its domain).

2. We say f is *one-one* if and only if whenever x and y are *distinct* elements of A, then fx and fy are *distinct* elements of B (i.e., if x, y are in A and $x \neq y$, then $fx \neq fy$). An equivalent form of this condition is that if x, y are in A and $fx = fy$ then $x = y$. (Intuitively, the condition for a function f to be one-one is that f never gives the same value to two different objects on which it acts.)

3. We call f an *identity* (*injection*) function if and only if for any x in A we have $fx = x$. Note that in this case A must be a subset of B and f is certainly one-one.

Let A be the set of all real numbers and let f map A into A with $fx = 3$ for all $x \in A$; then f is an example of a constant map. For the same set A, the function g which maps A onto A with $gx = 3x + 2$ for all $x \in A$ is easily seen to be a one-one map, since whenever $x \neq y$ we have $3x + 2 \neq 3y + 2$. However, the function h which maps A into itself with $hx = x^2$ for all $x \in A$ is not one-one; this is so since (for example) $h2 = h(-2)$ although $2 \neq -2$. Note also that neither g nor h is a constant map.

If A is any set and if f is a function which maps A into itself then we say f is an *operation on A*, or more precisely, a *unary operation on A*.

If A is any set and if f is a function whose domain is the set of all ordered pairs $\langle x, y\rangle$ for all $x, y \in A$, and if $f\langle x, y\rangle \in A$ for all $x, y \in A$, then we call f a *binary operation on A*. Often we simplify our notation and write fxy instead of $f\langle x, y\rangle$ in the case of a binary operation f.

The functions f, g, h described above, whose domain is the set A of real numbers and for which we have $fx = 3$, $gx = 3x + 2$, and $hx = x^2$ for all $x \in A$, are examples of unary operations. On the other hand if the domain of a function h is the set of all real numbers x, and if $hx = \sqrt{x}$ for every such x, then h is *not* a unary operation.

If D is the set of all natural numbers then the function T, which acts on the ordered pairs $\langle x, y\rangle$ for all $x, y \in D$ with $T\langle x, y\rangle = x + y$, is a binary operation on D. So also is the function E defined by $E\langle x, y\rangle = (x + 1)2y$, for another example. We note in passing that $T\langle x, y\rangle = T\langle y, x\rangle$ for all numbers x and y, since $x + y = y + x$; however, in general $E\langle x, y\rangle \neq E\langle y, x\rangle$ since, for example, $E\langle 1, 2\rangle = 8$ and $E\langle 2, 1\rangle = 6$ but $8 \neq 6$.

Exercises

Each of the following functions is assumed to have as its domain the set of those real numbers which, when substituted for the variable "x" or "y" in the expression which defines the function, yields a real number as the value of the expression. Give the domain and the range of each function.

1. The function f whose value, fx, at x is given by $fx = x^2$.
2. The function g whose value, gx, at x is given by $gx = -\sqrt{x}$.
3. The function e whose value, ex, at x is given by $ex = \sqrt{-x}$.
4. The function F whose value, Fx, at x is given by $Fx = \sin x$.
5. The function G whose value, Gz, at z is given by $Gz = 1$.
6. The function h whose value, hz, at z is given by $hz = \sqrt{9 - z^2}$.
7. The function j whose value, jx, at x is given by $jx = \sin x$.
8. The function H whose value, Hx, at x is given by $Hx = \sin^2 x + \cos^2 x$.
9. The function J whose value, Jy, at y is given by $Jy = \dfrac{y^2 + 4}{y^2 - 1}$.
10. The function k whose value, kx, at x is given by $kx = \log_{10} 10^x$.
11. The function K whose value, Ky, at y is given by $Ky = \sqrt{y^2}$.
12. The function p whose value, px, at x is given by $px = (\sqrt{x})^2$.
13. The function r whose value, ry, at y is given by $ry = \sec^2 y - \tan^2 y$.
14. Which of the above functions are one-one? Constant? Identity?
15. What can you say about the functions F and j?
16. Are k and p the same functions? If not, why not?
17. Which of the above functions are operations (on their domain)?
18. Let f be a function having as its domain the set of all ordered pairs $\langle x, y\rangle$ for all positive integers x and y. Which of the following functions f are (binary) operations on this domain?

(a) The function f whose value $f\langle x, y\rangle$ is given by $f\langle x, y\rangle = x - y$ for all positive integers x and y.
(b) The function f whose value $f\langle x, y\rangle$ is given by $f\langle x, y\rangle = x \cdot y$ for all positive integers x and y.
(c) The function f whose value $f\langle x, y\rangle$ is given by $f\langle x, y\rangle = x^y$ for all positive integers x and y.
(d) The function f whose value $f\langle x, y\rangle$ is given by $f\langle x, y\rangle = \dfrac{x}{y}$ for all positive integers x and y.

II

An Axiomatic Development of the Positive Integers

1. Axioms and Undefined Terms

The first and the most familiar of the great masterpieces of mathematical literature is Euclid's *Elements*. Its importance derives not so much from the actual theorems it contains—most of which were known before Euclid's time—but from the manner of its organization. This is the first book on mathematics in which an author attempts to present the material in a strictly logical, deductive fashion. It was Euclid's great contribution to recognize that all of the many theorems of geometry can be deduced from a few elementary statements he called, as do modern mathematicians, *axioms* or *postulates*. (No distinction is now made between these two terms; we shall most frequently use the term "axiom." The old description of an axiom as a "self-evident truth," and a postulate as an "assumption" is completely misleading. An axiom is not self-evident, nor does it need to be true—it is simply an assumption.) In the light of modern mathematics Euclid's logical organization of geometry, though faulty in many details, is considered one of the major breakthroughs on the frontiers of mathematics, and in a very important sense Euclid may be considered the first modern mathematician.

Just as Euclid was concerned with the logical structure of geometry, so modern mathematicians are concerned with the logical structure of all branches of mathematics. If, in arranging the theorems of a particular branch of mathematics in logical order, the proof of Theorem T requires the statement of Theorem S, then Theorem T should be placed after Theorem S. It is quite obvious that in order to arrange all the known theorems of a particular branch of mathematics in such a logical order there must be some initial statements which are *not proved* on the basis of previous theorems. The investigator carrying out this study calls these unproved statements his *axioms*, and his study is called an *axiomatic theory*.

The reader should not infer that only one logical arrangement of theorems in a particular branch of mathematics is possible—in other words, that only one set of axioms is possible. On the contrary, it can be shown that in any axiomatic theory there are many possible choices for the set of axioms.

Thus the fact that a certain statement is chosen as an axiom for a theory does not mean that there is anything intrinsically unprovable about it.

In subsequent sections of this chapter an axiomatic theory of the positive integers, 1, 2, 3 . . . , will be developed. From a set of four axioms the theory of positive integers will be deduced by use of logic and set theory alone. Euclid's geometric axioms are statements which seem intuitively to be correct facts about notions we have concerning certain objects we call *points* and *lines*. The reader will observe that our axioms about the positive integers will also seem to be intuitively correct statements about the counting numbers he uses in everyday life.

In addition to recognizing the need for unproved statements at the beginning of any logical organization of theorems, we must recognize a concomitant need for *undefined terms*. Any definition of a new term in a theory is given by using terms or words previously introduced. For example, in geometry the term "parallelogram" is defined as a quadrilateral which has opposite sides parallel. In this definition the words "quadrilateral," "opposite," "side," and "parallel" are used, and this is a valid definition only if these words have been previously introduced. A reader opening a geometry book at the page on which this definition appears would be expected to look back for the definitions of "quadrilateral," "opposite," "side," and "parallel." These in turn would be defined by using words previously introduced. Obviously there must be some terms at the beginning of the theory to start this chain of definitions. These are the undefined terms.

Any logically rigorous axiomatic treatment of a branch of mathematics begins with a clearly delineated list of such undefined terms. Most high-school texts on geometry point out carefully the need for axioms. Many, however, fail to note the equally important need for undefined terms. In most careful works on geometry, "line" and "point" are among the undefined terms.

Almost every axiomatic theory is concerned with certain sets of objects; for example, axiomatic geometry is concerned with sets of points and lines. Our axiomatic theory, starting in the next section, will be a study of the set of positive integers. In proving the theorems of such an axiomatic theory, the only permissible steps consist in applications of the laws of logic and of set theory to the axioms and definitions and theorems of the system. No appeal to intuitive knowledge of the objects under discussion may be made. Of course in *discovering* the steps of a proof the mathematician will usually have certain intuitive ideas in mind which lead him to find his proof; indeed, it is generally his intuitive ideas about the subject matter which lead him to guess what theorems can be proved in the first place. It is important to realize, however, that even though intuition may lead one to guess that a certain theorem is true, the actual steps in the proof of the theorem must be justified on the basis of logic applied to previous theorems, axioms, and definitions. This point will become clearer to the reader as he follows the axiomatic development in the sections that follow.

2. *Peano Axioms*

We shall now consider the theory of positive integers, both as an important example of the axiomatic method and as a means of gaining new insight into the familiar processes of arithmetic.

In 1889 an Italian mathematician, Giuseppe Peano, first developed a deductive theory of positive integers, starting with *number*, *successor*, *sum*, and *product* as undefined terms. Choosing a system of nine axioms, he showed how definitions and theorems could be developed so as to obtain a complete theory of the natural number system. We shall follow the spirit and the general method of Peano, with considerable modification of detail.

There are certain objects of our universe called *positive integers*. We will not attempt to say just *which* objects these integers are; hence "positive integers" will be one of the undefined terms of our theory. We shall use the letter "P" to denote the set of all those objects we call positive integers.

There is a certain element of P called the *unit element*, or *one*, and represented by the symbol "1". Since we do not specify *which* element of P this unit element is, "one" is also an undefined term.

Finally, there is a certain binary operation on P—that is, a function which produces a positive integer when acting on any two given positive integers (taken in a given order)— called the *addition operation* and denoted by the symbol "$+$". Since we do not say *which* function is called the "addition operation," this term, too, is undefined in our theory. We shall write $+\langle x, y\rangle$, or more simply $x + y$, to indicate the object in P obtained by applying the addition operation to the two elements x and y of P, in this order.

Thus our theory of positive integers has as its basis three undefined concepts: a certain set P, a certain element 1 of P, and a certain binary operation $+$ on P. Intuitively, we are thinking of the elements of P, the positive integers of this theory, as the ordinary counting numbers; and we think of 1 and $+$ in their everyday use. However, according to the nature of an axiomatic development our theorems must be obtained from definitions, axioms, and prior theorems by using only the laws of logic and set theory. We may never insert a statement in a proof on the grounds that it is "obviously" true because of the intuitive meaning of the terms. At a later time we shall indicate a great advantage which accrues to our theory by virtue of this restriction we impose on its proofs.

Our development will be based upon four axioms involving our undefined terms.

AXIOM P1. *If we select an arbitrary positive integer, and if we act with the addition operation on this number and one, the resulting integer is different from one.* In technical notation we can express this more compactly as follows: *For all* $x \in P$, $x + 1 \neq 1$. (Instead of speaking about "applying the addition operation to two positive integers, x and y," we shall use the more familiar language "adding y to x" from now on.)

AXIOM P2. *If we select two distinct positive integers, and if we add one to the first of these and also add one to the second, the numbers resulting from these operations will also be distinct from one another.* In technical notation: *For all* $x, y \in P$, *if* $x \neq y$ *then* $x + 1 \neq y + 1$. By elementary logic this axiom is equivalent to the following statement: *For all* $x, y \in P$, *if* $x + 1 = y + 1$ *then* $x = y$.[1]

We state the remaining two axioms directly in technical notation, as their rendering in English unassisted by symbols would be so cumbersome as to leave the essential meaning obscure.

AXIOM P3. *For all* $x, y \in P$, $x + (y + 1) = (x + y) + 1$. *Intuitively, this axiom is seen to express a special case of the familiar associative law for addition.*

AXIOM P4. *If G is any subset of P (i.e., any set of positive integers) such that*

(i) $1 \in G$, *and*

(ii) *whenever* $x \in G$ *then also* $x + 1 \in G$,

then $G = P$ (i.e., every positive integer is in G). We call this the *Axiom of Mathematical Induction*, because, as we shall see in the sequel, it is closely connected with the familiar principle of mathematical induction; indeed, the axiom is really nothing more than a precise way of stating this principle—although different formulations are admittedly possible.

A set G of positive integers which satisfies condition (**ii**) of Axiom P4 is said to be *closed under addition of 1*. Using this terminology, Axiom P4 may be rephrased as follows: *The only set of positive integers which contains 1 as an element and which is closed under addition of 1 is the set of all positive integers.*

Let us think intuitively about the counting numbers for a moment. Suppose that G is a set of these numbers, and that G is closed under addition of 1; i.e., whenever $x \in G$ then also $x + 1 \in G$. Suppose, too, that a certain number y is in G. Then applying the hypothesis that G is closed, we conclude that $y + 1$ is in G. Applying the hypothesis a second time we conclude that $(y + 1) + 1$, or in familiar terms $y + 2$, is in G. Another application shows that $y + 3$ is in G. And so on.

[1] The law of logic used here states that no matter what statements Q and R may be, the sentence "If not-Q then not-R" is equivalent to "If R then Q", in the sense that if either one of these sentences is true then the other must also be true.

In other words, if a set which is closed under addition of 1 contains a number y, it also contains every *greater* number. In particular, if a set which is closed under addition of 1 contains the number 1, then it contains every number whatever. In this way, we see intuitively that Axiom P4 expresses a true statement about the counting numbers.

Note, however, that the above considerations which help us to see the truth of Axiom P4 do not constitute a *proof* of this axiom within our theory. For one thing, the argument involves terms, such as 2, 3, and *greater than*, which are not terms of logic or set theory, not undefined terms of our theory, and which have not been defined in our theory; hence this argument on the face of it cannot be a proof in our theory. For another thing, at a certain point the argument employs the rather vague phrase "and so on." This phrase is not ordinarily considered a proper logical component of any axiomatic theory, and thus the argument has only heuristic status. In the next section we shall encounter genuine proofs as we begin to develop our theory from the axioms.

3. *Preliminary Theorems*

As children we learned intuitively that $1 + 1 = 2$, $2 + 1 = 3$, $2 + 2 = 4$, and so on. While plausible arguments are given to grade-school children to justify these statements, proofs—in the sense of logical deductions from prior premises—are not given. As we shall see, in our development the first two statements appear as definitions, while the statement that $2 + 2 = 4$ is a theorem. However, before we can prove any such theorem we must first state explicitly what numbers are represented in our axiom system by the symbols "2" and "4"—since these symbols have not yet made a formal entrance into our theory.

DEFINITION 2-3-1. $2 = 1 + 1$, $3 = 2 + 1$, *and* $4 = 3 + 1$. That is, we agree to use the symbol "2" as a name for the number obtained by applying the operation $+$ to the pair $\langle 1, 1\rangle$ of numbers.

The first theorem, which follows, is an example of a *particular* theorem—i.e., a theorem which states a fact concerning particular numbers of the set P. Later on we shall have examples of *general* theorems—i.e., theorems which state facts about all numbers in P.

THEOREM 2-3-2. $2 + 2 = 4$.

In proving theorems we shall use the format customarily used in elementary geometry books. The statements which make up the proof will be numbered, and opposite each step will appear the reason which justifies it.

A very frequently given reason will be "by the meaning of '='." For example, if we wish to combine two steps in a proof,

$$a = b$$

and

$$b = c$$

to obtain

$$a = c$$

the reason given for the last step would be "by the meaning of '=' from the two steps above." (The reader is invited to review the meaning of "=" by rereading Section 2 of Chapter I.) Because this reason will be stated so very frequently, we shall henceforth use the shorthand "by E" for the statement "by the meaning of '='." The letter "E" is chosen merely because it is the first letter of the word "equality".

Now let us proceed with the proof of Theorem 2-3-2.

1. $3 + 1 = 4$; by Definition 2-3-1.
2. $2 + 1 = 3$; by Definition 2-3-1.
3. $1 + 1 = 2$; by Definition 2-3-1.
4. $(2 + 1) + 1 = 3 + 1$; by line **2** and E.
5. $(2 + 1) + 1 = 4$; by E from lines **1** and **4**.
6. $(2 + 1) + 1 = 2 + (1 + 1)$; by Axiom P3.
7. $2 + (1 + 1) = 2 + 2$; by E from line **3**.
8. $(2 + 1) + 1 = 2 + 2$; by E from lines **6** and **7**.
9. $2 + 2 = 4$; by E from lines **5** and **8**.

In a similar manner, the reader could, for example, define the numbers 5 and 6 and then give proofs for the statements that $3 + 2 = 5$ and $4 + 2 = 6$. If he were so inclined, he might then continue with the necessary definitions and proofs of the rules for the addition of all the possible pairs of the numbers from 1 to 12—or even further. However, he would pretty soon find this a tiresome game because in all of these proofs the same idea is used over and over. To obtain new and more interesting methods of proof we turn our attention now to some examples of general theorems.

THEOREM 2-3-3. *For all* $x \in P$, $x \neq x + 1$. *That is, by adding* 1 *to any number we always get a number different from the one with which we start.*

Of course, from our intuitive knowledge of positive integers we are well aware of this theorem. But remember that in listing this statement as a theorem we are doing something more than asserting its truth. Our main concern is to show that these facts fit *logically* into our axiomatic framework. Trivial as Theorem 2-3-3 may seem, the fact that it *can be proved* on the basis of our axioms is far from trivial.

Before proceeding with the proof, a few remarks in preview are in order. Theorem 2-3-3 and many which follow are examples of a type of theorem which asserts that every element of P possesses a certain property q. The method of proof is to form the set G, consisting of all those elements from P which have this property q, and then to show that G is the same as P itself; for clearly, from the way in which G is defined, if we can show that $G = P$ then we have, in effect, shown that *every* element of P has the property q. First we show that $1 \in G$. Next we prove that whenever $x \in G$ then also $x + 1 \in G$. Then on the basis of Axiom P4 we may conclude that $G = P$.

As an illustration of this type of reasoning, let us consider the following statement: "All college students like mathematics." Letting $\bar{P}$ be the set of all college students, we can express this by: "For every $x \in \bar{P}$, x likes mathematics." Here the property q is the property of liking mathematics. We form the set G of all those college students who have this property and then try to show that this group G of students is the same as the set $\bar{P}$ of all college students. In order to show this we first interview Mr. Aaron A. Aab, the college student whose name appears at the very top of the alphabetical list of all college students. Mr. Aab says that he is crazy about mathematics, and that anyone who doesn't like it should have his head examined. This clearly puts Mr. Aab in the set G. Next, we attempt to prove that any time we find a college student who likes mathematics (and so is in the set G), the student whose name appears next on the alphabetical list also likes mathematics (and so is also in set G). If we could show this (we can't—as the statement is not quite true), it would follow that all students of $\bar{P}$ are in the set G, and this would prove the theorem.

Note that both steps of the induction proof are essential. In the second step we do not, as the reader may mistakenly suppose, assume that some student actually likes mathematics. Instead, we seek to prove that if any student does, then the one whose name appears next on the alphabetical list does also. As a matter of fact, this statement would be correct if *no* student likes mathematics, for a proposition of the form *if A then B* is true when both A and B are false (cf. the discussion of "if . . . then" in Section 5 of Chapter I). Thus the verification step that A. A. Aab likes mathematics is quite an essential part of the proof.

The two parts of the proof combine to establish the statement in full generality. For after having verified that A. A. Aab is in G, we find from the induction step that the college student whose name appears next on the list (Mr. Zelmer Z. Aab, a cousin) is also in G. Using the induction step again, we see that Mr. Adam B. Aac, whose name comes next, likewise is in G, and continuing in this way to examine the names of the students on the list, one after another, we finally verify that every student is in G.

Of course this illustration is only intended to provide an intuitive picture of the reasons why proofs by mathematical induction serve to establish general statements. In the actual proofs to be given we appeal only to axioms and laws of logic.

One other remark should be made before we consider the proof of Theorem 2-3-3. In the proof of this theorem, as in the proof of most general theorems, there are a number of different steps. As was indicated in the prefatory "A Note to the Reader," a few of these are key steps, revealing the basic structure of the proof. These are indicated by a double pointer. Other major steps are marked by a single pointer, while the subsidiary steps are unmarked. Thus it is possible to read the proof in three different ways. The double-marked statements, read alone, give the basic plan of the proof. The double-marked and marked steps, taken together, indicate not only the plan of the proof, but also how the plan is to be implemented. Finally, the reading of all steps gives the detailed proof.

We now give a detailed proof of Theorem 2-3-3.

▶▶**1.** Let G be the set of all positive integers x such that $x \neq x + 1$.
▶**2.** $1 \in G$; by line **1** and Axiom P1.
▶**3.** Let x be any element in G.
4. $x \neq x + 1$; by lines **1** and **3**.
▶**5.** $x + 1 \neq (x + 1) + 1$; by line **4** and Axiom P2.
▶**6.** $x + 1 \in G$; by lines **1** and **5**.
7. For any $x \in P$, if $x \in G$ then also $x + 1 \in G$; by lines **3** through **6**.
▶▶**8.** $G = P$; by lines **2** and **7** and Axiom P4.
9. For all $x \in P$, $x \neq x + 1$; by lines **1** and **8**.

Since this proof brings in many new ideas, let us review the meaning and the justification of each of its steps. In line **1** we simply agree to use the letter "G" as a name for a certain set of numbers, and indeed a number is put into G just in case it is different from the number obtained by adding 1 to itself. As explained above, our object is to show that actually all numbers are in G—for this is equivalent to proving our theorem. The letter "x" is used simply as a device for stating briefly which numbers are put into the set G.

Axiom P1 assures us that $1 \neq x + 1$ no matter *what* number x may be; hence *in particular*, $1 \neq 1 + 1$. That is, adding 1 to 1 gives us something different from 1 itself; hence 1 qualifies as an element of G. This is the content of line **2**.

In line **3** we agree to use "x" as the name of one of the elements which was put into G. We do not say *which* of the numbers in G is to be denoted by "x," and it does not matter which; so we use the word "any". The reader should imagine that the element x is chosen from G in an arbitrary way; but once chosen it is held fixed, and the same element is discussed in the following lines. Notice that in the earlier line **1** the letter "x" was used too, but in a different way.

In line **4** we simply say that the element chosen (and called "x") in the previous line is different from the number obtained by adding 1 to itself. Of course the reason is simply that x was chosen from G, and that all numbers in G have this property according to line **1**.

Axiom P2 assures us that if we start with two different numbers, and add 1 to each, the resulting two numbers are different from one another. By applying this axiom we pass from line **4** to **5**.

In line **6** we point out that the number $x + 1$ qualifies for admission as an element of the set G, since (according to line **5**) when we add 1 to it we get a number different from $x + 1$ itself.

Line **7** is essentially a summing up of the argument beginning on line **3** and ending on line **6**, since in this four-line argument we begin with any number chosen from G and then show that when we add 1 to it the resulting number must also be in G. Such a summing up is called an application of the *Deduction Theorem* of logic.

Line **8** is obtained by a simple application of Axiom P4, since lines **2** and **7** constitute the hypotheses of the axiom and line **8** the conclusion.

According to line **1**, every element of G has the property that when 1 is added to it a number results which is different from the first; according to line **8**, the set G is the same as the set P; hence we may conclude that every element of P has the stated property, and this is the content of line **9**.

We have been at some pains to explain fully each step in this proof, but the reader must learn to interpret the mathematical language of the steps themselves, as we shall discontinue giving additional explanatory material except when some new or special point arises.

We next present another theorem which will seem intuitively evident. But again the reader is reminded that although we may appeal to our intuitive knowledge of the positive integers to suggest possible theorems about these numbers, such theorems become a part of our axiomatic theory only after we have *proved* them on the basis of the axioms, previously proved theorems, and previous definitions.

THEOREM 2-3-4. *If $x \in P$ then either $x = 1$ or there is a $y \in P$ such that* $x = y + 1$. That is, any number is either 1, or it can be obtained from some other number by adding 1.

Let us call a number x of P a *successor* if there is a number $y \in P$ such that $x = y + 1$. We wish to prove that *every* element of P is either the element 1 or else is a successor. The idea of the proof is to form a set G by taking as its elements the number 1 as well as all those elements of P which are successors, and then showing that every element of P is in G (i.e., that $G = P$). The details are as follows.

Proof

▶▶**1.** Let G be the subset of P whose elements consist of 1 and all elements $y + 1$ (for any $y \in P$).

▶**2.** $1 \in G$; by line **1**.

▶**3.** Let y be any element of G.

▶**4.** $y + 1 \in G$; by line **1**.

5. For every $y \in P$, if $y \in G$ then $y + 1 \in G$; by lines **3** and **4**. (Application of Deduction Theorem of logic; cf. explanatory material following previous theorem.)

▶▶**6.** $G = P$; by lines **2** and **5** and Axiom P4.

7. If $x \in P$ then either $x = 1$ or else $x = y + 1$ for some $y \in P$; by lines **1** and **6**.

It is perhaps worth elaborating the justification for line **4**. We are interested in showing that a certain element of P, namely $y + 1$, is an element of G (where y is an element chosen in an arbitrary way from the set G, according to line **3**). In order to determine whether $y + 1$ qualifies as an element of the set G, we must refer to the definition of this set (given on line **1**). From that definition we see that two kinds of elements were put into G, namely the element 1 and those elements of P (called successors) which can be obtained by adding 1 to some other element of P. Now we see that the element $y + 1$ with which we are dealing on line **4** qualifies as an element of G because it is a successor—i.e., $y + 1$ can be obtained by adding 1 to some other element of P, namely by adding 1 to y.

Exercises

1. Define the symbols "5" and "6". Prove that $4 + 2 = 6$.

2. Theorem 2-3-4 was proved with the usual inclusive interpretation of the word "or". Prove that Theorem 2-3-4 is also true with the exclusive interpretation of "or" by showing that "not both" disjuncts can be true.

4. *Laws of Addition*

In our daily use of the counting numbers we make frequent use of certain rules or laws which are so taken for granted that most people do not even think of them as rules. One of these rules is the basis for giving meaning to the symbol "$2 + 3 + 4$", for example. Now we recall that addition has been introduced as a binary operation on the set of positive integers. Hence "$2 + 3$" is meaningful, and also "$(2 + 3) + 4$". In fact "$2 + 3$" denotes the element of P obtained by applying the binary operation of addition to the ordered pair $\langle 2, 3\rangle$. Similarly "$(2 + 3) + 4$" denotes the element of P obtained by applying the addition operation to the ordered pair of elements $\langle 2 + 3, 4\rangle$, while "$2 + (3 + 4)$" denotes that element obtained by operating with $+$ on the pair $\langle 2, 3 + 4\rangle$. We recognize intuitively (Could you prove it?) that carrying out these two pairs of additions leads to the same result. Because of this we may interpret the ambiguous notation "$2 + 3 + 4$" to mean either $2 + (3 + 4)$ or $(2 + 3) + 4$. Clearly the remarks we have made about the particular numbers, 2, 3, and 4, hold for any three numbers. Our next theorem is the statement of this fact.

THEOREM 2-4-1. THE ASSOCIATIVE LAW OF ADDITION. *For all* $x, y, z \in P$, $(x + y) + z = x + (y + z)$.

What mental processes might we go through in looking for a proof of this theorem? It certainly seems to be a plausible theorem, and we might expect that our axiomatic system has sufficient power to enable us to prove it. In fact, we note that Axiom P3, which says that $(x + y) + 1 = x + (y + 1)$ for any x, $y \in P$, is a special case of the theorem, so we know that the theorem holds for any $x, y \in P$ and for $z = 1$. Our method of attack, then, might be to use induction on the z.

Thus, in proving this theorem we shall make an application of the principle of mathematical induction as formulated in our Axiom P4. Now in order to apply this axiom we must describe a certain set G of elements of P. We notice that in the proof of Theorem 2-3-4 such a set was described on line **1**, and its description did not depend on any previously chosen object. However, in the present proof we shall first select elements x and y from P in an arbitrary way (line **1**) and then choose the elements of G in a certain manner (line **2**). In fact, in order to qualify as an element of G, an element z will have to be such that $(x + y) + z$ is the same as $x + (y + z)$, where x and y are the elements chosen on line **1**. After applying Axiom P4 we will discover that $G = P$ (line **16**), so that for *every* $z \in P$ we have $(x + y) + z = x + (y + z)$. Since x and y were not chosen in some special way, but were taken to be any elements of P whatever, we can infer that the equation $(x + y) + z = x + (y + z)$ holds for *any* elements x, y, z of P. The details of the proof are as follows:

Proof

▶▶ **1.** Let x, y be any elements in P.

▶▶ **2.** Having chosen x and y let G be the set of all those positive integers z in P such that $(x + y) + z = x + (y + z)$.

▶ **3.** $1 \in G$; by Axiom P3 and line **2**.

▶ **4.** Let z be any element in G.

5. $(x + y) + z = x + (y + z)$; by lines **2** and **4**.

6. $(x + y) + (z + 1) = [(x + y) + z] + 1$; by Axiom P3.

7. $[(x + y) + z] + 1 = [x + (y + z)] + 1$; by E from line **5**.

8. $(x + y) + (z + 1) = [x + (y + z)] + 1$; by lines **6** and **7** and E.

9. $[x + (y + z)] + 1 = x + [(y + z) + 1]$; by Axiom P3.

10. $(x + y) + (z + 1) = x + [(y + z) + 1]$; by lines **8** and **9** and E.

11. $(y + z) + 1 = y + (z + 1)$; by Axiom P3.

12. $x + [(y + z) + 1] = x + [y + (z + 1)]$; by line **11** and E.

▶**13.** $(x + y) + (z + 1) = x + [y + (z + 1)]$; by E from lines **10** and **12**.

▶**14.** $z + 1 \in G$; by lines **2** and **13**.

15. For any $z \in G$ we have also $z + 1 \in G$; by lines **4** through **14**. (Application of Deduction Theorem of logic.)

▶▶**16.** $G = P$; by lines **3** and **15** and Axiom P4.

17. For any $z \in P$, $(x + y) + z = x + (y + z)$; by lines **2** and **16**.

18. For any $x, y, z \in P$, $(x + y) + z = x + (y + z)$; by lines **1** and **17**.

The reader may well ask himself just how steps **6** and **9** follow from Axiom P3. This axiom says that for any $a, b \in P$, $a + (b + 1) = (a + b) + 1$. In line **6**, the element $x + y$ is the a, and z is the element b in this formulation of the axiom. In line **9**, x replaces the a and $y + z$ the b of the axiom. Some words of explanation about steps **17** and **18** may be in order also. Having first selected any $x, y \in P$, in line **2** we took G to be the set of all positive integers z having the property that $(x + y) + z = x + (y + z)$. Line **16** tells us that G and P are the same set, hence any element z of P possesses this property, as stated on line **17**. The x and y referred to on line **17** are those numbers selected on line **1**; but since this selection was made in an arbitrary way, we are entitled to pass to line **18**.

Granted that the reader may have followed the details of the above proof, he may still wonder why we chose to define G in the manner indicated on line **2**. For example, why not begin the proof by selecting any elements y and z from P and then forming the set G' of all those elements x such that $(x + y) + z = x + (y + z)$? The answer is that this is a perfectly reasonable way to begin to look for a proof, but that after trying it out we will be led to reject it. For in order to be able to apply Axiom P4 we shall want to proceed from the definition of G' to the assertion that $1 \in G'$ (i.e., that $(1 + y) + z = 1 + (y + z)$ for the chosen elements y and z). And here we see no apparent way to establish this fact on the basis of our axioms or previous theorems. In general, when we formulate induction proofs for theorems which begin with "For all $x, y \in P$ . . . ," or "For all $x, y, z \in P$ . . . ," it is not obvious, without actually attempting alternative possibilities, on which variable to "run" the induction.

We remark that in this proof Axioms P1 and P2 were not used. Only Axioms P3 and P4 were used. The significance of this remark will be brought out later.

We remark further that because of Theorem 2-4-1 we can give meaning to the symbol "$x + y + z$". This symbol is open to two interpretations, for it may mean either $(x + y) + z$ or $x + (y + z)$, but because of Theorem 2-4-1 it does not matter which of these interpretations is selected. However, most of the time in this book whenever more than two numbers are to be added the "association" will be indicated.

Lest the reader think that the associative law is a trivial statement of an obvious truth, it should be pointed out that there are many operations for which the associative property does not hold. For example, consider the operation of selection in the childhood game of "scissors, rock, and paper," where, as the reader doubtless recalls, "Scissors cut paper, paper covers rock, and rock breaks scissors." Using the + symbol to indicate the selection operation which when applied to any pair of "rock, scissors, paper," gives the one which wins, and abbreviating paper, rock, and scissors by the symbols P, R, and S, respectively, the rules of the game are given by the following statements:

$$R + S = R; \quad R + P = P; \quad \text{and } S + P = S.$$

Thus

$$(R + S) + P = R + P = P,$$

while

$$R + (S + P) = R + S = R,$$

so that $(R + S) + P \neq R + (S + P)$. For a mathematical example of a nonassociative operation, consider the operation of raising one given number to the power of a second given number. We have

$$(2^3)^2 = 8^2 = 64,$$

while

$$2^{(3^2)} = 2^9 = 512.$$

Thus $(2^3)^2 \neq 2^{(3^2)}$, and again the associative law fails.

Another property of addition the reader may be tempted to take for granted is the *commutative* property—the property that $x + y = y + x$ for all $x, y \in P$. From our daily intuitive contact with positive integers this is a very familiar property indeed; every school child knows that $3 + 4 = 4 + 3$. There are, however, operations on ordered pairs of numbers which do not obey the commutative law, subtraction being one example. Certainly $7 - 5$ is not the same as $5 - 7$. Another is the operation considered above, of raising one number to the power of a second; for $2^3 = 8$, while $3^2 = 9$, so that $2^3 \neq 3^2$. These examples should make clear that there is nothing universal about the commutative property; it holds only for certain operations. The mere fact that the commutative property for addition seems obvious does not guarantee that it actually holds for all pairs of numbers. This is something which must be proved.

THEOREM 2-4-2. THE COMMUTATIVE LAW OF ADDITION. *For all* $x, y \in P$, $x + y = y + x$.

A proof of this theorem is more easily presented by first proving a special case of the theorem which we formulate as a lemma. (A lemma is a theorem of little interest in itself but useful in the proof of an important theorem.)

LEMMA 2-4-2.1. *For all* $x \in P$, $x + 1 = 1 + x$.

Proof

▶▶ **1.** Let G be the set of all those numbers x such that $x + 1 = 1 + x$.
2. $1 + 1 = 1 + 1$; by E.
▶ **3.** $1 \in G$; by lines **1** and **2**.
▶ **4.** Let x be any element of G.
5. $x + 1 = 1 + x$; by lines **1** and **4**.
6. $(x + 1) + 1 = (1 + x) + 1$; by E from line **5**.
7. $(1 + x) + 1 = 1 + (x + 1)$; by Axiom P3.
▶ **8.** $(x + 1) + 1 = 1 + (x + 1)$; by E from lines **6** and **7**.
▶ **9.** $x + 1 \in G$; by lines **1** and **8**.
10. For every $x \in P$, if $x \in G$ then also $x + 1 \in G$; by lines **4** through **9** (Deduction Theorem).
▶▶ **11.** $G = P$; by lines **3** and **10** and Axiom P4.
12. For all $x \in P$, $x + 1 = 1 + x$; by lines **1** and **11**.

We now present a proof of Theorem 2-4-2 based upon this lemma.

Proof of Theorem 2-4-2

▶▶ **1.** Let x be any element of P.
▶▶ **2.** Having chosen x, let G be the set of integers such that for any number y we have $y \in G$ if and only if $x + y = y + x$.
▶ **3.** $x + 1 = 1 + x$; by Lemma 2-4-2.1.
▶ **4.** $1 \in G$; by lines **2** and **3**.
▶ **5.** Let y be any element of G.
6. $x + y = y + x$; by lines **2** and **4**.
7. $x + (y + 1) = (x + y) + 1$; by Axiom P3 (or Theorem 2-4-1).
8. $(x + y) + 1 = (y + x) + 1$; by E from line **6**.
9. $x + (y + 1) = (y + x) + 1$; by E from lines **7** and **8**.
10. $(y + x) + 1 = y + (x + 1)$; by Axiom P3 (or Theorem 2-4-1).
11. $y + (x + 1) = y + (1 + x)$; by E from line **3**.
12. $y + (1 + x) = (y + 1) + x$; by Theorem 2-4-1.
▶ **13.** $x + (y + 1) = (y + 1) + x$; by E from lines **9** through **12**.
▶ **14.** $y + 1 \in G$; by lines **2** and **13**.
15. For every $y \in P$, if $y \in G$ then also $y + 1 \in G$; by lines **5** through **14** (Deduction Theorem).

▶▶**16.** $G = P$; from lines **4** and **15** and Axiom P4.
17. For any $y \in P$, $x + y = y + x$; from lines **2** and **16**.
18. For any $x, y \in P$, $x + y = y + x$; from lines **1** and **17**.

The order of presentation of the steps in a proof is rarely the same as the order in which these steps are discovered when one is looking for the proof. For example, in proving Theorem 2-4-2 it would be natural (if one thought of the idea of using induction) to begin by setting down lines **1** and **2** of the proof just completed. At that time one would want to establish line **4** and would see that line **3** was necessary for this purpose. After seeing no way to justify line **3** readily, the idea would occur that a separate proof of this fact is necessary. Hence one would formulate the lemma and begin to look for a proof of it. But although one finds the lemma *after* lines **1** and **2** of the proof of the theorem, one writes it down *first* in order to have the result available at the time it is needed.

Hereafter, when several equations are combined by E (as in lines **9** through **13** above), we frequently will follow the familiar device of omitting the left members of some of these lines. Thus we would write:

9. $x + (y + 1)$	$= (y + x) + 1$;	by E from lines **7** and **8**.
10.	$= y + (x + 1)$;	by Axiom P3.
11.	$= y + (1 + x)$;	by E from line **3**.
12.	$= (y + 1) + x$;	by Theorem 2-4-1.
13. $x + (y + 1)$	$= (y + 1) + x$;	by E from lines **9** through **12**.

Comparing this shorthand version with the original, we see that our convention is this: *When a left member of an equation is omitted, it is understood to be the same as the right member of the equation on the previous line.*

As we have seen, an equivalent form of Axiom P2 is that if $x + 1 = y + 1$, then $x = y$. This is a particular case of our next theorem. Some teachers of elementary mathematics discourage the beginning student from using the word "cancellation" even when it is used in a correct sense, such as is described in the next theorem. This is done primarily because, from experience, it is found that the immature student is apt to use cancellation in ways that cannot be justified. In mathematical writing beyond the elementary level, however, it is convenient to refer to certain laws as *cancellation laws*.

THEOREM 2-4-3. THE RIGHT CANCELLATION LAW OF ADDITION. *For all $x, y, z \in P$, if $x + z = y + z$, then $x = y$.*

To prove this theorem we shall prove the following logically equivalent statement: For all $x, y, z \in P$, if $x \neq y$ then $x + z \neq y + z$. The substitution for the conditional "If R then Q" of the logically equivalent conditional "If not-Q then not-R" is frequently done in mathematics. The flow of logic in proceeding from the antecedent "not-Q" to the consequent "not-R" very often is easier to construct than that in proceeding from the antecedent "R" to the consequent "Q"—although of course, this is not always the case.

Proof

▶▶ **1.** Let x and y be any elements of P such that $x \neq y$.
▶▶ **2.** Having chosen x and y, let G be the subset of P such that for all z, $z \in G$ if and only if $x + z \neq y + z$.
3. $x + 1 \neq y + 1$; by line **1** and Axiom P2.
▶ **4.** $1 \in G$; by lines **2** and **3**.
▶ **5.** Let z be any element of G.
6. $x + z \neq y + z$; by lines **2** and **5**.
7. $(x + z) + 1 \neq (y + z) + 1$; by line **6** and Axiom P2.
8. $(x + z) + 1 = x + (z + 1)$ and $(y + z) + 1 = y + (z + 1)$; by Axiom P3.
▶ **9.** $x + (z + 1) \neq y + (z + 1)$; by E from lines **7** and **8**.
▶ **10.** $z + 1 \in G$; by lines **2** and **9**.
11. Whenever $z \in G$ then also $z + 1 \in G$; by lines **5** through **10**.
▶▶ **12.** $G = P$; by lines **4** and **11** and Axiom P4.
13. For all $x, y, z \in P$, if $x \neq y$ then $x + z \neq y + z$; by lines **1**, **2**, and **12**.
14. For all $x, y, z \in P$, if $x + z = y + z$ then $x = y$; by line **13**. (See the discussion preceding this proof.)

As an immediate result of this theorem and the commutative law of addition (Theorem 2-4-2) we have the following:

COROLLARY 2-4-3.1. THE LEFT CANCELLATION LAW OF ADDITION. *For all* $x, y, z \in P$, if $z + x = z + y$, *then* $x = y$.

EXERCISES

1. Prove Corollary 2-4-3.1.

2. The associative law of addition may be extended. Prove, for example, that for all $x, y, z, t \in P$,

$$\begin{aligned}[(x + y) + z] + t &= (x + y) + (z + t)\\ &= x + [(y + z) + t]\\ &= x + [y + (z + t)].\end{aligned}$$

Note that because of this extension of the associative law the ambiguous notation "$x + y + z + t$" may be employed without confusion.

3. Prove: For all $x, y, z \in P$, $x + (y + z) = z + (y + x)$.

4. Prove: For all $x, y, z \in P$, if $(x + y) + x = (y + x) + y$, then $x = y$.

5. Prove: For all $x, y \in P$, $x + y \neq x$.

6. *Prove: For all $x, y \in P$, if $x \neq y$, then $x + x \neq y + y$.

7. *Prove: For all $x \in P$, either $x = 1$, or $x = y + y$ for some $y \in P$, or $x = (y + y) + 1$ for some $y \in P$.
8. *Prove: For all $x, y \in P$, $x + x \neq (y + y) + 1$.

5. *The Relation "Less Than"*

We have an intuitive notion as to what we mean when we say that one positive integer is less than another. If the reader will recall our previous discussion of relations, he should recognize that this intuitive notion of "less than" actually has the form of a binary relation. It holds for certain ordered pairs, e.g., $\langle 2, 3\rangle$, since 2 is less than 3, but does not hold for others, say $\langle 5, 1\rangle$, since 5 is not less than 1. This concept is not among the primitive notions of our axiomatic theory; hence in order to discuss it within the framework of this theory we must introduce it as a *defined term.*

DEFINITION 2-5-1. *$<$ is the binary relation such that for all $x, y \in P$, $x < y$ if and only if there is a number $z \in P$ for which $x + z = y$. We shall say "x is less than y" for "$x < y$." Also, $>$ is that binary relation such that for all $u, v \in P$, $u > v$ if and only if $v < u$. We shall say "u is greater than v" for "$u > v$."*

As will be seen below, this definition functions in the following way in the development of our theory: Whenever we see the symbols "$x < y$" we may in effect regard this as shorthand for the statement "$x + z = y$ for some $z \in P$"; and conversely, whenever we have shown that $x + z = y$ for some $z \in P$ we may convey this information by writing "$x < y$." We now proceed to state and prove a few theorems concerning the relation $<$. The reader will recognize these as being some of the usual rules for inequalities.

THEOREM 2-5-2. *The relation $<$ is transitive. In other words, for all $x, y, z \in P$, if $x < y$ and $y < z$ then $x < z$.*

Proof

▶▶**1.** Let x, y, z be any elements of P such that $x < y$ and $y < z$.
▶**2.** There exists an element $u \in P$ such that $x + u = y$; by Definition 2-5-1 and line **1**.
▶**3.** There exists an element $v \in P$ such that $y + v = z$; by Definition 2-5-1 and line **1**.
4. $(x + u) + v = y + v$; by E from line **2**.
5. $(x + u) + v = x + (u + v)$; by the associative law of addition (Theorem 2-4-1).
6. $x + (u + v) = y + v$; by E from lines **4** and **5**.
7. $x + (u + v) = z$; by E from lines **3** and **6**.

▶▶**8.** There exists an element $w \in P$ such that $x + w = z$; from line **7**.
9. $x < z$; by Definition 2-5-1 and line **8**.

Before proceeding to the next theorem let us pause a moment to examine several of the steps in this proof. In line **1** we agree to use the symbols "x" and "y" to stand for an arbitrary pair of elements such that $x < y$. According to Definition 2-5-1 this means that there is some element z in P such that $x + z = y$; yet in line **2** we assert that here is an element u in P such that $x + u = y$. How come? Why u instead of z? To answer this question, we first observe that the sentences "There is an element $z \in P$ such that $x + z = y$" and "There is an element $u \in P$ such that $x + u = y$" mean *exactly* the same thing—namely, that there is an element of P which, when added to x, yields y. This explains why we are *permitted* to use the second sentence in line **2** even though the first sentence is what we get by a literal application of Definition 2-5-1. In the second place it is *desirable* to use "u" instead of "z" in "translating" the defined notation "$x < y$" in this context because the letter "z" is being used to denote some *other* element according to the hypothesis formulated in line **1**. A similar remark explains the use of "v" in line **3**.

How about the letter "u" which appears in lines **4** through **7**—for what does that stand? The answer is that it stands for an element of the kind whose existence is asserted in line **2**—that is, an element of P such that $x + u = y$. This use of the letter "u" in lines **4** through **7** is the result of a tacit agreement generally understood in mathematical writing. If we wished to be strict and make this agreement explicit we would rephrase line **2** to read "There exists an element $u \in P$ such that $x + u = y$, and we shall let u be such an element." In the same way the use of the letter "v" in lines **4** through **7** is based on an implicit understanding which refers back to line **3**.

THEOREM 2-5-3. THE TRICHOTOMY LAW. *For any $x, y \in P$, exactly one of the following relations holds: $x = y$, $x < y$, or $x > y$.*

A straightforward proof of this theorem can be given, but a large number of steps is necessary. To make the proof easier to follow, therefore, we shall first prove several lemmas.

The first lemma is merely a restatement of Theorem 2-3-4 using the definition of $<$. Hence, no proof will be given.

LEMMA 2-5-3.1. *For all $x \in P$, either $x = 1$ or $1 < x$.*

LEMMA 2-5-3.2. *For any $x, y \in P$, at least one of the following holds: $x = y$, $x < y$, or $y < x$.*

Proof of Lemma 2-5-3.2

▶▶ 1. Let x be any number in P.

▶▶ 2. Having chosen x, let G be the subset of P such that $y \in G$ if and only if at least one of the following holds: $x = y$, $x < y$, or $y < x$.

▶ 3. $1 \in G$; by Lemma 2-5-3.1 and line 2.

▶ 4. Let $y \in G$.

5. At least one of the following holds: $x = y$, $x < y$, or $y < x$; from lines 2 and 4.

▶ 6. *Case I.* Suppose $x = y$.

7. $x + 1 = y + 1$; by E from line 6.

8. For some element $z \in P$, $x + z = y + 1$; from line 7.

▶ 9. $x < y + 1$; from line 8 and the definition of $<$ (Definition 2-5-1).

▶ 10. $y + 1 \in G$; from lines 2 and 9.

▶ 11. *Case II.* Suppose $x < y$.

▶ 12. For some $z \in P$, $y = x + z$; from line 11 and the definition of $<$.

13. $y + 1 = (x + z) + 1$; by E from line 12.

14. $= x + (z + 1)$; by the associative law for addition.

15. $y + 1 = x + (z + 1)$; by E from lines 13 and 14.

16. For some element $u \in P$, $x + u = y + 1$; from line 15.

▶ 17. $x < y + 1$; by line 16 and the definition of $<$.

▶ 18. $y + 1 \in G$; from lines 2 and 17.

▶ 19. *Case III.* Suppose $y < x$.

▶ 20. For some $z \in P$, $x = y + z$; from line 19 and the definition of $<$.

21. $z = 1$ or $z = 1 + u$ for some $u \in P$; by Theorem 2-3-4.

▶ 22. *Subcase III.1.* Suppose $z = 1$.

▶ 23. $x = y + 1$; from lines 20 and 22 and E.

▶ 24. $y + 1 \in G$; from lines 2 and 23.

▶ 25. *Subcase III.2.* Suppose $z = 1 + u$ for some $u \in P$.

26. $x = y + (1 + u)$; from lines 20 and 25 and E.

27. $= (y + 1) + u$; by the associative law for addition.

28. $x = (y + 1) + u$; by E from lines 26 and 27.

▶ 29. $y + 1 < x$; from line 28 and the definition of $<$.

▶ 30. $y + 1 \in G$; from lines 2 and 29.

We are now in a position to pool the conclusions of the various cases and subcases. Lines **24** and **30** show that $y + 1 \in G$ in Case III no matter which subcase (III.1 or III.2) comes up; this fact, together with lines **10** and **18**, shows that $y + 1 \in G$ no matter which case (I, II, III) occurs. Hence we have:

▶**31.** For all y, if $y \in G$, then $y + 1 \in G$; by lines **4** through **10, 18, 24,** and **30.**

▶▶**32.** $G = P$; from lines **2, 3, 31,** and Axiom P4.

33. For the x chosen in line **1** we have, for any y, at least one of the following: $x = y$, $x < y$, or $y < x$; from lines **2** and **32.**

34. For any $x, y \in P$, either $x = y$, $x < y$, or $y < x$; from lines **1** and **33.**

The proof just given is our first example of a *proof by cases*, which is a frequently used method of proof. Although there are many steps they fall into sequence rather "naturally." Again the reader is reminded that in constructing a proof he may and should keep his intuitive ideas about the positive integers in mind; certainly this was done by the author of the last proof when he constructed it. Consider, for example, the steps after step **5**, where the goal is to prove that from the disjunction $x = y$, $x < y$, or $y < x$ it follows that $x = y + 1$, $x < y + 1$ or $y + 1 < x$. Certainly, the broad outlines of the proof come to mind almost immediately from our experience with the positive integers. The numerous steps merely formalize the intuitive argument in our mind.

LEMMA 2-5-3.3. *For any element $x \in P$, not $x < x$.*

Proof

1. Suppose there is an element $x \in P$ such that $x < x$.

2. There is an element $u \in P$ such that $x + u = x$; by line **1** and the definition of $<$.

3. For all $x, u \in P$, $x + u \neq x$; by Exercise 5, Section 4.

4. For any element $x \in P$, not $x < x$; by lines **1, 2,** and **3.**

The proof above is typical of proofs *by contradiction*, where we assume the theorem to be false and then arrive at a contradiction (i.e., two statements one of which is the denial of the other). In the proof of Lemma 2-5-3.3 we assume false the statement for any $x \in P$, not $x < x$; i.e., we assume the existence of an integer x such that $x < x$. (The reader is referred to the discussion of general and existential statements and their denial in Section 2 of the Introduction.) We then derive line **2** on the basis of this assumption. But line **3**, the negation of line **2**, has been previously established. Hence we conclude that the lemma must be true. This type of argument will be used in the proof of Theorem 2-5-3 below.

Proof of Theorem 2-5-3.

In view of Lemma 2-5-3.2 it only remains to be shown that for any pair $x, y \in P$ no more than one of the relations $x = y$, $x < y$, or $y < x$ can hold.

▶▶ **1.** Let x, y be any elements of P.

▶ **2.** *Case I.* Suppose $x = y$ and $x < y$.
3. $x < x$; by E from line **2**.
4. not $x < x$; by Lemma 2-5-3.3.
▶ **5.** It is false that $x = y$ and $x < y$; by lines **2** through **4**, since lines **3** and **4** are a contradiction obtained from the supposition on line **2**.

▶ **6.** *Case II.* Suppose $x = y$ and $y < x$. The pattern of the proof that it is false that $x = y$ and $y < x$ is exactly the same as in Case I, so we omit the details.

▶ **7.** *Case III.* Suppose $x < y$ and $y < x$.
8. $x < x$; by line **7** and the transitive law of $<$ (Theorem 2-5-2).
9. not $x < x$; by Lemma 2-5-3.3.
▶ **10.** It is false that $x < y$ and $y < x$; by lines **7** through **9**, since lines **8** and **9** are a contradiction.

▶▶ **11.** For any $x, y \in P$ not more than one of the relations $x = y$, $x < y$, or $y < x$ holds; by lines **1**, **5**, **6**, and **10**.
▶▶ **12.** For any $x, y \in P$, exactly one of the relations $x = y$, $x < y$, or $y < x$ holds; by line **11** and Lemma 2-5-3.2.

The proofs of the following theorems will be left as exercises.

THEOREM 2-5-4. *For all $x, y, z \in P$, if $x < y$ then $x + z < y + z$.*

THEOREM 2-5-5. THE RIGHT CANCELLATION LAW OF ADDITION FOR INEQUALITIES. *For all $x, y, z \in P$, if $x + z < y + z$ then $x < y$.*

EXERCISES

1. Prove that $1 < 2$.
2. Prove Theorem 2-5-4.
3. Prove Theorem 2-5-5.
4. Write a proof of Lemma 2-5-3.1.
5. Prove that if $x + y < z$ then $x < z$ and $y < z$.
6. Prove that if $x + y < z + u$ then either $x < z$ or $y < u$.

6. Subtraction

The reader is doubtless familiar with the concept of subtraction as a process related in a certain way to addition. For example, when we subtract 4 from 7 we are looking for *the number* which when added to 4 will give us 7. Clearly 3 is such a number and as we know intuitively, it is the only such number. More generally, when we consider subtracting y from x we are looking for *that number* z which when added to y yields x. In symbols we usually express this by writing $x - y = z$, where z is the number such that $y + z = x$; or, what amounts to the same thing, $y + (x - y) = x$. However, before we are justified in writing this we must know first that there is such a number z, and second that it is unique. Since we wish to introduce subtraction into our axiomatic theory in such a way that it bears this same intuitive relation to addition, a question that naturally arises is this: For what pairs of elements x, y in P is it true that there is a unique element z such that $y + z = x$? To answer this question we introduce the following theorem.

THEOREM 2-6-1. *For any $x, y \in P$ we have $y < x$ if and only if there is exactly one element $z \in P$ such that $y + z = x$.*

Proof

▶▶ **1.** Let x, y be any elements of P such that $y < x$.

▶▶ **2.** $y + z = x$ for some $z \in P$; by line **1** and the definition of $<$.

▶ **3.** Suppose u is *any* element of P such that $y + u = x$.

4. $y + u = y + z$; by E from lines **2** and **3**.

▶ **5.** $u = z$; by line **4** and the left cancellation law of addition (Corollary 2-4-3.1).

6. If u is any element of P such that $y + u = x$, then $u = z$; by the Deduction Theorem of Logic applied to lines **3** through **5**.

▶▶ **7.** There is exactly one element $z \in P$ such that $y + z = x$; by lines **2** and **6**.

8. If x, y are any elements of P such that $y < x$ then there is exactly one element $z \in P$ such that $y + z = x$; by the Deduction Theorem applied to lines **1** through **7**.

▶▶ **9.** If x, y are any elements of P for which there is exactly one $z \in P$ such that $y + z = x$, then $y < x$; by the definition of $<$.

10. For any $x, y \in P$ we have $y < x$ if and only if there is exactly one element $z \in P$ such that $y + z = x$; by lines **8** and **9**.

In view of Theorem 2-6-1 and the Trichotomy Law, Theorem 2-5-3, we see that if x, y are any pairs of *distinct* elements of P (so that $x \neq y$), then either there is exactly one element $u \in P$ such that $x + u = y$ or there is exactly one element $z \in P$ such that $y + z = x$ (but not both). *Intuitively then, for any pair* $x, y \in P$ *such that* $x \neq y$ *we can either subtract* x *from* y *or subtract* y *from* x, *but we cannot make both subtractions in* P. With this in mind, we define the subtraction function.

DEFINITION 2-6-2. *Let "−" (read as "the* **subtraction** *function") be the function whose domain consists of all ordered pairs* $\langle x, y\rangle$ *such that* $x, y \in P$ *and* $y < x$, *and whose value for any such ordered pair* $\langle x, y\rangle$ *is the unique element* z *such that* $x = y + z$.

Following the standard notation for functions we would write $z = -\langle x, y\rangle$ to indicate that z is the value of the subtraction function acting on the ordered pair $\langle x, y\rangle$; however, we will generally use the more conventional notation $z = x - y$. We refer to the element $x - y$ of P as x *minus* y, or as y *subtracted from* x.

Note again that the subtraction function as we have defined it does not act on *all* the ordered pairs $\langle x, y\rangle$ for all $x, y \in P$, as (for example) the operation $+$ does. Since an *operation* on P by definition does act on all ordered pairs of elements in P (see Section 5 of Chapter I), we refer to the subtraction *function* rather than to the subtraction *operation* on P.

The basic properties of subtraction which follow immediately from its definition are given in the following theorem.

THEOREM 2-6-3. *If* x, y, u *are any elements of* P *such that* $x + u = y$ *then* $u = y - x$. *If* x, y *are any elements of* P *such that* $x < y$, *then* $x + (y - x) = y$.

Proof

See Exercise 5 below.

In addition to this basic result there are many other theorems, both particular and general, involving the subtraction function. A very simple example of a particular theorem is:

THEOREM 2-6-4. $2 - 1 = 1$.

Proof

1. $1 + 1 = 2$; by definition of 2.
2. $2 - 1 = 1$; from line **1** and Theorem 2-6-3.

Theorem 2-6-4 implicitly contains the statement that the subtraction function may act on the ordered pair $\langle 2, 1\rangle$, and this is indeed possible since $1 < 2$; hence it can not act on the ordered pair $\langle 1, 2\rangle$, and so we cannot subtract 2 from 1 in P.

A general theorem involving subtraction is the following:

THEOREM 2-6-5. *If* $x < y$ *and* $z < x$ *then* $x - z < y - z$.

Proof

▶▶ **1.** Let x, y, z be any elements in P such that $x < y$ and $z < x$.

▶ **2.** There exist unique elements $u, v \in P$ such that $y = x + u$ and $x = z + v$; by line **1** by Theorem 2-6-1.

3. $v = x - z$; by line **2** and the definition of $-$.

4. $y = (z + v) + u$; by line **2** by E.

5. $y = z + (v + u)$; by line **4** by the associative law of addition.

6. $y - z = v + u$; by line **5** and the definition of $-$.

7. $v + u = (x - z) + u$; by line **3** by E.

▶ **8.** $y - z = (x - z) + u$; by lines **6** and **7** by E.

▶▶ **9.** $x - z < y - z$; by line **8** and the definition of $<$.

10. For all $x, y, z \in P$, if $x < y$ and $z < x$ then $x - z < y - z$; by lines **1** through **9** by the Deduction Law of logic.

Other general theorems are:

THEOREM 2-6-6. *For all $x, y, z \in P$, if $x < y$ and $y < z$ then $z - y < z - x$.*

THEOREM 2-6-7. *For all $x, y, z \in P$, if $z < y$ then $(x + y) - z = x + (y - z)$.*

THEOREM 2-6-8. *For all $x, y, z \in P$ such that $x + y < z$ we have $x < z$, $y < z - x$, and $z - (x + y) = (z - x) - y$.*

THEOREM 2-6-9. *If x, y, z are any elements of P such that $x < y$ and $y < z$, then $(y - x) < z$ and $z - (y - x) = (z - y) + x$.*

Let us see how we might begin to look for a proof of Theorem 2-6-7, for example. From our hypothesis $z < y$ we infer at once that $z + u = y$ for some $u \in P$, by the definition of $<$. This element u is, of course, the element $y - z$, as we easily show by the definition of $-$ (after applying one of the laws of addition; which?). Thus we see that the right side of the equation in the statement is $x + u$. But how do we get the left side? Well, if we knew of an element $v \in P$ such that $x + y = v + z$ this element would be $(x + y) - z$. But from $y = z + u$, which we have above, we get at once $x + y = x + (z + u)$ by E. A little thought should suffice to indicate how to complete the chain of reasoning, and there will then remain only the problem of writing the steps of the proof in logical order.

EXERCISES

1. Prove Theorem 2-6-6.
2. Prove Theorem 2-6-7.
3. Prove Theorem 2-6-8.

4. Is the subtraction function associative? Commutative?
5. Prove Theorem 2-6-3.
6. Prove Theorem 2-6-9.
7. Prove the following theorem. If $x, y \in P$ such that $x < y$, then $y - x < y$.

7. *The Relation "Less than or Equal to"*

We have already encountered both the *equals* relation and the *less than* relation. The disjunction of these two relations gives us the *less than or equal to* relation.

DEFINITION 2-7-1. *For any two elements* $x, y \in P$, *x is said to be* **less than or equal** *to y if and only if either* $x = y$ *or* $x < y$. We shall denote this relation by the symbol "$\leq$".

The reader will perhaps recall from the discussion in Chapter I concerning the use of the word "or" in mathematics that the disjunction "$x = y$ or $x < y$" is a statement which is true if both "$x = y$" and "$x < y$" are true, as well as if one of the statements "$x = y$", "$x < y$" is true and the other false. However, Theorem 2-5-3 of Section 5 tells us that actually the two statements "$x = y$" and "$x < y$" cannot both be true, so that in order to have $x \leq y$ we must have either $x = y$ and not $x < y$, or $x < y$ and not $x = y$.

Many theorems concerning the $\leq$ relation parallel those listed in Section 5 dealing with the $<$ relation. Most of the proofs proceed by cases, making use of the corresponding theorems for $<$; many will be left as exercises.

THEOREM 2-7-2. *The relation* $\leq$ *is transitive. In other words, for all* $x, y, z \in P$, *if* $x \leq y$ *and* $y \leq z$, *then* $x \leq z$.

Proof

See Exercise 1 below.

THEOREM 2-7-3. *For all* $x, y, z \in P$, *if* $x \leq y$, *then* $x + z \leq y + z$.

Proof

▶▶ 1. Let x, y be any elements in P such that $x \leq y$, and let z be any element of P whatever.

2. $x = y$ or $x < y$; by line **1** and the definition of $\leq$.

▶ 3. *Case I.* $x = y$.

4. $x + z = y + z$; by E from line **3**.

▶ 5. $x + z = y + z$ or $x + z < y + z$; by line **4**.

▶ 6. *Case II.* $x < y$.

7. $x + z < y + z$; by line **5** and Theorem 2-5-4.

▶ 8. $x + z = y + z$ or $x + z < y + z$; by line **7**.

▶▶ 9. In all cases, $x + z = y + z$ or $x + z < y + z$; by lines **2**, **3**, **5**, **6**, and **8**.

10. For all $x, y, z \in P$, if $x \leq y$ then $x + z \leq y + z$; by lines **1** and **9** and the definition of $\leq$.

Note: In passing from line **4** to line **5** or from line **7** to line **8**, we use the law of logic which asserts that Q implies Q or R, where Q, R are any sentences.

THEOREM 2-7-4. THE RIGHT CANCELLATION LAW OF ADDITION FOR $\leq$. *For all $x, y, z \in P$, if $x + z \leq y + z$, then $x \leq y$.*

Proof

See Exercise 2 below.

THEOREM 2-7-5. *For all $x, y \in P$, either $x \leq y$ or $y \leq x$.*

Proof

See Exercise 3 below.

The following two theorems have no parallel for the $<$ relation.

THEOREM 2-7-6. *For all $x \in P$, $x \leq x$ and $1 \leq x$.*

Proof of the First Part (for the remainder of the proof, see Exercise 4).

1. Let x be any element of P.
2. $x = x$; by E.
3. $x = x$ or $x < x$; by line **2**.
4. $x \leq x$; by line **3**, by Definition 2-7-1.

In the proof of the next theorem we make use of a law of logic which is sometimes referred to as the distributive law of conjunction over disjunction. This law states: If P, R, and S are any sentences, then the sentence "P and (R or S)" is logically equivalent to the sentence "(P and R) or (P and S)." On applying this law to the sentence "(P or Q) and (R or S)," where P, Q, R, and S are any sentences, we obtain the sentence "[(P or Q) and R] or [(P or Q) and S]." Here, the sentence "P or Q" plays the role of the sentence "P" in the statement of the law. Next, on making use of the commutative property of the word "and", we see that the sentence "[(P or Q) and R] or [(P or Q) and S]" is equivalent to the sentence "[R and (P or Q)] or [S and (P or Q)]". Finally, two more applications of the distributive law stated above give the sentence "(R and P) or (R and Q) or (S and P) or (S and Q)".

THEOREM 2-7-7. *For all $x, y \in P$, if $x \leq y$ and $y \leq x$, then $x = y$.*

Proof

▶▶**1.** Let x, y be any elements of P for which $x \leq y$ and $y \leq x$.

▶▶**2.** ($x < y$ or $x = y$) and ($y < x$ or $y = x$); by line **1** and the definition of $\leq$.

▶**3.** At least one of the following must hold:

(**a**) $x < y$ and $y < x$,
(**b**) $x < y$ and $y = x$,
(**c**) $x = y$ and $y < x$,
(**d**) $x = y$; by line **2** and distributive law of conjunction over disjunction discussed in the preceding paragraph.

▶**4.** (**a**) ($x < y$ and $y < x$) is false; by the Trichotomy Law (Theorem 2-5-3).

▶**5.** (**b**) ($x < y$ and $y = x$) is false; by the Trichotomy Law.

▶**6.** (**c**) ($x = y$ and $y < x$) is false; by the Trichotomy Law.

▶▶**7.** $x = y$; by lines **3**, **4**, **5**, and **6**.

8. For all $x, y \in P$, if $x \leq y$ and $y \leq x$ then $x = y$; by lines **1** and **7**.

The proof given of Theorem 2-7-7 is an instance of an indirect proof by cases. In proofs of this type, several cases are given of which one can show that at least one must hold. In the present proof, for example (see line **3**), there are four possible cases and it is clear by the laws of logic that at least one must hold. The proof then proceeds by showing that each case, except the desired one, leads to a contradiction and so is false. By the rules of logic we may then infer the desired result that the remaining case must be true.

This theorem is used frequently in mathematics. It often happens that the easiest way to show that two elements of P are equal is to show that the first is less than or equal to the second and that the second is less than or equal to the first.

The next theorem expresses a variant form of the Principle of Mathematical Induction which is often useful where Axiom P4 by itself seems ineffective.

THEOREM 2-7-8. *If G is a subset of P such that*

(**i**) $1 \in G$, *and*

(**ii**) *whenever x is a number such that $y \in G$ for all $y \leq x$, then also $x + 1 \in G$, then $G = P$.*

Before looking at the details of the proof of this theorem let us sketch the idea of the proof. To this end, suppose that we are given an arbitrary subset G of P which possesses the properties (**i**) and (**ii**) above. We wish to show that $G = P$, i.e., that every element of P is in G. In order to do this we employ a certain "trick." We pull out of G a certain subset H, consisting of those elements which have a certain special property. We then proceed to show that every element of P is in H! Since H is a subset of G, of course this shows that every element of P is in G.

At first sight this procedure may appear strange. If we can show that every element of P is in a certain subset of G, why can't we show directly that every element of P is in G without bothering to bring in the special subset H of G? To answer this question, we first note that in our proof the method used to show that every element of P is in H is to employ Axiom P4. In order to apply this axiom we must first show that (**a**) $1 \in H$ and (**b**) whenever $x \in H$ then also $x + 1 \in H$. If we tried to do without the special subset H we would have to show, instead of (**b**), that (**b′**) whenever $x \in G$ then also $x + 1 \in G$. Now as mentioned above, the elements put into H are chosen to have a certain special property. In proving (**b**) we select an element x from H and then, *making use of this special property*, we show that $x + 1$ is also in H. In trying to prove (**b′**) we find ourselves unable to proceed from the knowledge that x is in G to the conclusion that $x + 1$ is also in G because we do not know that x has the special property.

With this much discussion of the method of proof, let us examine the details.

Proof

▶▶ **1.** Let G be any subset of P satisfying hypotheses (**i**) and (**ii**) above.
▶▶ **2.** Form a set H consisting of all those numbers x such that $y \in G$ for all $y \leq x$.
▶ **3.** $1 \in H$; by lines **1** (**i**) and **2** and Exercise 5 below.
▶ **4.** Let x be any element of H.
5. For all $y \leq x$ we have $y \in G$; by line **2**.
6. $x + 1 \in G$; by line **1** (**ii**).
7. Let y be any element of P such that $y \leq x + 1$.
8. $y < x + 1$ or $y = x + 1$; by line **7** and Definition 2-7-1.
9. $y \leq x$ or $y = x + 1$; by line **8** and Exercise 9 below.
10. $y \in G$; by lines **5**, **6**, and **9**.
▶ **11.** For all $y \leq x + 1$ we have $y \in G$; by lines **7** and **10**.
▶ **12.** $x + 1 \in H$; by lines **2** and **11**.
13. Whenever $x \in H$ then also $x + 1 \in H$; by lines **4** through **12**.
▶▶ **14.** $H = P$; by Axiom P4 and lines **3** and **13**.
▶ **15.** Let z be any element of H.
16. For all $y \leq z$ we have $y \in G$; by lines **2** and **15**.
▶ **17.** $z \in G$; by line **16** and Theorem 2-7-6.
18. Whenever $z \in H$ we have also $z \in G$; by lines **15** through **17**.
▶▶ **19.** $G = P$; by lines **14** and **18**.

20. If G is any subset of P satisfying hypotheses (i) and (ii) above, then $G = P$; by lines **1** through **19.**

Theorem 2-7-8 is sometimes called the *strong form* of the Principle of Mathematical Induction. In comparing it with Axiom P4, note that in both cases we obtain the conclusion $G = P$. However, in applying P4 we must show that $x + 1 \in G$ whenever $x \in G$, while in applying Theorem 2-7-8 we need show $x + 1 \in G$ only for those x such that $y \in G$ for *all* $y \leq x$. Thus Theorem 2-7-8 gives the same conclusion as Axiom P4 with a weaker hypothesis. As an application of Theorem 2-7-8 we give a theorem which is sometimes expressed by saying that $\leq$ is a "well-order" for P.

THEOREM 2-7-9. *Let G be any subset of P which is nonempty, i.e., which is such that $x \in G$ for some $x \in P$. Then there is an element $z \in G$ such that $z \leq y$ for all $y \in G$.*

Proof

▶▶ **1.** Let G be any subset of P such that there is no $z \in G$ with the property that $z \leq y$ for all $y \in G$.

2. For any $y, z \in G$ either $z \leq y$ or $y < z$; by the definition of $\leq$ (Definition 2-7-1), the Trichotomy Law (Theorem 2-5-3), and the fact that G is a subset of P (line **1**).

3. If z is any element of G, there is an element $y \in G$ such that $y < z$; by lines **1** and **2**.

▶▶ **4.** Let H be the set of all those elements of P not in G.

5. There is no $y \in P$ such that $y < 1$; by the definition of $<$ and Axiom P1.

6. $1 \notin G$; by lines **3** and **5**.

▶ **7.** $1 \in H$; by lines **4** and **6**.

▶ **8.** Let x be any element of P such that $y \in H$ for all $y \leq x$.

9. For any $y \in P$, if $y < x + 1$ then $y \in H$; by line **8** and Exercise **9** below.

10. $x + 1 \notin G$; by lines **3**, **4**, and **9**.

▶ **11.** $x + 1 \in H$; by lines **4** and **10**.

12. Whenever x is a number such that $y \in H$ for all $y \leq x$, then $x + 1 \in H$; by lines **8** and **11**.

▶▶ **13.** $H = P$; by Theorem 2-7-8 (strong induction) and lines **7** and **12**.

14. There is no $x \in P$ such that $x \in G$; by lines **4** and **13**.

▶▶ **15.** If G is any subset of P which contains no element z such that $z \leq y$ for all $y \in G$, then G is empty; by lines **1** and **14**.

16. If G is any nonempty subset of P, then G contains an element z such that $z \leq y$ for all $y \in G$; by line **15**.

It can be shown that in any nonempty set G there is *only one* element z with the property described in Theorem 2-7-9. (This element is called the *least* element of G.) The proof of this is left as an exercise (Exercise 12).

EXERCISES

1. Prove Theorem 2-7-2.

2. Prove Theorem 2-7-4.

3. Prove Theorem 2-7-5.

4. Complete the proof of Theorem 2-7-6.

5. Prove that for all $y \in P$ we have $y \leq 1$ if and only if $y = 1$.

6. Prove that for all $x \in P$ we have $x \leq 4$ if and only if $x = 1$ or $x = 2$ or $x = 3$ or $x = 4$.

7. Write down a definition of the relation "greater than or equal to" ($\geq$).

8. State and prove the Left Cancellation Law of Addition for $\leq$.

9. Prove that for all $x, y \in P$ we have $y \leq x$ if and only if $y < x + 1$.

10. Define $\leq$ directly in terms of $+$ (without using the symbol "$<$").

11. State the distributive law of disjunction over conjunction. Is this a valid law of logic?

12. Show that in any nonempty set G there is only one element z of the kind described in Theorem 2-7-9.

13. The following statement is sometimes given as an alternative form of the Strong Induction Principle: Let G be any subset of P such that $x \in G$ whenever x is an element of P with the property that $y \in G$ for all $y < x$; then $G = P$. Prove this, using Theorem 2-7-8.

14.* Let G be any nonempty subset of P with the property that there exists an element $u \in P$ such that $z \leq u$ for all $z \in G$. Then there exists an element $s \in G$ such that $z \leq s$ for all $z \in G$. (A set G with the property described in the hypothesis of this problem is said to have an *upper bound*. Note that we assume there is an element *in* P, but must show the existence of an element *in* G.)

III

Models and Isomorphisms

1. Models of Axiomatic Systems

We pause here from our labor of deriving theorems from axioms in order to observe a remarkable fact about the significance of the theorems we are establishing. In Chapter II we set up axioms and derived theorems to show how different facts about the intuitively known domain of positive integers are connected with one another. But the axiomatic method possesses an importance and interest which far transcends the scope of this original purpose, as the following observation, which is equally relevant for any axiomatic theory, shows.

Consider, for example, Theorem 2-4-2, the Commutative Law of Addition, which asserts that if we apply the addition operation to any pair of positive integers, first in one order and then in the reverse order, the results will be the same. Just what are the positive integers and which is the addition operation to which this theorem applies? We did not define the terms *positive integer* and *addition operation* in our theory; in deriving Theorem 2-4-2, we assumed only that these things obeyed our axioms. *Hence the theorem holds for any objects and any operation which satisfy these axioms.* Thus we see that our derivation of Theorem 2-4-2 from axioms containing undefined terms not only furnishes information about the ordinary numbers and ordinary addition familiar from grade-school days, but simultaneously gives information about any *other* set of objects and binary operation which satisfy the axioms . . . providing we can find such other systems. Let us see.

In order to systematize our discussion let us agree to use the term *model* to refer to any system $\langle P, 1, +\rangle$ consisting of a set P, an element 1 of P, and a binary operation $+$ on P. If all of our Axioms P1 to P4 hold for a model we will say that it is a *Peano model*. Intuitively we feel that the set of counting numbers P with which we have had so much experience since childhood—the number 1 of everyday usage and the familiar operation $+$ used since our grade-school days—constitute such a triple and thus provide a Peano model. This, of course, is the model we had in mind when we wrote the axioms. But there are other models which appear intuitively to qualify as Peano models.

For example, let $P' = \{2, 4, 6, \ldots\}$, i.e., let P' be the set of even positive integers. Let $1' = 2$ and let $+'$ be the ordinary operation of addition. We can now verify intuitively that Axioms P1 to P4 hold when the undefined symbol "P" of the axioms is interpreted as P', and when the symbols "1" and "+" are respectively interpreted as $1'$ and $+'$, and thus that $\langle P', 1', +' \rangle$ is a Peano model. (For example, Axiom P3 asserts about this model that $(x +' y) +' 1' = x +' (y +' 1')$ for all $x, y \in P'$, and this is true because $(x + y) + 2 = x + (y + 2)$ for all even positive integers x and y.)

Still another Peano model can be constructed as follows. Let $P'' = \{2, 2^2, 2^3, 2^4, \ldots\}$, i.e., P'' is the set of all positive powers of 2. Let $1'' = 2$, and let $+''$ be the ordinary operation of multiplication. The reader is invited to check intuitively that the axioms hold for this interpretation of the undefined terms of our theory. He will thus find that $\langle P'', 1'', +'' \rangle$ is indeed a Peano model.

In our preceding examples the elements of P have all been numbers. However, there certainly exist Peano models in which the elements are not numbers. For example, let P''' be the set of all circles in some plane, with centers at some fixed point, the radii of which are positive integers. If a and b are any two such circles, let us denote by $a +''' b$ the circle of P''' whose radius equals the sum of the radii of the circles a and b. And let $1'''$ be the circle of P''' with radius 1. It is not hard to check intuitively that the system $\langle P''', 1''', +''' \rangle$ is a Peano model.

The reader may feel that in all of these examples of Peano models there is a certain similarity to our intuitive system of positive integers with the operation of addition. This is indeed the case—but it should not be too surprising, since it was with this intuitive system in mind that we were led to the particular set of axioms we assumed. Is there, then, some Peano model which is not simply a cleverly (?) disguised version of our familiar system of positive integers and ordinary addition? No. It can be shown that all Peano models have the same basic structure. (This point will be treated in more detail in the section on *isomorphisms*.)

In the preceding examples we mentioned only intuitive verification that the proposed systems are Peano models. Nothing was said about how one might actually give a proof—i.e., one as rigorous as those demanded for our theorems—that the axioms are actually satisfied by these models. We shall not examine this question here. However, in succeeding paragraphs of this section we discuss models of simpler axiomatic systems and prove rigorously that our models satisfy the axioms.

The important point to note here is the fact that any theorem derived by logic from the axioms is *true for all Peano models*, not the question whether this or that system is in fact a Peano model. Thus if we verify somehow that $\langle P'', 1'', +'' \rangle$ qualifies as a Peano model, then we can conclude, for example, that the statement "For all $x, y \in P''$, $x +'' y = y +'' x$" is true, by Theorem 2-4-2; for the commutative law of addition was proved for *any* model

$\langle P, 1, + \rangle$ which satisfies the Axioms P1 through P4, and so it will hold in particular for $\langle P'', 1'', +'' \rangle$. Thus, in the sequel, rather than consider our theory merely an axiomatic study of the positive integers, we might more properly regard it as the study of arbitrary Peano models. In this way we will emphasize that our theorems are true not only for the positive integers, our original model, but also for any Peano model.

Now consider for a moment a system of axioms simpler than Peano's, obtained simply by deleting Axioms P1 and P2. Any triple $\langle P, 1, + \rangle$ which satisfies Axioms P3 and P4 will be called an *induction model.* (The reader may recall that Axiom P4 is called the "induction axiom.") Many induction models can be constructed very simply, and we shall actually give three such examples. Obviously every Peano model is an induction model. But the converse is not true. To establish that some induction models are not Peano models we shall actually exhibit an induction model which does not satisfy Axiom P1 and another for which P2 is false.

As our first example of an induction model which is not a Peano model, let 1_1 be this book and let $P_1 = \{1_1\}$, i.e; P_1 is the set having this book as its one and only member. Let $+_1$ be the only possible binary operation on P_1, i.e., $1_1 +_1 1_1 = 1_1$. Then we see that Axioms P3 and P4 are satisfied trivially, i.e., $\langle P_1, +_1, 1_1 \rangle$ is an induction model. It is *not* a Peano model, however, in that it fails to satisfy Axiom P1, for we see that there *does* exist an element $x \in P_1$ such that $x +_1 1_1 = 1_1$. The reader will notice that here we are actually able to *prove* that our triple $\langle P_1, 1_1, +_1 \rangle$ is an induction model, in contrast to our examples for Peano models where we appealed to intuitive knowledge of counting numbers to justify our conclusions.

For our next example we shall consider a two element model. Let 1_2 be Donald Duck and B_2 be Bugs Bunny. Let $P_2 = \{1_2, B_2\}$ and let $+_2$ be the binary operation on P_2 such that

$$1_2 +_2 1_2 = B_2$$
$$1_2 +_2 B_2 = B_2 +_2 1_2 = 1_2$$
$$B_2 +_2 B_2 = B_2.$$

(*Note:* This description exemplifies the possibility of defining any binary operation on a finite set by describing how it acts on each ordered pair of the set.)

We shall now verify that Axioms P3 and P4 hold for P_2. To verify that Axiom P3 holds we must show that for all $x, y \in P_2$, $(x +_2 y) +_2 1_2 = x +_2 (y +_2 1_2)$. Since P_2 is finite we can actually verify this by letting x, y take on all values of P_2, one by one, and examining each case separately. Thus,

$$(1_2 +_2 1_2) +_2 1_2 = B_2 + 1_2 = 1_2$$

and

$$1_2 +_2 (1_2 + 1_2) = 1_2 +_2 B_2 = 1_2.$$

Hence, for $x = y = 1_2$, $(x +_2 y) +_2 1_2 = x +_2 (y +_2 1_2)$. There remain three cases:

1. $x = y = B_2$.
2. $x = B_2$, $y = 1_2$.
3. $x = 1_2$, $y = B_2$.

It will be left as an exercise for the reader to show that $(x +_2 y) +_2 1_2 = x +_2 (y +_2 1_2)$ for these cases and thus complete the verification that Axiom P3 holds for the model $\langle P_2, 1_2, +_2 \rangle$.

Next let us verify that Axiom P4 holds. Let G be a subset of P_2 such that $1_2 \in G$ and such that for all $x \in G$ we have also $x +_2 1_2 \in G$. Then we see that $1_2 \in G$ and $1_2 +_2 1_2 = B_2 \in G$. Thus $P_2 \subseteq G$. But G is a subset of P_2, i.e.; $G \subseteq P_2$. Therefore $P_2 = G$, by the Principle of Extensionality for sets. (See Chapter I, Section 3.) Hence Axiom P4 holds.

We have verified that Axioms P3 and P4 hold for $\langle P_2, 1_2, +_2 \rangle$. Hence this triple is an induction model. We see that it is *not* a Peano model, for $B_2 +_2 1_2 = 1_2$. Hence there exists an $x \in P_2$ such that $x +_2 1_2 = 1_2$, contrary to Axiom P1.

Some of the theorems we have proved in Chapter II were proved without the use of Axioms P1 and P2 and hence are true for induction models as well as for Peano models. Theorem 2-4-1, the Associative Law of Addition, and Theorem 2-4-2, the Commutative Law of Addition, are examples of such theorems. In our proof of Theorem 2-4-3, the Right Cancellation Law of Addition, we used Axiom P2, hence we cannot assert that this law holds for all induction models. The fact that we used Axiom P2 in proving Theorem 2-4-3 does not establish, however, that Theorem 2-4-3 fails to hold for all induction models, for there might exist some other proof of this theorem which makes no use of Axiom P1 or P2.

Let us consider the question whether the Right Cancellation Law holds for *all* induction models, i.e., the question whether it is possible to prove this law on the basis of Axioms P3 and P4 alone. In attempting to answer this question, two alternatives are open:

(1) we could attempt to produce a proof of this law on the basis of Axioms P3 and P4 alone, thus giving an affirmative answer to the question, or

(2) we could attempt to construct an induction model for which the theorem does not hold, thus answering the question in the negative.

If we suspect that the Right Cancellation Law of Addition does not hold for all induction models we would choose course (2) above to start our investigations. Since Axiom P2 is a special case of the Right Cancellation Law of Addition, if we can construct an induction model for which P2 fails, then automatically we have a model for which the cancellation law does not hold. On the other hand, if we construct an induction model for which P2 holds, then automatically the Right Cancellation Law holds for this particular model, since the proof given above for Theorem 2-4-3 makes use only of Axioms P2, P3, and P4.

We shall leave the reader to show, as exercises, that for the two examples of induction models already given, Axiom P2 does hold, and hence the Right Cancellation Law holds for these models.

For our final example we retain 1_2, B_2, and P_2 of the previous example but let $+_3$ be the binary operation on P_2 such that

$$1_2 +_3 1_2 = B_2$$
$$1_2 +_3 B_2 = B_2 +_3 1_2 = B_2$$
$$B_2 +_3 B_2 = B_2.$$

The proof that $\langle P_2, 1_2, +_3\rangle$ is an induction model follows the pattern of the proof, given above, that $\langle P_2, 1_2, +_2\rangle$ is an induction model, and we shall leave this as an exercise for the reader. We see, however, that $B_2 +_3 1_2 = 1_2 +_3 1_2$ but that $B_2 \neq 1_2$. Hence Axiom P2 fails. As mentioned earlier, since Axiom P2 is a special case of the cancellation law, we have now established that the cancellation law does *not* hold for every induction model.

The reader will observe that for each example of an induction model given above, either Axiom P1 or P2 is satisfied. This might lead one to the conjecture that perhaps the same is true of *every* induction model. This is indeed the case, but we shall not prove it here.

Before going on to further theorems about Peano models we wish to emphasize one of the most fundamental and important points about axiomatic studies. Since we actually prove theorems which hold for many models when we prove theorems from axioms containing undefined terms, we are actually developing simultaneously many potential applications of our study. If, for example, in a study of economics we find a situation which can be described by a model of a mathematical system which has been developed axiomatically, there is immediately available to the investigator of that situation the full body of theorems the mathematician has discovered in his purely abstract approach. Many of the modern applications of mathematics to practical problems come about precisely this way. To be sure, the impetus for initiating an abstract axiomatic theory often arises from the application itself, but it also happens frequently that the abstract study precedes a particular application made of it.

The reader who would like more information about the construction of induction models is referred to Appendix I with the warning that reading this supplementary note might be postponed until the concept of "isomorphism," which appears in the next section, has been encountered.

EXERCISES

1. Give the details of the proof that $\langle P_1, 1_1, +_1\rangle$ is an induction model.
2. Complete the proof of the statement that $\langle P_2, 1_2, +_2\rangle$ is an induction model.
3. Prove that $\langle P_2, 1_2, +_3\rangle$ is an induction model.

4. Prove that Axiom P2 holds for the models $\langle P_1, 1_1, +_1\rangle$ and $\langle P_2, 1_2, +_2\rangle$.

5. Prove that Axiom P1 holds for the model $\langle P_2, 1_2, +_3\rangle$.

6. Construct a three-element induction model. Which axiom, P1 or P2, holds for your model?

7. Show that if $P = \{1, 2, 3 \cdots 12\}$ and addition is the operation of adding time on a 12-hour clock, then $\langle P, 1, +\rangle$ is an induction model.

8. Using problem **7** as a guide, construct an induction model out of the set $\{1, 2, 3 \cdots m\}$ where m is any counting number.

9. Which Axiom, P1 or P2, holds for the models of problems **7** and **8**?

2. *Isomorphisms*

Let us consider two induction models. Model $\mathcal{A}$ will be $\langle P_1, 1, +\rangle$, where P_1 has as its elements the counting numbers 1, 2, and 3, and where the operation $+$ is understood to be the ordinary addition modified by the agreement that if the sum of two elements is greater than 3 it is to be reduced by 3. (This operation is known as *addition modulo 3.*) The operation can be summarized by the following table:

+	1	2	③
1	2	3	1
②	3	1	②
3	1	2	3

Thus, $2 + 3$, for example, is equal to 2 in model $\mathcal{A}$, as indicated by the circled elements in the table.

The induction model $\mathcal{B}$ will be $\langle P_2, 2p, \oplus\rangle$, where the elements of P_2 are a two-pint can, $2p$, a four-pint can, $4p$, and a six-pint can, $6p$, and where the operation $\oplus$, acting on an ordered pair $\langle x, y\rangle$ of elements of P_2, is the operation of filling the cans x and y with water, pouring together the water from both, and then finding the can which will just hold the combined water—or if none of the cans will hold the water then we pour the water into a six-pint container and find which can will just hold the overflow. The table which shows the result obtained by applying the $\oplus$ operation to the elements of P_2, is as follows:

$\oplus$	$2p$	$4p$	$6p$
$2p$	$4p$	$6p$	$2p$
$4p$	$6p$	$2p$	$4p$
$6p$	$2p$	$4p$	$6p$

Thus if four pints and six pints are poured together into a six-pint container there would be a four-pint overflow.

The reader may observe that the two models $\mathcal{A}$ and $\mathcal{B}$ are very similar in that the operation tables are essentially identical except for the names of the elements. In fact, the following table:

&	a	b	c
a	b	c	a
b	c	a	b
c	a	b	c

can be used for either model with the proper interpretation of the symbols "a", "b", "c", and "&". Thus we may say that both models, $\mathcal{A}$ and $\mathcal{B}$, "behave in the same way," although, strictly speaking, they are not the same model since they have quite different elements. We say that they are *isomorphic models*, or that there is an *isomorphism between them*. Literally, this means that they "*have the same structure.*"

Loosely speaking, an isomorphism between two models $\mathcal{A}$ and $\mathcal{B}$ of an arbitrary axiomatic system is a one-one function with domain A and range B which preserves any operations or relations that occur in the axiom system. For our present axiom system we make this precise in the following definition.

DEFINITION 3-2-1. *If* $\mathcal{A}_1 = \langle P_1, 1_1, +_1\rangle$ *and* $\mathcal{A}_2 = \langle P_2, 1_2, +_2\rangle$ *are any two models, then a function f with domain* P_1 *and range* P_2, *or, as we say, a function f mapping* P_1 *onto* P_2, *is an* **isomorphism** *between* $\mathcal{A}_1$ *and* $\mathcal{A}_2$ *if and only if:*

1. f *is a one-one function;*
2. $f(1_1) = 1_2$;
3. *for any* $x, y \in P_1$, *we have* $f(x +_1 y) = f(x) +_2 f(y)$.

If there exists an isomorphism of this kind we say that these two models are **isomorphic.**

In terms of this definition we can show precisely that the models $\mathcal{A}$ and $\mathcal{B}$ described above are isomorphic. In fact, we take f to be the function with domain P_1 and range P_2 such that $f(1) = 2p$, $f(2) = 4p$, and $f(3) = 6p$. To show that this function f is indeed an isomorphism will be left as an exercise for the reader.

In our definition of isomorphism, preference is apparently given to one model in that the function maps P_1 onto P_2, although we say that the isomorphism is "between the models" and this terminology suggests that neither model "comes first." This difficulty is apparent rather than real as is shown by the next theorem. Before we state this theorem we remark that since f maps P_1 *onto* P_2, then for each $x' \in P_2$ there is an $x \in P_1$ such that $f(x) = x'$; and because f is one-one this x is *unique.*

THEOREM 3-2-2. *Let f be an isomorphism between $\mathfrak{A}_1$ and $\mathfrak{A}_2$, and for each $x' \in P_2$ let $g(x')$ be the unique element x of P_1 such that $f(x) = x'$. Then g is an isomorphism between $\mathfrak{A}_2$ and $\mathfrak{A}_1$.*

Proof

►► **1.** Let f be an isomorphism between $\mathfrak{A}_1$ and $\mathfrak{A}_2$, where $\mathfrak{A}_1$ and $\mathfrak{A}_2$ are models.

►► **2.** Let g be the function with domain P_2 such that, for each $x' \in P_2$, $g(x')$ is the unique $x \in P_1$ for which $f(x) = x'$.

3. $f(1_1) = 1_2$; by Definition 3-2-1 and line **1**.

►► **4.** $g(1_2) = 1_1$; by lines **2** and **3**.

►► LEMMA 3-2-2.1. *g is a function mapping P_2 onto P_1.*

► **5.** Let x be any element of P_1.

► **6.** $f(x) = x'$ for some $x' \in P_2$; by line **1** and Definition 3-2-1.

► **7.** $g(x') = x$; by lines **2** and **6**.

8. For any x in P_1 there is an x' in P_2 such that $g(x') = x$; by lines **5** through **7**, by the Deduction Theorem of logic.

► **9.** g is a function mapping P_2 onto P_1; by lines **2** and **8** and the definition of a mapping "onto."

►► LEMMA 3-2-2.2. *g is one-one.*

► **10.** Let r' and s' be any two distinct elements of P_2; i.e., $r' \neq s'$.

11. There exist elements r and s in P_1 such that $f(r) = r'$ and $f(s) = s'$; since f is a function from P_1 onto P_2, by line **1**.

12. $g(r') = r$ and $g(s') = s$; by lines **2** and **11**.

13. If $r = s$ then $f(r) = f(s)$; by E.

14. If $f(r) \neq f(s)$ then $r \neq s$; by line **13**.

15. $f(r) \neq f(s)$; by lines **10** and **11**.

16. $r \neq s$; by lines **14** and **15**.

► **17.** $g(r') \neq g(s')$; by E from lines **12** and **16**.

18. For any $r', s' \in P_2$, if $r' \neq s'$ then $g(r') \neq g(s')$; by lines **10** through **17** by the Deduction Theorem of logic.

► **19.** g is one-one; by line **18** and the definition of a one-one function.

►► LEMMA 3-2-2.3. *For any $u', v' \in P_2$, $g(u' +_2 v') = g(u') +_1 g(v')$.*

► **20.** Let u' and v' be any elements of P_2.

21. There exist $u, v \in P_1$ such that $f(u) = u'$ and $f(v) = v'$; by lines **1** and **20**.

22. $g(u') = u$ and $g(v') = v$; by lines **2** and **21**.

23. $f(u +_1 v) = f(u) +_2 f(v)$; by line **1** and Definition 3-2-1.

24. $ = u' +_2 v'$; by E from lines **21**.

25. $f(u +_1 v) = u' +_2 v'$; by E from lines **23** and **24**.

26. $g(u' +_2 v') = u +_1 v$; by E from lines **2** and **25**.
27. $= g(u') +_1 g(v')$; by E from line **22**.
▶**28.** $g(u' +_2 v') = g(u') +_1 g(v')$; by E from lines **26** and **27**.
29. For any $u', v' \in P_2$, $g(u' +_2 v') = g(u') +_1 g(v')$; by lines **20** through **28** by the Deduction Theorem of logic.

Continuation of proof of theorem.

▶▶**30.** g is an isomorphism between $\mathfrak{A}_2$ and $\mathfrak{A}_1$; by line **4**, Lemmas 3-2-2.1, 3-2-2.2, and 3-2-2.3 and Definition 3-2-1.
31. The statement of Theorem 3-2-2 is now obtained by applying the Deduction Theorem of logic to lines **1** through **30**.

The function g in our last theorem is usually called the *inverse function* to f, and is often written f^{-1}. Not every function has an inverse—only one-one functions do. As the reader can readily establish, the inverse function to g is f; that is $(f^{-1})^{-1} = f$.

In our discussion of models (see the preceding section) we gave three examples of induction models which were not Peano models. The first model contained only one element, namely, this book. The second model contained two elements, Donald Duck and Bugs Bunny. Since it is impossible to have a one-one function mapping a pair onto a singleton, or mapping a singleton onto a pair, it is clear that these two induction models are not isomorphic. As indicated in Exercise 8 of the last section, for any counting number m there is an induction model with m elements. Hence, one can find many different *induction* models no two of which are isomorphic.

A natural question that arises is whether there are many *Peano* models no two of which are isomorphic. The answer is "No." Quite the contrary, although we will not give a proof of it here, it can be shown that *any two Peano models are isomorphic*. We express this fact by saying that the system of Axioms P1 through P4 is *categorical*.

THEOREM 3-2-3. *Suppose* $\mathfrak{A}_1 = \langle P_1, 1_1, +_1\rangle$ *and* $\mathfrak{A}_2 = \langle P_2, 1_2, +_2\rangle$ *are models, and let* f *be an isomorphism between* $\mathfrak{A}_1$ *and* $\mathfrak{A}_2$. *If* $\mathfrak{A}_1$ *is an induction model, then so is* $\mathfrak{A}_2$.

We shall prove this theorem in two parts. First we will show that $\mathfrak{A}_2$ satisfies Axiom P3; next we will show that $\mathfrak{A}_2$ satisfies Axiom P4.

Part 1. $\mathfrak{A}_2$ satisfies Axiom P3; i.e., for all $x', y' \in P_2$, $x' +_2 (y' +_2 1_2) = (x' +_2 y') +_2 1_2$.

Proof of Part 1

▶▶ **1.** Let f be an isomorphism between $\mathfrak{A}_1$ and $\mathfrak{A}_2$, and let $\mathfrak{A}_1$ be an induction model.

▶▶ **2.** Let x', y' be any elements in P_2.

▶ **3.** There exist unique elements $x, y \in P_1$ such that $f(x) = x'$ and $f(y) = y'$; by lines **1** and **2** and Definition 3-2-1. (See remark preceding Theorem 3-2-2.)

4. $f(1_1) = 1_2$; by line **1** and the definition of isomorphism (Definition 3-2-1).

▶ **5.** $(x +_1 y) +_1 1_1 = x +_1 (y +_1 1_1)$; by line **3**, since $\mathfrak{A}_1$ is an induction model (line **1**) and so satisfies Axiom P3.

▶ **6.** $f((x +_1 y) +_1 1_1) = f(x +_1 (y +_1 1_1))$; by E from line **5**.

7. $f((x +_1 y) +_1 1_1) = f(x +_1 y) +_2 f(1_1)$; by definition of isomorphism.

8. $= (f(x) +_2 f(y)) +_2 f(1_1)$; by E from the definition of isomorphism.

9. $= (x' +_2 y') +_2 1_2$; by E from lines **3**, **4**, and **8**.

▶ **10.** $f((x +_1 y) +_1 1_1) = (x' +_2 y') +_2 1_2$; by E from lines **7** to **9**.

11. $f(x +_1 (y +_1 1_1)) = f(x) +_2 f(y +_1 1_1)$; by definition of isomorphism.

12. $= f(x) +_2 (f(y) +_2 f(1_1))$; by E from the definition of isomorphism.

13. $= x' +_2 (y' +_2 1_2)$; by E from lines **3** and **4**.

▶ **14.** $f(x +_1 (y +_1 1_1)) = x' +_2 (y' +_2 1_2)$; by E from lines **11** through **13**.

▶▶ **15.** $(x' +_2 y') +_2 1_2 = x' +_2 (y' +_2 1_2)$; by E from lines **6, 10,** and **14**.

16. For all $x', y' \in P_2$, $(x' +_2 y') +_2 1_2 = x' +_2 (y' +_2 1_2)$; by the Deduction Theorem from lines **2** through **15**.

Part 2. If G_2 is any subset of P_2 such that

(i) $1_2 \in G_2$, and
(ii) whenever $x' \in G_2$ then also $x' +_2 1_2 \in G_2$,
then $G_2 = P_2$.

Proof of Part 2

▶▶ **1.** Let f be an isomorphism between $\mathfrak{A}_1$ and $\mathfrak{A}_2$, and let $\mathfrak{A}_1$ be an induction model.

▶▶ **2.** Let G_2 be any subset of P_2 such that **(i)** $1_2 \in G_2$, and **(ii)** whenever $x' \in G_2$ then also $x' +_2 1_2 \in G_2$.

▶ **3.** Let G_1 be the subset of P_1 whose elements are all those $x \in P_1$ for which $f(x) \in G_2$.

4. $f(1_1) = 1_2$; by line **1** and the definition of isomorphism (Definition 3-2-1).

5. $f(1_1) \in G_2$; by E from lines **2(i)** and **4**.
▶ 6. $1_1 \in G_1$; by lines **3** and **5**.
▶ 7. Let x be any element in G_1.
8. $f(x) \in G_2$; by lines **3** and **7**.
9. $f(x) +_2 1_2 \in G_2$; by line **2 (ii)** and **8**.
10. $f(x +_1 1_1) = f(x) +_2 1_2$; by line **1** and the definition of isomorphism (Definition 3-2-1).
11. $f(x +_1 1_1) \in G_2$; by E from lines **9** and **10**.
▶ 12. $x +_1 1_1 \in G_1$; by lines **3** and **11**.
13. Whenever $x \in G_1$, then also $x +_1 1_1 \in G_1$; by lines **7** through **12**, by the Deduction Theorem of logic.
▶ 14. $G_1 = P_1$; by lines **3, 6,** and **13**, since $\mathfrak{A}_1$ is an induction model (line **1**) and so satisfies Axiom P4.
▶ 15. Let y' be any element in P_2.
16. There is an element $y \in G_1$ such that $f(y) = y'$; by lines **1** and **14** and the definition of isomorphism (Definition 3-2-1).
▶ 17. $y' \in G_2$; by lines **3** and **16**.
18. For all $y' \in P_2$ we have $y' \in G_2$; by lines **15** and **17** by the Deduction Theorem.
▶▶ 19. $P_2 \subseteq G_2$; by line **18** and the definition of subset.
▶▶ 20. $G_2 = P_2$; by lines **2** and **19** and the Principle of Extensionality for sets.
21. If G_2 is any subset of P_2 such that **(i)** $1_2 \in G_2$; and **(ii)** whenever $x' \in G_2$ then also $x' +_2 1_2 \in G_2$; then $G_2 = P_2$; by lines **2** through **20**, by the Deduction Theorem.

The proof of Theorem 3-2-3 is immediately evident now from Parts 1 and 2 and the definition of an induction model.

We might ask whether the isomorphism relation on models is a transitive one. That is, if a model $\mathfrak{A}_1$ is isomorphic to $\mathfrak{A}_2$ and if $\mathfrak{A}_2$ is isomorphic to $\mathfrak{A}_3$ does it follow that $\mathfrak{A}_1$ and $\mathfrak{A}_3$ are isomorphic? That this is indeed the case is established in the following theorem.

THEOREM 3-2-4. *If* $\mathfrak{A}_1 = \langle P_1, 1_1, +_1\rangle$, $\mathfrak{A}_2 = \langle P_2, 1_2, +_2\rangle$, $\mathfrak{A}_3 = \langle P_3, 1_3, +_3\rangle$; *if f is an isomorphism between $\mathfrak{A}_1$ and $\mathfrak{A}_2$, and g is an isomorphism between $\mathfrak{A}_2$ and $\mathfrak{A}_3$, then there is an isomorphism between $\mathfrak{A}_1$ and $\mathfrak{A}_3$.*

Proof: See Exercise 2 below.

It is common practice among mathematicians to regard two isomorphic models as "essentially the same"; sometimes one even reads the statement that "we identify" two isomorphic models. This practice is widespread because any mathematical sentence (containing one or more of the undefined terms *number*, *addition*, and *one*) which is true of one model will be true of any other model isomorphic to the first. To prove this general statement lies beyond the scope of this book, but the reader will find it illustrated in Theorem 3-2-3, where it was shown that if Axiom P3 is true of a model $\mathfrak{A}$ then it will also be true of any model $\mathfrak{B}$ which is isomorphic to $\mathfrak{A}$; and similarly in the case of Axiom P4. Further illustrations are provided by Exercise 3 below.

The essential meaning expressed by the mathematician when he says that any two isomorphic models are "essentially the same" is that mathematically we are never interested in *what* kind of things the elements under discussion may be, but rather in *how* the things are combined or related to one another by the fundamental operations and relations of the mathematical theory. We may express this by saying that in mathematics we are interested in the "structure" rather than the "substance" of the systems we investigate. Herein lies an essential difference between mathematics and the empirical sciences. In other sciences the "structure" is used as an auxiliary tool. Also, with the collection of more and better data, the "structure" used in an empirical theory may be abandoned for another—for example, in physics, the structure of Newtonian physics was replaced by that of Relativity.

EXERCISES

1. Prove that the two models $\mathfrak{A}$ and $\mathfrak{B}$ given at the beginning of this section are isomorphic.

2. Give a proof for Theorem 3-2-4. [Hint: Consider the function h such that for every $x \in P_1$, $h(x) = g(f(x))$.]

3. Show that for any two models $\mathfrak{A}$ and $\mathfrak{B}$, if $\mathfrak{A}$ is a Peano model and f is an isomorphism between $\mathfrak{A}$ and $\mathfrak{B}$ then $\mathfrak{B}$ is a Peano model. (Use Theorem 3-2-3.)

4. Suppose that $\mathfrak{A}_1 = \langle P_1, 1_1, +_1 \rangle$ and $\mathfrak{A}_2 = \langle P_2, 1_2, +_2 \rangle$ are models, and that f is a function mapping $\mathfrak{A}_1$ into $\mathfrak{A}_2$ such that $f(1_1) = 1_2$ and $f(x +_1 1_1) = f(x) +_2 1_2$ for all $x \in P_1$. Show that if $\mathfrak{A}_2$ satisfies Axiom P4 then f maps $\mathfrak{A}_1$ onto $\mathfrak{A}_2$.

5. Suppose that $\mathfrak{A}_1$, $\mathfrak{A}_2$ and f are the same as in the preceding problem. Suppose, in addition, that f is one-one. Furthermore, suppose $\mathfrak{A}_1$ and $\mathfrak{A}_2$ satisfy Axiom P3. Then show that $\mathfrak{A}_1$ and $\mathfrak{A}_2$ are isomorphic.

6. Show that if $\mathfrak{B}_1 = \langle P_1, 1, + \rangle$ and $\mathfrak{B}_2 = \langle P_2, 1', +^1 \rangle$ are two Peano models, and if f and g both are isomorphisms between $\mathfrak{B}_1$ and $\mathfrak{B}_2$, then $f = g$.

7. Complete the proof of the statement that each of the models $\mathfrak{M}_1 = \langle P, 1, +_i \rangle$, $i = 1, 2, 3$, of Appendix I, satisfies Axiom P3.

8. Show that if $+$, $+'$, and $+''$ are distinct operations on $P = \{1, a, b\}$, then $\langle P, 1, + \rangle$ cannot be isomorphic to both $\langle P, 1, +' \rangle$ and $\langle P, 1, +'' \rangle$.

9. Show that if $+$ is any binary operation on $P = \{1, a, b\}$, and if $+'$ is defined by interchanging "a" and "b" throughout the table of values of $+$, then there is an isomorphism between $\langle P, 1, + \rangle$ and $\langle P, 1, +' \rangle$.

10.* Show in detail that the models $\mathfrak{M}$ and $\mathfrak{M}_0$ described in the last paragraph of the Appendix I, are isomorphic.

11.* It is shown in Appendix I that for each model $\mathfrak{M} = \langle P, 1, + \rangle$, where

$P = \{1, a, b\}$, there is a model $\mathfrak{M}' = \langle P, 1, +' \rangle$ such that f_2 is an isomorphism between $\mathfrak{M}$ and $\mathfrak{M}'$ (where $f_2 1 = 1$, $f_2 a = b$, $f_2 b = a$). Of course it may happen that $\mathfrak{M} = \mathfrak{M}'$, as one sees by considering the operation $+$ such that $x + y = 1$ for all $x, y \in P$. Show that of the 19,683 models $\langle P, 1, + \rangle$ there are 3^4, or 81, which are isomorphic to no other model in the set than themselves, while the remaining 19,602 models split up into 9,801 pairs of distinct but isomorphic models. Thus there are altogether 9,882 essentially different three-element models.

12. Show that $\mathfrak{M}_1$ of Appendix I satisfies Axiom P2 but not P1, while $\mathfrak{M}_2$ and $\mathfrak{M}_3$ each satisfy Axiom P1 but not P2.

13.* Generalize the results and methods of Appendix I to get a complete description of all k-element induction models for arbitrary positive integers k.

3. *Semi-Groups*

In our discussion of Peano models and induction models in Section 1 of this chapter we considered various mathematical systems, each consisting of a set of elements and a single binary operation on this set. In any such system the operation may or may not possess properties such as those expressed by the associative, commutative, and cancellation laws.

The systems we have considered, as well as many others, may be classified according to the properties they possess. Such a classification leads to the branch of mathematics known as *abstract algebra*, in which selected properties of mathematical systems are studied rather than individual systems. The terminology of abstract algebra—once the almost exclusive province of the graduate course—is creeping more and more into the elementary levels of mathematics, so that today even the high-school student may encounter such words as "group", "ring", "field", "semi-group", etc. It might be well to consider some of these concepts at this time, not only to acquaint the reader with some of the terms of abstract algebra, but also to afford a characterization of the mathematical systems we are considering in this book in terms of the categories studied by algebraists.

We begin by giving an intuitive idea of what is meant by a *group*; a precise definition will be given later, in Chapter XI. By a *group* we have in mind a mathematical system consisting of a set of elements, S, and a function $\circ$ which can act on any (ordered) pair of elements of S, such that the following four properties hold:

(i) S is *closed* under $\circ$; i.e., for any $a, b \in S$ we have also $(a \circ b) \in S$. (We can also express this condition by saying that $\circ$ is a binary operation on S. See Chapter I, Section 5.)

(ii) The associative law holds for $\circ$; i.e., for any $a, b, c \in S$ we have $(a \circ b) \circ c = a \circ (b \circ c)$.

(iii) S contains an element, z, called the *null element*, such that $a \circ z = a$ for any $a \in S$.

(**iv**) If a is any element of S there exists an element a' of S, called the *inverse* of a, such that $(a \circ a') = z$ (where z is the null element).

Clearly, the Peano models we have considered are *not* groups since they do not have any null element (there is no $z \in P$ such that $a + z = a$ for even a *single* $a \in P$, much less for *all* $a \in P$); and hence certainly their elements have no inverses. On the other hand the first induction model we considered (cf. p. 53), the system $\langle P_1, 1_1, +_1 \rangle$ where $P_1 = \{1_1\}$ and where $+_1$ is the binary operation defined by $(1_1 +_1 1_1) = 1_1$, is a group, as may be readily verified.

As another example of a group we might cite the number system consisting of the set of all integers (positive, negative, and zero), with the operation of addition. Our intuitive knowledge of this system tells us that the four properties characterizing a group (closure, associativity, and the existence of a null element and of inverses) all hold, with zero serving as the null element, and $-a$ as the inverse for each integer a.

We shall leave a more complete discussion of groups to a later time. We have introduced the word "group" at this time principally for terminological reasons. Actually, at the present level of development our concern is not with groups but rather with a more general class of mathematical systems known as *semi-groups*. The group concept was developed first; this explains why the name of the more general concept is a modified form of the name of the more special concept instead of *vice-versa*.

The system $\langle P, 1, + \rangle$ does not form a group, as we have indicated above, since it contains neither a null element nor inverse elements. It does, however, exhibit two of the four properties characterizing groups—closure and associativity. Thus we might consider it to be a kind of half-group. This observation suggests the need for classification such as given by the following definition.

DEFINITION 3-3-1. *A mathematical system $\langle S, \circ \rangle$ consisting of a set S of arbitrary elements and a binary operation $\circ$ on S is a* **semi-group** *if and only if the associative law holds for $\circ$, i.e., if and only if for any $a, b, c \in S$ $(a \circ b) \circ c = a \circ (b \circ c)$.* (Note that the property that S be closed under $\circ$ is implied by the statement that $\circ$ is an *operation* on S.)

Obviously any system which is a group is also a semi-group, although the converse need not be true as the example $\langle P, + \rangle$ itself shows.

Semi-groups may, of course, possess certain other properties, such as commutativity, the cancellation properties, etc. Accordingly, we can introduce a further classification.

DEFINITION 3-3-2. *A system $\langle S, \circ \rangle$ which is a semi-group is said to be a* **commutative** (*or an* **Abelian**) **semi-group,** *if and only if the additional property*

$a \circ b = b \circ a$, *for all* $a, b \in S$, *holds.* (*Note:* The adjective "Abelian" is derived from the name of a great Norwegian mathematician, Niels Abel, who was killed at the age of twenty-seven, and whose statue now stands at the head of the principal square in Oslo.)

DEFINITION 3-3-3. *A system* $\langle S, \circ\rangle$ *which is a semi-group is said to be a* **right cancellation semi-group** *if and only if, for any* $a, b, c \in S$ *such that* $a \circ b = c \circ b$ *we have* $a = c$. *Similarly, if* $a = c$ *whenever* a, b, *and* c *are elements of* S *such that* $b \circ a = b \circ c$, *we say that* $\langle S, \circ\rangle$ *is a* **left cancellation semi-group.** *A system which is both a right cancellation and a left cancellation semi-group will be referred to simply as a* **cancellation semi-group.**

Theorem 2-4-1 of Chapter II tells us that the particular system $\langle P, +\rangle$ is a semi-group. From Theorem 2-4-2 we see that this system is in fact a commutative semi-group, while Theorem 2-4-3 and Corollary 2-4-3.1 tell us that $\langle P, +\rangle$ is a cancellation semi-group.

In Chapter II we introduced the binary relation $<$ and we saw that it possessed certain ordering properties with respect to the system $\langle P, 1, +\rangle$. This suggests a further basis for classification of semi-groups, and hence another definition.

DEFINITION 3-3-4. *A system* $\langle S, \circ, R\rangle$ *consisting of a semi group* $\langle S, \circ\rangle$ *with which is associated a binary relation* R *on* S, *is said to be an* **ordered semi-group** *if and only if the relation* R *satisfies the following conditions:*

(**i**) *R is transitive (i.e., for any* $a, b, c \in S$ *such that* $a\ R\ b$ *and* $b\ R\ c$, *we have also* $a\ R\ c$;

(**ii**) *For any* $a, b \in S$ *we have one and only one of the following:* $a\ R\ b$, $b\ R\ a$, or $a = b$;

(**iii**) *For any* $a, b, c \in S$ *such that* $a\ R\ b$, *we have also* $(a \circ c)\ R\ (b \circ c)$ *and* $(c \circ a)\ R\ (c \circ b)$.

An examination of the definitions and theorems of Section 5 of Chapter II should convince us that the system $\langle P, +\rangle$, together with the associated relation, $<$, is indeed an ordered semi-group. (We shall use the notation $\langle P, +, <\rangle$ to denote this mathematical system.) For later reference we formulate this observation as a theorem.

THEOREM 3-3-5. *The system* $\langle P, +, <\rangle$ *is an ordered semi-group, while* $\langle P, +\rangle$ *is a commutative cancellation semi-group.*

Proof. See Exercise **1** below.

It may occur to us to wonder whether there is some binary relation, R, *other* than $<$, which also converts the semi-group $\langle P, +\rangle$ into an *ordered* semi-group $\langle P, +, R\rangle$. There is indeed, for the *greater than* relation, $>$, also satisfies conditions (**i**) through (**iii**) of Definition 3-3-4. But as we shall show below, these are the *only* two such relations. As a first step in proving this result, we consider the following theorem.

THEOREM 3-3-6. *Suppose that R is any binary relation on P such that* (**i**) *the system* $\langle P, +, R\rangle$ *is an ordered semi-group, and* (**ii**) *the relation R holds for the ordered pair* $\langle 1, 2\rangle$, *i.e.*, $1\ R\ 2$ *holds. Then R is the same relation as* $<$.

In effect this theorem states that $<$ is the only ordering relation of the semi-group $\langle P, +\rangle$ which holds for the pair of numbers $\langle 1, 2\rangle$. To prove this, we must show two things: (**i**) that whenever $a < c$, then $a\ R\ c$ also holds, and (**ii**), conversely, if $a\ R\ c$ holds, then $a < c$. In attempting to prove (**i**) we note that if $a < c$, then there exists an element $b \in P$ such that $c = a + b$. If we can establish that $a\ R\ (a + b)$ holds, we will have proved that $a\ R\ c$ holds. Thus we are led to consider the statement $a\ R\ (a + b)$. We might be able to show that this relation holds by induction on b, if we can first establish that $a\ R\ (a + 1)$. This analysis suggests that we break the proof of part (**i**) into three separate lemmas.

LEMMA 3-3-6.1. *If* $\langle P, +, R\rangle$ *is an ordered semi-group and* $1\ R\ 2$, *then for every* $a \in P$ *we have* $a\ R\ (a + 1)$.

Proof of Lemma 3-3-6.1

▶▶ **1.** Let R be a binary relation on P such that $\langle P, +, R\rangle$ is an ordered semi-group.

▶▶ **2.** Suppose $1\ R\ 2$ holds.

▶▶ **3.** Form the set G of all those elements $a \in P$ for which $a\ R\ (a + 1)$ holds.

4. $1\ R\ (1 + 1)$ holds; by E applied to line **2**, using the definition of 2 (Definition 2-3-1).

▶ **5.** $1 \in G$; by lines **3** and **4**.

▶ **6.** Assume that b is any element of G.

7. $b\ R\ (b + 1)$ holds; by lines **3** and **6**.

8. $(b + 1)\ R\ [(b + 1) + 1]$ holds; by lines **7** and **1**, together with Definition 3-3-4.

▶ **9.** $(b + 1) \in G$; by lines **8** and **3**.

10. If b is any element of G then also $(b + 1) \in G$; by the Deduction Theorem applied to lines **6** through **9**.

▶▶ **11.** $G = P$; by lines **5** and **10** and Axiom P4.

12. For every $a \in P$ we have $a\ R\ (a + 1)$; by lines **3** and **11**.

Lemma 3-3-6.1 now follows by applying the Deduction Theorem to lines **1**, **2**, and **12**.

LEMMA 3-3-6.2. *If $\langle P, +, R\rangle$ is an ordered semi-group and* $1 \; R \; 2$ *then for every* $a, b \in P$ *we have* $a \; R \; (a + b)$.

Proof of Lemma 3.3.6.2

▶▶ **1.** Let R be any binary relation on P such that $\langle P, +, R\rangle$ is an ordered semi-group.

▶▶ **2.** Suppose $1 \; R \; 2$ holds.

▶▶ **3.** Let a be any element of P.

▶▶ **4.** Form the set G of all those elements $b \in P$ for which $a \; R \; (a + b)$ holds.

▶ **5.** $1 \in G$; by lines **1** through **4**, and Lemma 3-3-6.1.

▶ **6.** Assume that c is any element of G.

7. $a \; R \; (a + c)$ holds; by lines **4** and **6**.

8. $(a + c) \; R \; [(a + c) + 1]$ holds; by lines **1** and **2** and Lemma 3-3-6.1.

9. $a \; R \; [(a + c) + 1]$ holds; by lines **7** and **8** and line **1**, together with the transitive property of R, Definition 3-3-3 (**i**).

10. $(a + c) + 1 = a + (c + 1)$; by Axiom P3.

▶**11.** $a \; R \; [a + (c + 1)]$; by E applied to lines **9** and **10**.

▶**12.** $(c + 1) \in G$; by lines **4** and **11**.

13. Whenever c is in G then also $(c + 1) \in G$; by the Deduction Theorem applied to lines **6** through **12**.

▶▶**14.** $G = P$; by lines **5** and **13**, and Axiom P4.

15. For every $b \in P$ we have $a \; R \; (a + b)$; by lines **4** and **14**.

Lemma 3-3-6.2 now follows by applying the Deduction Theorem to lines **1**, **2**, **3**, and **15**.

LEMMA 3-3-6.3. *If $\langle P, +, R\rangle$ is an ordered semi-group and* $1 \; R \; 2$ *then whenever* $a < c$ *we have* $a \; R \; c$.

Proof of Lemma 3-3-6.3

▶▶**1.** Let R be any binary relation on P such that $\langle P, +, R\rangle$ is an ordered semi-group.

▶▶**2.** Suppose $1 \; R \; 2$ holds.

▶▶**3.** Let a, c be any elements of P such that $a < c$.

4. $a + b = c$ for some $b \in P$; by line **3** and the definition of $<$ (Definition 2-5-1).

5. $a \; R \; (a + b)$; by lines **1** and **2** and Lemma 3-3-6.2.

▶▶**6.** $a \; R \; c$; by E applied to lines **4** and **5**.

7. If a, c are any elements of P such that $a < c$, then $a \; R \; c$ holds; by the Deduction Theorem applied to lines **3** through **6**.

Lemma 3-3-6.3 now follows by applying the Deduction Theorem to lines **1**, **2**, and **7**.

The above lemma gives us one part of Theorem 3-3-6. It remains only to show that whenever $a \; R \; c$ then we have $a < c$. This will be done in the following lemma. The method of proof will be to assume that a is not less than c, and arrive at a contradiction.

LEMMA 3-3-6.4 *If* $\langle P, +, R \rangle$ *is a semi-group and* $1 \; R \; 2$ *then whenever* $a \; R \; c$ *we have* $a < c$.

Proof of Lemma 3-3-6.4

▶▶ **1.** Let R be any binary relation on P such that $\langle P, +, R \rangle$ is an ordered semi-group.
▶▶ **2.** Suppose $1 \; R \; 2$ holds.
▶▶ **3.** Let a, c be any elements of P such that $a \; R \; c$ holds.
▶ **4.** Assume that $a < c$ does not hold.
▶ **5.** Either $c < a$ or $c = a$; by line **4** and the Trichotomy Law (Theorem 2-5-3).
6. Either $c \; R \; a$ or $c = a$; by line **5** and lines **1** and **2**, together with Lemma 3-3-6.3.
▶ **7.** Either both $a \; R \; c$ and $c \; R \; a$ hold, or both $a \; R \; c$ and $a = c$ hold; by lines **3** and **6**.
▶ **8.** But not both $a \; R \; c$ and $c \; R \; a$ hold, and not both $a \; R \; c$ and $a = c$ hold; by Definition 3-3-4 (**ii**) and line **1**.
9. If $a < c$ does not hold, the two contradictory statements of lines **7** and **8** follow; by the Deduction Theorem applied to lines **4** through **8**.
▶▶ **10.** $a < c$ holds; by line **9**.
11. Whenever $a \; R \; c$ we have $a < c$; by the Deduction Theorem applied to lines **3** through **10**.

The Lemma 3-3-6.4 now follows by applying the Deduction Theorem to lines **1**, **2**, and **11**.

Combining the last two lemmas gives us Theorem 3-3-6. A formal proof of this theorem is given below.

Proof of Theorem 3-3-6

1. Let R be any binary relation on P such that $\langle P, +, R \rangle$ is an ordered semi-group.
2. Suppose $1 \; R \; 2$.
3. For any $a, c \in P$ we have $a < c$ if and only if $a \; R \; c$; by lines **1** and **2** and Lemmas 3-3-6.3 and 3-3-6.4.
4. R is the same relation as $<$; by line **3** and the Principle of Extensionality for Relations (cf. Chapter I, Section 4), using line **1** and Definition 3-3-4.

Theorem 3-3-6 now follows by applying the Deduction Theorem to lines **1**, **2**, and **4**.

THEOREM 3-3-7. *Suppose R is any binary relation on P such that* $\langle P, +, R\rangle$ *is an ordered semi-group and* 2 R 1 *holds. Then R is the same relation as* $>$.

Proof

The proof closely parallels that of the preceding theorem and is left as an exercise. (Exercise 8 below.)

THEOREM 3-3-8. *If R is any binary relation on P such that* $\langle P, +, R\rangle$ *is an ordered semi-group then R must be one of the relations* $<$ *or* $>$.

Proof

1. Let R be any binary relation on P such that $\langle P, +, R\rangle$ is an ordered semi-group.

2. Either $1\ R\ 2$ or $2\ R\ 1$; by line **1** and Definition 3-3-4 (**ii**) since $2 \neq 1$.

3. R is either $<$ or $>$; by lines **1** and **2** and Theorems 3-3-6 and 3-3-7.

Theorem 3-3-8 now follows by applying the Deduction Theorem to lines **1** through **3**.

EXERCISES

1. Point out the specific definitions and theorems of Chapter II which enable us to say that $\langle P, +, <\rangle$ is an ordered, commutative, cancellation semi-group, thus proving Theorem 3-3-4.

2. Speaking intuitively, would the system $\langle P, \cdot\rangle$ consisting of the set of all positive integers and the multiplication operation form a group? A semi-group?

3. Consider the game of rocks, paper and scissors (cf. Chapter II, Section 4), where $\circ$ is the selection operation involved. Does this set of three elements and the operation $\circ$ form a semi-group?

4. Give an example of a noncommutative semi-group.

5. Show that every commutative left-cancellation semi-group is a cancellation semi-group.

6. Let $\langle S, \circ, R\rangle$ be any ordered semi-group. Show that if $a, b, c, d \in S$ and $a\ R\ b$ then $(a \circ c)\ R\ (b \circ d)$ when $c\ R\ d$.

7. Let $\langle S, \circ, R\rangle$ be any ordered cancellation semi-group, and suppose that a, b, c are elements of S such that $(a \circ c)\ R\ (b \circ c)$. Show that we must have $a\ R\ b$.

8. Prove Theorem 3-3-7.

9. Let $\langle S, \circ, R\rangle$ be any ordered semi-group. Define a binary relation R' on S by the rule that for any $a, b \in S$ we have $a\ R'\ b$ if and only if $a \neq b$ and not $a\ R\ b$. Show that $\langle S, \circ, R'\rangle$ is also an ordered semi-group.

IV

Further Development of the Positive Integers: Multiplication Theory

1. Multiplication

We now proceed with our axiomatic treatment of the positive integers by introducing the defined concept of *multiplication*. We remark first that we could have begun our theory with *multiplication* as an undefined term, along with *number*, *one*, and *addition*, adding to our postulates P1 through P4 further postulates involving the multiplication symbol. However, since it is more satisfying to have as few undefined terms as possible in an axiomatic theory, we prefer to follow the alternative course of introducing multiplication as a *defined* concept. But how is this to be done? Let us begin with some intuitive considerations.

If we recall our grade-school experience with the positive integers, we remember that multiplication was introduced only after we learned how to add. For example, we learned that $2 \cdot 3$ means $3 + 3$, i.e., the addition of two three's. And then, after many examples of this kind we learned the general rule for multiplying any pair of positive integers x and y: $x \cdot y$ means the sum of x terms each having value y—even though we never actually formulated the general statement in precisely this way.

It should not be too surprising, then, to find that it is possible to introduce the concept of multiplication into our theory in terms of addition. However, if we attempt to find a definition closely patterned after the grade-school explanation we encounter certain difficulties. For the notion of summing x terms, for arbitrary x, implicitly involves the notion of *counting*, and this is a concept not yet available in our axiomatic theory. We must, therefore, consider some other form of definition.

Curiously enough, we can get a hint as to how to proceed by asking what axioms we would have added to P1 through P4 *if* we had taken *multiplication* as an additional undefined term. To this end, consider the following sentences:

(i) For all $x \in P$, $\quad x \cdot 1 = x$; and

(ii) For all $x, y \in P$, $\quad x \cdot (y + 1) = (x \cdot y) + x$.

On the one hand we recognize that these are true statements about the positive integers as we have come to know them intuitively through long experience. [Indeed, (**ii**) becomes a special case of the familiar distributive law if we replace the final "x" by "$x \cdot 1$"—to which it is equal according to (**i**).] On the other hand one can argue intuitively that (**i**) and (**ii**) together enable us to compute the product of *any* pair of positive integers (providing we know how to add any pair).

For example, suppose we wish to compute the product $4 \cdot 3$. From (**i**) we see that $4 \cdot 1 = 4$. Then we compute $4 \cdot 2$ by first writing 2 as $1 + 1$ and next making use of (**ii**). Thus $4 \cdot 2 = 4 \cdot (1 + 1) = 4 \cdot 1 + 4 = 4 + 4 = 8$. Now it is evident how we can compute $4 \cdot 3$: $4 \cdot 3 = 4 \cdot (2 + 1) = 4 \cdot 2 + 4 = 8 + 4 = 12$. From this example we see how it would be possible to compute the product of any two positive integers from (**i**) and (**ii**) (and the knowledge of how to add any pair).

The above considerations suggest that (**i**) and (**ii**) might be reasonable propositions to adopt as axioms *if* we had selected *multiplication* as one of the undefined terms of our system. But how does this help us to obtain a *definition* of this concept in our present system?

To answer this, we first observe that multiplication is a binary operation on P—i.e., it is a function which acts on any ordered pair of positive integers and produces a positive integer as the result of the action. But there are many such operations—how can we single out the one we wish to call multiplication? Here we see how to make use of (**i**) and (**ii**)—multiplication is a binary operation f on P such that

(**i′**) For all $x \in P$, $f\langle x, 1\rangle = x$; and
(**ii′**) For all $x, y \in P$, $f\langle x, y + 1\rangle = f\langle x, y\rangle + x$.

But perhaps there are many binary operations f on P which satisfy (**i′**) and (**ii′**)—how can we select multiplication from among these? Fortunately, we do not have to answer the last question, for we can prove (within our axiomatic theory) that there is only one binary operation f on P which satisfies (**i′**) and (**ii′**).

The idea of our definition of multiplication is now clear. We first *prove* that there is one and only one binary operation on P which satisfies (**i′**) and (**ii′**), and then define multiplication to be that unique operation. If we denote this operation, as usual, by "$\cdot$", it then follows immediately from our definition that the sentences (**i**) and (**ii**) will hold in our theory. But this time they will have the status of theorems involving a defined term instead of axioms involving only undefined terms.

We have indicated that in order to prepare the ground for our definition of multiplication it is necessary first to prove the existence and uniqueness of a binary operation on P satisfying (**i′**) and (**ii′**). It may at first appear that there is no need for a proof of existence in view of our intuitive knowledge that multiplication satisfies these conditions—but of course this knowledge refers only to one Peano model, and we are trying to give proofs based only upon our axioms in order to gain information about all Peano models. This procedure, i.e., the establishment of the existence and uniqueness of a certain kind of object, before naming it in a definition, occurs frequently in mathematics. For an example the reader is referred to Theorem 2-6-1 where the existence and uniqueness of a certain kind of number are shown to prepare the ground for Definition 2-6-2, the definition of the subtraction function.

THEOREM 4-1-1. *There is one and only one binary operation f on P such that*

(**i**) $f\langle x, 1\rangle = x$ *for all* $x \in P$, *and*
(**ii**) $f\langle x, y + 1\rangle = f\langle x, y\rangle + x$ *for all* $x, y \in P$.

The proof of this theorem, although not difficult, is long, and appears in Appendix II.

As discussed in the paragraphs preceding Theorem 4-1-1, we are now able to define multiplication and we do so.

DEFINITION 4-1-2. *We define* $\cdot$ *to be the unique binary operation on* P *described in Theorem* 4-1-1. *We agree to write* "$x \cdot y$" *instead of* "$\cdot\langle x, y\rangle$". *With this notation we have*

(**i**) $x \cdot 1 = x$ *for all* $x \in P$, *and*
(**ii**) $x \cdot (y + 1) = (x \cdot y) + x$ *for all* $x, y \in P$.

We shall sometimes say "x *times* y" *for* "$x \cdot y$" *and also call* $x \cdot y$ **the product** *of* x *and* y.

A careful check of the proof of Theorem 4-1-1 reveals that the only axioms used are P3 and P4. Thus, Definition 4-1-2 may be given for induction models as well as for Peano models. Let us compute the multiplication table for the induction model $\langle P_2, 1_2, +_2\rangle$ given in Section **1** of Chapter III. For consistency of notation let us use the symbol "$\cdot_2$" for the multiplication operation in this model. The interpretation of (**i**) and (**ii**) in Definition 4-1-2 then become

(**i**) $x \cdot_2 1_2 = x$ for all $x \in P_2$, and
(**ii**) $x \cdot_2 (y +_2 1_2) = (x \cdot_2 y) +_2 x$ for all $x, y \in P_2$.

We shall copy the addition table for this model from Section 1 for easy reference:

$+_2$	1_2	B_2
1_2	B_2	1_2
B_2	1_2	B_2

And now we see:

$$1_2 \cdot_2 1_2 = 1_2; \qquad \text{by } (\mathbf{i})$$

$$B_2 \cdot_2 1_2 = B_2; \qquad \text{by } (\mathbf{i})$$

$$\begin{aligned} 1_2 \cdot_2 B_2 &= 1_2 \cdot_2 (1_2 +_2 1_2); && \text{by } E \text{ and the table for } +_2 \\ &= (1_2 \cdot_2 1_2) +_2 1_2; && \text{by } (\mathbf{ii}) \\ &= 1_2 +_2 1_2 \\ &= B_2; && \text{from the table for } +_2 \end{aligned}$$

$$\begin{aligned} B_2 \cdot_2 B_2 &= B_2 \cdot_2 (1_2 +_2 1_2) \\ &= (B_2 \cdot_2 1_2) +_2 B_2 \\ &= B_2 +_2 B_2 \\ &= B_2; && \text{by the table for } +_2. \end{aligned}$$

And now, summarizing these results in a table, we get

$\cdot_2$	1_2	B_2
1_2	1_2	B_2
B_2	B_2	B_2

Now let us return to the axiomatic development of well known laws of arithmetic for positive integers. The first of these is a law involving both operations of our theory, addition and multiplication.

THEOREM 4-1-3. THE RIGHT DISTRIBUTIVE LAW OF MULTIPLICATION OVER ADDITION. *For all* $x, y, z \in P$, $(x + y) \cdot z = x \cdot z + y \cdot z$.

Proof

▶▶ **1.** Let x and y be any elements of P.
▶▶ **2.** Having chosen x and y, let G be the subset of P consisting of those elements z in P for which $(x + y) \cdot z = x \cdot z + y \cdot z$.
3. $(x + y) \cdot 1 = x + y$; by definition of "$\cdot$" [Definition 4-1-2 (**i**)].
4. $= x \cdot 1 + y \cdot 1$; by Definition 4-1-2 (**i**) and by E.
▶ **5.** $(x + y) \cdot 1 = x \cdot 1 + y \cdot 1$; by E from lines 3 and 4.
▶ **6.** $1 \in G$; by lines 2 and 5.
▶ **7.** Let z be any element of G.
8. $(x + y) \cdot z = x \cdot z + y \cdot z$; by lines 2 and 7.
9. $(x + y) \cdot (z + 1) = (x + y) \cdot z + (x + y)$; by Definition 4-1-2 (**ii**).
10. $= (x \cdot y + y \cdot z) + (x + y)$; by E from line 8.
11. $= (x \cdot z + x) + (y \cdot z + y)$; by the associative and commutative laws of addition (Theorems 2-4-1 and 2-4-2).

12. $= x \cdot (z + 1) + y \cdot (z + 1)$; by E and Definition 4-1-2 (**ii**).

▶**13.** $(x + y) \cdot (z + 1) = x \cdot (z + 1) + y \cdot (z + 1)$; by E from lines **9** through **12**.

▶**14.** $z + 1 \in G$; by lines **2** and **13**.

15. Whenever $z \in G$, then also $z + 1 \in G$; by lines **7** through **14**, using the Deduction Theorem.

▶▶**16.** $G = P$; by lines **2**, **6**, and **15** and Axiom P4.

17. For all $z \in P$, $(x + y) \cdot z = x \cdot z + y \cdot z$; by lines **2** and **16**.

18. For all $x, y, z \in P$, $(x + y) \cdot z = x \cdot z + y \cdot z$; by lines **1** and **17**.

And now we prove the familiar Commutative Law of Multiplication.

THEOREM 4-1-4. THE COMMUTATIVE LAW OF MULTIPLICATION. *For all* $x, y \in P$, $x \cdot y = y \cdot x$.

Before plunging into a proof of this theorem, we will consider possible methods of attack. By now we have become quite familiar with proofs by induction, and it would seem reasonable to use this technique. We might try induction either on x or y—let us arbitrarily select y. The verification step of the induction proof requires us to show that $x \cdot y = y \cdot x$ for $y = 1$, i.e., that $x \cdot 1 = 1 \cdot x$. But this statement itself requires proof, with induction on x as a likely method of attack. Accordingly, we find it convenient to list and prove the following lemma, before giving a proof of the theorem itself.

LEMMA 4-1-4.1. *For all* $x \in P$, $x \cdot 1 = 1 \cdot x$.

Proof

▶▶ **1.** Let G be the subset of P consisting of all numbers x such that $x \cdot 1 = 1 \cdot x$.

▶ **2.** $1 \cdot 1 = 1 \cdot 1$; by E.

▶ **3.** $1 \in G$; by lines **1** and **2**.

▶ **4.** Let x be any element of G.

5. $1 \cdot x = x \cdot 1$; by lines **1** and **4**.

6. $= x$; by Definition 4-1-2 (**i**).

7. $1 \cdot x = x$; by E from lines **5** and **6**.

8. $(x + 1) \cdot 1 = x + 1$; by Definition 4-1-2 (**i**).

9. $= 1 \cdot x + 1$; by E from line **7**.

10. $= 1 \cdot (x + 1)$; by Definition 4-1-2 (**ii**).

▶**11.** $(x + 1) \cdot 1 = 1 \cdot (x + 1)$; by E from lines **8** through **10**.

▶**12.** $x + 1 \in G$; by lines **1** and **11**.

13. Whenever $x \in G$ then also $x + 1 \in G$; by lines **4** through **12**, using the Deduction Theorem.
▶▶14. $G = P$; by lines **1**, **3**, and **13** and Axiom P4.
15. For all $x \in P$, $x \cdot 1 = 1 \cdot x$; by lines **1** and **14**.

We now proceed with a proof of the theorem.

Proof of Theorem 4-1-4

▶▶ 1. Let x be any element of P.
▶▶ 2. Having chosen x, let G be the set of all those numbers y for which $x \cdot y = y \cdot x$.
▶ 3. $x \cdot 1 = 1 \cdot x$; by Lemma 4-1-4.1.
▶ 4. $1 \in G$; by lines **2** and **3**.
▶ 5. Let y be any element of G.
6. $x \cdot y = y \cdot x$; by lines **2** and **5**.
7. $1 \cdot x = x$; by E from Lemma 4-1-4.1 and Definition 4-1-2 (**i**).
8. $x \cdot (y + 1) = x \cdot y + x$; by Definition 4-1-2 (**ii**).
9. $= y \cdot x + x$; by E from line **6**.
10. $= y \cdot x + 1 \cdot x$; by E from line **7**.
11. $= (y + 1) \cdot x$; by Theorem 4-1-3.
▶12. $x \cdot (y + 1) = (y + 1) \cdot x$; by E from lines **8** to **11**.
▶13. $y + 1 \in G$; by lines **2** and **12**.
14. For all $y \in G$, $y + 1 \in G$; by lines **5** through **13**, using the Deduction Theorem.

▶▶15. $G = P$; by lines **2**, **4**, and **14** and Axiom P4.
16. For all $y \in P$, $x \cdot y = y \cdot x$; by lines **2** and **15**.
17. For all $x, y \in P$, $x \cdot y = y \cdot x$; by lines **1** and **16**.

The following theorem can now be proved easily and the proof will be left as an exercise for the reader.

THEOREM 4-1-5. THE LEFT DISTRIBUTIVE LAW OF MULTIPLICATION OVER ADDITION. *For all* $x, y, z \in P$, $x \cdot (y + z) = x \cdot y + x \cdot z$.

Proof. See Exercise 1 below.

And now we come to another theorem familiar to us from our grade-school experience with integers.

THEOREM 4-1-6. THE ASSOCIATIVE LAW OF MULTIPLICATION. *For all* $x, y, z \in P$, $x \cdot (y \cdot z) = (x \cdot y) \cdot z$.

Proof

▶▶ 1. Let x, y be any elements of P.

▶▶ **2.** Having chosen x and y, let G be the subset of P containing all those $z \in P$ for which $x \cdot (y \cdot z) = (x \cdot y) \cdot z$.

3. $y \cdot 1 = y$; by Definition 4-1-2 (**i**).
4. $x \cdot (y \cdot 1) = x \cdot y$; by line **3** by E.
5. $= (x \cdot y) \cdot 1$; by Definition 4-1-2 (**i**).
▶ **6.** $x \cdot (y \cdot 1) = (x \cdot y) \cdot 1$; by E from lines **4** and **5**.
▶ **7.** $1 \in G$; by lines **2** and **6**.
▶ **8.** Let z be any element of G.
9. $x \cdot (y \cdot z) = (x \cdot y) \cdot z$; by lines **2** and **8**.
10. $y \cdot (z + 1) = y \cdot z + y$; by Definition 4-1-2 (**ii**).
11. $x \cdot [y \cdot (z + 1)] = x \cdot (y \cdot z + y)$; by E from line **10**.
12. $= x \cdot (y \cdot z) + x \cdot y$; by Theorem 4-1-5.
13. $= (x \cdot y) \cdot z + x \cdot y$; by E from line **9**.
14. $= (x \cdot y) \cdot (z + 1)$; by Definition 4-1-2 (**ii**).
▶ **15.** $x \cdot [y \cdot (z + 1)] = (x \cdot y) \cdot (z + 1)$; by E from lines **11** through **14**.
▶ **16.** $z + 1 \in G$; by lines **2** and **15**.
17. Whenever $z \in G$, then also $z + 1 \in G$; by lines **8** through **16**, using the Deduction Theorem.
▶▶ **18.** $G = P$; by Axiom P4 from lines **2**, **7**, and **17**.
19. For all $z \in P$, $x \cdot (y \cdot z) = (x \cdot y) \cdot z$; by lines **2** and **18**.
20. For all $x, y, z \in P$, $x \cdot (y \cdot z) = (x \cdot y) \cdot z$; by lines **1** and **19**.

We have already pointed out that Definition 4-1-2 is a valid definition for induction models as well as for Peano models (since the proof of Theorem 4-1-1, on which the definition depends, holds for all induction models). A careful check of the proofs of Theorems 4-1-3 through 4-1-6 reveals that only Axioms P3 and P4 were used; Axioms P1 and P2 were not used, even implicitly. Thus we see that these theorems hold for all induction models as well as for Peano models. The following theorem is an example of one which holds for all Peano models but, as will be clear from Exercise 3 below, not for all induction models. (See the remarks in Section 1, Chapter III, concerning the Right Cancellation Law of Addition and induction models.)

THEOREM 4-1-7. THE RIGHT CANCELLATION LAW OF MULTIPLICATION. *For all* $x, y, z \in P$, *if* $x \cdot z = y \cdot z$, *then* $x = y$; *or equivalently, for all* $x, y, z \in P$, *if* $x \neq y$, *then* $x \cdot z \neq y \cdot z$.

Proof

▶▶ **1.** Let x, y, z be any elements of P such that $x \neq y$.
2. Either $x < y$ or $y < x$; by line **1** and the Trichotomy Law (Theorem 2-5-3).

▶ **3.** Without loss of generality we may assume $y < x$. (See remark after proof.)

4. $x = y + u$ for some $u \in P$; by line **3** and the definition of $<$ (Definition 2-5-1).

5. $x \cdot z = (y + u) \cdot z$; by E from line **4**.

6. $\quad = y \cdot z + u \cdot z$; by the right distributive law (Theorem 4-1-3).

7. $x \cdot z = y \cdot z + u \cdot z$; by E from lines **5** and **6**.

8. $x \cdot z = y \cdot z + v$ for some $v \in P$; by line **7**.

▶ **9.** $y \cdot z < x \cdot z$; by line **8** and the definition of $<$ (Definition 2-5-1).

▶▶ **10.** $x \cdot z \neq y \cdot z$; by line **9** and Theorem 2-5-3.

11. For all $x, y, z \in P$, if $x \neq y$ then $x \cdot z \neq y \cdot z$; by lines **1** through **10**, using the Deduction Theorem.

Remark: After line **2** a complete proof would proceed by considering two cases, $x < y$ and $y < x$, and showing that in *each* case we may conclude that $x \cdot z \neq y \cdot z$. However, in this instance the proof for the case $x < y$ follows step for step the proof given for the case considered, simply by interchanging the roles of x and y. In situations such as this mathematicians customarily give the proof for only one case and indicate that the other case is essentially the same by using the phrase "without loss of generality. . .".

COROLLARY 4-1-7.1. THE LEFT CANCELLATION LAW OF MULTIPLICATION. *For all $x, y, z \in P$, if $x \cdot y = x \cdot z$ then $y = z$.*

We now state some theorems the proofs of which will be left as exercises.

THEOREM 4-1-8. *For all $x, y, z \in P$, if $x < y$ then $x \cdot z < y \cdot z$, and $z \cdot x < z \cdot y$.*

THEOREM 4-1-9. *For all $x, y, z \in P$, if $x \cdot z < y \cdot z$ or if $z \cdot x < z \cdot y$ then $x < y$.*

THEOREM 4-1-10. *For all $x, y, z \in P$, if $x < y$, then $z \cdot (y - x) = z \cdot y - z \cdot x$ and $(y - x) \cdot z = y \cdot z - x \cdot z$.*

THEOREM 4-1-11. *For all $x, y, u, v \in P$, if $x < y$ and $u \leq v$ then $x \cdot u < y \cdot v$.*

THEOREM 4-1-12. *For all $x, y \in P$, if $y \neq 1$ then $x < x \cdot y$.*

THEOREM 4-1-13. *For all $x, y \in P$, $x \leq x \cdot y$ and $y \leq x \cdot y$.*

Remark: In beginning our axiomatic theory of positive integers we took as undefined terms *number*, *one*, and *addition*, where addition is a binary operation on the set of all numbers. There is another, logically simpler, method of beginning the theory, in which we replace addition by the undefined term *successor*, where successor is a unary operation on the set of all numbers. Such an alternative approach was actually adopted by Peano. (See p. 23.)

If we use "S" to denote the successor operation then intuitively, for any $x \in P$, we think of Sx as the element of P which "comes next" after x. In this system we take as axioms, instead of P1 through P4, the following:

S1. For all $x \in P$, $Sx \neq 1$.
S2. For all $x, y \in P$, if $x \neq y$ then $Sx \neq Sy$.
S3. If G is any subset of P such that

(i) $1 \in G$, and
(ii) whenever $x \in P$, then $Sx \in P$,

then $G = P$.

Of course in such an approach to the axiomatic theory of numbers it is necessary to introduce addition as a defined concept. The method of doing this resembles the method whereby we introduced multiplication into our present system. That is, we first show on the basis of Axioms $S1$ through $S3$ that there is one and only one binary operation f on P such that

(i) $f\langle x, 1\rangle = Sx$ for all $x \in P$, and
(ii) $f\langle x, Sy\rangle = S(f\langle x, y\rangle)$ for all $x, y \in P$,

and we then define addition to be this operation. If we denote it, as usual, by "+", we obtain at once

(**a**) $x + 1 = Sx$ for all $x \in P$, and
(**b**) $x + Sy = S(x + y)$ for all $x, y \in P$.

By combining (**a**) and (**b**) we easily obtain

$$x + (y + 1) = (x + y) + 1 \text{ for all } x, y \in P.$$

Thus the Axiom P3 of our present system becomes a theorem in the new system. Similarly, by combining S1, S2, and S3 with (**a**) we obtain as theorems in the new system the Axioms P1, P2, and P4 of our present system. From this it is clear that all theorems of our present system will be provable in the new system.

Why, then, did we not begin in the logically simpler way? For pedagogical reasons. We would have been faced at the very beginning of our theory with the relatively difficult task of proving an analogue of Theorem 4-1-1.

EXERCISES

1. Prove Theorem 4-1-5.

2. Interpret multiplication for the model $\langle P_2, 1_2, +_2\rangle$ of Section 1 of Chapter III and construct the multiplication table.

3. Exhibit an induction model for which Theorem 4-1-7 fails.

4. Interpret "$\cdot$" for the Peano model $\langle P'', 1'', +''\rangle$ of Section 1, Chapter III and find the product of 2^3 and 2^2.

5. Prove Theorem 4-1-8.

6. Prove Theorem 4-1-9.

7. Prove Theorem 4-1-10.

8. Prove Theorem 4-1-11.

9. Prove Theorem 4-1-12.

10. Prove Theorem 4-1-13.

11. Show that for all $x \in P$, $x + x = 2 \cdot x$.

12. Show that for all $x, y \in P$, $(x + y) \cdot (x + y) = [x \cdot x + 2 \cdot (x \cdot y)] + y \cdot y$.

13. Show that for all $x, y \in P$, if $y < x$, then $(x + y) \cdot (x - y) = x \cdot x - y \cdot y$.

14. Show that for all $x, y \in P$, $x \cdot y = 1$ if and only if both $x = 1$ and $y = 1$.

15. Show that for all $x, y \in P$, $x \cdot y = x$ if and only if $y = 1$.

2. *Division*

In looking back through Sections 4, 5, and 6 in Chapter II the reader will observe that after the familiar laws of addition were developed the theory of addition was extended by introducing first the relation *less than* and later the binary function *subtraction*. The question that naturally arises at this stage is this: Now that we have developed the elementary properties of multiplication, is it possible to enrich the theory by introducing a relation and a binary function analogous respectively to the relation *less than* and the function *subtraction*? The answer to this question is "Yes." Furthermore, we shall see that the theories of this new relation and this new function closely parallel the theories of the relation *less than* and the function *subtraction* as we studied them in Sections 4 and 5 of the last chapter.

DEFINITION 4-2-1. *We define $\mid$ to be the binary relation such that for all $x, y \in P$, $x \mid y$ if and only if $x \cdot u = y$ for some $u \in P$. We shall say "x* **divides** *y" or "x is a* **factor** *of y" or "y is a* **multiple** *of x" when the relation $x \mid y$ holds.*

If we compare the definitions of the relations $<$ (Definition 2-5-1) and $\mid$ we see that the latter is identical to the former except for having "$\cdot$" in place of "$+$". The close analogy between these two relations is illustrated by the following theorem which should be compared with the statement and proof of Theorem 2-5-2.

THEOREM 4-2-2. THE TRANSITIVE LAW FOR $\mid$. *For all $x, y, z \in P$, if $x \mid y$ and $y \mid z$ then $x \mid z$.*

Proof

▶▶**1.** Let x, y, z be any elements of P such that $x \mid y$ and $y \mid z$.
▶▶**2.** $x \cdot u = y$ for some $u \in P$ and $y \cdot w = z$ for some $w \in P$; by line **1** and Definition 4-2-1.
3. $(x \cdot u) \cdot w = y \cdot w$; by E from line **2**.
▶▶**4.** $x \cdot (u \cdot w) = z$; by E and the associative law for $\cdot$ from lines **2** and **3**.
5. For some $v \in P$, $x \cdot v = z$; by line **4**.
▶▶**6.** $x \mid z$; by Definition 4-2-1 and line **5**.
7. If x, y, z are any elements of P such that $x \mid y$ and $y \mid z$ then $x \mid z$; by the Deduction Theorem applied to lines **1** through **6**.

An example of a theorem in the theory of the relation *less than* that does not have an analogue in the theory of the relation *divides* is the Trichotomy Law. In other words, it is *not* the case that for all $x, y \in P$, either $x \mid y$ or $x = y$ or $y \mid x$; or, equivalently, it is the case that for some $x, y \in P$ we have *not* $x \mid y$, *not* $x = y$, and *not* $y \mid x$. For example, let $x = 2$ and $y = 3$; then *not* $2 \mid 3$, *not* $2 = 3$, and *not* $3 \mid 2$ (see Exercise 1).

The next theorem is an example showing that the relation $\mid$ sometimes obeys laws resembling those which hold for the relation $\leq$ instead of $<$. (Compare Theorem 2-7-7.)

THEOREM 4-2-3. *For all* $x, y \in P$, *if* $x \mid y$ *and* $y \mid x$ *then* $x = y$.

Proof

▶▶ **1.** Let x and y be any elements of P such that $x \mid y$ and $y \mid x$.
▶▶ **2.** $x \cdot u = y$ for some $u \in P$ and $y \cdot v = x$ for some $v \in P$; by line **1** and Definition 4-2-1.
3. $(x \cdot u) \cdot v = x$; by E from line **2**.
4. $x \cdot (u \cdot v) = x$; by the associative law for $\cdot$ from line **3**.
5. $x = x \cdot 1$; by the definition of $\cdot$ [Definition 4-1-2 (**i**)].
6. $x \cdot (u \cdot v) = x \cdot 1$; by E from lines **4** and **5**.
7. $u \cdot v = 1$; from line **6** by the left cancellation law of $\cdot$.
▶▶ **8.** $u = 1$, and $v = 1$; by line **7** and Exercise 14 (Section 1, Chapter IV).
▶ **9.** $x \cdot 1 = y$; by E from lines **2** and **8**.
▶▶**10.** $x = y$; by E from lines **5** and **9**.
11. For all $x, y \in P$, if $x \mid y$ and $y \mid x$ then $x = y$; by the Deduction Theorem applied to lines **1** through **10**.

Another example of a theorem which states a property of which is shared by $\leq$ is the following (compare Theorem 2-7-6).

THEOREM 4-2-4. *For all* $x \in P$, $1 \mid x$ *and* $x \mid x$.

Proof. See Exercise 2 below.

The following two theorems should be compared to Theorems 2-5-4 and 2-5-5.

THEOREM 4-2-5. *For all* $x, y, z \in P$, *if* $x \mid y$ *then* $x \cdot z \mid y \cdot z$.

Proof

▶▶1. Let x, y, z be any elements of P such that $x \mid y$.
▶2. $x \cdot u = y$ for some $u \in P$; by Definition 4-2-1 from line **1**.
3. $(x \cdot u) \cdot z = y \cdot z$; by E from line **2**.
4. $x \cdot (u \cdot z) = y \cdot z$; by the associative law for $\cdot$ from line **3** and E.
5. $x \cdot (z \cdot u) = y \cdot z$; by the commutative law for $\cdot$ from line **4** and E.
▶6. $(x \cdot z) \cdot u = y \cdot z$; by line **5**, the associative law for $\cdot$ and E.
▶▶7. $x \cdot z \mid y \cdot z$; by Definition 4-2-1 and line **6**.
8. For all $x, y, z \in P$, if $x \cdot y$ then $x \cdot z \mid y \cdot z$; by the Deduction Theorem applied to lines **1** through **7**.

The next theorem is the converse of Theorem 4-2-5.

THEOREM 4-2-6. *For all* $x, y, z \in P$, *if* $x \cdot z \mid y \cdot z$ *then* $x \mid y$.

Proof

▶▶1. Let x, y, z be any elements of P such that $x \cdot z \mid y \cdot z$.
▶2. $(x \cdot z) \cdot u = y \cdot z$ for some $u \in P$; by Definition 4-2-1 and line **1**.
3. $(x \cdot u) \cdot z = y \cdot z$; by line **2** by the associative and commutative laws of $\cdot$.
▶4. $x \cdot u = y$; by line **3** by the right cancellation law of $\cdot$.
▶▶5. $x \mid y$; by Definition 4-2-1 and line **4**.
6. For all $x, y, z \in P$, if $x \cdot z \mid y \cdot z$ then $x \mid y$; by the Deduction Theorem applied to lines **1** through **6**.

The next two theorems state properties of the relation $\mid$ familiar to us from our intuitive experience with the positive integers.

THEOREM 4-2-7. *For all* $x, y, z \in P$, *if* $x \mid y$ *and* $x \mid z$ *then* $x \mid (y + z)$.

Proof

▶▶1. Let x, y, z be any elements of P such that $x \mid y$ and $x \mid z$.
▶2. $x \cdot u = y$ for some $u \in P$ and $x \cdot v = z$ for some $v \in P$; by line **1** and Definition 4-2-1.
3. $x \cdot u + x \cdot v = y + z$; by E from line **2**.
▶4. $x \cdot (u + v) = y + z$; by line **3** and the left distributive law of multiplication over addition.

▶▶5. $x \mid (y + z)$; by line **4** and Definition 4-2-1.

6. For all $x, y, z \in P$, if $x \mid y$ and $x \mid z$ then $x \mid (y + z)$; by the Deduction Theorem applied to lines **1** through **5**.

THEOREM 4-2-8. *For all $x, y, z \in P$, if $x \mid y$ and $x \mid z$ and if $y < z$ then $x \mid (z - y)$.*

Proof

▶▶ **1.** Let y, z be any elements of P such that $y < z$.
▶▶ **2.** Let x be any element of P such that $x \mid y$ and $x \mid z$.
▶ **3.** $x \cdot u = y$ for some $u \in P$ and $x \cdot v = z$ for some $v \in P$; by line **2** and Definition 4-2-1.
▶ **4.** $y + w = z$ for some $w \in P$; by line **1** and the definition of $<$.
5. $w = z - y$; by line **4** and Theorem 2-6-3.
6. $x \cdot u < x \cdot v$; by E from lines **1** and **3**.
7. $w = x \cdot v - x \cdot u$; by E from lines **3** and **5**.
8. $u < v$; from line **6** by the left cancellation law of $\cdot$ over $<$ (Theorem 4-1-9).
▶ **9.** $w = x \cdot (v - u)$; by line **7** and **8** by Theorem 4-1-10.
▶**10.** $x \mid w$; by line **9** and Definition 4-2-1.
▶▶**11.** $x \mid (z - y)$; by E from lines **5** and **10**.
12. For all $x, y, z \in P$, if $x \mid y$ and $x \mid z$ and if $y < z$ then $x \mid (z - y)$; by the Deduction Theorem applied to lines **1** and **2** through **11**.

Now that we have incorporated into our theory the relation *divides*, which we have seen is analagous in the theory of multiplication to the relation *less than* in the theory of addition, we wish to introduce the analogue of the subtraction function. But before we do this it is necessary to prove the following theorem which parallels Theorem 2-6-1.

THEOREM 4-2-9. *For all $x, y \in P$, if $y \mid x$ then there is one and only one $u \in P$ such that $y \cdot u = x$.*

Proof

▶▶**1.** Let x, y be any elements of P such that $y \mid x$.
▶▶**2.** $y \cdot u = x$ for some $u \in P$; by line **1** and Definition 4-2-1.
▶▶**3.** Suppose, also, that v is an element for which $y \cdot v = x$.
4. $y \cdot u = y \cdot v$; by E from lines **2** and **3**.
▶▶**5.** $u = v$; by line **4** and the left cancellation law for $\cdot$ (Corollary 4-1-7.1).
6. If v is any element of P for which $y \cdot v = x$ then $v = u$; by the Deduction Theorem applied to lines **3** through **5**.
7. There is one and only one element $u \in P$ such that $y \cdot u = x$; by lines **2** and **6**.

8. For all $x, y \in P$, if $y \mid x$ then there is one and only one $u \in P$ such that $y \cdot u = x$; by the Deduction Theorem applied to lines **1** through **7**.

Using this result we can formulate the following definition.

DEFINITION 4-2-10. *We define* $\div$ *to be the binary function whose domain consists of all ordered pairs* $\langle x, y \rangle$ *for which* $y \mid x$, *and whose values are given by the rule that* $x \div y$ *is the unique element* u *of* P *such that* $y \cdot u = x$. *(See Theorem 4-2-9.) We shall say "*x **divided by** y*" for the element* $x \div y$.

The following theorem states the most basic properties of $\div$.

THEOREM 4-2-11. *If* x, y, u *are any elements of* P *such that* $y \cdot u = x$ *then* $u = x \div y$. *If* x, y *are any elements of* P *such that* $y \mid x$, *then* $y \cdot (x \div y) = x$.

Proof. See Exercise 3 below.

The next four theorems are analogues of corresponding theorems concerning the subtraction function. (Compare Theorems 2-6-5 through 2-6-8.)

THEOREM 4-2-12. *For all* $x, y, z \in P$, *if* $y \mid x$ *and* $z \mid y$ *then* $y \div z \mid x \div z$.

Proof. See Exercise 4 below.

THEOREM 4-2-13. *For all* $x, y, z \in P$, *if* $z \mid y$ *then* $(x \cdot y) \div z = x \cdot (y \div z)$.

Proof

▶▶**1.** Let x, y, z be any elements of P such that $z \mid y$.
▶**2.** $z \cdot u = y$ for some $u \in P$; by line **1** and Definition 4-2-1.
3. $x \cdot (z \cdot u) = x \cdot y$; by E from line **2**.
4. $z \cdot (x \cdot u) = x \cdot y$; by line **3** and the associative and commutative laws for $\cdot$.
▶**5.** $u = y \div z$; by line **2** and Theorem 4-2-11.
▶**6.** $x \cdot u = x \cdot (y \div z)$; by E from line **5**.
▶**7.** $x \cdot u = (x \cdot y) \div z$; by line **4** and Theorem 4-2-11.
▶▶**8.** $(x \cdot y) \div z = x \cdot (y \div z)$; by E from lines **6** and **7**.
9. If x, y, z are any elements of P such that $z \mid y$, then $(x \cdot y) \div z = x \cdot (y \div z)$; by the Deduction Theorem applied to lines **1** through **8**.

THEOREM 4-2-14. *For all* $x, y, z \in P$, *if* $y \mid x$ *and* $x \mid z$ *then* $z \div x \mid z \div y$.

Proof. See Exercise 5 below.

THEOREM 4-2-15. *For all* $x, y, z \in P$, *if* $(x \cdot y) \mid z$ *then* $x \mid z$, $y \mid (z \div x)$ *and* $z \div (x \cdot y) = (z \div x) \div y$.

Proof. See Exercise 6 below.

The next two theorems have no parallels in the earlier theory of subtraction, as they involve both additive and multiplicative theory. However, they are familiar to us from our early experience with the positive integers.

THEOREM 4-2-16. *If* x, y, z *are any elements of* P *such that* $x \mid y$ *and* $x \mid z$, *then* $(y \div x) + (z \div x) = (y + z) \div x$.

Proof

▶▶**1.** Let x, y, z be any elements of P such that $x \mid y$ and $x \mid z$.
▶**2.** $x \cdot u = y$ and $x \cdot v = z$ for some $u, v \in P$; by line **1** and Definition 4-2-1.
▶**3.** $u = y \div x$ and $v = z \div x$; by Theorem 4-2-11 from line **2**.
4. $x \cdot u + x \cdot v = y + z$; by E from line **2**.
5. $x \cdot (u + v) = y + z$; from line **4** by the left distributive law of $\cdot$ over $+$.
▶**6.** $u + v = (y + z) \div x$; by line **5** and Theorem 4-2-11.
▶▶**7.** $(y \div x) + (z \div x) = (y + z) \div x$; by E from lines **3** and **6**.
8. If x, y, z are any elements of P such that $x \mid y$ and $x \mid z$, then $(y \div x) + (z \div x) = (y + z) \div x$; by the Deduction Theorem applied to lines **1** through **7**.

THEOREM 4-2-17. *If* x, y, z *are any elements of* P *such that* $x \mid y$ *and* $x \mid z$, *and if* $z < y$, *then* $(y \div x) - (z \div x) = (y - z) \div x$.

Proof. See Exercise 7 below.

EXERCISES

1. Show that not $2 \mid 3$ and not $2 = 3$ and not $3 \mid 2$.
2. Prove Theorem 4-2-4.
3. Prove Theorem 4-2-11.
4. Prove Theorem 4-2-12.
5. Prove Theorem 4-2-14.
6. Prove Theorem 4-2-15.
7. Prove Theorem 4-2-17.

3. *Semi-Groups under the Operation of Multiplication*

In our original discussion of semi-groups (Chapter III, Section 3) the binary operation involved was not specified. In fact, a new symbol, "$\circ$", was used in Definition 3-3-1 to indicate the unspecified operation. The reader may recall that the mathematical system $\langle S, \circ \rangle$, consisting of an arbitrary set S of elements and an arbitrary binary operation, $\circ$, on S, forms a semi-group if and only if the associative law holds for the operation $\circ$.

We have already seen that the system $\langle P, +\rangle$ is a semi-group, and indeed it can be classified as a commutative, cancellation semi-group. (See Definitions 3-3-2 and 3-3-3 and Theorem 3-3-5.) A natural question, now that we have defined a new operation (multiplication) on P, is whether the system $\langle P, \cdot\rangle$ is also a semi-group. That this is indeed so may be verified readily. (See Definition 3-3-1.) In fact, the system $\langle P, \cdot\rangle$ has an additional characteristic, namely, it possesses a null element. The number 1 is the null element of the semi-group $\langle P, \cdot\rangle$ since $a \cdot 1 = a$ for any $a \in P$.

By this observation we see that the system $\langle P, \cdot\rangle$ has three of the four properties characteristic of a group: closure, associativity, and the existence of a null element. (See discussion preceding Definition 3-3-1.) It might seem semantically plausible to classify such a system as a "Three-quarter-group." However, we shall use the terminology given in the definition which follows.

DEFINITION 4-3-1. *A system $\langle S, \circ\rangle$ which is a semi-group is said to be a* **semi-group with null element** *if and only if there exists an element $z \in S$ such that $a \circ z = a$, for any $a \in S$.*

We are now able to state that the system $\langle P, \cdot\rangle$ possesses the characteristics indicated in the following theorem.

THEOREM 4-3-2. *The system $\langle P, \cdot\rangle$ is a commutative, cancellation semi-group with null element.*[1] *The null element is the number* 1.

The proof of this theorem is left to the Exercises.

EXERCISES

1. Prove Theorem 4-3-2.

2. Could the mathematical system consisting of the set of elements P and the division function $\div$, be considered a semi-group?

3. Consider the system $\langle N, +_N\rangle$, where N is the set of all positive integers and 0, and $+_N$ is the binary operation of addition on N. Using your intuitive understanding of addition involving zero, determine whether this system is a semi-group and if so which additional properties it has.

4. In Theorem 3-3-4 it was shown that the system $\langle P, +, <\rangle$ is an ordered semi-group. Is the same true of the system $\langle P, \cdot, <\rangle$?

[1] The null element is sometimes referred to as the identity element.

V

Elementary Concepts of Number Theory

1. Least Common Multiple and Greatest Common Divisor

Two notions with which we come into fairly early contact in grade school are those of the *least common multiple* and the *greatest common divisor* of two positive integers. If, for example, we take the two integers 4 and 6, the least common multiple is 12 (the smallest integer divisible by both 4 and 6), and the greatest common divisor is 2 (the largest integer dividing both 4 and 6). We now introduce the first of these concepts into our axiomatic theory.

DEFINITION 5-1-1. *If x, y, z are any elements of P such that $x \mid z$ and $y \mid z$, we call z a* **common multiple** *of x and y.* Clearly, any two elements x and y of P have at least one common multiple, namely $x \cdot y$. *We define* **lcm** *to be the binary operation on P such that, for all $x, y \in P$, $\text{lcm}\langle x, y\rangle$ is the least of the common multiples of x and y, and refer to the element $\text{lcm}\langle x, y\rangle$ as the* **least common multiple** *of x and y.*

Remark: Since the set of common multiples of any pair of numbers x and y contains at least one element, as noted above, we are assured by Theorem 2-7-9 that the set of common multiples has a least element. (And by Exercise 12, p. 50, there is only one least element.) Thus, Definition 5-1-1 is justified. In some books on number theory $\text{lcm}\langle x, y\rangle$ is defined to be that common multiple of x and y which divides all other common multiples of x and y. However, at this stage of our axiomatic development we are not assured that there is a common multiple with this property. Actually it is possible to prove that $\text{lcm}\langle x, y\rangle$, as we have defined it, has this property; but we must first establish certain other results to prepare the way. The reader will recognize that the definition given in 5-1-1 for lcm is the one generally taught in the grades and is closest to our intuitive notions about the concept.

The next theorem states the two most basic properties of lcm and follows quickly from Definition 5-1-1.

THEOREM 5-1-2. *For all $x, y \in P$ we have the following:*

(i) $x \mid \text{lcm}\langle x, y\rangle$, *and* $y \mid \text{lcm}\langle x, y\rangle$, *and*
(ii) *whenever z is any element of P such that $x \mid z$ and $y \mid z$ then* $\text{lcm}\langle x, y\rangle \leq z$.

Proof. See Exercise 2.

Although we did not introduce it at the time we were studying addition there is a concept in the theory of addition which closely resembles the notion of lcm in the theory of multiplication. Let $\max\langle x, y\rangle$ be the greater of two numbers x, y. Then we see that **(i)** $x \leq \max\langle x, y\rangle$ and $y \leq \max\langle x, y\rangle$, and **(ii)** whenever z is any number such that $x \leq z$ and $y \leq z$ then $\max\langle x, y\rangle \leq z$. Thus we see that max has properties parallel to the properties of lcm given in Theorem 5-1-2. Despite this fact we would find, if we developed the theory of max, that actually it has little depth. On the other hand we shall see that the theory of lcm has considerable depth. It is useful to keep the parallel in mind, however, for simple properties of max often suggest corresponding laws for lcm. The next two theorems are examples of laws whose analogues hold in the theory of max.

THEOREM 5-1-3. THE IDEMPOTENT LAW FOR LCM. *For all $x \in P$,* $\text{lcm}\langle x, x\rangle = x$.

Proof

▶▶**1.** Let x be any element of P.
2. $x \mid x$; by Theorem 4-2-4.
3. x is a common multiple of x and x; by line **2** and Definition 5-1-1.
▶▶**4.** $\text{lcm}\langle x, x\rangle \leq x$; by line **3** and Theorem 5-1-2 (**ii**).
5. $x \mid \text{lcm}\langle x, x\rangle$; by Theorem 5-1-2 (**i**).
▶▶**6.** $x \leq \text{lcm}\langle x, x\rangle$; by line **5**, Definition 4-2-1, and Theorem 4-1-12.
▶▶**7.** $x = \text{lcm}\langle x, x\rangle$; by lines **4** and **6** and Theorem 2-7-7.

As we shall see, lcm has many of the familiar properties of the binary operations we have studied earlier. The next theorem states one of these properties.

THEOREM 5-1-4. THE COMMUTATIVE LAW FOR LCM. *For all $x, y \in P$,* $\text{lcm}\langle x, y\rangle = \text{lcm}\langle y, x\rangle$.

Proof. See Exercise 3.

Remark on the proof of Theorem 5-1-4. The principal law of logic used in the proof is the *commutative law of conjunction*. As the reader will see if he constructs a proof of this theorem, the decisive step is the use of the fact: If $[x \mid \text{lcm}\langle x, y\rangle$ and $y \mid \text{lcm}\langle x, y\rangle]$ then $[y \mid \text{lcm}\langle x, y\rangle$ and $x \mid \text{lcm}\langle x, y\rangle]$. This illustrates the fact that algebraic laws about numbers, such as Theorem 5-1-4, often reflect laws of logic which themselves have an algebraic form.

What can be said about associativity of lcm? To be sure, if we use our intuitive knowledge of lcm for three given integers, such as 4, 6, and 9, we note that $\text{lcm}\langle 4, 6\rangle = 12$ and $\text{lcm}\langle 12, 9\rangle = 36$, while $\text{lcm}\langle 6, 9\rangle = 18$ and $\text{lcm}\langle 4, 18\rangle = 36$, so that associativity appears to exist; but is it true that for *all* $x, y, z \in P$ we have $\text{lcm}\langle \text{lcm}\langle x, y\rangle, z\rangle = \text{lcm}\langle x, \text{lcm}\langle y, z\rangle\rangle$? We can get a further intuitive feeling about the truth of this statement by considering the simpler notion of max. It is easily verified that for all $x, y, z \in P$, $\max\langle \max\langle x, y\rangle, z\rangle = \max\langle x, \max\langle y, z\rangle\rangle$, for in fact each side of this equation represents the greatest of the numbers x, y, and z. Thus we would be led to guess (correctly) that lcm is associative. However, we shall delay the proof of associativity of lcm until after we have introduced the notion of *division with remainder*.

In the theory of addition there is a dual concept to that of max, namely, min, where $\min\langle x, y\rangle$ is the smaller of the numbers x, y. Similarly, in the theory of multiplication there is a dual notion to that of lcm, namely that of greatest common divisor, gcd. We would like to define $\text{gcd}\langle x, y\rangle$ as the greatest of the numbers z such that $z \mid x$ and $z \mid y$, but before we can do this in our axiomatic theory we must establish that there *is* such a greatest number z—and furthermore that it is unique. This we shall do in the next theorem.

THEOREM 5-1-5. *Let x, y be any elements of P. Let G be the set of all those elements $z \in P$ such that $z \mid x$ and $z \mid y$. Then there is one and only one element $s \in G$ such that $z \leq s$ for every $z \in G$.*

Before proving this theorem we shall prove a lemma which will be useful not only in proving Theorem 5-1-5, but elsewhere. (This lemma was given as Exercise 14, Section 7, Chapter II. Because of its importance, the proof of this lemma will be given here.)

LEMMA 5-1-5.1. *Let G be any nonempty subset of P with the property that there exists an element $u \in P$ such that $z \leq u$ for all $z \in G$. Then there exists an element $s \in G$ such that $z \leq s$ for all $z \in G$.* [A set G with the property described in the hypothesis of this lemma is said to have an *upper bound in P*. The element s is said to be a *maximum element of G*. Note that we assume that there is an element u *in* P, but must show the existence of an element s *in* G.]

Proof

▶▶ **1.** Let G be any nonempty subset of P with the property that there is an element $u \in P$ such that $z \leq u$ for all $z \in G$.

▶▶ **2.** Let H be the set of all those numbers $w \in P$ such that $z \leq w$ for all $z \in G$.

3. $u \in H$; by lines **1** and **2**.

▶▶ 4. There exists an element $s \in H$ such that $s \leq v$ for every $v \in H$; by line **3** and Theorem 2-7-9.

5. Either $s = 1$ or $s \neq 1$; by logic.

▶ 6. *Case I.* Suppose $s = 1$.

7. For all $z \in G$, $z \leq 1$; by lines **2**, **4**, and **6**.

8. For all $z \in G$, $z = 1$; by lines **7** and Exercise 5, page 50.

9. $1 \in G$; by lines **1** and **8**.

▶ 10. $s \in G$; by E, from lines **6** and **9**.

▶ 11. *Case II.* Suppose $s \neq 1$.

▶ 12. $s = w + 1$ for some $w \in P$; by line **11** and Theorem 2-3-4.

▶ 13. Assume that $s \notin G$.

14. For every $z \in G$ we have $z \neq s$; by line **13**.

15. For every $z \in G$ we have $z \leq s$; by lines **2** and **4**.

16. For every $z \in G$ we have $z < s$; by lines **14** and **15** and definition of $\leq$.

17. For every $z \in G$ we have $z < w + 1$; by E, from lines **12** and **16**.

18. For every $z \in G$, $z \leq w$; by line **17** and Exercise 9, page 50.

19. $w \in H$; by lines **2** and **18**.

▶ 20. $w < s$; by line **12** and the definition of $<$.

▶ 21. not $s \leq w$; by line **20**, Trichotomy Law, and the definition of $\leq$.

22. $w \notin H$; by lines **21** and **4**.

23. If $s \notin G$ then (**i**) $w \in H$, and (**ii**) $w \notin H$; by the Deduction Theorem applied to lines **13** through **19** and **22**.

▶ 24. $s \in G$; by line **23**.

▶▶ 25. In all cases $s \in G$; by lines **5**, **6**, **10**, **11**, and **24**.

▶▶ 26. There exists an element $s \in G$ for which $z \leq s$ for all $z \in G$; by lines **2**, **4**, and **25**.

27. If G is any nonempty subset of P with the property that there exists an element $u \in P$ such that $z \leq u$ for all $z \in G$, then there exists an element $s \in G$ such that $z \leq s$ for all $z \in G$; by the Deduction Theorem applied to lines **1** through **26**.

Now, using the lemma just proved, we give a

Proof of Theorem 5-1-5.

▶▶ 1. Let x, y be any elements of P.

▶▶ 2. Let G be the set of all those elements $z \in P$ for which $z \mid x$ and $z \mid y$.

▶ **3.** $1 \in G$; by line **2** and Theorem 4-2-4.

4. $x \mid x \cdot y$; by definition of $\mid$.

5. If z is any element of P such that $z \mid x$ (and $z \mid y$) then $z \mid x \cdot y$; by line **4** and the transitive law of $\mid$.

▶ **6.** If z is any element of P such that $z \mid x$ and $z \mid y$ then $z \leq x \cdot y$; by line **5**, definition of $\mid$, E, and Theorem 4-1-13.

7. G is not empty and there exists an element $u \in P$ such that $z \leq u$ for all $z \in G$; by lines **2**, **3**, and **6**.

▶▶ **8.** There exists an element $s \in G$ such that $z \leq s$ for all $z \in G$; by line **7** and Lemma 5-1-5.1.

▶▶ **9.** Let t be any number such that $t \in G$ and $z \leq t$ for every $z \in G$.

10. $t \leq s$; by lines **8** and **9**.

11. $s \leq t$; by lines **8** and **9**.

▶▶ **12.** $s = t$; by lines **10** and **11** and Theorem 2-7-7.

13. If t is any number such that $t \in G$ and $z \leq t$ for every $z \in G$, then $t = s$; by the Deduction Theorem applied to lines **9** through **12**.

14. s is the one and only number such that $s \in G$ and $z \leq s$ for all $z \in G$; by lines **8** and **13**.

15. If x, y are any elements of P, and if G is the set of all those elements $z \in P$ such that $z \mid x$ and $z \mid y$, then there is one and only one element $s \in G$ such that $z \leq s$ for every $z \in G$; by the Deduction Theorem applied to lines **1** and **2** through **14**.

We are now in a position to define greatest common divisor.

DEFINITION 5-1-6. *If x, y, z are any elements of P such that $z \mid x$ and $z \mid y$ then we call z a* **common divisor** *of x and y. We define* **gcd** *to be the binary operation on P such that for every $x, y \in P$,* $\gcd\langle x, y\rangle$ *is the unique common divisor s of x and y such that $z \leq s$ for every common divisor z of x and y.* (Note that this definition is justified by Theorem 5-1-5.) *We call this divisor s the* **greatest common divisor** *of x and y.*

The next two theorems parallel Theorems 5-1-3 and 5-1-4 respectively.

THEOREM 5-1-7. THE IDEMPOTENT LAW FOR GCD. *For all $x \in P$,* $\gcd\langle x, x\rangle = x$.

THEOREM 5-1-8. THE COMMUTATIVE LAW FOR GCD. *For all $x, y \in P$,* $\gcd\langle x, y\rangle = \gcd\langle y, x\rangle$.

Proofs. See Exercises 4 and 5.

We now come to a topic with which we have had considerable experience in grade-school arithmetic. It is also one of the most important theorems for our future development of the theory of numbers. Although we have not introduced the words "quotient" and "remainder" into our theory as yet (and indeed we will postpone this for some time), the reader will recognize that the numbers q and r in the next theorem are the numbers which are usually called the *quotient* and *remainder* (upon dividing y by x).

THEOREM 5-1-9. *If x, y are any elements of P such that $x < y$ and not $x \mid y$, then there exist elements q and r in P such that*

(i) $y = q \cdot x + r$, *and*
(ii) $r < x$.

Note that each of the hypotheses "$x < y$" and "not $x \mid y$" is needed because our axiomatic theory deals only with positive integers. In a system containing the number 0 the conclusions (i) and (ii) would be true for any numbers x, y such that $x \neq 0$.

Proof

▶▶ 1. Let x, y be any elements of P such that $x < y$ and not $x \mid y$.
2. $y \leq y \cdot x$; by Theorem 4-1-13.
▶▶ 3. There is a number t such that (a) $y \leq t \cdot x$, and (b) whenever s is any number such that $y \leq s \cdot x$ then $t \leq s$; by line 2 and Theorem 2-7-9.
4. If $t = 1$ then $y \leq x$; by line 3(a), E, Lemma 4-1-4.1, and the definition of $\cdot$.
5. *Not* $y \leq x$; by line 1, the Trichotomy Law, and the definition of $\leq$.
6. $t \neq 1$; by lines 4 and 5.
▶▶ 7. $t = q + 1$ for some $q \in P$; by line 6 and Theorem 2-3-4.
8. $t \cdot x \neq y$; by line 1 and the definition of $\mid$ and the commutative law of $\cdot$.
9. $y < t \cdot x$; by lines 3(a) and 8 and the definition of $\leq$.
10. $q < t$; by line 7 and the definition of $<$.
11. *Not* $t \leq q$; by line 10, the Trichotomy Law, and the definition of $\leq$.
12. If $y \leq q \cdot x$ then $t \leq q$; by line 3(b).
13. *Not* $y \leq q \cdot x$; by lines 11 and 12.
▶▶ 14. $q \cdot x < y$; by line 13, the Trichotomy Law, and the definition of $\leq$.
▶▶ 15. $q \cdot x + r = y$ for some $r \in P$; by line 14 and the definition of $<$.
16. $y < (q + 1) \cdot x$; by E from lines 7 and 9.
17. $q \cdot x + r < (q + 1) \cdot x$; by E from lines 15 and 16.

18. $q \cdot x + r < q \cdot x + x$; by E from line **17**, the commutative law of multiplication and the definition of $\cdot$.

▶▶ **19.** $r < x$; by line **18**, the commutative law of addition, and the right cancellation law of addition over $<$.

20. If x, y are any elements of P such that $x < y$ and *not* $x \mid y$ then there exist elements q and r in P such that **(i)** $y = q \cdot x + r$ and **(ii)** $r < x$; by the Deduction Theorem applied to lines **1** through **15** and **19**.

We have seen that the theorem just proved can be expressed in the language of grade-school arithmetic by saying that if x and y are positive integers such that $x < y$ and *not* $x \mid y$, then we can find a quotient q and remainder r (both positive integers) to indicate the result of attempting to divide y by x. But for given numbers x and y can we sometimes find two different quotients, or two different remainders? The effect of the following theorem is to supply a negative answer for this question.

THEOREM 5-1-10. *If* x, y, q, r, q', r' *are any elements of* P *such that*

(i) $y = q \cdot x + r$ **(i′)** $y = q' \cdot x + r'$
(ii) $r < x$ **(ii′)** $r' < x$,

then $q = q'$ and $r = r'$.

The basic idea of our proof is to show that the assumption $q < q'$, as well as the assumption $q' < q$, leads to a contradiction. We will then infer from the Trichotomy Law that $q = q'$. From this it will be simple to conclude that $r = r'$.

Proof

▶▶ **1.** Let x, y, q, r, q', r' be any elements of P satisfying **(i)**, **(ii)**, **(i′)**, and **(ii′)** above.

▶▶ **2.** $q \cdot x + r = q' \cdot x + r'$; by E from line **1**, parts **(i)** and **(i′)**.

▶▶ **3.** Let us suppose that $q < q'$.

▶ **4.** $q + u = q'$ for some $u \in P$; by line **3** and the definition of $<$.

5. $(q + u) \cdot x = q' \cdot x$; by E from line **4**.

6. $q \cdot x + u \cdot x = q' \cdot x$; by line **5** and Theorem 4-1-3.

7. $(q \cdot x + u \cdot x) + r' = q' \cdot x + r'$; by E from line **6**.

8. $(q \cdot x + u \cdot x) + r' = q \cdot x + r$; by E from lines **2** and **7**.

9. $q \cdot x + (u \cdot x + r') = q \cdot x + r$; by E from line **8** and the associative law of addition.

10. $u \cdot x + r' = r$; by line **9** and the left cancellation law of addition (Corollary 2-4-3.1).

▶ **11.** $u \cdot x < r$; by line **10**, and the definition of $<$.

12. $x \leq u \cdot x$; by Theorem 4-1-13.

13. $x \leq r$; by lines **11** and **12**, the definition of $\leq$, and the transitive law for $\leq$.

▶**14.** *Not* $r < x$; by line **13**, the definition of $\leq$, and the Trichotomy Law.

15. If $q < q'$ then *not* $r < x$; by the Deduction Theorem applied to lines **3** through **14**.

▶▶**16.** *Not* $q < q'$; by lines **15** and **1** (**ii**).

▶▶**17.** By the same reasoning we show: *not* $q' < q$. (See discussion at end of proof.)

18. Either $q < q'$ or $q = q'$ or $q' < q$; by the Trichotomy Law.

▶▶**19.** $q = q'$; by lines **16**, **17**, and **18**.

▶▶**20.** $q \cdot x + r = q \cdot x + r'$; by E from lines **2** and **19**.

▶▶**21.** $r = r'$; by line **20** and Corollary 2-4-3.1.

22. If x, y, q, r, q', r' are any elements of P satisfying (**i**), (**ii**), (**i'**), and (**ii'**) then $q = q'$ and $r = r'$; by the Deduction Theorem applied to lines **1** through **19** and **21**.

The use of the words "by the same reasoning" on line **17** deserves some comment. The meaning here is that if in lines **3** through **16** we interchange "q" with "q'" and "r" with "r'" throughout, the resulting sequence of lines will constitute a proof of the statement "*not* $q' < q$"; the justification for each step will be the same as that used in the corresponding step of lines (**3**) through (**16**), except that in the last step we must use line **1** (**ii'**) instead of line **1** (**ii**). In general the phrase "by the same reasoning" is not used with a fixed, precise meaning but is employed whenever a writer feels that the part of the proof which is supplied is "more or less the same as" the part of the proof which is omitted.

We are now in a position to show that the least common multiple of two positive integers is a factor of any other common multiple of those numbers.

THEOREM 5-1-11. *If x, y, z are any elements of P such that $x \mid z$ and $y \mid z$, then* $\text{lcm}\langle x, y\rangle \mid z$.

Proof

▶▶ **1.** Let x, y, z be any elements of P such that $x \mid z$ and $y \mid z$.

2. $\text{lcm}\langle x, y\rangle \leq z$; by line **1** and Theorem 5-1-2.

▶▶ **3.** Suppose *not* $\text{lcm}\langle x, y\rangle \mid z$.

4. $\text{lcm}\langle x, y\rangle \neq z$; by line **3** and Theorem 4-2-4.

5. $\text{lcm}\langle x, y\rangle < z$; by lines **2** and **4** and the definition of $\leq$.

▶ **6.** There exist $q, r \in P$ such that (**i**) $z = q \cdot \text{lcm}\langle x, y\rangle + r$ and (**ii**) $r < \text{lcm}\langle x, y\rangle$; by lines **3** and **5** and Theorem 5-1-9.

7. $q \cdot \text{lcm}\langle x, y\rangle < z$; by line **6** (**i**) and Definition 2-5-1.

8. $r = z - (q \cdot \mathrm{lcm}\langle x, y\rangle)$; by line **6** (**i**) and Theorem 2-6-3.
9. $x \mid \mathrm{lcm}\langle x, y\rangle$; by Theorem 5-1-2 (**i**).
10. $\mathrm{lcm}\langle x, y\rangle \mid q \cdot \mathrm{lcm}\langle x, y\rangle$; by the commutative law of multiplication and the definition of $\mid$.
11. $x \mid q \cdot \mathrm{lcm}\langle x, y\rangle$; by lines **9** and **10** and the transitive law for $\mid$.
12. $x \mid [z - (q \cdot \mathrm{lcm}\langle x, y\rangle)]$; by lines **1**, **7**, and **11** and Theorem 4-2-8.
13. $x \mid r$; by E, lines **8** and **12**.
14. By the same reasoning (lines **9** through **13**) we show $y \mid r$.
15. $\mathrm{lcm}\langle x, y\rangle \leq r$; by lines **13** and **14** and Theorem 5-1-2 (**ii**).
▶**16.** *Not* $r < \mathrm{lcm}\langle x, y\rangle$; by line **15** and the Trichotomy Law.
▶▶**17.** If *not* $\mathrm{lcm}\langle x, y\rangle \mid z$ then $r < \mathrm{lcm}\langle x, y\rangle$ and *not* $r < \mathrm{lcm}\langle x, y\rangle$; by the Deduction Theorem applied to lines **3** through **6** (**ii**) and **16**.
▶▶**18.** $\mathrm{lcm}\langle x, y\rangle \mid z$; by line **17**.
19. If x, y, z are any elements of P such that $x \mid z$ and $y \mid z$ then $\mathrm{lcm}\langle x, y\rangle \mid z$; by the Deduction Theorem applied to lines **1** through **18**.

Using the theorem just proved we can demonstrate the associative law for the operation lcm (which was discussed after the proof of Theorem 5-1-4.)

THEOREM 5-1-12. *For any* $x, y, z \in P$,
$$\mathrm{lcm}\langle \mathrm{lcm}\langle x, y\rangle, z\rangle = \mathrm{lcm}\langle x, \mathrm{lcm}\langle y, z\rangle\rangle.$$

The idea of this proof is to demonstrate the equation by showing that each side is in the relation $\leq$ to the other. To show that the left side is less than or equal to the right side, for example, it suffices to show that the latter is a common multiple of $\mathrm{lcm}\langle x, y\rangle$ and z, for then we may use Theorem 5-1-2 (**ii**). The details are as follows.

Proof

▶▶ **1.** Let x, y, z be any elements of P.
2. $z \mid \mathrm{lcm}\langle y, z\rangle$; by Theorem 5-1-2 (**i**).
3. $\mathrm{lcm}\langle y, z\rangle \mid \mathrm{lcm}\langle x, \mathrm{lcm}\langle y, z\rangle\rangle$; by Theorem 5-1-2 (**i**).
▶ **4.** $z \mid \mathrm{lcm}\langle x, \mathrm{lcm}\langle y, z\rangle\rangle$; by lines **2** and **3** and Theorem 4-2-2.
5. $y \mid \mathrm{lcm}\langle y, z\rangle$; by Theorem 5-1-2 (**i**).
6. $\mathrm{lcm}\langle y, z\rangle \mid \mathrm{lcm}\langle x, \mathrm{lcm}\langle y, z\rangle\rangle$; by Theorem 5-1-2 (**i**).
7. $y \mid \mathrm{lcm}\langle x, \mathrm{lcm}\langle y, z\rangle\rangle$; by lines **5** and **6** and Theorem 4-2-2.
8. $x \mid \mathrm{lcm}\langle x, \mathrm{lcm}\langle y, z\rangle\rangle$; by Theorem 5-1-2 (**i**).
▶ **9.** $\mathrm{lcm}\langle x, y\rangle \mid \mathrm{lcm}\langle x, \mathrm{lcm}\langle y, z\rangle\rangle$; by lines **7** and **8** and Theorem 5-1-11.
▶▶**10.** $\mathrm{lcm}\langle \mathrm{lcm}\langle x, y\rangle, z\rangle \leq \mathrm{lcm}\langle x, \mathrm{lcm}\langle y, z\rangle\rangle$; by lines **4** and **9** and Theorem 5-1-2 (**ii**).

▶▶**11.** By similar reasoning we show that $\text{lcm}\langle x, \text{lcm}\langle y, z\rangle\rangle \leq \text{lcm}\langle \text{lcm}\langle x, y\rangle, z\rangle$.

▶▶**12.** $\text{lcm}\langle \text{lcm}\langle x, y\rangle, z\rangle = \text{lcm}\langle x, \text{lcm}\langle y, z\rangle\rangle$; by lines **10** and **11** and Theorem 2-7-7.

13. If x, y, z are any elements of P then $\text{lcm}\langle \text{lcm}\langle x, y\rangle, z\rangle = \text{lcm}\langle x, \text{lcm}\langle y, z\rangle\rangle$; by the Deduction Theorem applied to lines **1** through **12**.

The last two theorems about lcm have precise analogues for the operation gcd which we now state without proof.

THEOREM 5-1-13. *If x, y, z are any elements of P such that $z|x$ and $z|y$, then $z|\text{gcd}\langle x, y\rangle$.*

Proof. See Exercise 7.

THEOREM 5-1-14. *For any $x, y, z \in P$,*
$$\text{gcd}\langle \text{gcd}\langle x, y\rangle, z\rangle = \text{gcd}\langle x, \text{gcd}\langle y, z\rangle\rangle.$$

Proof. See Exercise 8.

The following theorem leads to a practical method for calculating the greatest common divisor of two given numbers.

THEOREM 5-1-15. *Let x, y be any elements of P such that $x < y$.*

(**a**) *If $x \mid y$ then $\text{gcd}\langle x, y\rangle = x$.*
(**b**) *If not $x \mid y$ then there exist numbers q, r such that*

(i) $y = q \cdot x + r$,
(ii) $r < x$, *and* $\text{gcd}\langle x, y\rangle = \text{gcd}\langle r, x\rangle$.

In order to use this theorem for computing it is necessary to know, in addition to the theoretical material developed so far in our axiomatic theory, a detailed and systematic notation for the elements of P (such as the Arabic notation), and a method for computing quotients and remainders in this notation. At a later point we shall indicate how such notation and computational techniques can be incorporated into our axiomatic theory. But at this point, relying on grade-school knowledge of these matters, we shall illustrate the use of Theorem 5-1-15 to compute the greatest common divisor of 96 and 162.

Since division of 162 by 96 leaves a remainder of 66 we obtain $\text{gcd}\langle 96, 162\rangle = \text{gcd}\langle 66, 96\rangle$ by Theorem 5-1-15 (**b**). Since division of 96 by 66 leaves a remainder of 30 we obtain similarly $\text{gcd}\langle 66, 96\rangle = \text{gcd}\langle 30, 66\rangle$. Continuing in this way we get the following string of equations: $\text{gcd}\langle 96, 162\rangle = \text{gcd}\langle 66, 96\rangle = \text{gcd}\langle 30, 66\rangle = \text{gcd}\langle 6, 30\rangle$. But $6 \mid 30$, hence $\text{gcd}\langle 6, 30\rangle = 6$ by Theorem 5-1-15 (**a**). Thus we finally obtain $\text{gcd}\langle 96, 162\rangle = 6$.

We now turn to a proof of Theorem 5-1-15.

Proof of Part (**a**).

▶▶**1.** Let x, y be any elements of P such that $x < y$ and $x \mid y$.
2. $x \mid x$; by Theorem 4-2-4.
▶▶**3.** $x \mid \gcd\langle x, y\rangle$; by lines **1** and **2** and Theorem 5-1-13.
▶▶**4.** $\gcd\langle x, y\rangle \mid x$; by definition of gcd (Definition 5-1-6).
▶▶**5.** $\gcd\langle x, y\rangle = x$; by lines **3** and **4**, and Theorem 4-2-3.
6. If x, y are any elements of P such that $x < y$ and $x \mid y$ then $\gcd\langle x, y\rangle = x$; by the Deduction Theorem applied to lines **1** through **5**.

Proof of Part (**b**).

▶▶ **1.** Let x, y be any elements of P such that $x < y$ and *not* $x \mid y$.
▶▶ **2.** There exist $q, r \in P$ such that (**i**) $y = q \cdot x + r$ and (**ii**) $r < x$; by line **1** and Theorem 5-1-9.
▶ **3.** $\gcd\langle x, r\rangle \mid x$; by definition of gcd (Definition 5-1-6).
4. $x \mid q \cdot x$; by Definition 4-2-1 and Theorem 4-1-4.
5. $\gcd\langle x, r\rangle \mid q \cdot x$; by lines **3** and **4** and Theorem 4-2-2.
6. $\gcd\langle x, r\rangle \mid r$; by definition of gcd (Definition 5-1-6).
7. $\gcd\langle x, r\rangle \mid (q \cdot x + r)$; by lines **5** and **6** and Theorem 4-2-7.
▶ **8.** $\gcd\langle x, r\rangle \mid y$; by E from lines **2** (**i**) and **7**.
▶▶ **9.** $\gcd\langle x, r\rangle \mid \gcd\langle x, y\rangle$; by Theorem 5-1-13 and lines **3** and **8**.
▶**10.** $\gcd\langle x, y\rangle \mid x$; by definition of gcd (Definition 5-1-6).
11. $\gcd\langle x, y\rangle \mid q \cdot x$; by lines **10** and **4** and Theorem 4-2-2.
12. $\gcd\langle x, y\rangle \mid y$; by definition of gcd (Definition 5-1-6).
13. $q \cdot x < y$; by line **2** (**i**) and Definition 2-5-1.
14. $r = y - q \cdot x$; by line **2** (**i**), the commutative law of addition, and Theorem 2-6-3.
15. $\gcd\langle x, y\rangle \mid (y - q \cdot x)$; by lines **11**, **12**, and **13** and Theorem 4-2-8.
▶**16.** $\gcd\langle x, y\rangle \mid r$; by E from lines **14** and **15**.
▶▶**17.** $\gcd\langle x, y\rangle \mid \gcd\langle r, x\rangle$; by lines **10** and **16** and Theorem 5-1-13.
▶▶**18.** $\gcd\langle x, y\rangle = \gcd\langle r, x\rangle$; by lines **9** and **17**, and Theorem 4-2-3.
19. If x, y are any elements of P such that $x < y$ and *not* $x \mid y$, then there exist $q, r \in P$ such that (**i**) $y = q \cdot x + r$, (**ii**) $r < x$, and $\gcd\langle x, y\rangle = \gcd\langle r, x\rangle$; by the Deduction Theorem applied to lines **1** and **2** through **18**.

As we have seen, Theorem 5-1-15 furnishes us with a practical method for computing the greatest common divisor of a given pair of numbers. The next theorem gives us a method for computing the least common multiple of a given pair of numbers by reducing the problem to that of finding the greatest common divisor of the pair.

THEOREM 5-1-16. *For all* $x, y \in P$, $\operatorname{lcm}\langle x, y\rangle = (x \cdot y) \div \operatorname{gcd}\langle x, y\rangle$.

Proof

▶▶ **1.** Let x, y be any elements of P.
▶▶ **2.** Let $d = \operatorname{gcd}\langle x, y\rangle$.
3. $x = a \cdot d$ and $y = b \cdot d$ for some $a, b \in P$; by line **2**, the definition of gcd (Definition 5-1-6), and the definition of $|$.
▶▶ **4.** Let $z = (x \cdot y) \div d$.
5. $z = [(a \cdot d) \cdot (b \cdot d)] \div d$; by E from lines **3** and **4**.
6. $\quad = (a \cdot d) \cdot [(b \cdot d) \div d]$; by Theorem 4-2-13.
7. $\quad = (a \cdot d) \cdot b$; by E and the definition of $\div$.
8. $\quad = (b \cdot d) \cdot a$; by the commutative and associative laws for $\cdot$.
9. $z = x \cdot b$ and $z = y \cdot a$; by E from lines **3** and **5** through **7** and **8**.
10. $x \mid z$ and $y \mid z$; by line **9** and the definition of $|$.
▶ **11.** z is a common multiple of x and y; by line **10** and the definition of common multiple (Definition 5-1-1).
▶▶ **12.** Let $w = \operatorname{lcm}\langle x, y\rangle$.
▶ **13.** $w \mid z$; by lines **11** and **12** and Theorem 5-1-11.
▶ **14.** $z = w \cdot g$ for some $g \in P$; by line **13** and the definition of $|$.
15. $w = e \cdot x$ and $w = f \cdot y$ for some $e, f \in P$; by line **12** and the definition of lcm (Definition 5-1-1).
16. $z = (e \cdot x) \cdot g$ and $z = (f \cdot y) \cdot g$; by E from lines **14** and **15**.
17. $x \cdot b = (e \cdot x) \cdot g$ and $y \cdot a = (f \cdot y) \cdot g$; by E from lines **9** and **16**.
18. $b = e \cdot g$ and $a = f \cdot g$; by the commutative, associative, and left cancellation laws for $\cdot$ from line **17**.
19. $b \cdot d = (e \cdot g) \cdot d$ and $a \cdot d = (f \cdot g) \cdot d$; by E from line **18**.
20. $y = e \cdot (g \cdot d)$ and $x = f \cdot (g \cdot d)$; by E and the associative law for $\cdot$ from lines **3** and **19**.
21. $g \cdot d$ is a common divisor of x and y; from line **20** and the definition of common divisor (Definition 5-1-6).
22. $g \cdot d \leq d$; by lines **21** and **2** and the definition of gcd (Definition 5-1-6).
23. $d \leq g \cdot d$; by Theorem 4-1-13.
24. $g \cdot d = d$; by lines **22** and **23** and Theorem 2-7-7.
25. $d \cdot g = d \cdot 1$; by E from line **24**, the commutative law of $\cdot$, and the definition of $\cdot$ (**i**).
▶ **26.** $g = 1$; by line **25** and the left cancellation law of $\cdot$.
▶▶ **27.** $z = w$; by E from lines **26** and **14** and the definition of $\cdot$ (**i**).
28. $z = \operatorname{lcm}\langle x, y\rangle$; by E from lines **12** and **27**.
▶▶ **29.** $\operatorname{lcm}\langle x, y\rangle = (x \cdot y) \div \operatorname{gcd}\langle x, y\rangle$; by E from lines **2**, **4**, and **28**.

30. For all $x, y \in P$, $\text{lcm}\langle x, y\rangle = (x \cdot y) \div \text{gcd}\langle x, y\rangle$; by the Deduction Theorem applied to lines **1** through **29**.

As an illustration of the use of this theorem let us apply it to find the lcm of the ordered pair of integers $\langle 20, 48\rangle$, using our intuitive knowledge of the number system. By inspection we note that $\text{gcd}\langle 20, 48\rangle = 4$ and $x \cdot y = 960$. Hence $\text{lcm}\langle 20, 48\rangle = 960 \div 4 = 240$, which can be seen to be the least common multiple of 20 and 48.

EXERCISES

1. Compute lcm and gcd for the following pairs of numbers:

(**a**) $\langle 24, 60\rangle$

(**b**) $\langle 36, 210\rangle$

(**c**) $\langle 168, 264\rangle$.

2. Prove Theorem 5-1-2.
3. Prove that the lcm operation is commutative (Theorem 5-1-4).
4. Prove the Idempotent Law for gcd (Theorem 5-1-7).
5. Prove that the gcd operation is commutative (Theorem 5-1-8).
6. Give details to establish line **11** in the proof of Theorem 5-1-12.
7. Prove Theorem 5-1-13.
8. Prove that the gcd operation is associative (Theorem 5-1-14).
9.* Let x, y be any two numbers such that $(a \cdot x) - (b \cdot y) = 1$ for some numbers a, b. Show that $\text{gcd}\langle x, y\rangle = 1$. (Conversely, if $\text{gcd}\langle x, y\rangle = 1$ then either $(a \cdot x) - (b \cdot y) = 1$ or $(a \cdot y) - (b \cdot x) = 1$ for some $a, b \in P$; but this is more difficult to show.)

2. *Primes*

One branch of the theory of positive integers which dates back to antiquity, and which still interests mathematicians, is the theory of primes. There is a vast literature on the subject which we shall merely sample here.

The reader doubtless will recall that certain positive integers, other than 1, which have the property that they have no integral divisors other than 1 and themselves, are called *prime* numbers. Examples of prime numbers are 2, 3, 19, 37. A number such as 51 is called a *composite* number. It is not a prime, since it has a divisor other than 1 and 51. We shall introduce the concept of *prime* into our theory by means of a definition.

DEFINITION 5-2-1. *An element $x \in P$ is called* **prime** *if and only if $x \neq 1$ and the only elements y such that $y \mid x$ are $y = 1$ and $y = x$.* (Sometimes this definition is given as follows: *x is* **prime** *if and only if $x \neq 1$ and whenever $x = u \cdot v$ then either $u = 1$ or $v = 1$.* It is easily seen that these two statements are equivalent.)

THEOREM 5-2-2. *If y is any element of P other than* 1, *then there is a prime x such that $x \mid y$.*

Proof

▶▶ **1.** Let y be any element of P other than 1.
▶▶ **2.** Let G be the set of all those numbers u such that $u \mid y$ and $u \neq 1$.
3. $y \mid y$; by Theorem 4-2-4.
4. G is not empty; by lines **1**, **2**, and **3**.
▶▶ **5.** There is an element $x \in G$ such that $x \leq t$ for all $t \in G$; by line **4** and Theorem 2-7-9.
6. $x \mid y$ and $x \neq 1$; by lines **2** and **5**.
▶ **7.** Let z be any factor of x other than 1; e.g., let z be any element of P such that $z \mid x$ and $z \neq 1$.
8. $z \mid y$; by lines **6** and **7** and the transitive law of $\mid$.
9. $z \in G$; by lines **2**, **7**, and **8**.
10. $x \leq z$; by lines **5** and **9**.
11. $z \leq x$; by line **7**, the definition of $\mid$, and Theorem 4-1-13.
▶ **12.** $z = x$; by lines **10** and **11** and Theorem 2-7-7.
13. If z is any factor of x and $z \neq 1$ then $z = x$; by the Deduction Theorem applied to lines **7** through **12**.
14. The only factors of x are 1 and x; by line **13**.
▶▶ **15.** x is prime; by lines **6** and **14** and Definition 5-2-1.
16. x is prime and $x \mid y$; by lines **15** and **6**.
17. If y is any element of P other than 1 then there is a prime x such that $x \mid y$; by the Deduction Theorem applied to lines **1** through **16**.

Later on in the development of the theory of numbers, Theorem 5-2-2 will be used to prove that any number y has at least one factorization into primes. At this point we cannot formulate this result precisely because we do not have available in our axiomatic theory a precise concept of a product of an arbitrary number of factors.

The next theorem will be used later to show that any prime decomposition (or factorization) is unique (except possibly for the order of the prime factors).

THEOREM 5-2-3. *If x, y, z are any elements of P such that x is prime and $x \mid (y \cdot z)$, then either $x \mid y$ or $x \mid z$.*

Proof

▶▶ **1.** Let x, y, z be any elements of P such that x is prime and $x \mid (y \cdot z)$.
▶▶ **2.** Assume *not* $x \mid y$.
3. $\gcd\langle x, y\rangle \mid x$ and $\gcd\langle x, y\rangle \mid y$; by the definition of gcd.

4. For any number t, if $t \mid x$ then $t = 1$ or $t = x$; by line **1** and Definition 5-2-1.
5. $\gcd\langle x, y\rangle = 1$ or $\gcd\langle x, y\rangle = x$; by lines **3** and **4**.
6. If $\gcd\langle x, y\rangle = x$ then $x \mid y$; by line **3**.
7. $\gcd\langle x, y\rangle \neq x$; by lines **2** and **6**.
8. $\gcd\langle x, y\rangle = 1$; by lines **5** and **7**.
▶ **9.** $y \mid (y \cdot z)$; by the definition of $\mid$.
▶**10.** $\text{lcm}\langle x, y\rangle \mid (y \cdot z)$; by lines **1** and **9**, and Theorem 5-1-11.
11. $\text{lcm}\langle x, y\rangle = (x \cdot y) \div \gcd\langle x, y\rangle$; by Theorem 5-1-16.
12. $\qquad = (x \cdot y) \div 1$; by E from line **8**.
13. $(x \cdot y) \cdot 1 = x \cdot y$; by the definition of $\cdot$ (**i**).
14. $(x \cdot y) \div 1 = x \cdot y$; by line **13** and definition of $\div$.
▶**15.** $\text{lcm}\langle x, y\rangle = x \cdot y$; by E from lines **11**, **12**, and **14**.
▶**16.** $(x \cdot y) \mid (y \cdot z)$; by E from lines **10** and **15**.
▶▶**17.** $x \mid z$; by line **16**, the commutative law of $\cdot$, and Theorem 4-2-6.
18. If *not* $x \mid y$ then $x \mid z$; by the Deduction Theorem applied to lines **2** through **17**.
▶▶**19.** Either $x \mid y$ or $x \mid z$; by logic from line **18**.
20. If x, y, z are any elements of P such that $x \mid (y \cdot z)$ and x is a prime, then either $x \mid y$ or $x \mid z$; by the Deduction Theorem applied to lines **1** through **19**.

A very famous theorem concerning primes, first proved by Euclid, states that there are infinitely many prime numbers. We can formulate this proposition in the language of our theory as follows: *For every* $x \in P$ *there is a* y *such that* $x < y$ *and* y *is prime.* We shall postpone the proof of this theorem until we have introduced certain concepts needed to carry through Euclid's demonstration.

EXERCISES

1. Prove that 3 is a prime.

2. Suppose that $u, v, w \in P$ and that x and y are primes such that $(x \cdot y) \mid (u \cdot v \cdot w)$. Prove that either $(x \cdot y) \mid (u \cdot v)$ or $(x \cdot y) \mid (u \cdot w)$ or $(x \cdot y) \mid (v \cdot w)$.

3. *Further Concepts*

We recall that the symbolism "x^2" was introduced into elementary algebra as follows: For any number x we let "x^2" stand for "$x \cdot x$". From our more advanced viewpoint we recognize that "square" is really a unary operation on P. If we were to introduce it into our theory we might do so as follows:

DEFINITION: *Let* sq *be the unary operation on* P *such that for all* $x \in P$, $sq\langle x\rangle = x \cdot x$. *Notation:* We write "$x^2$" for "$sq\langle x\rangle$".

Next we could give a definition for x^3, then x^4, and then carry this idea as many steps as we like. But we could not in this way bring the general concept of exponentiation, which is a binary operation, into our theory. How is this to be done? If the reader recalls Section 1, Chapter IV, where multiplication was introduced, he can probably anticipate how we will define x^y for any $x, y \in P$. We first prove the existence of a unique binary operation which has certain properties (familiar to us from our intuitive experience with exponentiation), and then we shall define the exponentiation operation to be this operation.

THEOREM 5-3-1. *There is one and only one binary operation f on P such that*

(**i**) $f\langle x, 1\rangle = x$ *for all* $x \in P$, *and*
(**ii**) $f\langle x, y + 1\rangle = f\langle x, y\rangle \cdot x$ *for all* $x, y \in P$.

We shall not include a proof of this theorem here—not even in the Appendix. The proof is somewhat longer and more involved than the proof of Theorem 4-1-1 (the corresponding result on which the definition of multiplication is based, which does appear in the Appendix)[1]. We do wish to remark, however, that Theorem 5-3-1, unlike Theorem 4-1-1, does not hold for all induction models. (This means that its proof must be based on other axioms than merely P3 and P4; as a matter of fact all four axioms must be used.) It is not hard to exhibit an induction model for which Theorem 5-3-1 fails. See Exercise 1 below.

Assuming that Theorem 5-3-1 is part of our theory, we are now able to give a definition of the general exponentiation function.

DEFINITION 5-3-2. *We define* **exp** *to be the unique binary operation on P described in Theorem* 5-3-1. *Thus we have*

(**i**) $\exp\langle x, 1\rangle = x$ *for all* $x \in P$, *and*
(**ii**) $\exp\langle x, y + 1\rangle = \exp\langle x, y\rangle \cdot x$ *for all* $x, y \in P$.

Notation: We sometimes write "x^y" instead of "$\exp\langle x, y\rangle$". Thus we have

(**i**) $x^1 = x$ for all $x \in P$, and
(**ii**) $x^{y+1} = x^y \cdot x$ for all $x, y \in P$.

The reader will recognize the next two theorems from elementary algebra. Their proofs are straightforward applications of mathematical induction.

THEOREM 5-3-3. *For all* $x, y, z \in P$, $\exp\langle x, y + z\rangle = \exp\langle x, y\rangle \cdot \exp\langle x, z\rangle$ (*or* $x^{y+z} = x^y \cdot x^z$).

[1] The reader who wishes to see such a proof can find one in Kershner, R. B. and Wilcox, L. R., *The Anatomy of Mathematics*, New York; The Ronald Press Company, 1950. See also Henkin, Leon, "*On Mathematical Induction*," *The American Mathematical Monthly*, Vol. 67 (1960), p. 323.

Proof

▶▶ **1.** Let x, y be any elements of P.

▶▶ **2.** Having chosen x and y, let G be the set of all those $z \in P$ such that $x^{y+z} = x^y \cdot x^z$.

3. $x^1 = x$; by Definition 5-3-2 (**i**).

4. $x^{y+1} = x^y \cdot x$; by Definition 5-3-2 (**ii**).

▶ **5.** $x^{y+1} = x^y \cdot x^1$; by E from lines **3** and **4**.

▶ **6.** $1 \in G$; by lines **2** and **5**.

▶ **7.** Let u be any element of G.

8. $x^{y+u} = x^y \cdot x^u$; by lines **2** and **7**.

9. $y + (u + 1) = (y + u) + 1$; by Axiom P3.

10. $x^{y+(u+1)} = x^{(y+u)+1}$; by E from line **8**.

11. $= x^{y+u} \cdot x$; by Definition 5-3-2 (**ii**).

12. $= (x^y \cdot x^u) \cdot x$; by E from line **8**.

13. $= x^y \cdot (x^u \cdot x)$; by Theorem 4-1-6.

14. $= x^y \cdot x^{u+1}$; by Definition 5-3-2 (**ii**) and E.

▶ **15.** $x^{y+(u+1)} = x^y \cdot x^{u+1}$; by E from lines **10** through **14**.

▶ **16.** $u + 1 \in G$; by lines **2** and **15**.

17. Whenever $u \in G$ then also $u + 1 \in G$; by the Deduction Theorem applied to lines **7** through **16**.

▶▶ **18.** $G = P$; by Axiom P4 and lines **6** and **17**.

19. For all $z \in P$, $x^{y+z} = x^y \cdot x^z$; by lines **2** and **18**.

20. For all $x, y, z \in P$, $x^{y+z} = x^y \cdot x^z$; by lines **1** and **19**.

THEOREM 5-3-4. *For all* $x, y, z \in P$, $\exp\langle x, y \cdot z\rangle = \exp\langle \exp\langle x, y\rangle, z\rangle$ (*or* $x^{y \cdot z} = (x^y)^z$).

Proof. See Exercise 2 below.

So far we have introduced two defined operations into our theory, namely multiplication and exponentiation. In each case, before stating the definition of the operation, a certain theorem asserting existence and uniqueness was proved (or at least stated). Recall, for example, that before stating the definition of multiplication (Definition 4-1-2) we proved the theorem (Theorem 4-1-1) that there exists one and only one function f with the properties

(**i**) $f\langle x, 1\rangle = x$ for all $x \in P$, and
(**ii**) $f\langle x, y + 1\rangle = f\langle x, y\rangle + x$ for all $x, y \in P$.

Notice that (**i**) gives an explicit formula for obtaining the value of the function f for any $\langle x, 1\rangle$, and that (**ii**) gives the value of f at $\langle x, y + 1\rangle$ *provided* we know the value at $\langle x, y\rangle$. The two parts of Theorem 5-3-1 (which provides the basis for introducing exp in Definition 5-3-2) function in just the same way.

Can we introduce still other functions in this way? Suppose, for example, that we wish to define a binary function θ with the properties:

(**i′**) $x \theta 1 = 2 \cdot x + 3$ for all $x \in P$, and
(**ii′**) $x \theta (y + 1) = (x \theta y) + x \cdot y$ for all $x, y \in P$.

Here again we see that (**i′**) gives the value of the function for any $\langle x, 1\rangle$, and that (**ii′**) gives the value of θ for all $\langle x, y + 1\rangle$ "in terms of" the value of θ at $\langle x, y\rangle$. In other words, we see that (**i′**) and (**ii′**) seem to have the same general character as (**i**) and (**ii**) above. But, can we be assured that there is one (and only one) function with properties (**i′**) and (**ii′**)? Intuitively, we may feel that the answer is yes. But is it possible to prove this within our axiomatic framework? It turns out that the answer is yes. Indeed, not only is it possible to prove this special theorem for the function θ, but it is possible to prove a general theorem called the *Principle of Definition by Induction* (or the *Principle of Definition by Recursion*) which establishes the existence and uniqueness of functions in all cases where a pair of equations is given having the same general character as (**i**) and (**ii**) above. We shall not give a precise formulation of the Principle of Definition by Induction here, for it has a rather abstract character. Nor shall we even hint at the proof.[2] But we shall refer to this principle in indicating the justification for further definitions of functions.

Not all functions which can be introduced by the Principle of Definition by Induction are useful in the development of number theory. For example, our last function, introduced by (**i′**) and (**ii′**) above, would have very little use beyond this point. Now, however, we will define a unary function by means of this principle, which does play an important role in the further development of our theory.

DEFINITION 5-3-5. *We define (by recursion) a unary operation on P, the* **factorial** *operation (denoted by "!"), as follows:*

(**i**) $1! = 1$, *and*
(**ii**) $(x + 1)! = x! \cdot (x + 1)$ *for all* $x \in P$.

(Here we have followed the usual notation by putting the symbol "!" after, instead of in front of, the symbol for the number on which the function acts.)

To be complete here we should mention that by the general principle of definition by induction there is a unique function f on P such that (**i**) $f\langle 1\rangle = 1$, and (**ii**) $f\langle x + 1\rangle = f\langle x\rangle \cdot (x + 1)$ for all $x \in P$. But in ordinary mathematical writing we usually proceed as we have done here. That is, we simply give the pair of "recursion equations" (**i**) and (**ii**) for the function, with the assumption that the reader understands that the existence and

[2] Ibid.

uniqueness of such a function can be established by appeal to the general theorem.

We now state and prove a theorem concerning our new function.

THEOREM 5-3-6. *If x, y are any elements of P such that $y \leq x$, then $y \mid (x!)$.*

Proof

▶▶ **1.** Let G be the subset of all those elements $x \in P$ such that for every $y \leq x$ we have $y \mid (x!)$.
▶ **2.** Let y be any number such that $y \leq 1$.
3. $y = 1$; by line **2** and Exercise 5, page 50.
4. $1! = 1$; by Definition 5-3-5 (**i**).
5. $1 \mid 1$; by Theorem 4-2-4.
▶ **6.** $y \mid 1!$; by E from lines **3**, **4**, and **5**.
7. For every $y \leq 1$ we have $y \mid 1!$; by the Deduction Theorem applied to lines **2** through **6**.
▶ **8.** $1 \in G$; by lines **1** and **7**.
▶ **9.** Let x be any element of G.
10. For every $y \leq x$ we have $y \mid (x!)$; by lines **1** and **9**.
▶ **11.** Let z be any number such that $z \leq x + 1$.
12. $z = x + 1$ or $z < x + 1$; from line **11** by definition of $\leq$.
13. $z = x + 1$ or $z \leq x$; by line **12** and Exercise 9, page 50.

▶ **14.** *Case I.* Suppose $z = x + 1$.
15. $(x + 1)! = x! \cdot (x + 1)$; by Definition 5-3-5 (**ii**).
16. $(x + 1) \mid (x + 1)!$; by line **15**, the commutative law of $\cdot$, and the definition of $\mid$.
▶ **17.** $z \mid (x + 1)!$; by E from lines **14** and **16**.

▶ **18.** *Case II.* Suppose $z \leq x$.
19. $z \mid (x!)$; by lines **10** and **18**.
20. $(x + 1)! = x! \cdot (x + 1)$; by Definition 5-3-5 (**ii**).
21. $x! \mid (x + 1)!$; by line **20** and the definition of $\mid$.
▶ **22.** $z \mid (x + 1)!$; by lines **19** and **21** and the transitive law of $\mid$.

23. In all cases $z \mid (x + 1)!$; by lines **13**, **14** through **17**, and **18** through **22**.
24. For every $z \leq x + 1$ we have $z \mid (x + 1)!$; by the Deduction Theorem applied to lines **11** through **23**.
▶ **25.** $x + 1 \in G$; by lines **1** and **24**.
26. Whenever $x \in G$ then also $x + 1 \in G$; by applying the Deduction Theorem to lines **9** through **25**.

▶▶**27.** $G = P$; by lines **8** and **26** and Axiom P4.
28. If x, y are any elements of P such that $y \leq x$, then $y \mid (x!)$; by lines **1** and **27**.

We can use Theorem 5-3-6 to prove Euclid's theorem on primes. But first we must establish the converse of Theorem 5-1-9, which is our next theorem.

THEOREM 5-3-7. *If x, y, q, r are elements of P such that*

(**i**) $y = q \cdot x + r$ *and*
(**ii**) $r < x$,

then $x < y$ and not $x \mid y$.

Proof

▶▶ **1.** Let x, y, q, r be any elements of P such that (**i**) $y = q \cdot x + r$ and (**ii**) $r < x$.
2. $x \leq q \cdot x$; by Theorem 4-1-13.
3. (**a**) $x < q \cdot x$ or (**b**) $x = q \cdot x$; from line **2** by the definition of $\leq$.
4. $q \cdot x < y$; by line **1** (**i**) and the definition of $<$.
▶▶ **5.** $x < y$; by lines **3**(**a**) and **4** by the transitive law for $<$; or from lines **3**(**b**) and **4** by E.
▶▶ **6.** Suppose $x \mid y$.
7. $x \cdot z = y$ for some $z \in P$; by line **6** and the definition of $\mid$.
8. $x \cdot z = q \cdot x + r$; by E from lines **1** (**i**) and **7**.
9. $x \cdot z = x \cdot q + r$; by E from line **8** and the commutative law of $\cdot$.
10. $x \cdot z - x \cdot q = r$; by line **9** and Theorem 2-6-3.
11. $x \cdot (z - q) = r$; by E from line **10** and Theorem 4-1-10.
▶**12.** $x \mid r$; by line **11** and the definition of $\mid$.
▶▶**13.** $x \leq r$; by line **12**, the definition of $\mid$, and Theorem 4-1-13.
14. If $x \mid y$ then $x \leq r$; by the Deduction Theorem and lines **6** through **13**.
▶▶**15.** *Not* $x \leq r$; by line **1** (**ii**), the Trichotomy Law and the definition of $\leq$.
▶▶**16.** *Not* $x \mid y$; by lines **14** and **15**.
17. If x, y, q, r are any elements of P such that (**i**) $y = q \cdot x + r$ and (**ii**) $r < x$, then $x < y$ and *not* $x \mid y$; by applying the Deduction Theorem to lines **1** through **5** and **16**.

As remarked after Theorem 5-2-3, Euclid's theorem asserting the infinitude of prime numbers can be formulated within our theory as follows.

THEOREM 5-3-8. *If x is any element of P there is a prime y such that $x < y$.*

Proof

▶▶ **1.** Let x be any element of P.

▶▶ **2.** Let $z = x! + 1$.

3. $1 < z$; by line **2**, the definition of $<$, and Theorem 2-4-2.

4. $1 \neq z$; by line **3** and the Law of Trichotomy.

▶▶ **5.** There is a prime y such that $y \mid z$; by line **4** and Theorem 5-2-2.

▶▶ **6.** *Assume* $y \leq x$.

7. $y \mid x!$; by line **6** and Theorem 5-3-6.

8. $y \cdot q = x!$ for some $q \in P$; by line **7** and the definition of $\mid$.

9. $x! + 1 = q \cdot y + 1$; by E and the commutative law of $\cdot$ from line **8**.

10. $1 \neq y$; by line **5** and the definition of prime.

11. $1 < y$; by line **10** and Lemma 2-5-3.1.

▶▶ **12.** *Not* $y \mid (x! + 1)$; by lines **9** and **11** and Theorem 5-3-7.

13. If $y \leq x$ then *not* $y \mid (x! + 1)$; by the Deduction Theorem applied to lines **6** through **12**.

14. *Not* $y \leq x$; by lines **2**, **5**, and **13**.

▶▶ **15.** $x < y$; by line **14**, the definition of $\leq$, and the Trichotomy Law.

16. If x is any element of P there is a prime y such that $x < y$; by the Deduction Theorem applied to lines **1** through **5** and **15**.

EXERCISES

1. Exhibit an induction model for which Theorem 5-3-1 fails. *Hint:* After selecting an induction model, assume the existence of a binary operation f of the kind mentioned in Theorem 5-3-1 and try to derive a contradiction.

2. Prove Theorem 5-3-4.

VI

Finite Sequences: General Sums and Products[1]

1. Segments and Sequences

The operations of addition and multiplication are *binary* operations, that is, they act on ordered *pairs* of elements of P and each such action produces an element of P. By use of the associative laws of addition and multiplication we have been able to assign meanings to expressions involving an ordered triple of elements such as "$x + y + z$" and "$x \cdot y \cdot z$"; the former, for example, denotes the same element as either of the expressions "$(x + y) + z$" or "$x + (y + z)$". We could, if we wish, introduce a special symbol (say ⊕) for the ternary operation whose values are given by the equation $\oplus\langle x, y, z\rangle = x + y + z$ for all $x, y, z \in P$. Can we extend this concept to sums of four terms, say? It is fairly obvious that we can. For if x, y, z, w are any elements of P, then the binary operation of addition can be applied to the ordered pair $\langle x + y + z, w\rangle$ to produce an element which might be denoted "$x + y + z + w$". The associative law tells us that all possible interpretations of this symbol—$[(x + y) + z] + w$, $[x + (y + z)] + w$, $x + [(y + z) + w]$, $x + [y + (z + w)]$, $[x + y] + [z + w]$—produce the same element of P, so that we are justified in the use of the notation "$x + y + z + w$". (See Exercise 2, Chapter II, Section 4.)

The reader may correctly conclude that it is possible to speak of the sum of 5 terms, or 19 terms, or of any *fixed* number of terms within our present axiomatic system. For example, once the expression "$x + y + z + w$" is introduced as the name of an element of P, then "$(x + y + z + w) + u$," where $u \in P$, will also denote an element of P, and we would agree to denote this by "$x + y + z + w + u$." Clearly, by adding one element at a time in this way we can arrive at the sum of 19 terms, or 37 terms, or any *fixed* number of terms. However, each time we increase the number of terms admitted to a sum we need a new definition. What we would like is a *single*

[1] The reader is reminded (cf. A Note to the Reader) that the proofs of the theorems in this Chapter might well be omitted. In fact, the continuity of the book will not be disturbed if Chapter VI is omitted entirely—until specific reference is made to it.

definition which enables us to deal with a *general sum*, the sum of *any* number of terms.

Before we attempt to state such a definition, let us consider several difficulties which arise. In the first place, when we speak of the *number* of terms in a sum, we are dealing with a concept which has not been formally introduced. Intuitively, some kind of counting process is suggested—and counting has not yet been made a part of our axiomatic framework. Secondly, we are concerned with some kind of array or sequence of elements of P, the "terms" of our general sum. We need a device which will enable us to indicate just which elements of P are to be added.

To overcome these difficulties we find it convenient to develop the concepts of *segment* and *sequence*. A segment will be defined as a certain kind of subset of P, while a sequence will be defined as a function over the elements of some segment (whose values will be the individual terms of a general sum). The formal definitions of these concepts follow.

DEFINITION 6-1-1. *If x is any element of P, the* **segment of x**, *written* **seg(x)**, *is defined to be the set of all those $y \in P$ such that $y \leq x$.*

This definition says that seg(x) is a subset of P consisting of x itself and all those elements which are less than x. Thus, if x is 4, seg(x) is the set $\{1, 2, 3, 4\}$. (Compare Exercise 6, Chapter II, Section 7.)

DEFINITION 6-1-2. *If x is any element of P, an* **x-sequence** *is defined to be any function X whose domain is seg(x) and whose values are in P.* [In other words, X is a function mapping seg(x) into P.] Often we shall use a subscript notation, such as "X_x," "Y_x," "Z_x," to indicate that we are dealing with x-segments. *By a* **finite sequence** *we simply mean a function which is an x-sequence for some $x \in P$.*

As an example, suppose again that $x = 4$. The domain of any 4-sequence consists of the numbers 1, 2, 3, 4; in particular, a 4-sequence is a function which assigns to each of the elements 1, 2, 3, 4 a value from P. To define a particular 4-sequence, X_4, we give a table of values, as follows:

$$X_4(1) = 17, \qquad X_4(2) = 24, \qquad X_4(3) = 57, \qquad X_4(4) = 2.$$

It is often convenient to abbreviate this table by the notation:

$$X_4 = \langle 17, 24, 57, 2 \rangle.$$

In general, if X_x is any x-sequence, and if for every u in seg(x) (i.e., for every $u \leq x$) one has $X_x(u) = a_u$, we use the abbreviative notation:

$$X_x = \langle a_1, a_2, \ldots, a_x \rangle$$

in place of writing out a table of values of X_x. This notation makes it clear that we can think intuitively of an x-sequence as an ordinary sequence containing x terms (each of which is a positive integer).

EXERCISES

1. Is an x-sequence an operation, as well as a function? Justify your answer.
2. What is the domain of a 6-sequence?

2. *General Sums and Products*

Before giving a formal definition of general sum, let us consider several special cases which might suggest to us a form which such a definition might take. The expression $a_1 + a_2 + a_3$ can be used to denote the element of P obtained by adding the sum of a 2-sequence, $\langle a_1, a_2\rangle$, and an element a_3. Similarly, $a_1 + a_2 + a_3 + a_4$ could be interpreted as $(a_1 + a_2 + a_3) + a_4$, the sum of an element which is the sum of a 3-sequence, $\langle a_1\, a_2, a_3\rangle$, and a_4. On the other hand, the sum of a 1-sequence, $\langle a_1\rangle$ should be a_1 itself.

Let us use $\sum$ (the Greek capital sigma) as the symbol for the general sum function. Then we might define $\sum$ by means of the two statements:

(i′) $\sum \langle a_1\rangle = a_1$, and
(ii′) $\sum \langle a_1, a_2, \ldots, a_y, a_{y+1}\rangle = (\sum \langle a_1, \ldots, a_y\rangle) + a_{y+1}$,

for all $a_1, \ldots, a_{y+1}$ in P. Notice that (i′) gives an explicit formula for the sum of any 1-sequence, and in fact states that the sum is simply equal to the single term of such a sequence. Statement (ii′) tells how to compute the sum of any $(y + 1)$-sequence, *provided* we know the value of the sum of a certain y-sequence (in fact, the y-sequence obtained by "deleting" the last term of the given $(y + 1)$-sequence). This is the typical form of a recursive definition (cf. the discussion in Section 3, Chapter V, about the Principle of Definition by Recursion or Induction).

With this informal discussion of general sum in mind, let us formally introduce it as follows:

DEFINITION 6-2-1. *We define (by induction) $\sum$ to be the (unique) function which assigns to every finite sequence X a value $\sum(X)$ in P, as follows:*

(i) *If X_1 is any 1-sequence, $\sum(X_1) = X_1(1)$.*
(ii) *If X_{y+1} is any $(y + 1)$-sequence, where y is any element of P, and if Y_y is the y-sequence such that $Y_y(u) = X_{y+1}(u)$ for all $u \le y$, then $\sum(X_{y+1}) = \sum(Y_y) + X_{y+1}(y + 1)$.*

We refer to $\sum$ (X) as the **general sum of X.**

Note that the sequence X_{y+1} of (ii) is the $\langle a_1, \ldots, a_{y+1}\rangle$ of (ii′), and the Y_y of (ii) is the $\langle a_1, \ldots, a_y\rangle$ of (ii′). If $X_n = \langle a_1, a_2, \ldots, a_n\rangle$, we often use the familiar summation notation "$\sum_{i=1}^{n} a_i$" to denote the number $\sum(X)$.

As an example, let us see how we would use Definition 6-2-1 to obtain the sum of a 4-sequence, say $X_4 = \langle a_1, a_2, a_3, a_4 \rangle$. We have:

$$\begin{aligned}\textstyle\sum(X_4) &= \textstyle\sum \langle a_1, a_2, a_3, a_4\rangle \\ &= (\textstyle\sum \langle a_1, a_2, a_3\rangle) + a_4, \quad \text{by Definition 6-2-1 (ii), or (ii}'), \\ &= ((\textstyle\sum \langle a_1, a_2\rangle) + a_3) + a_4, \quad \text{by Definition 6-2-1 (ii) or (ii}'), \\ &= (((\textstyle\sum \langle a_1\rangle) + a_2) + a_3) + a_4, \quad \text{by Definition 6-2-1 (ii), or (ii}'), \\ &= ((a_1 + a_2) + a_3) + a_4, \quad \text{by Definition 6-2-1 (i) or (i}').\end{aligned}$$

By using the associative law we can now get other formulas for $\sum(X_4)$, such as $[(a_1 + a_2) + (a_3 + a_4)]$.

The definition of *general product*, which we give next, closely parallels the definition of general sum given above.

DEFINITION 6-2-2. *We define (by induction) a function* $\prod$ *which assigns to every finite sequence* X *a value* $\prod(X)$, *as follows:*

(i) *If* X_1 *is a* 1-*sequence, then* $\prod(X_1) = X_1(1)$.
(ii) *If* X_{y+1} *is a* $(y + 1)$-*sequence, for any* $y \in P$, *and if* Y_y *is the* y-*sequence such that* $X_{y+1}(u) = Y_y(u)$ *for every* $u \leq y$, *then*
$$\textstyle\prod(X_{y+1}) = \prod(Y_y) \cdot (X_{y+1}(y + 1)).$$

We refer to $\prod(X)$ *as the* **general product of X.**

The remarks concerning the definition of a general sum are appropriate here, with obvious modifications.

In the above discussion we have been concerned essentially with *ordered* x-tuples of elements of P, for the terms of an x-sequence are given a natural order by the relation $<$ which orders the domain of the x-sequence. If the order of terms in an x-sequence is changed, what effect, if any, does this have on the general sum or general product of that sequence? Before considering this, let us define the notion of a *rearrangement* of a given sequence.

DEFINITION 6-2-3. *Let* X *and* Y *be finite sequences. We write "*$X \sim Y$*" (read "*X *is a* **rearrangement** *of* Y*") to mean the following:*

(i) *There is a* $z \in P$ *such that* X *is a* z-*sequence and* Y *is a* z-*sequence, and*
(ii) *There is a one-one mapping,* f, *of* seg(z) *onto* seg(z) *such that* $X_z(u) = Y_z(f(u))$ *for all* $u \leq z$.

As an example, suppose that $z = 4$ and that f is the function mapping seg(4) onto seg(4) such that

$$f(1) = 2, \qquad f(2) = 3, \qquad f(3) = 1, \qquad f(4) = 4.$$

If $X = \langle a_1, a_2, a_3, a_4\rangle$ and $Y = \langle b_1, b_2, b_3, b_4\rangle$ then to say that $X(u) = Y(f(u))$ for all $u \leq 4$ means that $a_1 = b_2$, $a_2 = b_3$, $a_3 = b_1$, $a_4 = b_4$. Thus we could write $X = \langle b_2, b_3, b_1, b_4\rangle$. This should make it clear why we speak of X as a rearrangement of $Y = \langle b_1, b_2, b_3, b_4\rangle$.

THEOREM 6-2-4. *If X and Y are any finite sequences such that $X \sim Y$, then $\sum(X) = \sum(Y)$ and $\prod(X) = \prod(Y)$.*

A proof is more easily given if we first establish the following result.

LEMMA 6-2-4.1. *If $X = \langle a_1, a_2, \ldots, a_z\rangle$ and $Y = \langle a_1, a_2, \ldots, a_{i-1}, a_{i+1}, \ldots, a_z, a_i\rangle$ are z-sequences then $X \sim Y$.*

Outline of Proof of Lemma

1. Let f be the function mapping seg(z) into itself, such that
$f(u) = u$ for any $u < i$, and
$f(u) = u + 1$ for any $u \geq i$ such that $u \neq z$, and
$f(u) = i$ if $u = z$.

2. Clearly f is a one-one mapping of seg(z) into itself, since it assigns a unique value in seg(z) to each element of seg(z), and since $f(u) \neq f(v)$ whenever $u \neq v$. Also, f maps seg(z) *onto* seg(z), since each element of seg(z) is a value of f. Finally, $Y(u) = X(f(u))$ for all $u \in$ seg(z).

Hence, by Definition 6-2-3, $X \sim Y$.

Outline of Proof of Theorem

I. To show: $\sum(X) = \sum(Y)$ whenever X and Y are finite sequences such that $X \sim Y$.

▶▶ **1.** Let G be the set of all those numbers z such that whenever X, Y are z-sequences for which we have $X \sim Y$, then we also have $\sum(X) = \sum(Y)$.

2. If X, Y are any 1-sequences for which $X \sim Y$ then $X(1) = Y(1)$, as the only one-one mapping of seg(1) onto itself is the identity function (i.e., the only rearrangement of a one-termed sequence is itself).

3. By Definition 6-2-1, $\sum(X) = X(1)$ and $\sum(Y) = Y(1)$. So we have $\sum(X) = \sum(Y)$; by line **2**.

4. Whenever X and Y are 1-sequences such that $X \sim Y$, then $\sum(X) = \sum(Y)$; by the Deduction Theorem applied to lines **1** through **3**.

▶ **5.** $1 \in G$; by lines **1** and **4**.

▶ **6.** Let z be any element of G.

7. Let X, Y be any $(z + 1)$-sequences for which $X \sim Y$, and suppose $X = \langle a_1, \ldots, a_{z+1}\rangle$ and $Y = \langle b_1, \ldots, b_{z+1}\rangle$.

8. $\sum(X) = \sum\langle a_1, \ldots, a_z\rangle + a_{z+1}$ and $\sum(Y) = \sum\langle b_1, \ldots, b_z\rangle + b_{z+1}$; by Definition 6-2-1 (**ii**).

9. *Case I.* Suppose $a_{z+1} = b_{z+1}$. Then from line **7** and Definition 6-2-3 it is easy to see that $\langle a_1, \ldots, a_z \rangle \sim \langle b_1, \ldots, b_z \rangle$, and hence $\sum \langle a_1, \ldots, a_z \rangle = \sum \langle b_1, \ldots, b_z \rangle$, by lines **1** and **6**.

10. $\sum(X) = \sum(Y)$; by E from lines **8** and **9**.

11. *Case II.* Suppose $a_{z+1} \neq b_{z+1}$, in which case $b_{z+1} = a_i$ for some $i \leq z$; from line **7** and Definition 6-2-3. (Since X is a rearrangement of Y, if the last term of X is different from the last term of Y, then one of the first z terms of X is the same as the last term of Y.)

12. Then $\sum(X) = \sum \langle a_1, \ldots, a_{z+1} \rangle$; by line **7**.

$= (\sum \langle a_1, \ldots, a_z \rangle) + a_{z+1}$; by Definition 6-2-1 (**ii**).

$= (\sum \langle a_1, \ldots, a_{i-1}, a_{i+1}, \ldots, a_z, a_i \rangle) + a_{z+1}$; by E from Lemma 6-2-4.1 and lines **6** and **1**.

$= ((\sum \langle a_1, \ldots, a_{i-1}, a_{i+1}, \ldots, a_z \rangle) + a_i) + a_{z+1}$; by Definition 6-2-1 (**ii**).

$= ((\sum \langle a_1, \ldots, a_{i-1}, a_{i+1}, \ldots, a_z \rangle) + a_{z+1}) + a_i$; by the associative and commutative laws of addition.

$= (\sum \langle a_1, \ldots, a_{i-1}, a_{i+1}, \ldots, a_z, a_{z+1} \rangle) + a_i$; by Definition 6-2-1 (**ii**).

$= \sum(Y)$; by Case I (since $a_i = b_{z+1}$ by line **11**).

13. Hence, in either case, $\sum(X) = \sum(Y)$; by lines **9**, **10**, **11**, and **12**.

▶**14.** If X and Y are any $(z+1)$-sequences for which $X \sim Y$, then $\sum(X) = \sum(Y)$; by the Deduction Theorem applied to lines **7** through **13**.

▶**15.** $(z + 1) \in G$; by lines **1** and **14**.

16. Whenever $z \in G$ then also $z + 1 \in G$; by the Deduction Theorem applied to lines **6** through **15**.

▶▶**17.** $G = P$; by Axiom P4 and lines **5** and **16**.

18. If X, Y are any z-sequences (for any $z \in P$) such that $X \sim Y$, then $\sum(X) = \sum(Y)$; by lines **1** and **17**.

19. If X, Y are any finite sequences such that $X \sim Y$, then $\sum(X) = \sum(Y)$; by line **18** and Definition 6-1-2.

A proof of the second part of Theorem 6-2-4, that $\prod(X) = \prod(Y)$, would follow the same pattern, and can be obtained if we replace "$\sum$" by "$\prod$" and "$+$" by "$\cdot$" in the above proof. This is left to the reader to prove. (See Exercise 1 below.)

Our intuitive knowledge of multiplication suggests that this *binary* operation is closely related to the *general* sum function for certain special finite sequences, since if X is the y-sequence $\langle x, x, x, x, \ldots, x\rangle$ we would expect that $\sum(X) = x \cdot y$. Similarly, we might expect that the binary operation of exponentiation, as well as the unary factorial operation, both of which were defined in Section 3 of Chapter V, could be interpreted as general products for certain special finite sequences. In the case of exponentiation, let X be the y-sequence $\langle x, x, \ldots, x\rangle$. Then, apparently, $\prod(X) = x \cdot x \cdot x \cdot \ldots \cdot x = x^y$. If X is the x-sequence $\langle 1, 2, 3, \ldots, x\rangle$ then $(\prod X) = 1 \cdot 2 \cdot 3 \cdot \ldots \cdot x$, which we are accustomed to calling $x!$. That all of these possibilities actually do occur is shown by this next theorem.

THEOREM 6-2-5. *Let X be a y-sequence, and suppose that there is some $z \in P$ such that $X(u) = z$ for every $u \leq y$. Then $\sum(X) = y \cdot z$ and $\prod(X) = z^y$. Also, if Y is a y-sequence such that $Y(u) = u$ for every $u \leq y$, then $\prod(Y) = y!$.*

Outline of Proof (of first part of theorem)

▶▶ **1.** Let z be any element of P.

▶▶ **2.** Let G be the set of all those numbers y such that for every y-sequence X such that $X(u) = z$ for every $u \leq y$ we have $\sum(X) = y \cdot z$.

3. Suppose X is any 1-sequence such that $X(1) = z$. Then by Definition 6-2-1 (**i**) we have $\sum(X) = X(1)$. But $X(1) = z = 1 \cdot z$, and so $\sum(X) = 1 \cdot z$.

▶ **4.** $1 \in G$; by lines **2** and **3**.

▶ **5.** Let y be any element of G.

6. Let X be any $(y + 1)$-sequence such that $X(u) = z$ for all $u \leq y + 1$.

7. By Definition 6-2-1 (**ii**) $\sum(X) = \sum(Y) + X(y + 1)$, where Y is the y-sequence such that $Y(u) = X(u) = z$ for all $u \leq y$.

8. $\sum(Y) = y \cdot z$; by lines **2**, **5**, and **7**.

9. $\sum(X) = y \cdot z + z$; by E from lines **6**, **7**, and **8**.
$= (y + 1) \cdot z$; by the Definition and commutative law of multiplication.

▶ **10.** If X is any $(y + 1)$-sequence such that $X(u) = z$ for all $u \leq y + 1$, then $\sum(X) = (y + 1) \cdot z$; by the Deduction Theorem and lines **6** through **9**.

▶ **11.** $y + 1 \in G$; by lines **2** and **10**.

12. If y is any element of G, then also $y + 1 \in G$; by the Deduction Theorem applied to lines **5** through **11**.

▶▶ **13.** $G = P$; by lines **4** and **12** and Axiom P4.

14. If y is any element of P and X is any y-sequence such that $X(u) = z$ for every $u \leq y$, then $\sum(X) = y \cdot z$; by lines **2** and **13**.

The proof of the other two parts of Theorem 6-2-5 is left to the reader. (See Exercises 2 and 3 below.)

From two given sequences, an x-sequence X_x and a y-sequence Y_y, it is possible to construct a third sequence, called the *concatenation of* X_x *and* Y_y, by "adjoining" the values of Y_y to those of X_x. This concept is stated more precisely in the following:

DEFINITION 6-2-6. *If* X_x *is an x-sequence and* Y_y *is a y-sequence then the* **concatenation** *of* X_x *and* Y_y, *denoted by the formula* "X_xY_y" *is defined to be the* $(x + y)$*-sequence such that*

$$(X_xY_y)(u) = \begin{cases} X_x(u), \text{ if } u \leq x \\ Y_y(u - x), \text{ if } u > x \text{ and } u \leq x + y. \end{cases}$$

In somewhat less precise notation, if

$$X_x = \langle a_1, a_2, \ldots, a_x\rangle$$

and

$$Y_y = \langle b_1, b_2, \ldots, b_y\rangle$$

then

$$X_xY_y = \langle a_1, a_2, \ldots, a_x, b_1, b_2, \ldots, b_y\rangle.$$

It is worth noting that the concatenation of an x-sequence and a y-sequence is a function whose domain is seg$(x + y)$, and whose values include the values of each of the two given sequences.

From the above notation one might expect that the general sum of the concatenation of two given sequences is the sum of the general sums of each of the given sequences, for $a_1 + a_2 + \cdots + a_x + b_1 + \cdots + b_y$ is intuitively the same as $(a_1 + \cdots + a_x) + (b_1 + \cdots + b_y)$. That this is indeed the case is established in our axiomatic theory by the following theorem:

THEOREM 6-2-7. *For any finite x-sequence,* X_x, *and any finite y-sequence,* Y_y, $\sum(X_xY_y) = \sum(X_x) + \sum(Y_y)$.

The proof of this theorem is carried out by induction on y. The details are as follows.

Proof

▶▶ **1.** Let x be any element of P, and let X_x be any x-sequence; say $X_x = \langle a_1, a_2, \ldots, a_x\rangle$.

▶▶ **2.** Having chosen x and X_x, let G be the subset of P consisting of all those elements $y \in P$ such that for every y-sequence Y_y we have $\sum(X_xY_y) = \sum(X_x) + \sum(Y_y)$.

▶ **3.** Consider any 1-sequence Y_1, say $Y_1 = \langle b_1\rangle$.

4. $X_xY_y = \langle a_1, a_2, \ldots, a_x, b_1\rangle$; by lines **1** and **3** and Definition 6-2-6.

5. $\sum(X_xY_y) = (\sum \langle a_1, a_2, \ldots, a_x\rangle) + b_1$; by E from line **4** and Definition 6-2-1 (**ii**).

6. $\sum(Y_1) = b_1$; by line **3** and Definition 6-2-1 (**i**).

7. $\sum(X_x) + \sum(Y_1) = (\sum \langle a_1, \ldots, a_x\rangle) + b_1$; by E from lines **1** and **6**.

▶ **8.** $\sum(X_xY_1) = \sum(X_x) + \sum(Y_1)$; by E from line **5** and **7**.

▶ **9.** $1 \in G$; by lines **2** and **8**.

10. Let y be any element of G.

11. For any y-sequence Y_y we have $\sum(X_xY_y) = \sum(X_x) + \sum(Y_y)$; by lines **2** and **10**.

▶ **12.** Let Z_{y+1} be any $(y + 1)$-sequence; say $Z_{y+1} = \langle c_1, \ldots, c_y, c_{y+1}\rangle$. And let Y_y be the y-sequence, $\langle c_1, \ldots, c_y\rangle$, such that $Y_y(u) = Z_{y+1}(u)$ for every $u \leq y$.

13. $\sum(X_xZ_{y+1}) = \sum \langle a_1, \ldots, a_x, c_1, \ldots, c_{y+1}\rangle$; by lines **1** and **12** and Definition 6-2-6.

14. $= (\sum \langle a_1, \ldots, a_x, c_1, \ldots, c_y\rangle) + c_{y+1}$; by Definition 6-2-1 (**ii**).

15. $= (\sum(X_xY_y)) + c_{y+1}$; by E from lines **1** and **12**, and Definition 6-2-6.

16. $= (\sum(X_x) + \sum(Y_y)) + c_{y+1}$; by line **11** and E.

17. $= \sum(X_x) + (\sum(Y_y) + c_{y+1})$; by Theorem 2-4-1 and E.

18. $= \sum(X_x) + ((\sum \langle c_1, \ldots, c_y\rangle) + c_{y+1})$; by line **12** and E.

19. $= \sum(X_x) + \sum \langle c_1, \ldots, c_{y+1}\rangle$; by Definition 6-2-1 (**ii**) and E.

▶ **20.** $\sum(X_xZ_{y+1}) = \sum(X_x) + \sum(Z_{y+1})$; by E from lines **12** through **19**.

21. If Z_{y+1} is *any* $(y + 1)$-sequence, then $\sum(X_xZ_{y+1}) = \sum(X_x) + \sum(Z_{y+1})$; by the Deduction Theorem applied to lines **12** through **20**.

▶ **22.** $y + 1 \in G$; by lines **2** and **21**.

23. If y is any element of G, then $y + 1 \in G$; by the Deduction Theorem and lines **10** through **22**.

▶▶ **24.** $G = P$; by Axiom P4 and lines **9** and **23**.

25. For every $y \in P$ and every y-sequence Y_y we have $\sum(X_xY_y) = \sum(X_x) + \sum(Y_y)$; by lines **2** and **24**.

26. For every $x, y \in P$, every x-sequence X_x, and every y-sequence Y_y, we have $\sum(X_xY_y) = \sum(X_x) + \sum(Y_y)$; by lines **1** and **25**.

The proof of the theorem for multiplication which corresponds to Theorem 6-2-7 is similar, and will be left to the reader as an exercise.

THEOREM 6-2-8. *For any finite x-sequence, X_x, and any finite y-sequence, Y_y,* $\prod(X_x Y_y) = \prod X_x \cdot \prod Y_y$.

Proof. See Exercise 5 below.

Our next theorem is sometimes referred to briefly as "the prime decomposition theorem." In intuitive terms it states that any number other than 1 can be factored (or "decomposed") into primes. We shall state it here in the precise terminology of our axiomatic theory, and outline a proof.

THEOREM 6-2-9. *If x is any element of P other than* 1, *then there exists an element $w \in P$, and there exists a w-sequence W, such that:*

(**i**) *$W(u)$ is prime for every $u \leq w$, and*
(**ii**) $\prod(W) = x$.

Proof

▶▶ **1.** Let G be the set of those $y \in P$ such that $y \neq 1$ but for which there is *no* finite sequence W of primes satisfying $y = \prod(W)$.

▶▶ **2.** *Assume* G is nonempty.

▶▶ **3.** There exists a least element of G, i.e., an element $x \in G$ such that $x \leq v$ for all $v \in G$; by line **2** and Theorem 2-7-9.

▶ **4.** There is a prime z such that $z \mid x$, i.e., $x = a \cdot z$ for some element $a \in P$; by lines **1** and **3** and Theorem 5-2-2.

5. Suppose $a = 1$.

6. $x = 1 \cdot z = z$; by E from lines **4** and **5**, the commutative law of $\cdot$ and the definition of $\cdot$.

7. Let W be the 1-sequence such that $W(1) = z$, so that W is a sequence of primes; by line **4**.

8. $\prod(W) = z$; by the definition of $\prod$ and line **7**.

9. $x = \prod(W)$; by E from lines **6** and **8**.

10. If $a = 1$ then $x = \prod(W)$, where W is a 1-sequence of primes; by the Deduction Theorem applied to lines **5** through **7** and **9**.

▶ **11.** $a \neq 1$; by lines **1**, **3**, and **10**.

12. $z \neq 1$; by line **4** and the definition of prime.

13. $a < x$; by lines **4** and **12** and Theorem 4-1-12 and E.

▶ **14.** Since x is the least element in G and $a < x$ we have $a \notin G$, that is, there is an element $q \in P$ and a q-sequence Q such that (**i**) $Q(u)$ is prime for every $u \leq q$, and (**ii**) $\prod(Q) = a$; by lines **1**, **3**, **11**, and **13**.

▶15. Let V be the $(q + 1)$-sequence defined as follows:
$V(u) = Q(u)$ for all $u \leq q$, and
$V(q + 1) = z$.
16. $V(u)$ is prime for all $u \leq q + 1$; by lines **4**, **14**, and **15**.
17. $\prod(V) = \prod(Q) \cdot z$; by the definition of $\prod$ and line **15**.
▶18. $\prod(V) = a \cdot z = x$; by E from lines **4**, **14 (ii)**, and **17**.
▶▶19. $x \notin G$; by lines **1**, **16**, and **18**.
20. If G is nonempty there is an element $x \in G$ such that $x \notin G$; by the Deduction Theorem applied to lines **2** and **3** through **19**.
▶▶21. G is empty; by line **20**.
22. For any element x of P other than 1, there is an element $w \in P$, and there is a w-sequence W, such that:
(**i**) $W(u)$ is prime for every $u \leq w$, and
(**ii**) $\prod(W) = x$; by lines **1** and **21**.

The following theorem, 6-2-10, states that the prime decomposition found in Theorem 6-2-9 is essentially unique. In texts on number theory, Theorems 6-2-9 and 6-2-10 are sometimes combined and called the Fundamental Theorem of Arithmetic.

THEOREM 6-2-10. *Suppose X is an x-sequence and Y is a y-sequence, and suppose that $X(u)$ is prime for every $u \leq x$ and that $Y(u)$ is prime for every $u \leq y$. If $\prod(X) = \prod(Y)$ then $X \sim Y$.*

In order to prove this theorem we shall first establish a lemma.

LEMMA 6-2-10.1. *For any $x \in P$, if X is an x-sequence such that $X(u)$ is prime for all $u \leq x$, and if p is any prime in P such that $p \mid \prod(X)$, then $p = X(u)$ for some $u \leq x$.*

Proof

▶▶ 1. Let G be the set of those numbers x for which the condition of the Lemma holds, i.e., $x \in G$ if and only if whenever $p \mid \prod(X)$, where p is prime and X is an x-sequence of primes, then $p = X(u)$ for some $u \leq x$.
2. Let X be any 1-sequence such that $X(1)$ is prime, and let p be any prime such that $p \mid \prod(X)$.
3. $\prod(X) = X(1)$; by the definition of $\prod$ and line **2**.
4. $p \mid X(1)$; by lines **2** and **3** by E.
5. $p = X(1)$; by lines **2** and **4** and the definition of prime.
▶ 6. If X is any 1-sequence of primes, and if p is any prime such that $p \mid \prod(X)$, then $p = X(1)$; by the Deduction Theorem applied to lines **2** through **5**.
▶ 7. $1 \in G$; by lines **1** and **6**.

▶ **8.** Let x be any element in G.

9. If X is any x-sequence such that $X(u)$ is prime for every $u \leq x$, and if p is any prime such that $p \mid \prod(X)$, then we have $p = X(u)$ for some $u \leq x$; by lines **1** and **8**.

10. Consider any $(x + 1)$-sequence Y such that $Y(u)$ is prime for all $u \leq x + 1$, and let q be any prime such that $q \mid \prod(Y)$.

11. $\prod(Y) = \prod(X) \cdot Y(x + 1)$, where X is the x-sequence such that $X(u) = Y(u)$ for all $u \leq x$; by line **10** and the definition of $\prod$.

12. $q \mid [\prod(X) \cdot Y(x + 1)]$; by E from lines **10** and **11**.

13. $q \mid \prod(X)$ or $q \mid Y(x + 1)$; by line **12** and Theorem 5-2-3.

14. If $q \mid \prod(X)$ then $q = X(u)$ for some $u \leq x$; by line **9**.

15. If $q \mid Y(x + 1)$ then $q = Y(x + 1)$; by line **10** and the definition of prime.

16. $q = Y(u)$ for some $u \leq x + 1$; by lines **13**, **14**, and **15** and the definition of $\leq$.

▶**17.** If Y is any $(x + 1)$-sequence of primes and q is any prime such that $q \mid \prod(Y)$, then $q = Y(u)$ for some $u \leq x + 1$; by the Deduction Theorem and lines **10** through **16**.

▶**18.** $(x + 1) \in G$; by lines **1** and **17**.

19. Whenever $x \in G$ then also $x + 1 \in G$; by the Deduction Theorem applied to lines **8** through **18**.

▶▶**20.** $G = P$; by lines **7** and **19** and Axiom P4.

21. The condition of the lemma holds for all $x \in P$; by lines **1** and **20**.

Outline of Proof of Theorem 6-2-10

▶▶ **1.** Let G be the set of all those numbers x such that there exists an x-sequence X satisfying the following conditions: $X(u)$ is prime for every $u \leq x$, and $\prod(X) = \prod(Y)$ for some sequence Y of primes, but *not* $X \sim Y$.

▶▶ **2.** *Suppose* G is not empty.

▶▶ **3.** G has a least element, say x (so that $x \in G$ and $x \leq y$ for all $y \in G$); by line **2** and Theorem 2-7-9.

▶ **4.** Assume $x = 1$.

▶ **5.** There exists a 1-sequence X such that: $X(1)$ is prime, $\prod(X) = \prod(Y)$ for some sequence Y of primes, but *not* $X \sim Y$; by lines **1**, **3**, and **4**.

6. $\prod(X) = X(1)$; by line **5** and the definition of $\prod$.

7. $X(1) = \prod(Y)$; by E from lines **5** and **6**.

8. Y is a 1-sequence; by lines **5** and **7** and Exercise 6 below.

9. $\prod(Y) = Y(1)$; by line **8** and the definition of $\prod$.

10. $X(1) = Y(1)$; by E from lines **7** and **9**.

▶**11.** $X \sim Y$; by the definition of $\sim$ and lines **5**, **8**, and **10**.

12. If $x = 1$ then there is an x-sequence X such that *not* $X \sim Y$ and such that $X \sim Y$; by the Deduction Theorem applied to lines **4** and **5** through **11**.

▶▶**13.** $x \neq 1$; by line **12**.

▶▶**14.** $x = w + 1$ for some $w \in P$; by line **13** and Theorem 2-3-4.

▶▶**15.** There is a $(w + 1)$-sequence X, say $X = \langle a_1, a_2, \ldots, a_w, a_{w+1}\rangle$, such that a_u is prime for each $u \leq w + 1$, and there is a sequence Y of primes, say $Y = \langle b_1, \ldots, b_y\rangle$, such that $\prod(X) = \prod(Y)$ but *not* $X \sim Y$; by lines **3** and **14**.

16. $\prod(X) = \prod(\langle a_1, a_2, \ldots, a_w\rangle) \cdot a_{w+1}$; by line **15** and the definition of $\prod$.

17. $(\prod\langle a_1, a_2, \ldots, a_w\rangle) \cdot a_{w+1} = \prod\langle b_1, b_2, \ldots, b_y\rangle$; by E from lines **15** and **16**.

18. $a_{w+1} \mid \prod\langle b_1, b_2, \ldots, b_y\rangle$; by line **17** and the definition of $|$.

19. $a_{w+1} = b_k$ for some $k \leq y$; by line **18** and Lemma 6-2-10.1.

20. $\prod\langle b_1, b_2, \ldots, b_y\rangle = \prod\langle b_1, b_2, \ldots, b_{k-1}, b_{k+1}, \ldots, b_y, b_k\rangle$; by the definition of $\sim$ and Theorem 6-2-4.

21. $\prod\langle b_1, b_2, \ldots, b_{k-1}, b_{k+1}, \ldots, b_y, b_k\rangle) = \langle\prod b_1, b_2, \ldots, b_{k-1}, b_{k+1}, \ldots, b_y\rangle) \cdot b_k$; by the definition of $\prod$.

22. $(\prod\langle a_1, a_2, \ldots, a_w\rangle) \cdot a_{w+1} = (\prod\langle b_1, b_2, \ldots, b_{k-1}, b_{k+1}, \ldots, b_y\rangle) \cdot b_k$; by E from lines **17**, **20**, and **21**.

23. $\prod\langle a_1, a_2, \ldots, a_w\rangle = \prod\langle b_1, b_2, \ldots, b_{k-1}, b_{k+1}, \ldots, b_y\rangle$; by the Right Cancellation Law for $\cdot$ from lines **19** and **22**.

24. Let $W = \langle a_1, a_2, \ldots, a_w\rangle$ and $V = \langle b_1, b_2, \ldots, b_{k-1}, b_{k+1}, \ldots, b_y\rangle$.

25. $w < x$; by line **14** and the definition of $<$.

26. $w \notin G$; by lines **3** and **25**.

27. W is a w-sequence of primes, V is a sequence of primes, and $\prod(W) = \prod(V)$; by lines **15**, **23**, and **24**.

28. $V \sim W$; by lines **1**, **26**, and **27**.

▶▶**29.** $X \sim Y$; by lines **15**, **19**, **24**, and **28**, and the definition of $\sim$.

30. If G is nonempty then there are sequences X, Y such that *not* $X \sim Y$ and $X \sim Y$; by the Deduction Theorem applied to lines **2** through **15** and **29**.

▶▶**31.** G is empty; by line **30**.

▶▶**32.** If X is any x-sequence and Y is any y-sequence, and if $X(u)$ is prime for every $u \leq x$ and $Y(u)$ is prime for every $u \leq y$, and if $\prod(X) = \prod(Y)$, then $X \sim Y$; by lines **1** and **31**.

Exercises

1. Show that if $X \sim Y$ then $\prod(X) = \prod(Y)$.

2. Show that if X is a y-sequence such that $X(u) = z$ for every $z \leq y$, then $\prod(X) = z^y$.

3. Show that if Υ is a y-sequence such that $\Upsilon(u) = u$ for every $u \leq y$, then $\prod(\Upsilon) = y$.

4. Show that if $\mathcal{Z}$ is a z-sequence such that $\mathcal{Z}(u) = (2 \cdot u) + 1$ for every $u \leq z$, then $\sum(\mathcal{Z}) = z^2 + (2 \cdot z)$.

5. Prove Theorem 6-2-8.

6. If q is any prime, if Υ is a y-sequence such that $\Upsilon(u)$ is prime for every $u \leq y$ and if $\prod(\Upsilon) = q$, then Υ is a 1-sequence.

VII

Applied Arithmetic: Counting[1]

1. The Number of Elements of a Set

Until now we have been dealing with what might be called a theory of "pure arithmetic." That is, we have been concerned purely with facts about formal operations and relations involving numbers, without regard to the question of how these concepts can be related to problems dealing with non-numerical phenomena. However, when we *use* arithmetic in our daily lives we encounter ideas which have not yet been touched on here. One of these ideas is that of counting, which constitutes what is perhaps the most basic type of application of arithmetic—the determination of the cardinality (the "how manyness") of an arbitrary set of objects.

Before defining what we mean by the number of elements of a set, let us refer back to the introductory remarks of the preceding chapter. The reader may recall that in seeking to define a general sum (or product) it was found convenient to introduce the concept of a segment. We denoted by seg(x), for any $x \in P$, the set of all those $y \in P$ such that $y \leq x$. (Cf. Definition 6-1-1.) Thus, for example, seg(4) is the set $\{1, 2, 3, 4\}$. It is quite natural to use the segment concept to give some indication of the number of elements of a set. Precisely how this is done is shown by the following definition.

DEFINITION 7-1-1. *If G is any set, and if x is any element of P, we define the phrase* **G has exactly x elements** (*or:* **the number of elements in G is x**) *to mean that there exists a one-one mapping of seg(x) onto G. Such a one-one mapping is called a* **counting function** *for G. If a set G has exactly x elements then x is sometimes called the* **cardinal number** *of the set G.*

For example, suppose that a, b, c are any distinct objects (i.e., $a \neq b$, $a \neq c$, and $b \neq c$). Suppose, too, that G is the set with a, b, c as its only elements (i.e., $G = \{a, b, c\}$). Then we can show that *G has exactly 3 elements;* for seg(3) $= \{1, 2, 3\}$, and if f is the function with domain seg(3) such that

[1] This chapter may be omitted entirely, although the reader may find the definitions and the statements of the theorems of considerable interest.

$f(1) = a$, $f(2) = c$, and $f(3) = b$, we easily see that f maps seg(3) onto G and that f is one-one. Notice that the function f serves the same purpose as a finger does when we count the elements of G by reciting aloud "one" while pointing to a, reciting "two" while pointing to c, and reciting "three" while pointing to b. The six different functions which map seg(3) onto G correspond to the six different orders in which we may count the elements of G.

Using Definition 7-1-1 there is one kind of set which we can count very easily, as the following theorem indicates.

THEOREM 7-1-2. *For any $x \in P$, seg(x) has exactly x elements.*

Proof. See Exercise 1 below.

The following theorem asserts the intuitively obvious fact that the number of elements in a set is unique—but though the fact may appear obvious the proof is far from simple.

THEOREM 7-1-3. *If G is any set such that G has exactly x elements and G also has exactly y elements, then $x = y$.*

Before proving this theorem it is convenient to establish several lemmas.

LEMMA 7-1-3.1. *If G, H, and K are any sets such that there is a one-one mapping f of G onto H and a one-one mapping g of H onto K, then the function h with domain G such that for any $a \in G$ we have $h(a) = g(f(a))$ is a one-one mapping of G onto K.*

Outline of Proof

1. Let G, H, and K be any sets such that there is a one-one mapping f of G onto H and a one-one mapping g of H onto K. Let h be the function with domain G such that $h(a) = g(f(a))$ for any $a \in G$.
2. If a, b are any elements of G such that $a \neq b$ then $f(a) \neq f(b)$ since f is one-one. Then, since g is one-one, $g(f(a)) \neq g(f(b))$. Hence $h(a) \neq h(b)$ and so h is one-one.
3. If p is any element in K, then since g is *onto* K there is an element $r \in H$ such that $g(r) = p$. Similarly, since f is onto H, there is an element $a \in G$ such that $f(a) = r$. Hence, $h(a) = g(f(a)) = g(r) = p$, and so h maps G onto K.

LEMMA 7-1-3.2. *If G and H are any sets, if there is a one-one mapping f of G onto H, and if either G or H has exactly x elements, then* **each** *of the sets G and H has exactly x elements.*

Outline of Proof

1. Suppose G is a set with exactly x elements, so that there is a one-one

mapping g of seg(x) onto G. Let H be a set such that there is a one-one mapping f of G onto H.

2. The function h with domain seg(x) such that $h(u) = f(g(u))$ for all $u \leq x$ is then (by Lemma 7-1-3.1) a one-one mapping of seg(x) onto H. Hence H has exactly x elements.

3. Suppose that H, rather than G, is assumed to have exactly x elements so that there is a one-one mapping k of seg(x) onto H. By Theorem 3-2-2 and line **1**, the function f^{-1} is a one-one mapping of H onto G. Hence the function f' such that $f'(u) = f^{-1}(k(u))$ for all $u \leq x$ is a one-one mapping of seg(x) onto G which shows G has exactly x elements.

LEMMA 7-1-3.3. *If G and H are any sets such that there is a one-one mapping of G onto H, if a is any element of G and if b is any element of H, then there is a one-one mapping g of G onto H such that $g(a) = b$.*

Outline of Proof

1. Let G and H be any sets such that there is a one-one mapping f of G onto H; let a be any element in G and b any element in H.

2. If $f(a) = b$ then f is the required mapping. Suppose, therefore, that $f(a) = c$ where $c \neq b$. Then there is an element $p \in G$ such that $f(p) = b$ (since f is *onto* H), and of course $p \neq a$ (since $f(a) \neq b$).

3. Let g be the function whose domain is G such that

$g(t) = f(t)$ if t is any element of G other than a or p,
$g(t) = b$ if $t = a$, and
$g(t) = c$ if $t = p$.

Clearly, g is a one-one mapping of G onto H and $g(a) = b$.

LEMMA 7-1-3.4. *If x is any number and G is any proper subset of seg(x) (i.e., if $G \subseteq$ seg(x) but $G \neq$ seg(x)), then there is no one-one mapping of seg(x) onto G.*

Outline of Proof

1. Let K be the set of all those numbers x such that for every proper subset G of seg(x) there is no one-one mapping of seg(x) onto G.

2. Since seg$(1) = \{1\}$, the only proper subset of seg(1) is the empty set. Clearly there is no mapping f of seg(1) onto the empty set, for if f were such a mapping we would have $f(1) \in$ empty set (when in fact the empty set has *no* elements). Hence $1 \in K$.

3. Let x be any element of K and let G be any proper subset of seg$(x + 1)$. *Suppose* there is a one-one mapping f of seg$(x + 1)$ onto G. Since $1 \neq x + 1$ we have $f(1) \neq f(x + 1)$, and so G has at least two elements.

4. *Case I.* Suppose $x + 1 \in G$. Then since G is a proper subset of $\text{seg}(x + 1)$ there is an element $w \leq x$ such that $w \notin G$. Hence the set $G - \{x + 1\}$ (i.e., the set obtained from G by deleting the number $x + 1$) is a proper subset of $\text{seg}(x)$. Moreover, by Lemma 7-1-3.3, we can assume $f(x + 1) = x + 1$. (That is, if f does not itself have this property we can find another one-one mapping of $\text{seg}(x + 1)$ onto G which does.) Then the function g with domain $\text{seg}(x)$, such that $g(u) = f(u)$ for every $u \leq x$, is a one-one mapping of $\text{seg}(x)$ onto $G - \{x + 1\}$. But this is impossible since $x \in K$ (see definition of K) and $G - \{x + 1\}$ is a proper subset of $\text{seg}(x)$. Hence our assumption that the function f exists is false, and so $(x + 1) \in K$ in this case.

5. *Case II.* Suppose $x + 1 \notin G$. In this case G is evidently a subset of $\text{seg}(x)$. If $f(x + 1) = v$, then $v \in G$, and so $G - \{v\}$ is a proper subset of $\text{seg}(x)$. The function h with domain $\text{seg}(x)$ such that $h(u) = f(u)$ for every $u \leq x$ is then a one-one function mapping $\text{seg}(x)$ onto $G - \{v\}$. Again, we have a contradiction with our hypothesis that $x \in K$ (see the definition of K) since $G - \{v\}$ is a proper subset of $\text{seg}(x)$. Hence $x + 1 \in K$ in this case also.

6. In either case we have $x + 1 \in K$. Since x was *any* element of K, we see that whenever $x \in K$ we have also $x + 1 \in K$. By step (**2**), $1 \in K$. Hence we can apply the Induction Axiom P4 and obtain $K = P$. That is, for all $x \in P$, if G is any proper subset of $\text{seg}(x)$ there is no one-one mapping of $\text{seg}(x)$ onto G.

With the aid of these four lemmas we can now indicate a proof for our theorem.

Outline of Proof of Theorem 7-1-3

1. Suppose G is any set such that G has exactly x elements and also G has exactly y elements. Then there is a one-one mapping g of $\text{seg}(x)$ onto G and a one-one mapping f of $\text{seg}(y)$ onto G.

2. *Suppose* $x \neq y$. Then either $x < y$ or $y < x$. Without loss of generality we can assume that $y < x$. Let h be the function with domain $\text{seg}(x)$ such that for all $u \leq x$, $h(u) = f^{-1}(g(u))$. Since f^{-1} and g are one-one and onto functions, then by Lemma 7-1-3.1 so also is h. In fact, h is a one-one mapping of $\text{seg}(x)$ onto $\text{seg}(y)$.

3. But $\text{seg}(y)$ is a proper subset of $\text{seg}(x)$, since from $y < x$ we infer that $x \notin \text{seg}(y)$ while for every $u \in \text{seg}(y)$ we have also $u \in \text{seg}(x)$. Hence we have a contradiction with Lemma 7-1-3.4. Thus our assumption that $x \neq y$ is false and so $x = y$.

The previous theorem shows us that no set can have two different numbers of elements. But are there sets which have *no* number of elements?

THEOREM 7-1-4. *There are sets G (of numbers) such that no matter which element x we select from P it is* **not** *the case that G has exactly x elements. P itself, and the null set, are examples of such sets.*

Outline of Proof

1. *Suppose* first that for some $x \in P$ there is a one-one mapping of seg(x) onto the null set. Since $1 \in$ seg(x), it follows that $f(1)$ is an element of the null set. But this is impossible since the null set contains no elements. Hence for no x is there a one-one mapping of seg(x) onto the null set. That is, for any $x \in P$ it is *not* the case that the null set has exactly x elements.
2. *Suppose* next that for some $x \in P$ there is a one-one mapping f of seg(x) onto P. Clearly $x \neq 1$, for otherwise the domain of f would be $\{1\}$ and so we would have $f(1) = 1$ and $f(1) = 2$ (because f is onto P), which is impossible since f is one-one and $1 \neq 2$. Thus $x > 1$. Since $x \in$ seg(x) we have $f(x) = y$ for some $y \in P$.
3. Let h be the function with domain P such that
   $h(u) = u$ for every $u < y$, and
   $h(u) = u + 1$ for every $u \geq y$.
   It is easy to see that h is a one-one mapping of P onto the set $P - \{y\}$.
4. Let k be the function defined on seg(x) such that $k(u) = h(f(u))$ for every $u \leq x$. By Lemma 7-1-3.1, k is a one-one mapping of seg(x) onto the set $P - \{y\}$.
5. Let g be the function defined on seg(x) such that $g(u) = f^{-1}(k(u))$ for every $u \leq x$. Again by Lemma 7-1-3.1, since f^{-1} is one-one, we conclude that g is a one-one mapping of seg(x) onto a subset of seg(x). Moreover, since $x = f^{-1}(y)$ and $y \notin P - \{y\}$, we see that $x \neq g(u)$ for all $u \leq x$. Thus g is a one-one mapping of seg(x) onto a *proper* subset of seg(x). But this is impossible by Lemma 7-1-3.4. Our assumption that there is a one-one mapping of seg(x) onto P must be false, since it has led to a consequence which we know is false. In other words, we have shown that for *no* x does P have exactly x elements.

We say that a set G is *finite* if either G is empty or if, for some positive integer x, G has exactly x elements. We say that a set G is *infinite* if it is not finite, i.e., if G is nonempty and if for no $x \in P$ is it the case that G has exactly x elements. The preceding theorem shows that P itself is an infinite set. As the reader no doubt realizes, most (but not all) of the theorems of this chapter deal with finite sets.

Our next theorem states a fact which again seems intuitively obvious—that the number of elements of a subset is not greater than the number of elements of the set itself.

THEOREM 7-1-5. *If G is any set with exactly x elements and if H is any nonempty subset of G, then there is a number $y \in P$ such that H has exactly y elements and $y \leq x$.*

To prove this we first establish the following lemma which, by Theorem 7-1-2, is a special case of our theorem.

LEMMA 7-1-5.1. *If x is any number and J is any nonempty subset of seg(x), then there exists a $y \leq x$ such that J has exactly y elements.*

Outline of Proof

▶▶ **1.** Let G be the set of all those numbers x such that for every nonempty subset J of seg(x) there exists a $y \leq x$ such that J has exactly y elements.

▶ **2.** Since the only nonempty subset of seg(1) is seg(1) itself, since seg(1) has exactly 1 element by Theorem 7-1-2, and finally since $1 \leq 1$, we see that $1 \in G$.

▶ **3.** Let x be any element of G. We wish to show that $x + 1 \in G$ also.

▶ **4.** Let J be any nonempty subset of seg$(x + 1)$. If $J =$ seg$(x + 1)$ then J has exactly $x + 1$ elements (by Theorem 7-1-2 again). So we consider the case where $J \neq$ seg$(x + 1)$, and in this case we shall show that J has exactly y elements for some $y < x + 1$. (This will establish that $x + 1 \in G$.)

5. *Case I.* Suppose $x + 1 \notin J$. In this case J is a nonempty subset of seg(x), and so there exists a $y \leq x$ such that J has exactly y elements (by lines **1** and **3**). But $x < x + 1$ and so $y < x + 1$.

6. *Case II.* Suppose $(x + 1) \in J$. Since $J \neq$ seg$(x + 1)$ there is a $z < x + 1$ such that $z \notin J$. Moreover, since $z < x + 1$ we have $z \leq x$ and so $z \in$ seg(x).

7. Let K be the subset of seg(x) such that for any $u \leq x$ we have $u \in K$ if and only if either $u \in J$ *or* $u = z$. Since $z \in K$, K is a *nonempty* subset of seg(x) and hence for some $y \leq x$ K has exactly y elements; (by lines **1** and **3**).

8. Now let f be the function mapping J into K such that:

$f(n) = n$ for every $n \in J$ such that $n \neq x + 1$, and
$f(n) = z$ if $n = x + 1$.

9. We can see that f is a one-one mapping of J into K. For if $n_1 \neq n_2$ and each is different from $x + 1$ then $f(n_1) = n_1$ and $f(n_2) = n_2$, and so $f(n_1) \neq f(n_2)$. On the other hand if $n \in J$ and $n \neq x + 1$ then $f(n) = n \in J$, but $z \notin J$ and so $f(n) \neq z$, i.e., $f(n) \neq f(x + 1)$. Thus f is one-one. Furthermore, f is *onto* K. For if $n \in K$ then either $n \in J$ or $n = z$; in the former case $f(n) = n$, and in the latter case $f(x + 1) = n$. Hence every element of K is a value of f and so f is *onto* K.

10. Since f is a one-one mapping of J onto K, and since K has exactly y elements, we see by Lemma 7-1-3.2 that J also has exactly y elements. But $y \leq x$. Hence $y < x + 1$.

▶▶ **11.** As mentioned in line **4**, cases I and II together show that $x + 1 \in G$. Thus whenever $x \in G$ we have also $x + 1 \in G$. Since $1 \in G$ by line **2**, it follows by the Induction Axiom that $G = P$. That is, for all $x \in P$, if J is a nonempty subset of seg(x) then for some $y \leq x$ J has exactly y elements.

Outline of Proof of Theorem 7-1-5

1. Let G be any set with exactly x elements and H any nonempty subset of G. Then there is a one-one mapping f of seg(x) onto G. If $H = G$, then H has exactly x elements and so we consider the case where $H \neq G$ and show that in this case H has exactly y elements for some $y < x$.

2. Let J be the subset of seg(x) consisting of all those $y \leq x$ such that $f(y) \in H$. Since H is nonempty so also is J. Hence by Lemma 7-1-5.1, we see that J has exactly y elements for some $y \leq x$.

3. Now let h be the mapping of H into J such that $h(u) = f^{-1}(u)$ for every $u \in H$. Since f^{-1} is a one-one mapping of G onto seg(x), and since $H \subseteq G$, it follows that whenever u, v are distinct elements of H we have $f^{-1}(u) \neq f^{-1}(v)$ and hence $h(u) \neq h(v)$. Thus h is one-one. Furthermore, h maps H *onto* J. For if $y \in J$, then from the definition of J there must be a $u \in H$ such that $f^{-1}(u) = y$, and so $h(u) = y$. Since J has exactly y elements and h is a one-one mapping of H onto J it follows by Lemma 7-1-3.2 that G also has exactly y elements.

EXERCISES

1. Show that for any $x \in P$ seg(x) has exactly x elements.

2.* Show that if G is the set of all one-one mappings of seg(x) onto seg(x), then G has exactly $x!$ elements.

2. *Addition and Multiplication*

We now come to a classical theorem about counting which provides the basis upon which most children are introduced to the arithmetical operation of addition. In order to formulate this theorem we first define two basic notions of the theory of sets.

If G and H are any sets then by $G \cup H$, the *union* of G and H, we mean the set of all those elements that are either in G or in H (i.e., $G \cup H$ is formed by "combining" the elements of G and H into one set). By $G \cap H$, the *intersection* of G and H, we mean the set of all those elements that are in both G and H, (i.e., $G \cap H$ is the "common part" of the sets G and H). If $G \cap H$ is the empty set, i.e., if $G \cap H = \phi$, so that G and H have no elements in common, then we say that G and H are *disjoint*.

It is customary, in explaining addition to a child, to start with two disjoint sets (perhaps four marbles in one pile, and three in another), form the union of these sets (bring the piles together), and then to say that the number of elements in the union is the sum of the number of elements in each of the two original sets. The following theorem furnishes the justification for this procedure.

THEOREM 7-2-1. *If G and K are any disjoint sets such that G has exactly x elements and K has exactly z elements, then $G \cup K$ has exactly $x + z$ elements.*

Outline of Proof

1. Let G and K be any disjoint sets such that G has exactly x elements and K has exactly z elements. Then there is a one-one mapping f of seg(x) onto G and a one-one mapping g of seg(z) onto K.

2. Let h be the function with domain seg$(x + z)$ such that

$$h(n) = f(n) \text{ for every } n \leq x, \text{ and}$$
$$h(n) = g(n - x) \text{ for every } n \in \text{seg}(x + z) \text{ such that } x < n.$$

To see that the second part of this definition is permissible, consider any n such that $x < n$ and $n \leq x + z$. Then either (**i**) $n < x + z$, in which case $n - x < z$, or (**ii**) $n = x + z$ and so $n - x = z$. In either case $n - x \leq z$ and so $g(n - x)$ is defined. By the Trichotomy Law it follows that h is defined for each element of seg$(x + z)$.

3. If a is any element of $G \cup K$, then either $a \in G$ or $a \in K$ by definition of "union". On the other hand a cannot be in *both* G and K since these sets are disjoint. Now if $a \in G$ then for some $n \leq x$ we have $f(n) = a$ and so $h(n) = a$. If $a \in K$, then for some $m \leq z$ we have $g(m) = a$. But then $x + m \leq x + z$ and $x < x + m$, so that $h(x + m) = g((x + m) - x) = g(m) = a$. Therefore, h maps seg $(x + z)$ *onto* $G \cup K$.

4. It remains only to show that h is one-one. Now we know that f is one-one on seg(x) and g is one-one on seg(z). Also, for any $a \in$ seg(x) and any $b \in$ seg(z) we have $f(a) \neq g(b)$ since $f(a) \in G$, $g(b) \in K$

and $G \cap K = \phi$. Hence, h is a one-one mapping of seg$(x + z)$ onto $G \cup H$. This means that $G \cup H$ has exactly $x + z$ elements.

The following theorem concerns the number of elements in the union of two given sets which are *not* disjoint.

THEOREM 7-2-2. *If G and K are any sets such that G has exactly x elements and K has exactly z elements, and if G and K are* **not** *disjoint, then there are numbers u and v in P such that $G \cup K$ has exactly u elements, $G \cap K$ has exactly v elements, and $u + v = x + z$.*

Outline of Proof

1. Let G be any set with exactly x elements, K any set with exactly z elements, and suppose that G and K are not disjoint so that $G \cap K$ has at least one element.

2. *Case I.* Suppose that one of the sets G or K is a subset of the other. Without loss of generality we may assume $G \subseteq K$. Then $G \cup K = K$ and $G \cap K = G$. Hence, taking $u = z$ and $v = x$ we have: $G \cup K$ has exactly u elements, $G \cap K$ has exactly v elements, and $u + v = x + z$.

3. *Case II.* Suppose that neither of the sets G, K is a subset of the other. Let G' be the set of all those elements of G which are not in $G \cap K$, and let K' be the set of all those elements of K which are not in $G \cap K$. Since neither set G or K is a subset of the other, G' and K' must be nonempty.

4. Since $G' \subseteq G$, $K' \subseteq K$, and $G \cap K \subseteq G$, we infer by Theorem 7-1-5 that each of the sets G', K', $G \cap K$ is finite. That is, there exist numbers w, v, and y such that G' has exactly w elements, $G \cap K$ has exactly v elements, and K' has exactly y elements.

5. Since $G = G' \cup (G \cap K)$ while G' and $G \cap K$ are disjoint, we can apply Theorem 7-2-1 to obtain $x = w + v$. Similarly, K' and $G \cap K$ are disjoint, and $K = K' \cup (G \cap K)$, so that $z = y + v$.

6. Since G' and K' are disjoint $G' \cup K'$ has exactly $w + y$ elements. Also $G \cup K = (G' \cup K') \cup (G \cap K)$ while $G' \cup K'$ and $G \cap K$ are disjoint, so that $G \cup K$ has exactly $(w + y) + v$ elements.

7. From step 5 we have $x = w + v$ and $z = y + v$, so that $x + z = (w + v) + (y + v) = [(w + y) + v] + v$ by use of the associative and commutative laws for $+$. Setting $u = (w + y) + v$ we get $x + z = u + v$; $G \cup K$ has exactly u elements (by step **6**); and $G \cap K$ has exactly v elements (by step **4**).

In the preceding two theorems we have observed that addition is employed to count the elements in the union of two given sets. Under what conditions do we use multiplication for counting purposes? The following theorem provides an answer. In passing, it might be noted that this theorem can be used to justify what is sometimes referred to as the fundamental principle of permutations—if one event can occur in any of h different ways and if, after it has occurred, another event can occur in any of k different ways, then both events can occur, in the stated order, in any of $h \cdot k$ different ways.

THEOREM 7-2-3. *If G and K are any sets such that G has exactly x elements and K has exactly z elements, then the set of all ordered pairs $\langle a, b\rangle$ such that $a \in G$ and $b \in K$ has exactly $x \cdot z$ elements.* [The set of all such ordered pairs is often called the **cartesian product** of G and K, and is denoted "$G \times K$."]

As in the case of earlier theorems in this chapter a lemma proves very useful in the proof.

LEMMA 7-2-3.1. *If G is any set with $x + 1$ elements, and if a is any element of G, then the set $G - \{a\}$ has x elements.*[2]

Outline of Proof

1. Let G be any set with exactly $x + 1$ elements and let a be any element of G. Since there is a one-one mapping of $\text{seg}(x + 1)$ onto G, it follows by Lemma 7-1-3.3 that there is a one-one mapping f of $\text{seg}(x + 1)$ onto G such that $f(x + 1) = a$.

2. Let h be the mapping of $\text{seg}(x)$ onto $G - \{a\}$ such that, for any $n \in \text{seg}(x)$, $h(n) = f(n)$. Clearly, since f is one-one, so also is h. Hence $G - \{a\}$ has exactly x elements.

Outline of Proof of Theorem 7-2-3

▶▶**1.** Let z be any number and K any set with exactly z elements.

▶▶**2.** Let H be the set of all those $x \in P$ such that for every set G with exactly x elements the set $G \times K$ has exactly $x \cdot z$ elements.

▶**3.** Consider any set G with exactly one element, say $G = \{b\}$. Then the mapping f of K into $G \times K$ such that for any $r \in K$ we have $f(r) = \langle b, r\rangle$ is certainly one-one and maps K onto $G \times K$. (For if $r_1 \neq r_2$ then $\langle b, r_1\rangle \neq \langle b, r_2\rangle$ and so $f(r_1) \neq f(r_2)$; also, if $\langle b, r\rangle$ is any element of $G \times K$ then $\langle b, r\rangle = f(r)$ and $r \in K$.) Since K has exactly z elements it then follows by Lemma 7-1-3.2 that $G \times K$ has exactly z elements. And since $z = 1 \cdot z$, we see that $G \times K$ has $x \cdot z$ elements.

[2] The set $G - \{a\}$ is the subset of G obtained from G by deleting the element a.

▶4. Now let x be any element of H, suppose that G is any set with exactly $x + 1$ elements, and consider any element a of G. Letting G' be the set $G - \{a\}$, we see by Lemma 7-2-3.1 that G' has exactly x elements. Since $x \in H$, we see (by line **2**) that $G' \times K$ has exactly $x \cdot z$ elements.

5. We now show that $G \times K = (G' \times K) \cup (\{a\} \times K)$. Since $G' \subseteq G$ and $\{a\} \subseteq G$, any element in either $G' \times K$ or $\{a\} \times K$ is in $G \times K$. That is $(G' \times K) \cup (\{a\} \times K) \subseteq G \times K$. On the other hand, if $\langle s, t\rangle$ is any element in $G \times K$ we have $\langle s, t\rangle \in (G' \times K) \cup (\{a\} \times K)$. (For if $s \neq a$, then $s \in G'$ and so $\langle s, t\rangle \in G' \times K$, while if $s = a$ then $\langle s, t\rangle = \langle a, t\rangle \in \{a\} \times K$.) Hence, $G \times K \subseteq (G' \times K) \cup (\{a\} \times K)$ and so the equality holds.

6. It is easy to see that $(G' \times K)$ and $(\{a\} \times K)$ have no elements in common. (For if $\langle s, t\rangle \in G' \times K$ then $s \neq a$ and so $\langle s, t\rangle \notin \{a\} \times K$.) By step **4**, $(G' \times K)$ has exactly $x \cdot z$ elements, and by step **3**, $\{a\} \times K$ has exactly $1 \cdot z$ elements. Hence by step **5** and Theorem 7-2-1 we compute that $G \times K$ has exactly $(x \cdot z) + (1 \cdot z)$ elements. But $(x \cdot z) + (1 \cdot z) = (x + 1) \cdot z$ and so $G \times K$ has exactly $(x + 1) \cdot z$ elements.

▶7. Since G was any set with $(x + 1)$ elements (line **4**), this shows that $(x + 1) \in H$ (line **2**).

▶▶8. Thus whenever $x \in H$ we also have $x + 1 \in H$. Since $1 \in H$ (by step **3**) we may apply the Induction Axiom P4 to obtain $H = P$. That is, for any numbers x and z, any set G with exactly x elements, and any set K with exactly z elements, the set $G \times K$ has exactly $x \cdot z$ elements.

In the final theorem of this chapter we show how the arithmetical operation of exponentiation may be used in counting the number of elements in a certain set.

THEOREM 7-2-4. *If G is any set with exactly x elements and if K is any set with exactly z elements then the set of all functions which map K into G has exactly x^z elements.* (We denote this set of functions by "G^K".)

LEMMA 7-2-4.1. *Let G and K be any nonempty sets. Suppose a is any element of K, and let $K' = K - \{a\}$. Then there is a one-one mapping α from G^K onto $G^{K'} \times G^{\{a\}}$.*

Outline of Proof

1. Let f be any element of G^K so that f is a function mapping K into G. Associated with any such f we define two other functions, f' and f''. We let f' be the function mapping K' into G such that $f'(b) = f(b)$ for every $b \in K'$, and we let f'' be the function mapping $\{a\}$ into G

such that $f''(a) = f(a)$. Clearly $f' \in G^{K'}$ and $f'' \in G^{\{a\}}$. Now let α be the mapping of G^K into $G^{K'} \times G^{\{a\}}$ such that $\alpha(f) = \langle f', f'' \rangle$ for every $f \in G^K$.

2. We first show that α is one-one. Indeed, if f_1 and f_2 are any elements of G^K such that $f_1 \neq f_2$, then (by the principle of extensionality for functions) for some $b \in K$ we must have $f_1(b) \neq f_2(b)$. If $b \in K'$, then $f_1'(b) \neq f_2'(b)$ and so $f_1' \neq f_2'$. If, on the other hand, $b \notin K'$, then $b = a$ so that $f_1(a) \neq f_2(a)$ and therefore $f_1'' \neq f_2''$. In either case $\langle f_1', f_1'' \rangle \neq \langle f_2', f_2'' \rangle$ and hence $\alpha(f_1) \neq \alpha(f_2)$. Therefore α is one-one.

3. Finally, to show that α maps G^K *onto* $G^{K'} \times G^{\{a\}}$, let $\langle g, h \rangle$ be any element of $G^{K'} \times G^{\{a\}}$. Let f be the function mapping K into G such that for any $b \in K$, $f(b) = g(b)$ if $b \in K'$ and $f(b) = h(a)$ if $b = a$. Clearly then, $f' = g$ and $f'' = h$ so that $\alpha(f) = \langle g, h \rangle$. This proves that α is *onto* $G^{K'} \times G^{\{a\}}$ and completes the proof of the lemma.

Outline of Proof of Theorem 7-2-4

▶▶**1.** Let x be any number in P and let G be any set with exactly x elements.

▶▶**2.** Let H be the set of all those $z \in P$ such that for every set K with exactly z elements the set G^K has exactly x^z elements.

▶**3.** Consider any set K with exactly 1 element, say $K = \{a\}$. To define a function mapping K into G, we need only specify which element of G is produced when the function acts on a. Now since G has exactly x elements, there is a one-one mapping f of seg(x) onto G. For each $y \leq x$, let f_y be the function mapping K into G such that $f_y(a) = f(y)$. And let α be the mapping of seg(x) into G^K such that for any $y \in$ seg(x), $\alpha(y) = f_y$. We shall show that α is one-one and maps seg(x) *onto* G^K.

4. If g is any element in G^K then $g(a) \in G$. But f maps seg(x) onto G, and so for some $y \leq x$, $f(y) = g(a)$. Since $f_y(a) = g(a)$ by line **3**, and since a is the only element in the domain of g (or of f_y), we get $g = f_y$. Hence $\alpha(y) = g$. But g was *any* element of G^K. Hence α maps seg(x) *onto* G^K.

▶**5.** To see that α is one-one, let y_1 and y_2 be any elements of seg(x) such that $y_1 \neq y_2$. Since f is one-one, $f(y_1) \neq f(y_2)$ and so $f_{y_1}(a) \neq f_{y_2}(a)$. But this means that $f_{y_1} \neq f_{y_2}$, and so $\alpha(y_1) \neq \alpha(y_2)$. Thus, α is a one-one mapping of seg(x) onto G^K, and hence G^K has exactly x elements. But $x = x^1$ and so G^K has exactly x^1 elements. Since K was *any* set with exactly 1 element (line **3**), we see from line **2** that $1 \in H$.

▶**6.** Now let z be any number in H. In order to show that $z + 1 \in H$ also, consider any set K with exactly $z + 1$ elements, and any element a of K. Then by Lemma 7-2-3.1, $K' = K - \{a\}$ has exactly z elements.

7. Since $z \in H$ and K' has exactly z elements we see (by line **2**) that $G^{K'}$ has exactly x^z elements. Since $1 \in H$ (line **5**), we see by line **2** that $G^{\{a\}}$ has exactly x^1 elements. By Theorem 7-2-3, $G^{K'} \times G^{\{a\}}$ has exactly $x^z \cdot x^1$ elements. But $x^z \cdot x^1 = x^{z+1}$ and so $G^{K'} \times G^{\{a\}}$ has exactly x^{z+1} elements.

▶**8.** By Lemma 7-2-4.1 there is a one-one mapping of G^K onto $G^{K'} \times G^{\{a\}}$, and so by Lemma 7-1-3.2, G^K has exactly x^{z+1} elements. Since K was *any* set with $z + 1$ elements (line **6**), it follows that $z + 1 \in H$ (line **2**).

▶▶**9.** Thus whenever $z \in H$ we have also $z + 1 \in H$. From step **5** we have $1 \in H$, and so (by the Induction Axiom P4), $H = P$. Hence for any numbers x and z, if G is any set with exactly x elements and K is any set with exactly z elements then G^K has exactly x^z elements.

EXERCISES

1.* Show that if G has exactly x elements, and if H is the set of all subsets of G, then H has exactly 2^x elements. *Hint*: Show that there is a one-one mapping of H onto $[\text{seg}(2)]^G$, and then use Theorem 7-2-1.

2. For any $x \in P$, let G_1, G_2, and G_3 be any sets each having exactly x elements, and such that $G_i \cap G_j = \phi$ whenever $i \neq j$. Show that $(G_1 \cup G_2) \cup G_3$ has exactly $3x$ elements.

VIII

The Natural Numbers: An Extension of the Number System

1. Introductory Remarks

In our daily use of arithmetic we need and use numbers other than the positive integers. In particular, we frequently encounter the number zero which shows up in commercial transactions, on the sports page, on test papers, and on innumerable other occasions. Among the familiar intuitive properties of the number zero is the fact that $0 + 1 = 1$. Is there a number with this property in the system determined by our axioms? Axiom P1 states that there is no number x in P such that $x + 1 = 1$, so there is certainly *no number in* P with this property. We do know, from Theorem 2-3-4, that for any number y *other than* 1 there does exist a number x in P such that $x + 1 = y$; in the language of high-school algebra, if $y \neq 1$, the "equation" $x + 1 = y$ does have a "root" in P. But if we wish to find a root of the equation $x + 1 = 1$ we must search for it somewhere other than in P. *We must enlarge our number system* in order to obtain a new number which can serve as a root of this equation. (The reader should note that although we have used the terms "equation" and "root," they have not been formally introduced into our theory. We use them in order to present the topic of number system extensions in terms which are familiar from elementary mathematics.)

In this chapter we shall concern ourselves with the problem of extending the number system which we have been studying so as to obtain a new number system in which, speaking intuitively, the equation $x + 1 = 1$ possesses a root. To achieve such an extension it will be necessary not only to enlarge our set of elements, P, to a new set, which we shall denote by "$\mathcal{N}$", but it will be necessary also to extend our binary operations $+$ and $\cdot$ to new operations which can act on any pair of elements of the enlarged set.

It might be well for the reader to refer back to the discussion of operations in Section 5 of Chapter I. A binary operation on a set A, it will be recalled, is a function whose domain is the set of all ordered pairs $\langle x, y \rangle$, for all $x, y \in A$ (and its range is a set of elements of this same set A). From the Principle of Extensionality for Functions it follows that a function (and hence an operation) is completely determined by the set of objects on which it acts, and the objects which it produces when it acts on each of these things. Since we must enlarge the set of objects on which the operations $+$ and $\cdot$ may act, we shall pass from the domain of these functions to a new domain, and hence *we need new functions*. These will be defined, after we have specified our set N, by specifying the elements which they produce as they act on each ordered pair of elements of N. To emphasize that these new operations are different from the original $+$ and $\cdot$ we shall use the symbols $+_N$ and $\cdot_N$ to denote them. This, to be sure, is a somewhat awkward notation, but it is essential, at this stage in our development, in order to keep clearly in mind that these are *new* operations, acting on all ordered pairs of elements *of the enlarged set* N, rather than the operations $+$ and $\cdot$ which are defined only for pairs of elements of the smaller set P.

Let us use the term *number system* to refer to any system consisting of a set of elements and two binary operations each of which can act on any ordered pair of these elements. Thus we have been considering the number system $\langle P, +, \cdot\rangle$, which we might conveniently denote by "$\mathcal{P}$", and we are seeking to construct a new number system $\langle N, +_N, \cdot_N\rangle$, denoted by "$\mathfrak{N}$".

As we have already indicated, we wish the set N to be an *enlargement* of P. That is, we wish to keep all of our original numbers in the new system, but to have new numbers also. In the language of set theory, we wish to form N in such a way that P is a *subset* of N $(P \subseteq N)$. Is there to be some similar relation between $+_N$ and $+$, and between $\cdot_N$ and $\cdot$? Indeed there is!

Since $+_N$ may act on any ordered pair of elements of N, and since we will have $P \subseteq N$, it follows that *in particular* $+_N$ can act on any ordered pair of elements *of* P. Now our purpose in changing from one number system to another is to obtain a new system which contains a root of a certain equation, but we have no wish to change the rules of addition *of the original numbers*. Hence we specify that whenever the operation $+_N$ acts on an ordered pair of numbers *which are in* P it shall give the same value as the original operation $+$ acting on this pair. In symbols: For all $x, y \in P$ we want $x +_N y = x + y$. Of course if x and y are elements of N but one of them is *not* in P then it makes no sense to write $x +_N y = x + y$ since the original operation *cannot act* on the pair $\langle x, y\rangle$ unless *both* x *and* y *are in* P.

In the same way we shall want to know that whenever $x, y \in P$ then $x \cdot_N y = x \cdot y$. Thus the number systems $\langle P, +, \cdot\rangle$ and $\langle N, +_N, \cdot_N\rangle$ will satisfy three conditions:

(**a**) For every $x \in P$ we have also $x \in N$ (i.e., $P \subseteq N$);
(**b**) For every $x, y \in P$ we have $x +_N y = x + y$;
(**c**) For every $x, y \in P$ we have $x \cdot_N y = x \cdot y$.

We express this relation between the two number systems by saying that $\langle N, +_N, \cdot_N\rangle$ *is an extension of* $\langle P, +, \cdot\rangle$.

The problem of obtaining a new number system in which the equation

$x +_N 1 = 1$ possesses a root can be made precise in more than one way, and it will be instructive to consider three alternative formulations. The simplest form of the problem is this:

Problem I. Can we find a number system $\langle N, +_N, \cdot_N \rangle$ with the following properties?

(i) $\langle N, +_N, \cdot_N \rangle$ is an extension of $\langle P, +, \cdot \rangle$, and
(ii) there is a number $z \in N$ such that $z +_N 1 = 1$.

As we shall see, there are many solutions to Problem I. To obtain one of these solutions we shall begin by constructing a set N, taking as its elements the elements of P and just *one other* element not in P.

Now one question which may naturally occur to the reader at this point is the following: Which new object shall we put into N? The answer is—it does not matter! For our interest in a number system is directed toward the problem of how we reckon with numbers—i.e., how the numbers are connected to one another by the basic operations—not in what kind of objects the numbers are. Technically, we express this interest by saying that we shall not distinguish between two number systems which are isomorphic; and of course systems can be isomorphic even though they have altogether different kinds of elements.

Granted that it does not matter *which* new element we add to the elements of P in forming N, we must still decide on one. Just how can we go about finding an element not in P? The reader will recall that the elements in P were not specified in our axiomatic theory, since "positive integer" was an undefined term. Thus, if we pick an element in a random fashion we run the danger of selecting an object which is already in P. For example, we could not select the Washington Monument for we have no guarantee that this object is not already in P. Do we know that there are any objects at all that are not in P? The answer is that there certainly are such objects. As we shall see when we come to the study of Set Theory (Chapter IX), no set can be an element of itself. Hence, P, for one thing, is an object which is not in P.

As we have mentioned, it is not important for us to know just which objects are not in P, in order to solve Problem I—it is sufficient to know that there is at least one such object. Let us therefore designate one of these objects by the symbol "0", and let N be the set consisting of all elements of P together with this element 0; in the symbolism of Set Theory, $N = P \cup \{0\}$. (Note that in other solutions we are free to take more than one new element in forming N from P.)

Now let us define $+_N$ to be the binary operation on N such that, for any $x, y \in N$,

$$x +_N y = \begin{cases} x + y \text{ if } x, y \text{ are both in } P; \\ 1 \text{ if either } x = 0 \text{ or } y = 0. \end{cases}$$

And similarly, let us define $\cdot_N$ by the rule

$$x \cdot_N y = \begin{cases} x \cdot y \text{ if } x, y \text{ are both in } P; \\ 0 \text{ if } x = 0 \text{ or } y = 0, \quad \text{for any } x, y \in N. \end{cases}$$

We see at once that conditions (**i**) and (**ii**) of Problem I are satisfied. Hence we have found a solution to Problem I.

The solution we have found is by no means unique. We have already indicated that some solutions can be found by adding more than one new element to P to obtain N (and extending the definition of $+_N$ and $\cdot_N$ to these new elements in an arbitrary way). Still another solution, different from the one given, can be obtained, for example, by using the set N and the operation $+_N$ as we defined them, but defining $\cdot_N$ as follows:

$$x \cdot_N y = \begin{cases} x \cdot y \text{ for all } x, y \in P; \\ 3 \text{ if } x = 0 \text{ or } y = 0. \end{cases}$$

No doubt the reader feels some dissatisfaction with all of the solutions we have presented for Problem I. If he analyzes the cause of this dissatisfaction he will find two reasons. First, in any of the proposed solutions we have $0 +_N 2 = 1$, and this does not "fit" with our intuitive knowledge of the number 0. Secondly, even if we had no previous intuitive knowledge of the way $+_N$ should act on an ordered pair $\langle x, y\rangle$ when one of the numbers is 0, we would be dissatisfied with our solutions for another reason: We find that many of the important laws which hold for the operations $+$ and $\cdot$ in the number system $\langle P, +, \cdot\rangle$ do not hold for the operations $+_N$ and $\cdot_N$ in the extensions $\langle N, +_N, \cdot_N\rangle$ found above.

Consider, for example, our first solution. We see immediately from the definitions of the operations $+_N$ and $\cdot_N$ that the commutative laws for these operations *do* hold. However, from the definition of $+_N$ we see that

$$(1 +_N 1) +_N 0 = (1 + 1) +_N 0 = 2 +_N 0 = 1,$$

and

$$1 +_N (1 +_N 0) = 1 +_N 1 = 1 + 1 = 2$$

so that

$$(1 +_N 1) +_N 0 \neq 1 +_N (1 +_N 0).$$

In other words, it is not the case that for all $x, y, z \in N$ we have $(x +_N y) +_N z = x +_N (y +_N z)$. That is, the associative law for $+_N$ fails in the system $\langle N, +_N, \cdot_N\rangle$. This observation suggests a modification of Problem I.

Problem II. Can we find a number system $\langle N, +_N, \cdot_N\rangle$ such that conditions (**i**) and (**ii**) of Problem I hold and in addition such that the following various basic laws all hold:

(iii) (**a**) The Commutative Law for $+_N$,
(**b**) The Commutative Law for $\cdot_N$,
(**c**) The Associative Law for $+_N$,
(**d**) The Associative Law for $\cdot_N$,
(**e**) The Left and Right Distributive Laws for $\cdot_N$ over $+_N$,
(**f**) The Left and Right Cancellation Laws for $+_N$, and
(**g**) The Left and Right Cancellation Laws for $\cdot_N$

It is evident that condition (**iii**) places quite a restriction on the kind of models considered. Our intuitive knowledge of arithmetical operations involving 0 might suggest that the cancellation properties listed in (**g**) fail to hold. The reader may not be surprised to learn, therefore, that in fact there is *no* solution to Problem II. Thus by adding condition (**iii**) to Problem I we pass from a problem with many solutions to one with *no* solutions. Naturally the question arises whether condition (**iii**) can be relaxed somewhat so as to obtain a problem with "essentially one" solution. (Just what meaning we give to the phrase "essentially one solution" will be discussed later.)

It turns out, as we shall see below, that the modification which we need make on condition (**iii**) in order to obtain a problem with an essentially unique solution is a minor one, namely, the deletion of part (**g**).

Problem III. Can we find a set N, a pair of binary operations $+_N$, and $\cdot_N$ on N, and an element $z \in N$ such that conditions (**i**) and (**ii**) of Problem I hold and, in addition, such that the following condition (**iii′**) holds?

(iii′) The following laws are all satisfied:
(**a**) The Commutative Law for $+_N$,
(**b**) The Commutative Law for $\cdot_N$,
(**c**) The Associative Law for $+_N$,
(**d**) The Associative Law for $\cdot_N$,
(**e**) The Left and Right Distributive Laws for $\cdot_N$ over $+_N$, and
(**f**) The Left and Right Cancellation Laws for $+_N$.

In addition to solving Problem III, we shall show that the solution obtained is "essentially unique." Furthermore, the condition (**iii**) (**g**) of Problem II (i.e., the Right Cancellation Law for $\cdot_N$) does *not* hold in the number system obtained as our solution to III. Obviously if Problem III has only one solution, and if (**iii**) (**g**) does not hold for this, then Problem II has no solution (as stated above).

EXERCISES

1. Does the associative law for $\cdot_N$ hold in the first solution given to Problem I? In the second?

2. Do any of the cancellation laws hold for the first solution to Problem I?

3. Make up a third solution to Problem I in which the commutative law for $+_N$ does not hold, but the left cancellation law for $+_N$ does hold.

4. List several other objects which you are *sure* could not be elements of P.

2. *The System* $\mathfrak{N} = \langle N, +_N, \cdot_N \rangle$

Let us set about the task of solving Problem III by defining a set N and two binary operations $+_N$ and $\cdot_N$ in a way which our intuitive experience naturally suggests.

DEFINITION 8-2-1. *The number system* $\mathfrak{N} = \langle N, +_N, \cdot_N \rangle$ *is to be obtained by selecting a set* N *and two binary operations* $+_N$, $\cdot_N$ *as follows:*

I. *Definition of* N. *Let* N *be any set* $P \cup \theta$, *where* θ *is a unit set containing a single element* 0 *which is some object not in* P. *Clearly* $P \subseteq N$. *The element* 0 *which is in* N *but not in* P *we shall call* **zero**. *The elements of* $N = \{0, 1, 2, 3, \ldots\}$ *will be called* **natural numbers.**[1]

II. *Definition of* $+_N$. *The binary operation* $+_N$ *on* N *is defined by the following rule:*

(i) *For any* $x, y \in P$ *we set* $x +_N y = x + y$; (i.e., the addition operation in the new number system, when acting on elements of P, yields the same results as the addition operation $+$ whose domain is P).

(ii) *For any* $x \in N$ *we set*

(a) $x +_N 0 = x$, *and*

(b) $0 +_N x = x$.

III. *Definition of* $\cdot_N$. *The binary operation* $\cdot_N$ *on* N *is defined by the following rule:*

(i) *For any* $x, y \in P$ *we set* $x \cdot_N y = x \cdot y$;

(ii) *For any* $x \in N$ *we set*

(a) $x \cdot_N 0 = 0$, *and*

(b) $0 \cdot_N x = 0$.

The number system $\langle N, +_N, \cdot_N \rangle$, as defined above, is now completely determined. Certainly it seems to be consistent with our intuitive knowledge of zero, and of the arithmetical operations involving zero. That this system is actually a solution to Problem III is a fact which will therefore seem plausible, but which must be verified by logical proof. This is done in the sequence of theorems which complete this section.

[1] This use of the term *natural numbers* is common but by no means universal. Many authors use this phrase to describe the elements of $P = \{1, 2, 3, \ldots\}$, which we have called the *positive integers*.

THEOREM 8-2-2. *The system* $\langle N, +_N, \cdot_N \rangle$ *is an extension of* $\langle P, +, \cdot \rangle$.

Outline of Proof

By our definition of *extension*, the system $\langle N, +_N, \cdot_N \rangle$ is an extension of $\langle P, +, \cdot \rangle$ if and only if the following three conditions hold:

(i) $P \subseteq N$,
(ii) For any $x, y \in P$ we have $x +_N y = x + y$,
(iii) For any $x, y \in P$ we have $x \cdot_N y = x \cdot y$.

Each of these conditions follows immediately from parts **I**, **II**, and **III**, respectively, of Definition 8-2-1.

Theorem 8-2-2 assures us that the system $\langle N, +_N, \cdot_N \rangle$ satisfies part **(i)** of Problem III. To see that **(ii)** holds also we have only to notice that $0 +_N 1 = 1$ by Definition 8-2-1 (**III**). To show that part **(iii)** is satisfied also it is necessary to establish that various commutative, associative, distributive, and cancellation properties hold for the new system. That this is indeed the case is shown by the following theorems.

THEOREM 8-2-3. *If* x, y *and* z *are any elements of* N, *then:*

(i) $x +_N y = y +_N x$,
(ii) $x \cdot_N y = y \cdot_N x$,
(iii) $(x +_N y) +_N z = x +_N (y +_N z)$,
(iv) $(x \cdot_N y) \cdot_N z = x \cdot_N (y \cdot_N z)$,
(v) $z \cdot_N (x +_N y) = z \cdot_N x +_N z \cdot_N y$,
(vi) $(x +_N y) \cdot_N z = x \cdot_N z +_N y \cdot_N z$, *and*
(vii) $x \cdot_N 1 = x$.

Proof

We shall give proofs of **(iii)** and **(vii)** only. The proofs of the other parts of the theorem are very similar, and will be left to the reader in the exercises. The general method of proof is to consider all possible cases for x, y and z (as to whether each is an element of P, or is 0), and to make use of the corresponding law for the number system $\langle P, +, \cdot \rangle$.

Proof of **(iii)**

We divide the proof into several cases. For clarity we shall treat each case in a separate lemma.

LEMMA 8-2-3.1. *If* x, y, z *are any elements of* P, *then* $(x +_N y) +_N z = x +_N (y +_N z)$.

Proof

▶▶**1.** Let x, y, z be any elements of P.

▶2. $x +_N y = x + y$ and $y +_N z = y + z$; by line **1** and the definition of $+_N$.

3. $x + y$ and $y + z$ are elements of P; by line **1**, since $+$ is an operation on P.

4. $x +_N y$ and $y +_N z$ are elements of P; by E applied to lines **2** and **3**.

▶5. $(x +_N y) +_N z = (x +_N y) + z$ and $x +_N (y +_N z) = x + (y +_N z)$; by lines **1** and **4** and the definition of $+_N$.

▶6. $(x +_N y) +_N z = (x + y) + z$ and $x +_N (y +_N z) = x + (y + z)$; by E applied to lines **2** and **5**.

7. $(x + y) + z = x + (y + z)$; by line **1** and Theorem 2-4-1.

▶▶8. $(x +_N y) +_N z = x +_N (y +_N z)$; by E applied to lines **6** and **7**.

9. If x, y, z are any elements of P then $(x +_N y) +_N z = x +_N (y +_N z)$; by the Deduction Theorem applied to lines **1** through **8**.

LEMMA 8-2-3.2. *If* $x = 0$ *and if* y, z *are any elements of* N *then* $(x +_N y) +_N z = x +_N (y +_N z)$.

Proof

▶▶1. Let $x = 0$ and let y, z be any elements of N.

2. $(x +_N y) +_N z = (0 +_N y) +_N z$; by E and line **1**.

3. $0 +_N y = y$; by line **1** and the definition of $+_N$.

▶4. $(x +_N y) +_N z = y +_N z$; by E applied to lines **2** and **3**.

5. $x +_N (y +_N z) = 0 +_N (y +_N z)$; by E and line **1**.

6. $0 +_N (y +_N z) = y +_N z$; by the definition of $+_N$.

▶7. $x +_N (y +_N z) = y +_N z$; by E applied to lines **5** and **6**.

▶▶8. $(x +_N y) +_N z = x +_N (y +_N z)$; by E applied to lines **4** and **7**.

9. If $x = 0$ and y, z are any elements of N then $(x +_N y) +_N z = z +_N (y +_N z)$; by the Deduction Theorem applied to lines **1** through **8**.

LEMMA 8-2-3.3 *If* $y = 0$ *and* x, z *are any elements of* N *then* $(x +_N y) +_N z = x +_N (y +_N z)$.

Proof. Similar to that of Lemma 8-2-3.2.

LEMMA 8-2-3.4. *If* $z = 0$ *and* x, y *are any elements of* N *then* $(x +_N y) +_N z = x +_N (y +_N z)$.

Proof. Similar to that of Lemma 8-2-3.2.

Now the lemmas are combined to yield a proof of Theorem 8-2-3 as follows.

Proof of Theorem

1. Let x, y, z be any elements of N.
2. Either x, y, z are elements of P, or $x = 0$, or $y = 0$, or $z = 0$; by Definition 8-2-1.
3. $(x +_N y) +_N z = x +_N (y +_N z)$; by lines **1** and **2** and Lemmas 8-2-3.1, 2, 3, and 4.
4. If x, y, z are any elements of N then $(x +_N y) +_N z = x +_N (y +_N z)$; by the Deduction Theorem applied to lines **1** through **3**.

The type of proof we have presented here is called a *proof by cases.* We have considered four different cases (Lemmas 8-2-3.1 through 4), in each of which the conclusion of **(iii)** is seen to hold. These cases are not mutually exclusive—for example, ($x = 0$ and $y = 0$ and $z = 1$) falls under both Lemmas 8-2-3.2 and 3—but that is immaterial. What is essential is that our four cases are exhaustive—that is, for *any* $x, y, z \in N$, *at least one* of the four cases is applicable. This is obviously the situation, for by Definition 8-2-1 (I) any three elements of N are either all elements of P, or at least one of them is zero. Thus the proof of part **(iii)** has been completed for all possible cases.

Proof of **(vii)**

Again, this will be a proof by cases, but since only two cases are involved we shall not use the device of introducing separate lemmas.

▶▶ **1.** Let x be any element of N.
▶▶ **2.** Either $x = 0$ or $x \neq 0$.

▶ **3.** *Case I.* Assume $x = 0$.
4. $x \cdot_N 1 = 0 \cdot_N 1$; by E from line **3**.
5. $0 \cdot_N 1 = 0$; by the definition of $\cdot_N$ (Definition 8-2-1).
▶ **6.** $x \cdot_N 1 = 0$; by E from lines **4** and **5**.
7. $x \cdot_N 1 = x$; by E from lines **3** and **6**.
▶▶ **8.** If $x = 0$ then $x \cdot_N 1 = x$; by the Deduction Theorem applied to lines **3** through **7**.

▶ **9.** *Case II.* Assume $x \neq 0$.
10. $x \in P$; by lines **1** and **9** and the definition of N (Definition 8-2-1).
11. $1 \in P$; by definition of the number system $\langle P, 1, + \rangle$.
▶ **12.** $x \cdot_N 1 = x \cdot 1$; by lines **10** and **11** and the definition of $\cdot_N$.
▶ **13.** $x \cdot 1 = x$; by Definition 4-1-2.
14. $x \cdot_N 1 = x$; by E applied to lines **12** and **13**.
▶▶ **15.** If $x \neq 0$ then $x \cdot_N 1 = x$; by the Deduction Theorem applied to lines **9** through **14**.

16. If x is any element of N then $x \cdot_N 1 = x$; by the Deduction Theorem applied to lines **1** through **2**, **8**, and **15**.

Next, let us consider cancellation laws for the system $\mathfrak{N}$. Our intuitive experience with the natural numbers suggests that the cancellation laws for $+_N$ might be expected to hold, but that the cancellation laws for $\cdot_N$ must be modified to exclude division by zero. The exact situation is described in the next theorem.

THEOREM 8-2-4.

Part I. For any $x, y, z \in N$,

(i) *if* $x +_N z = y +_N z$, *then* $x = y$ (*the Right Cancellation Law for* $+_N$),
(ii) *if* $z +_N x = z +_N y$, *then* $x = y$ (*the Left Cancellation Law for* $+_N$).

Part II. For any $x, y \in N$, *and for any* $z \in P$ (*i.e., for any* z *in* N *other than* 0),

(i) *if* $x \cdot_N z = y \cdot_N z$, *then* $x = y$ (*the Right Cancellation Law for* $\cdot_N$),
(ii) *if* $z \cdot_N x = z \cdot_N y$, *then* $x = y$ (*the Left Cancellation Law for* $\cdot_N$).

Part III. The Cancellation Laws for $\cdot_N$ *do* **not** *hold for* **all** *elements* x, y, z *of* N.

Proof

First, let us prove Part III. To do this, it will be sufficient to exhibit three elements x, y and z of N for which the cancellation laws for $\cdot_N$ fail. Consider, for example, the elements 0, 1, 2. Clearly $0 \cdot_N 1 = 0 \cdot_N 2$, since both $0 \cdot_N 1$ and $0 \cdot_N 2$ are equal to 0 by Definition 8-2-1 (III), but it is *not* true that $1 = 2$, which we could infer from the equation $0 \cdot_N 1 = 0 \cdot_N 2$ if the left cancellation law held for these elements 0, 1, 2. Similarly, it is easy to see that the right cancellation law fails for these elements.

To prove Parts I and II it will be enough to prove just one of the two statements under each part. The other follows at once from the commutativity of $+_N$ and $\cdot_N$ (Theorem 8-2-3).

Proof of Part I (**ii**)

We are to show that for all $x, y, z \in N$, if $z +_N x = z +_N y$ then $x = y$. This can be done by proving the equivalent statement: for all $x, y, z \in N$, if $x \neq y$, then $z +_N x \neq z +_N y$. We shall use the latter form, hypothesizing that x, y, z are any elements of N such that $x \neq y$. The proof will be by cases. The first case will be handled in detail, but the proofs in the remaining cases will be outlined informally.

Case I. $x, y, z \in P$.

1. Let x, y, z be any elements of P such that $x \neq y$.
2. $z +_N x = z + x$ and $z +_N y = z + y$; by line **1** and the definition of $+_N$ (Definition 8-2-1).

3. $z + x \neq z + y$; by line **1** and the left cancellation law for $+$ (Corollary 2-4-3.1).
4. $z +_N x \neq z +_N y$; by E applied to lines **2** and **3**.
5. If x, y, z are any elements of P such that $x \neq y$ then $z +_N x \neq z +_N y$; by the Deduction Theorem applied to lines **1** through **4**.

Case II. Suppose $z = 0$. Then $z +_N x = 0 +_N x = x$ and $z +_N y = 0 +_N y = y$. But $x \neq y$. Therefore, $z +_N x \neq z +_N y$.

Case III. Suppose $z \neq 0$ and $x = 0$. Then $y \in P$ (since $x \neq y$) and $z \in P$. Hence $z +_N x = z +_N 0 = z$, and $z +_N y = z + y$. But $z + y \neq z$, by the Trichotomy Law, since $z < z + y$ (by the definition of $<$). Hence $z +_N x \neq z +_N y$.

Case IV. Suppose $z \neq 0$ and $y = 0$. The proof of this case is similar to that of Case III.

Cases **I** through IV are exhaustive, and so in all cases we have $z +_N x \neq z +_N y$.

Proof of Part II (**ii**)

We shall take x, y, z as any elements of N such that $z \cdot_N x = z \cdot_N y$ and $z \neq 0$. As before, we shall give a proof by cases, writing it up in detail for the case $x, y \in P$ and merely outlining the proof for the remaining cases.

Case I. $x, y \in P$.

1. Let x, y, z be any elements of P such that $z \cdot_N x = z \cdot_N y$.
2. $z \cdot_N x = z \cdot x$ and $z \cdot_N y = z \cdot y$; by line **1** and the definition of $\cdot_N$ (Definition 8-2-1).
3. $z \cdot x = z \cdot y$; by E from lines **1** and **2**.
4. $x = y$; by the left cancellation law for $\cdot$ (Corollary 4-1-7.1).
5. If x, y, z are any elements of P such that $z \cdot_N x = z \cdot_N y$, then $x = y$; by the Deduction Theorem applied to lines **1** through **4**.

Case II. Suppose $x \in P$ and $y = 0$. Then $z \cdot_N x = z \cdot x$ and $z \cdot_N y = 0$. But $z \cdot x \in P$, since the binary operation $\cdot$ is acting here on a pair of elements of P, and $0 \notin P$. Hence $z \cdot x \neq 0$; i.e., $z \cdot_N x \neq z \cdot_N y$. But this contradicts our choice of x, y, z. Thus our choice of x, y, z precludes Case II: this case cannot arise.

Case III. Suppose $x = 0$ and $y \in P$. By an argument similar to that used in Case II we can show that this also cannot arise when x, y, z are chosen so that $z \cdot_N x = z \cdot_N y$.

Case IV. Suppose $x = 0$ and $y = 0$. Then clearly $x = y$.

Cases I through IV are exhaustive, so we see that in every possible case $x = y$ and the proof of Part II (**ii**) is complete.

We have now shown, in Theorems 8-2-2, 8-2-3, and 8-2-4, that the system $\mathfrak{N} = \langle \mathcal{N}, +_N, \cdot_N \rangle$ which is defined in Definition 8-2-1 meets all the requirements for a solution of Problem III with the exception of condition (**ii**). As remarked above, this condition is simply checked by noticing that $0 +_N 1 = 1$, by Definition 8-2-1. Actually, a much more powerful result than this follows readily from our definition of $\mathfrak{N}$, as we see in the next theorem.

THEOREM 8-2-5. *There exists a unique element $z \in \mathcal{N}$ such that for any element a of $\mathcal{N}$ we have $z +_N a = a$.*

Outline of Proof

Take $z = 0$. Then for any $a \in \mathcal{N}$ we have $z +_N a = 0 +_N a = a$, by Definition 8-2-1.

There remains the question of uniqueness. Could there be some element z_1 in $\mathcal{N}$, *other* than 0, such that $z_1 +_N a = a$? *Suppose* that such an element z_1 exists. Then since $0 +_N a = a$ by definition of $+_N$ we obtain $z_1 +_N a = 0 +_N a$ by E. Using the right cancellation law for $+_N$ we then obtain $z_1 = 0$, contradicting our assumption that $z_1 \neq 0$. This contradiction shows that 0 is the *unique* solution of the equation $z +_N a = a$.

EXERCISES

1. Prove part (v) of Theorem 8-2-3.
2. How would you define an ordering relation $<_N$ for the number system $\langle \mathcal{N}, +_N, \cdot_N \rangle$? After giving a definition prove that this relation is transitive. (Compare Theorem 2-5-2.)

3. *On the Uniqueness of the System $\langle N, +_N, \cdot_N \rangle$.*

Now let us turn to the one remaining question suggested by Problem III. We have established, by Theorems 8-2-2 through 8-2-5, that the system $\langle \mathcal{N}, +_N, \cdot_N \rangle$ which is given by Definition 8-2-1 is indeed a solution to the problem. But is this the *only* solution? Might there be some other extension, entirely different from $\langle \mathcal{N}, +_N, \cdot_N \rangle$, which would also serve our purpose? This question is answered in the following theorem which shows that, in a certain sense, the solution given to Problem III is unique.

THEOREM 8-3-1. *Let $\langle Q, +_Q, \cdot_Q \rangle$ be any number system such that*

(**i**) *$\langle Q, +_Q, \cdot_Q \rangle$ is an extension of $\langle P, +, \cdot \rangle$;*
(**ii**) *There is an element z_Q in Q such that $z_Q +_Q 1 = 1$;*

(iii) *The commutative, associative, and cancellation laws hold for* $+_Q$, *and the left and right distributive laws hold for* $\cdot_Q$ *over* $+_Q$.

Then we must have

$$\text{(a)} \begin{cases} x +_Q y = x + y \text{ if } x, y \in P \\ z_Q +_Q y = y \text{ for all } y \in Q \\ x +_Q z_Q = x \text{ for all } x \in Q; \end{cases}$$

$$\text{(b)} \begin{cases} x \cdot_Q y = x \cdot y \text{ if } x, y \in P \\ z_Q \cdot_Q y = z_Q \text{ if } y \in Q \\ x \cdot_Q z_Q = z_Q \text{ if } x \in Q; \end{cases}$$

(c) *There is an isomorphism* h *of* $\langle N, +_N, \cdot_N\rangle$ *into* $\langle Q, +_Q, \cdot_Q\rangle$; *in fact,* h *will be a one-one mapping of* N *into* Q *such that, for all* $x, y \in N$ $h(x +_N y) = h(x) +_Q h(y)$ *and* $h(x \cdot_N y) = h(x) \cdot_Q h(y)$. *Furthermore,* $h(0) = z_Q$.

We shall outline the proof of this theorem.

Part (a).

Case I. Suppose $x, y \in P$. Then the proof is obvious by (**i**).

Case II. Suppose y is any element of Q. Then

$$\begin{aligned} 1 +_Q (z_Q +_Q y) &= (z_Q +_Q 1) +_Q y; \quad \text{by (iii).} \\ &= 1 +_Q y; \quad \text{by (ii) and E.} \end{aligned}$$

Hence

$$z_Q +_Q y = y; \quad \text{by (iii).}$$

Case III. Suppose x is any element of Q. In this case the proof is similar to that of Case II.

Part (b).

Case I. Suppose $x, y \in P$. Then the proof is obvious because of (**i**).

Case II. Suppose y is any element of Q. Then

$$\begin{aligned} z_Q \cdot_Q y +_Q 1 \cdot_Q y &= (z_Q +_Q 1) \cdot_Q y; \quad \text{by (iii).} \\ &= 1 \cdot_Q y; \quad \text{by (ii) and E.} \\ &= z_Q +_Q 1 \cdot_Q y; \quad \text{by } (a) \text{ which has already been proved.} \end{aligned}$$

Hence,

$$z_Q \cdot_Q y = z_Q; \quad \text{by (iii).}$$

Case III. Suppose x is any element of Q. Then we get $x \cdot_Q z_Q = z_Q$ by reasoning similar to Case II.

Part (c). We define h to be the function with domain N such that for any $x \in N$,

$$h(x) = \begin{cases} x \text{ if } x \in P \\ z_Q \text{ if } x = 0. \end{cases}$$

Clearly h maps $\mathcal{N}$ into $\mathcal{Q}$, since h is defined to act on any element of $\mathcal{N}$ and in each case the result of the action is an element of $\mathcal{Q}$. Also h is one-one; i.e., whenever $x, y \in \mathcal{N}$ and $x \neq y$, then $h(x) \neq h(y)$. To show this, suppose first that both x and y are in P. Then $h(x) = x$ and $h(y) = y$. And since $x \neq y$, we have $h(x) \neq h(y)$. If, on the other hand one of x, y is 0, say $x = 0$, and y is any element in P, then $h(x) = z_Q$ and $h(y) = y$. Now if $z_Q = y$, then $y + 1 = 1$, by (**ii**). But $y \in P$ and so $y + 1 \neq 1$ by Axiom P1. Hence $z_Q \neq y$, and therefore $h(x) \neq h(y)$.

Now we wish to show that for any $x, y \in \mathcal{N}$ we have $h(x +_N y) = h(x) +_Q h(y)$.

Case I. Suppose $x, y \in P$. Then

$h(x +_N y) = h(x + y)$; by (**i**).
$= x + y$; by the definition of h, since $x + y \in P$.
$= h(x) + h(y)$; by E, since $h(x) = x$ and $h(y) = y$.
$= h(x) +_Q h(y)$; again by (**i**).

Case II. Suppose $x = 0$ and y is any element of $\mathcal{N}$. Then

$h(x +_N y) = h(0 +_N y)$; by E.
$= h(y)$; since $0 +_N y = y$ by the definition of $+_N$.
$= z_Q +_Q h(y)$; by (*a*).

$= h(0) +_Q h(y)$; by the definition of h.
$= h(x) +_Q h(y)$; by E.

Case III. Suppose $x \in \mathcal{N}$ and $y = 0$. Then by reasoning similar to that used in Case II we get $h(x +_N y) = h(x) +_Q h(y)$.

We shall leave as an exercise for the reader to show that for all $x, y \in \mathcal{N}$ we have $h(x \cdot_N y) = h(x) \cdot_Q h(y)$. (See Exercise 2.) Then the proof of Theorem 8-3-1 will be complete.

Let us fix our attention now on Part (**c**) of the last theorem. The function h described in Part (**c**) is called an *isomorphism* of the number system $\langle \mathcal{N}, +_N, \cdot_N \rangle$ *into* the number system $\langle \mathcal{Q}, +_Q, \cdot_Q \rangle$ which *carries* 0 into z_Q. The fact that such an isomorphism exists, according to Part (**c**), does *not* entitle us to say that the number systems $\langle \mathcal{N}, +_N, \cdot_N \rangle$ and $\langle \mathcal{Q}, +_Q, \cdot_Q \rangle$ are *isomorphic*, because h is not necessarily *onto* $\mathcal{Q}$; i.e., there may be numbers in $\mathcal{Q}$ which are not values of the function h. Thus we are not entitled to say that the system $\langle \mathcal{Q}, +_Q, \cdot_Q \rangle$ and $\langle \mathcal{N}, +_N, \cdot_N \rangle$ are "essentially the same." But even though the system $\langle \mathcal{Q}, +_Q, \cdot_Q \rangle$ may not be the same number system as $\langle \mathcal{N}, +_N, \cdot_N \rangle$, the fact that there exists such an isomorphism h may be interpreted by saying that the two systems present "essentially the same" *solution to Problem III.* In this sense we might say that the system $\langle \mathcal{N}, +_N, \cdot_N \rangle$ is a sort of minimal solution to Problem III in that any other system which solves the problem contains a part which is isomorphic to it.

EXERCISES

1. Find number systems $\langle Q, +_Q, \cdot_Q \rangle$ which satisfy all of the hypotheses of Theorem 8-3-1, except that
   (a) the commutative law for $\cdot_Q$ fails;
   (b) the commutative law for $\cdot_Q$ holds, but the associative law for $\cdot_Q$ fails.
2. Complete the proof of (c) in Theorem 8-3-1.
3. Give a detailed proof of Theorem 8-3-1.

4. *Ordering Relations*

We have seen how multiplication, which was a defined concept in the number system $\langle P, +, \cdot \rangle$ (addition, the reader may recall, was an undefined concept), can be extended to a defined operation in the system $\langle N, +_N, \cdot_N \rangle$. What can be said about some of the other defined concepts? Can they, too, be extended to similar concepts in the new system?

In this section we shall consider extensions of the ordering relations. Intuitively, it seems obvious that the relations $<$ and $\leq$ can be extended to the system $\langle N, +_N, \cdot_N \rangle$. But would these extensions be *new* relations, or are they simply the same old relations? In the latter case, of course, we could simply use the already established notation.

The *less than* relation, which was defined to hold for certain ordered pairs of elements *of P* (and not for others), is *not* identical with a binary relation *on N*. For in the case of an ordered pair of elements of N, if one or both of these elements is 0 then we have no information as to whether the relation $<$ holds for the ordered pair or not. In general, two binary relations which are defined on different fields cannot be the same.

Accordingly, we adopt the notation $<_N$ to indicate the *less than* relation whose field is N, and we define this relation, in terms of the relation $<$ whose field is P, as follows.

DEFINITION 8-4-1. *We define $<_N$ to be the binary relation on N such that*
- (i) *If x, y are any elements of P, then $x <_N y$ if and only if $x < y$. (We say that $<_N$ is an* **extension** *of $<$.)*
- (ii) *If $x = 0$ and y is any element of P, then $x <_N y$.*
- (iii) *If x is any element of N and $y = 0$, then* **not** *$x <_N y$.*

As regards the form of this definition, notice that all ordered pairs $\langle x, y \rangle$ have been divided into three mutually exclusive and exhaustive classes, (i), (ii), and (iii), and in each class we have specified precisely for which ordered pairs the relation $<_N$ holds and for which it does not.

The theorems regarding this extended notion of *less than*, $<_N$, resemble the corresponding theorems regarding $<$ and we shall combine many of them into one.

THEOREM 8-4-2.

(**a**) $<_N$ *is an extension of* $<$: *Whenever* $x, y \in P$ *then* $x <_N y$ *if and only if* $x < y$.

(**b**) $<_N$ *is transitive: If* x, y, z *are any elements of* N *such that* $x <_N y$ *and* $y <_N z$, *then also* $x <_N z$.

(**c**) $<_N$ *satisfies the Trichotomy Law: For any* $x, y \in N$, *either* $x <_N y$ *or* $x = y$ *or* $y <_N x$—*and no two of these hold simultaneously.*

(**d**) *For all* $x, y, z \in N$ *we have* $(x +_N z) <_N (y +_N z)$ *if and only if* $x <_N y$.

(**e**) *If* x, y, z *are any elements of* N *such that* $z \neq 0$, *then* $x \cdot_N z <_N y \cdot_N z$ *if and only if* $x <_N y$.

(**f**) *For all* $x, y \in N$, $x <_N y$ *if and only if* $x +_N u = y$ *for some* $u \in P$.

Proof

Part (**a**) is immediate from Part (**i**) of Definition 8-3-1. The proofs of the remaining parts of the theorems proceed by cases. We shall carry out the proof for Part (**f**) and leave the remaining parts for the reader. (See Exercise 3 below.)

Proof of (**f**)

▶▶ **1.** Let x, y be any elements of N.

▶▶ **2.** Either $x, y \in P$, or $x = 0$ and $y \in P$, or $y = 0$ and $x \in N$; by the definition of N.

▶ **3.** *Case I.* Assume $x, y \in P$.

4. $x <_N y$ if and only if $x < y$; by line **3** and the definition of $<_N$.

5. $x <_N y$ if and only if $x + u = y$ for some $u \in P$; by line **4** and the definition of $<$.

▶ **6.** If $x, y \in P$, then $x <_N y$ if and only if $x + u = y$ for some $u \in P$; by the Deduction Theorem applied to lines **3** through **5**.

▶ **7.** *Case II.* Assume $x = 0$ and $y \in P$.

8. $x <_N y$; by the definition of $<_N$, from **7**.

9. $x +_N y = 0 +_N y$; by line **7** and E.

10. $0 +_N y = y$; by the definition of $+_N$.

11. $x +_N y = y$ so that $x +_N u = y$ for some $u \in P$; by lines **9**, **10**, and **7**.

▶ **12.** If $x = 0$ and $y \in P$, then $x <_N y$ if and only if there exists an element $u \in P$ such that $x +_N u = y$; by the Deduction Theorem applied to lines **7** through **8** and **11**.

▶ **13.** *Case III.* Assume $y = 0$ and $x \in N$.

14. *Not* $x <_N y$; by line **13** and the definition of $<_N$.

15. Let u be any element of P.
16. $x +_N u \in P$; by lines **13** and **15** and the definition of $+_N$.
17. $x +_N u \neq 0$; by line **16** and the definition of N.
18. $x +_N u \neq y$; by E from lines **13** and **17**.
19. If u is any element of P then $x +_N u \neq y$; by the Deduction Theorem applied to lines **15** through **18**.
20. If $y = 0$ and $x \in N$, then *not* $x <_N y$ if and only if for all $u \in P$ we have $x +_N u \neq y$; by the Deduction Theorem applied to lines **13** through **19**.
▶**21.** If $y = 0$ and $x \in N$, then $x <_N y$ if and only if $x +_N u = y$ for some $u \in P$; by line **20**.

▶▶**22.** For all $x, y \in N$ we have $x <_N y$ if and only if $x +_N u = y$ for some $u \in P$; by lines **1, 2, 6, 12,** and **21**.

In comparing (**d**) and (**e**) of the previous theorem we see almost a strict analogy—except for the condition $z \neq 0$ in the hypothesis of (**e**). This might lead one to think that with a different definition of the relation $<_N$ the analogy between (**d**) and (**e**) would be perfect, i.e., we might be able to delete the condition $z \neq 0$ in the hypothesis of (**e**). But the next theorem tells us that it is useless to seek such a definition: it turns out that there is only one extension of $<$ for which (**d**) holds.

THEOREM 8-4-3. *If $<'$ is any binary relation on N such that:*

(**a**) *$<'$ is an extension of $<$, and*
(**b**) *For all $x, y, z \in N$ we have $x +_N z <' y +_N z$ if and only if $x <' y$,* then $<' = <_N$.

Outline of Proof

Let $<'$ be any binary relation on N satisfying (**a**) and (**b**) above.

Case I. Suppose that $x, y \in P$. Then we have $x <' y$ if and only if $x < y$, by (**a**). Hence $x <' y$ if and only if $x <_N y$ by Definition 8-4-1 (**i**).

Case II. Suppose that $x = 0$ and that y is any element of P. Then

$x +_N 1 = 0 +_N 1 = 1$; by the definition of $+_N$.
$y +_N 1 = y + 1$; by the definition of $+_N$.

But $1 < y + 1$ by the definition of $<$ and the commutative law of addition. Hence

$(x +_N 1) < (y + 1)$; by E, and so
$(x +_N 1) <' (y + 1)$; by (**a**) above.

But then $x <' y$ by (**b**) above. On the other hand in Case **II** we have $x <_N y$ by Definition 8-4-1 (**ii**). Hence we have shown in Case **II** that $x <' y$ if and only if $x <_N y$.

Case III. Suppose that x is any element of N and that $y = 0$. Let us *assume* that $x <' y$. Then by (**b**) above we have $x +_N 1 <' y +_N 1 = 0 +_N 1 = 1$. But $x +_N 1 \in P$ and so $x +_N 1 < 1$ by (**a**) above. On the other hand since $(x +_N 1) \in P$ we have $1 \leq x +_N 1$ by Theorem 2-7-6, and so *not* $x +_N 1 < 1$ by the Trichotomy Law. This contradiction shows that the assumption $x <' y$ made above is wrong. That is, we have *not* $x <' y$. On the other hand we have *not* $x <_N y$, in Case III, by Definition 8-4-1 (**iii**). Hence in Case III we have $x <' y$ if and only if $x <_N y$.

In defining the *less than or equal to* relation associated with P, in Chapter II, Section 7, we identified it with the disjunction of the *equals* relation and the *less than* relation. We shall follow the same procedure in defining $\leq_N$.

DEFINITION 8-4-4. *We define $\leq_N$ to be the binary relation on N such that for any $x, y \in N$ we have $x \leq_N y$ if and only if (either $x <_N y$ or $x = y$).*

A list of the fundamental properties of the $\leq_N$ relation is given by the following theorem.

THEOREM 8-4-5.

(**a**) *$\leq_N$ is an extension of the relation $\leq$* (i.e., *whenever $x, y \in P$ we have ($x \leq_N y$ if and only if $x \leq y$))*.
(**b**) *For any $x \in N$ we have $0 \leq_N x$.*
(**c**) *If x is any element of N other than 0, then* **not** *$x \leq_N 0$.*
(**d**) *$\leq_N$ is transitive.*
(**e**) *For any $x, y \in N$ either $x \leq_N y$ or $y \leq_N x$.*
(**f**) *If x and y are elements of N such that $x \leq_N y$ and $y \leq_N x$, then $x = y$.*
(**g**) *For any $x, y, z \in N$ we have $x +_N z \leq_N y +_N z$ if and only if $x \leq_N y$.*
(**h**) *If x, y, z are any elements of N such that $z \neq 0$, then $x \cdot_N z \leq_N y \cdot_N z$ if and only if $x \leq_N y$.*
(**i**) *For any $x, y \in N$ we have $x \leq_N y$ if and only if $x +_N u = y$ for some $u \in N$.*

We shall leave the proofs of most of the parts of this theorem to the reader, giving only an outline of a proof of part (**d**) as an indication to the reader as to how he might proceed. To prove (**d**), let x, y, z be any elements of N such that $x \leq_N y$ and $y \leq_N z$. We are to show that $x \leq_N z$. This will be done by cases, as indicated below.

Case I. Suppose x, y, z are any elements of P. Then, by Theorem 2-7-2 and Part (**a**) of this theorem we have $x \leq_N z$.

Case II. Suppose $x = 0$ and $y, z \in N$. Then $x \leq_N z$ since $0 \leq_N z$ for any $z \in N$ by part (**b**) of this theorem.

Case III. Suppose $y = 0$ and $x, z \in N$. Since $x \leq_N y$, by hypothesis, we have $x \leq_N 0$, and hence $x = 0$, by part (**c**) of this theorem. Thus this case reduces to Case II.

Case IV. Suppose $z = 0$ and $x, y \in \mathcal{N}$. Since $y \leq_N z$, by hypothesis, we have $y \leq_N 0$. Hence $y = 0$, by part (**c**) of this theorem. This case reduces to Case III.

Since the four cases exhaust all the possibilities for $x, y, z \in \mathcal{N}$, part (**d**) of the theorem has been proved.

The next theorem states that the relation $\leq_N$ is completely characterized by properties (**a**), (**b**), and (**c**) of the above theorem.

THEOREM 8-4-6. *If $<'$ is any binary relation such that* (**a**), (**b**), *and* (**c**) *of Theorem* 8-4-5 *hold, then* $\leq' = \leq_N$.

The proof is left to the reader.

EXERCISES

1.* Prove Theorem 8-4-6.
2. Prove Part (**b**) of Theorem 8-4-2.
3. Prove Part (**c**) of Theorem 8-4-2.

5. *The Subtraction Function*

In the system $\mathcal{P} = \langle P, +, \cdot \rangle$ we defined the subtraction function, $-$, whose domain consists of those ordered pairs $\langle x, y \rangle$ (where x and y are elements of P) such that $y < x$, and whose value for such an ordered pair $\langle x, y \rangle$ of this domain is the unique element z of P such that $x = y + z$. (See Definition 2-6-2.) In our extended system $\mathfrak{N} = \langle \mathcal{N}, +_N, \cdot_N \rangle$ the domain over which we would like to define the subtraction function consists of selected ordered pairs of elements *of* $\mathcal{N}$, rather than of P. With a change of domain we no longer have the original subtraction function of course, and in consequence we must define precisely what we mean by the subtraction function of the system $\mathfrak{N}$.

DEFINITION 8-5-1. *Let the* **subtraction function over N,** *to be denoted by* "$-_N$", *be the function whose domain consists of all ordered pairs* $\langle x, y \rangle$ (*where* x *and* y *are elements of* $\mathcal{N}$) *such that* $y \leq_N x$, *and whose values are given as follows: For any* $x, y \in \mathcal{N}$ *such that* $y \leq_N x$,

$$x -_N y = \begin{cases} x - y, \text{ if } x, y \in P \text{ and } y < x, \\ 0, \text{ if } x = y, \\ x, \text{ if } x \in P \text{ and } y = 0. \end{cases}$$

Note that by combining Definitions 8-4-1 and 8-4-4 we may infer that whenever $y \leq_N x$ then one of these three things must occur: (**i**) $x, y \in P$ and

$y < x$, **(ii)** $x = y$, **(iii)** $x \in P$ and $y = 0$. Furthermore, by Theorem 2-5-3 and Definition 8-2-1 no two of these can occur simultaneously. This justifies the form of our definition of $-_N$, since a unique value $x -_N y$ is provided for each $\langle x, y \rangle$ in the domain of $-_N$. Note, too, that the subtraction function, $-_N$, is *not defined* to have a value for an ordered pair $\langle x, y \rangle$ if $x <_N y$.

The properties of the subtraction function, $-_N$, for the most part parallel those of the original subtraction function, $-$, of the system $\mathcal{P}$, and are intuitively familiar to us. Some of the more important properties are indicated by the following theorem.

THEOREM 8-5-2.

- **(a)** *$-_N$ is an extension of $-$ (i.e., whenever $\langle x, y \rangle$ is in the domain of $-$ it is also in the domain of $-_N$ and we have $x -_N y = x - y$).*
- **(b)** *For any $x \in N$ we have $x -_N 0 = x$ and $x -_N x = 0$.*
- **(c)** *If x, y, u are elements of N such that $y +_N u = x$ then $u = x -_N y$.*
- **(d)** *If $x, y \in N$ and $y \leq_N x$ then $y +_N (x -_N y) = x$.*
- **(e)** *If $y \leq_N x$ and $z \leq_N y$ then $y -_N z \leq_N x -_N z$, and $x -_N y \leq_N x -_N z$.*
- **(f)** *If $z \leq_N y$ then $(x +_N y) -_N z = x +_N (y -_N z)$.*
- **(g)** *If $z \leq_N y$ then $x \cdot_N (y -_N z) = (x \cdot_N y) -_N (x \cdot_N z)$.*
- **(h)** *If x, y, z are elements of N such that $x \leq_N y$ and $y \leq_N z$, then $y -_N x \leq_N z$, and $z -_N (y -_N x) = (z -_N y) +_N x$.*

We shall prove only one part of this theorem; the proofs of the remaining parts will be left as exercises.

Proof of (**d**). This is a proof by cases.

▶▶ 1. Let x, y be any elements of N such that $y \leq_N x$.
▶▶ 2. Either $x = y$ or $y <_N x$; by line **1** and Definition 8-4-4.

▶ 3. *Case I.* Assume $x = y$.
4. $x -_N y = 0$; by line **3** and the definition of $-_N$ (Definition 8-5-1).
5. $y +_N (x -_N y) = y +_N 0$; by line **4** and E.
6. $= y$; by the definition of $+_N$ (Definition 8-2-1).
7. $y +_N (x -_N y) = y$; by lines **5** and **6** and E.
8. $y +_N (x -_N y) = x$; by lines **3** and **7** and E.
▶ 9. If $x = y$ then $y +_N (x -_N y) = x$; by the Deduction Theorem applied to lines **3** through **8**.

▶ **10.** *Case II.* Assume $y <_N x$.
▶ **11.** Either $x, y \in P$ and $y < x$, or $y = 0$ and $x \in P$; by line **10** and the definition of $<_N$ (Definition 8-4-4).

▶12. *Subcase IIa.* Assume $y = 0$ and $x \in P$.

13. $y +_N (x -_N y) = 0 +_N (x -_N 0)$; by line **12** and E.

14. $x -_N 0 = x$; by part (**b**) of this theorem.

15. $0 +_N x = x$; by the definition of $+_N$ (Definition 8-2-1).

16. $y +_N (x -_N y) = x$; by E from lines **13** through **15**.

▶17. If $y = 0$ and $x \in P$ then $y +_N (x -_N y) = x$; by the Deduction Theorem applied to lines **12** through **16**.

▶18. *Subcase IIb.* Assume $x, y \in P$ and $y < x$.

19. $x -_N y = x - y$; by **18** and the definition of $-_N$ (Definition 8-5-1).

20. $x -_N y \in P$; by E from line **19** and the definition of $-$ (Definition 2-6-2).

21. $y +_N (x -_N y) = y + (x -_N y)$; by lines **18** and **20** since $+_N$ is an extension of $+$ (Definition 8-2-1).

22. $= y + (x - y)$; by E from line **19**.

23. $= x$; by line **18** and Theorem 2-6-3.

24. $y +_N (x -_N y) = x$; by E from lines **21** through **23**.

▶25. If $x, y \in P$ and $y < x$, then $y +_N (x -_N y) = x$; by the Deduction Theorem applied to lines **18** through **24**.

26. If either $x, y \in P$ and $y < x$, or $y = 0$ and $x \in P$, then $y +_N (x -_N y) = x$; by lines **17** and **25**.

27. $y +_N (x -_N y) = x$; by lines **11** and **26**.

▶28. If $y <_N x$ then $y +_N (x -_N y) = x$; by the Deduction Theorem applied to lines **10** through **27**.

▶▶29. If either $x = y$ or $y <_N x$ then $y +_N (x -_N y) = x$; by lines **9** and **28**.

30. $y +_N (x -_N y) = x$; by lines **2** and **29**.

31. If x, y are any elements of $\mathcal{N}$ such that $y \leq_N x$ then $y +_N (x -_N y) = x$; by the Deduction Theorem applied to lines **1** through **30**.

EXERCISES

1.* Let f be the function whose domain consists of all those ordered pairs $\langle x, y\rangle$ such that x and y are elements of $\mathcal{N}$ for which $y \leq_N x$, and whose value for any $\langle x, y\rangle$ in this domain is the unique $u \in \mathcal{N}$ such that $y +_N u = x$. (The existence of such an element u is shown in Theorem 8-4-5 (**i**); its uniqueness follows easily from Theorem 8-2-4 Part I.) Show that for every $\langle x, y\rangle$ in the domain of f we have $f(x, y) = x -_N y$, and hence that $f = -_N$. (This result indicates that the definition of f could be used as an alternative definition for the subtraction function in developing our theory of natural numbers.)

2. Prove Part (**b**) of Theorem 8-5-2.

3. Prove Part (**c**) of Theorem 8-5-2.

4. Prove Part (**h**) of Theorem 8-5-2.

6. *Division with a Remainder*

It would be possible to continue our discussion of the system $\mathfrak{N} = \langle N, +_N, \cdot_N\rangle$ as we did for the positive integers, by defining a division relation for elements of N which would be an extension of the relation $|$ (Definition 4-2-1). We could then proceed to obtain various theorems concerning this relation analogous to Theorems 4-2-2 through 4-2-9. Next would come the definition of a division function, $\div_N$, extending the function $\div$ (Definition 4-2-10), and we could prove various properties about $\div_N$ similar to Theorems 4-2-11 through 4-2-16. In turn, the concepts gcd and lcm (Definitions 5-1-1 and 5-1-6) and many of their properties can be extended to the system $\mathfrak{N}$.

However, it would be too time-consuming for us to parallel exactly our development of $\mathcal{P}$. Instead, we shall proceed directly to the important concept of division with a remainder.

When this idea was first introduced, in Theorem 5-1-9, the zero element was not present in our number system. This fact made it necessary to state a much more restricted theorem (Theorem 5-1-9) than is possible in our extended system. We are now in a position to prove an extremely important and useful theorem.

THEOREM 8-6-1. *For any $x, y \in N$ such that $x \neq 0$ there exists a unique pair of elements $q, r \in N$ such that*

(**i**) $y = q \cdot_N x +_N r$, *and*
(**ii**) $r <_N x$.

(Note that it is no longer necessary, as was the case in formulating Theorem 5-1-9, to assume that x is less than y or that x does not divide y.)

The proof of this important theorem is outlined below.

Case I. Suppose $x, y \in P$ such that $x < y$ and not $x \mid y$. Then, by Theorems 5-1-9 and 5-1-10 there exist unique elements q and r in P such that

(**i**) $y = q \cdot x + r$ and
(**ii**) $r < x$.

Hence, since $+_N$ and $\cdot_N$ are extensions of $+$ and $\cdot$ respectively, and since $<_N$ is an extension of $<$, we have

(i) $y = q \cdot_N x +_N r$ and
(ii) $r <_N x$.

Now we know that q and r are the only elements *in* P which satisfy (i) and (ii). It remains to show that neither r nor q can be 0. If we had $r = 0$, then $y = q \cdot_N x = q \cdot x$ and so $x \mid y$, contrary to the supposition that *not* $x \mid y$. Hence $r \neq 0$. Similarly, if we had $q = 0$ then $y = r$ by (i) and hence $x > y$ by (ii) contrary to hypothesis. Thus, $q \neq 0$.

Case II. Suppose $x, y \in P$ and $x \mid y$. Then $y = q \cdot x$ for some $q \in P$. Hence $y = q \cdot_N x +_N 0$ where $0 <_N x$, by Definitions 8-2-1 and 8-4-1 (ii). Now we wish to show that these numbers q and 0 are the *only* numbers with the properties (i) and (ii) of the theorem. To do this, suppose that u, v are *any* natural numbers (i.e., elements of $\mathcal{N}$) such that $y = u \cdot_N x +_N v$ and $v <_N x$. Now if $u = 0$, then $y = 0 \cdot_N x +_N v = 0 +_N v = v$. Then $v = q \cdot x$ and so $x \leq_N v$. But $v <_N x$. This contradiction with the Trichotomy Law arises from the supposition that $u = 0$. Hence $u \neq 0$; i.e., $u \in P$.

Suppose that $v \neq 0$. Then $q \cdot x = u \cdot_N x +_N v = u \cdot x + v$. Therefore, $(q - u) \cdot x = v$ and so $x \leq v$. But by hypothesis $v < x$, so that we obtain a contradiction with the Trichotomy Law. Hence $v = 0$.

And now, $q \cdot x = u \cdot x$ and so by the right cancellation law for multiplication we have $q = u$. Thus we have shown that if u, v are *any* natural numbers such that $y = u \cdot_N x +_N v$ and $v <_N x$, then we must have $v = 0$ and $u = q$. That is, q and 0 are the *only* natural numbers satisfying (i) and (ii).

Case III. Suppose y is any element in $\mathcal{N}$ and $y < x$. Then the proof of existence and uniqueness of q and r is left to the reader. (See Exercise 3 below.)

Cases I through III exhaust the possibilities (since $x \neq 0$ by hypothesis), Cases I and II together providing for all cases where $x \leq y$. Hence the theorem is proved.

Theorem 8-6-1 provides the justification for the following definition.

DEFINITION 8-6-2. *We define binary functions* $\mathbf{quo}_N$ *and* $\mathbf{rem}_N$, *each of which has as its domain the set of all those ordered pairs* $\langle x, y\rangle$ *of elements of* $\mathcal{N}$ *for which* $x \neq 0$. *For any such pair* $\langle x, y\rangle$, $\mathrm{quo}_N\langle x, y\rangle$ *and* $\mathrm{rem}_N\langle x, y\rangle$ *are defined to be the unique elements* q *and* r *respectively such that*

(i) $y = q \cdot_N x +_N r$ *and*
(ii) $r <_N x$.

Thus from this definition we see that for any $x, y \in N$ such that $x \neq 0$:

(i) $y = \text{quo}_N\langle x, y\rangle \cdot_N x +_N \text{rem}_N\langle x, y\rangle$ *and*
(ii) $\text{rem}_N\langle x, y\rangle <_N x$.

We say that $\text{quo}_N\langle x, y\rangle$ *and* $\text{rem}_N\langle x, y\rangle$ *are the* **quotient** *and* **remainder** *respectively,* **on dividing y by x.**

Theorem 8-6-1 and Definition 8-6-2 which is based upon it, provide us with the assurance (as long as we are working in the system $\mathfrak{N}$) that the division process always leads to a unique quotient and remainder. In fact, when we "divide" a number, y, by another number, x, we are, in effect, finding the unique numbers q and r, or $\text{quo}_N\langle x, y\rangle$ and $\text{rem}_N\langle x, y\rangle$ as we shall hereafter call them, which satisfy the conditions (**i**) and (**ii**) above.

EXERCISES

1.* One way to define the division relation $|_N$ for the system N is to say that $|_N$ is the binary relation such that, for all $y \in N$, we have $x |_N y$ if and only if $x \cdot_N u = y$ for some $u \in N$. Give an *alternative* definition, by cases, using the idea that $|_N$ is an extension of the relation $|$. Formulate and prove some of the laws for $|_N$.

2. Give two definitions of the division function $\div_N$ for the system N. Formulate and prove some of the laws for this function.

3. Following the outline of the proof of 8-6-1, write out a detailed proof for Case III.

7. *Exponentiation in* $\mathfrak{N}$

The reader may recall that in our development of $\mathcal{P}$ we defined the exponentiation operation as a binary operation acting on ordered pairs of elements of P, and proceeded to obtain the customary "laws" of exponents (cf. Chapter V, Section 3). At that stage, zero was not an element of the domain over which the exponentiation operation was defined, and consequently we were not confronted with the question of the meaning of such expressions as x^0 or 0^y—in particular, of 0^0. We shall now see what meanings we are to give to these expressions in the following definition, which is an extension of Definition 5 3 2.

DEFINITION 8-7-1. *We define* $\textbf{exp}_N$ *to be the binary operation on* N *such that for any* $x, y \in N$,

$$\text{exp}_N\langle x, y\rangle = \begin{cases} \text{exp}\langle x, y\rangle \text{ if } x, y \in P \\ 0 \text{ if } x = 0 \text{ and } y \in P \\ 1 \text{ if } y = 0. \end{cases}$$

Remarks on this definition: We notice that by Definition 8-7-1 we have $0^0 = 1$ or, in the notation of the definition, $\text{exp}_N\langle 0, 0\rangle = 1$. In high-school mathematics 0^0 is usually not defined. Certainly we could have followed this practice here, restricting the domain of $\exp_N$ by excluding $\langle 0, 0\rangle$. But there is nothing to prevent us from assigning a value to 0^0. It is true that if we set $0^0 = 3$, say, it would turn out that two of the most basic laws of exponents would fail to hold. On the other hand either of the values 0 or 1 for 0^0 is consistent with these basic laws [(**a**) and (**b**) of the next theorem]. Thus the situation is quite different from the case of "$0 \div 0$" where no possible value can be assigned which is consistent with the basic laws for the operation $\div$.

Using the above definition of the extended operation of exponentiation we shall now prove the customary "laws" for this operation. The reader may find the statement of these laws a bit more familiar if it is recalled that our notation "$\exp_N\langle x, y\rangle$" is equivalent to the customary "x^y" (where $x, y \in N$).

THEOREM 8-7-2. *For all* $x, y, z \in N$

(**a**) $\exp_N\langle x, y +_N z\rangle = \exp_N\langle x, y\rangle \cdot_N \exp\langle x, z\rangle$,

(**b**) $\exp_N\langle x, y \cdot_N z\rangle = \exp_N\langle \exp_N\langle x, y\rangle, z\rangle$,

(**c**) $\exp_N\langle x, 0\rangle = 1$,

(**d**) $\exp_N\langle x, 1\rangle = x$.

Furthermore, $\exp_N$ *is an extension of* exp.

Outline of the Proof of this Theorem

We see that $\exp_N$ is an extension of exp immediately from Definition 8-7-1 and the meaning of extension.

The proof of Parts (**a**), (**b**), and (**c**) is by cases. We shall outline the proof of the theorem for one case and leave the listing of the other cases and their proofs as an exercise for the reader. It is suggested that the reader fill in the reason for each step in the proof outline which follows.

Case I. Suppose $x, y \in P$ and $z = 0$. Then

$$\begin{aligned}\exp_N\langle x, y +_N z\rangle &= \exp_N\langle x, y +_N 0\rangle \\ &= \exp_N\langle x, y\rangle.\end{aligned}$$

Also

$$\begin{aligned}\exp_N\langle x, y\rangle \cdot_N \exp_N\langle x, z\rangle &= \exp_N\langle x, y\rangle \cdot_N \exp_N\langle x, 0\rangle \\ &= \exp_N\langle x, y\rangle \cdot_N 1 \\ &= \exp_N\langle x, y\rangle\end{aligned}$$

Thus

$$\exp_N\langle x, y +_N z\rangle = \exp_N\langle x, y\rangle \cdot_N \exp_N\langle x, z\rangle$$

and we have proved (**a**) for this case.

To prove (**b**) for this case we see that

$$\begin{aligned}\exp_N\langle x, y \cdot_N z\rangle &= \exp_N\langle x, y \cdot_N 0\rangle \\ &= \exp_N\langle x, 0\rangle \\ &= 1\end{aligned}$$

and

$$\begin{aligned}\exp_N\langle \exp_N\langle x, y\rangle, z\rangle &= \exp_N\langle \exp_N\langle x, y\rangle, 0\rangle \\ &= 1.\end{aligned}$$

Thus,

$$\exp_N\langle x, y \cdot_N z\rangle = \exp_N\langle \exp_N\langle x, y\rangle, z\rangle.$$

Parts (**c**) and (**d**) are immediate consequences of Definition 8-7-1 and the fact that $\exp_N$ is an extension of exp.

For the other cases and their proofs, see Exercise 2.

Our next theorem shows that if we want our extension of the notion of exp to have properties (**a**), (**c**), and (**d**) of Theorem 8-7-2, then there is only one way to define this extension.

THEOREM 8-7-3. *If* exp′ *is any binary operation on* N *which is an extension of* exp *satisfying conditions* (**a**), (**c**), *and* (**d**) *of Theorem* 8-7-2, *then* $\exp' = \exp_N$.

Outline of Proof

Let exp′ be any extension of exp satisfying conditions (**a**), (**c**), and (**d**) of Theorem 8-7-2. We wish to show that for all $x, y \in N$ we have $\exp'\langle x, y\rangle = \exp_N\langle x, y\rangle$.

Case I. Suppose x, y are any elements of P. Then, since exp′ and $\exp_N$ are extensions of exp, we have

$$\exp'\langle x, y\rangle = \exp\langle x, y\rangle = \exp_N\langle x, y\rangle.$$

Case II. Suppose x is any element of P and $y = 0$. Then

$$\begin{aligned}\exp'\langle x, y\rangle &= \exp'\langle x, 0\rangle \\ &= 1; \quad \text{by } (\mathbf{c}). \\ &= \exp_N\langle x, y\rangle; \quad \text{by Theorem 8-7-2 } (\mathbf{c}).\end{aligned}$$

Case III. Suppose $x = 0$ and y is any element of N.

Subcase III.1. Suppose $y = 0$. Then

$$\begin{aligned}\exp'\langle x, y\rangle &= \exp'\langle 0, 0\rangle \\ &= 1; \quad \text{by } (\mathbf{c}). \\ &= \exp_N\langle x, y\rangle; \quad \text{by Theorem 8-7-2 } (\mathbf{c}).\end{aligned}$$

Subcase III.2. Suppose $y = 1$. Then

$$\begin{aligned}\exp'\langle x, y\rangle &= \exp'\langle 0, 1\rangle \\ &= 0; \quad \text{by } (\mathbf{d}). \\ &= \exp_N\langle x, y\rangle; \quad \text{by Theorem 8-7-2 } (\mathbf{d}).\end{aligned}$$

Subcase III.3. Suppose $y \in P$ and $y \neq 1$. Then $y = u + 1$ for some $u \in P$.

$$\begin{aligned}\exp'\langle x, y\rangle &= \exp'\langle 0, u +_N 1\rangle; \quad \text{since } +_N \text{ is an extension of } +. \\ &= \exp'\langle 0, u\rangle \cdot_N \exp'\langle 0, 1\rangle; \quad \text{by } (\mathbf{a}). \\ &= \exp'\langle 0, u\rangle \cdot_N 0; \quad \text{by } (\mathbf{d}). \\ &= 0; \quad \text{by the definition of } \cdot_N. \\ &= \exp_N\langle x, y\rangle; \quad \text{by the definition of } \exp_N.\end{aligned}$$

EXERCISES

1. In Chapter V, Definition 5-3-2 was preceded by Theorem 5-3-1 in which we established the existence of a unique binary operation of a certain kind; and it was this operation which we defined as exp, the exponentiation operation. Strictly speaking, is it necessary to prove an analogous theorem before making Definition 8-7-1? Why, or why not?

2. Complete the proof of Theorem 8-7-2.

8. *Semi-Groups in* $\mathfrak{N}$

The reader may recall that the system $\langle P, +, <\rangle$ can be classified, in the terminology of abstract algebra, as an ordered, commutative, cancellation semi-group (cf. Theorem 3-3-5). This simply means that the elements of P, together with the $+$ operation and the associated $<$ relation, form a mathematical system possessing certain properties which occur also in various other systems and which have been given this identifying name. Again, in Chapter IV, Section 3, we considered the mathematical system $\langle P, \cdot\rangle$ from the viewpoint of the algebraist. We found (cf. Theorem 4-3-2) that this system formed a commutative, cancellation semi-group with a null element, 1.

Now that we have enlarged our number system to include the number 0, and have introduced new operations, $+_N$ and $\cdot_N$, it becomes natural to inquire whether the extended systems $\langle N, +_N\rangle$ and $\langle N, \cdot_N\rangle$ are subject to the same classification as our earlier systems. Let us seek an intuitive answer to this question before we state the pertinent theorems.

In the system $\langle N, +_N\rangle$ we have the zero element, 0, and so are able to find an element $z \in N$ such that $a +_N z = a$ for all $a \in N$. At the same time, the operation $+_N$ has the same closure, associativity, commutativity and cancellation properties as did the $+$ operation on P. Thus we would expect that $\langle N, +_N\rangle$ would exhibit the same algebraic properties as $\langle P, +\rangle$, and in addition would possess a null element. In the case of $\langle N, \cdot_N\rangle$, however, the situation is different. The enlargement of the set of numbers to include 0 does not add to the list of properties which the system possesses, but on the contrary, reduces this list, for the cancellation property no longer holds.

THEOREM 8-8-1. *The system* $\langle \mathcal{N}, +_N, <_N \rangle$ *is an ordered, commutative, cancellation semi-group with null element,* 0.

THEOREM 8-8-2. *The system* $\langle \mathcal{N}, \cdot_N \rangle$ *is a commutative semi-group with null element,* 1.

These two Theorems are simple to verify when the relevant definitions are at hand, and the proofs will be left to the reader in the form of exercises.

EXERCISES

1. Prove Theorem 8-8-1.
2. Prove Theorem 8-8-2.
3. Prove that $\langle \mathcal{N}, \cdot_N \rangle$ is not a cancellation semi-group.
4. Is the system $\langle P, \cdot_N \rangle$ a cancellation semi-group?
5. No mention was made of an ordering relation associated with the system $\langle \mathcal{N}, \cdot_N \rangle$. Why?

9. *Arabic Numerals*[1]

We have used the word "number" to indicate an element of a set on which certain operations are defined. In particular, when we speak of the "natural numbers" we are referring to elements of the set $\mathcal{N}$. Closely associated with the concept of number is that of *numeral*, but, contrary to a common belief, the concepts of number and numeral are *not* identical. Speaking in very general terms, a numeral may be described as a *name* of a number. We have an analogous situation in nonmathematical terminology. When we say "Tom is my son," "Tom" is a three letter word used to refer to a particular boy—it is a sequence of letters, not a person.

Lest the reader think that this is a trivial distinction, let us point out that it is quite possible to use many *different* names to refer to the *same* element of a set of numbers. For example, consider the following array of marks; ||||| ||||| || . The answer to the question "How many marks are in this array?" would be given by the numeral "12" in our familiar Arabic decimal system, and by the expression "XII" in the Roman numeral system. In an octal system, i.e., a system based on eight, rather than ten, we note that there is one group of eight marks, plus four additional marks, and so we would use the numeral "14" to answer the question. In a binary number system (widely used in today's high-speed digital computers), the reply would be "1100". Thus we have many different names for the same object —just as the same boy might be described as "my darling Thomas" by his mother, and as "that fool kid" by a neighbor.

[1] This section may be omitted without interfering with the continuity of the book.

Although there are many different ways of selecting symbols to denote the elements of N, we shall here consider only the Arabic decimal numerals. Numerals, in this notation, provide a means of referring to *all* natural numbers while employing special symbols which refer to only *ten* of the elements of N. So far we have formally introduced the symbols "0", "1", "2", "3", and "4". We shall now add six symbols to this list, and introduce the concept of *digit*.

DEFINITION 8-9-1.

(i) $5 = 4 + 1$, $6 = 5 + 1$, $7 = 6 + 1$, $8 = 7 + 1$, $9 = 8 + 1$, *and* $T = 9 + 1$.

(ii) *By a* **digit** *we mean any element* x *of* N *such that* $x <_N T$. *(It is not difficult to prove that* x *is a digit if and only if* $x = 0$, *or* $x = 1$, *or* $x = 2$, *or* $x = 3$, *or* $x = 4$, *or* $x = 5$, *or* $x = 6$, *or* $x = 7$, *or* $x = 8$, *or* $x = 9$.)

Although we have discussed the concept of *numeral* from an intuitive point of view, we have not yet formally introduced it. Before we do, it might be advisable for the reader to refer back to the concept of a *sequence*. In Chapter VI, Section 1, we defined an x-sequence to be a function, X_x, whose domain is the set $\{1, 2, \ldots, x\}$ and whose values are in P. Thus an example of a 4-sequence might be the function X_4 such that $X_4(1) = 7$, $X_4(2) = 3$, $X_4(3) = 5$, $X_4(4) = 1$, which we abbreviate as $\langle 7, 3, 5, 1\rangle$. If we broaden this definition (6-1-2) to say that an x-sequence has values *in* N (rather than in P), we can define numerals to be certain x-sequences.

DEFINITION 8-9-2. *A (decimal)* **numeral** *is an* x*-sequence,* X_x, *where* x *may be any element in* P, *such that* $X_x(u)$ *is a digit for every* $u \leq x$. *We call* x *the* **length** *of the numeral* X_x. *By a* **proper numeral,** *we mean any numeral of length* 1, *or any numeral of length* $x > 1$ *such that* $X_x(x) \neq 0$. *We denote the set of all numerals by* "**Nu**".

Examples of numerals are: $\langle 7, 3, 5, 1\rangle$ (a proper numeral of length 4); $\langle 7, 3, 5, 1, 0\rangle$ (an improper numeral of length 5); $\langle 7\rangle$ (a proper numeral of length 1); $\langle 0\rangle$ (a proper numeral of length 1); and $\langle 0, 3, 5\rangle$ (a proper numeral of length 3). $\langle 4, 12, 5\rangle$ is *not* a numeral. (Why?)

Just what connection is there between "numeral" and "number?" If a numeral is to be the name of a number, then there must be some sort of correspondence between the two—that is, there must be some function which has as its domain the numerals and as its range the numbers (i.e., a function which maps Nu into N). Before we define such a function, let us examine what we know intuitively about numerals. Consider "752" as an example. We recognize this as an abbreviated name for the number $7 \cdot 10^2 + 5 \cdot 10 + 2$. We will find it convenient here (although perhaps a bit confusing) to think of this as $2 + 5 \cdot 10 + 7 \cdot 10^2$, and so to represent it by the 3-sequence $\langle 2, 5, 7\rangle$ (instead of the sequence $\langle 7, 5, 2\rangle$). One other point before we define the function which maps Nu into $\mathcal{N}$. An expression such as "$2 + 5 \cdot 10 + 7 \cdot 10^2$" is an example of what we have called a *general sum.* It might be well for the reader to review the discussion of general sums in Chapter VI.

DEFINITION 8-9-3. *We define a function* **nr** *which maps Nu into* $\mathcal{N}$ *as follows:*

If X is any numeral, and x = the length of X, we let $\mathbf{X}^*$ *be the x-sequence such that*

$$X^*(u) = \begin{cases} X(u) \cdot_{\mathcal{N}} T^{u-1} & \text{if } u > 1, \\ X(u) & \text{if } u = 1, \end{cases}$$

for every $u \leq x$. *And then we define* $\mathbf{nr}(X) = \sum(X^*)$.

A fundamental theorem about the function nr is the following, which shows that *every* number corresponds to a numeral, and in fact to exactly one proper numeral.

THEOREM 8-9-4. *For each* $x \in \mathcal{N}$ *there exists one and only one proper numeral* Y *such that* $\text{nr}(Y) = x$. *If* Z *is any numeral other than* Y, *then we have* $\text{nr}(Z) = x$ *if and only if* $\text{length}(Z) > \text{length}(Y)$ *and for every* $u \leq \text{length}(Z)$

$$Z(u) = \begin{cases} Y(u) & \text{if } u \leq \text{length}(Y), \\ 0 & \text{if } u > \text{length}(Y). \end{cases}$$

Outline of Proof

The idea of the proof is this. We shall define a function nl which acts on any element $x \in \mathcal{N}$ to yield a certain proper numeral $\text{nl}(x)$. Then, by showing that $\text{nr}(\text{nl}(x)) = x$, we will show the existence of the proper numeral Y asserted to exist in the theorem, for Y may simply be taken as $\text{nl}(x)$. Next, by showing that for any proper numeral X we have $\text{nl}(\text{nr}(X)) = X$, we will show the uniqueness of Y which is claimed in the theorem; for if we had two proper numerals Y and Y_1 such that both $\text{nr}(Y) = x$ and $\text{nr}(Y_1) = x$, we would obtain $\text{nl}(\text{nr}(Y)) = \text{nl}(x)$ and $\text{nl}(\text{nr}(Y_1)) = \text{nl}(x)$, and hence $Y = \text{nl}(x)$ and $Y_1 = \text{nl}(x)$, so that $Y = Y_1$. Once the existence and uniqueness of Y are established in this way, the demonstration of the relation between Z and Y which is mentioned in the theorem becomes a simple matter, and we leave this to the reader. (See Exercise 1 below.)

In order to define the function nl we must first associate with each $x \in \mathcal{N}$ an element $i_x \in P$ which we call the *index* of x. In fact, we define i_x to be the least number $y \in P$ such that $x < T^y$. The existence of such a least number y will be assured by Theorem 2-7-9 *if* we can show that the class of all those numbers $y \in P$ for which $x < T^y$ is a nonempty class. But this is a simple matter since we have $x < T^x$ for every $x \in P$ as the reader may easily show. (See Exercise 2 below.)

Having defined the index i_x, in the above manner, for any $x \in N$, we now define $\text{nl}(x)$ by induction on i_x. For every x, $\text{nl}(x)$ will be a numeral of length i_x.

(i) Suppose $i_x = 1$, so that $x < T^1$. Then we let $\text{nl}(x)$ be the numeral $\langle x \rangle$.

(ii) Suppose $i_x = z + 1$, so that $x < T^{z+1}$ but $x \geq T^z$. In this case $\text{rem}\langle T^z, x\rangle < T^z$, so that the index of $\text{rem}\langle T^z, x\rangle$ is some number $u \leq z$. Say $\text{nl}(\text{rem}\langle T^z, x\rangle) = \langle c_1, \ldots, c_u\rangle$, and let $\langle b_1, \ldots, b_z\rangle$ be the numeral $\langle c_1, \ldots, c_u\rangle$ if $u = z$, or let $\langle b_1, \ldots, b_z\rangle = \langle c_1, \ldots, c_u, 0, 0, \ldots, 0\rangle$ if $u < z$. Then we define $\text{nl}(x)$ to be $\langle b_1, \ldots, b_z, \text{quo}\langle T^z, x\rangle\rangle$.

Parts **(i)** and **(ii)** together define the function nl by induction. We note, however, that this is a definition by *strong induction*, rather than by ordinary induction. For in **(ii)** we do *not* define the value of nl for a number x of index $z + 1$ in terms of the value of nl for a number of index z, but rather the definition is in terms of the value of nl for a number of index u, where we know only that u is some number less than or equal to z. This type of definition can be justified by a general theorem just as can definitions by ordinary induction. The relation between the two kinds of inductive definition is analogous to the two types of proof by induction (as exemplified by Axiom P4 and Theorem 2-7-8).

The general theorem justifying recursive definitions tells us that there is a unique function nl which assigns to every $x \in N$ a numeral $\text{nl}(x)$. The fact that $\text{nl}(x)$ is always a *proper* numeral follows at once from the observation that in Part **(ii)** of this definition the digit $\text{quo}\langle T^z, x\rangle$ is not 0 (because $x \geq T^z$).

Now that the function nl is available we proceed to establish three lemmas concerning this function and nr. Together the lemmas yield a proof of our theorem.

LEMMA 8-9-4.1. *For every $x \in N$ we have* $\text{nr}(\text{nl}(x)) = x$.

Outline of Proof

The proof proceeds by strong induction (see Theorem 2-7-8) on the index of x.

1. We form the set G of all those numbers $y \in P$ such that for every x of index y we have $\text{nr}(\text{nl}(x)) = \text{x}$. Clearly the lemma is equivalent to the proposition that $G = P$.

2. We first show that $1 \in G$. In fact, if x is of index 1 then $\text{nl}(x) = \langle x\rangle$ by **(i)** above, and $\text{nr}\langle x\rangle = \sum\langle x\rangle = x$ by definitions of nr and $\sum$ respectively. Thus $\text{nr}(\text{nl}(x)) = x$ for any x of index 1, whence $1 \in G$ by step **1** above.

3. Now (as usual in a proof by strong induction) let z be any element of G such that for every $u \leq z$ we have $u \in G$. We will show that for such a number z we must also have $z + 1 \in G$. To do this, consider any x of index $z + 1$, so that $x < T^{z+1}$ but $T^z \leq x$. We have $\mathrm{rem}\langle T^z, x\rangle < T^z$, so that the index of $\mathrm{rem}\langle T^z, x\rangle$ is some number $u \leq z$, and hence this index u is in G (by choice of z). By definition of G (step **1**) this means that if $\langle c_1, \ldots, c_u\rangle = \mathrm{nl}(\mathrm{rem}\langle T^z, x\rangle)$ then we have $\mathrm{nr}\langle c_1, \ldots, c_u\rangle = \mathrm{rem}\langle T^z, x\rangle$. Now if $u = z$, set $\langle b_1, \ldots, b_z\rangle = \langle c_1, \ldots, c_u\rangle$, but if $u < z$ we set $\langle b_1, \ldots, b_z\rangle = \langle c_1, \ldots, c_u, 0, 0, \ldots, 0\rangle$. Then we have $\mathrm{nr}\langle b_1, \ldots, b_z\rangle = \mathrm{nr}\langle c_1, \ldots, c_u\rangle$, by definition of nr, so that also $\mathrm{nr}\langle b_1, \ldots, b_z\rangle = \mathrm{rem}\langle T^z, x\rangle$.

4. By **(ii)**, $\mathrm{nl}(x) = \langle b_1, \ldots, b_z, \mathrm{quo}\langle T^z, x\rangle\rangle$. To compute $\mathrm{nr}(\mathrm{nl}(x))$ by Definition 8-9-3 we first form the sequence $(\mathrm{nl}(x))^* = \langle b_1, \ldots, b_z \cdot T^{z-1}, \mathrm{quo}\langle T^z, x\rangle \cdot T^z\rangle$, and then

$$\begin{aligned}\mathrm{nr}(\mathrm{nl}(x)) = \textstyle\sum (\mathrm{nl}(x))^* &= \textstyle\sum \langle b_1, \ldots, b_z\rangle^* + \mathrm{quo}\langle T^z, x\rangle \cdot T^z; \quad \text{by definition of } \textstyle\sum.\\ &= \mathrm{nr}\langle b_1, \ldots, b_z\rangle + \mathrm{quo}\langle T^z, x\rangle \cdot T^z\\ &= \mathrm{rem}\langle T^z, x\rangle + \mathrm{quo}\langle T^z, x\rangle \cdot T^z; \quad \text{by step } \mathbf{3}.\\ &= x; \quad \text{by the definition of quo and rem.}\end{aligned}$$

Since we have shown $\mathrm{nr}(\mathrm{nl}(x)) = x$ for every x of index $z + 1$, we infer that $z + 1 \in G$. This essentially completes the proof of Lemma 8-9-4.1 by strong induction (Theorem 2-7-8).

As mentioned above, this lemma tells us at once that for every $x \in N$ there is a proper numeral Υ such that $\mathrm{nr}(\Upsilon) = x$.

LEMMA 8-9-4.2. *If Z is any numeral of length z, then* $\mathrm{nr}(Z) < T^z$.

The proof, which is by induction on z, is left to the reader. (Exercise 3 below.)

LEMMA 8-9-4.3. *For every proper numeral Υ we have* $\mathrm{nl}(\mathrm{nr}(\Upsilon)) = \Upsilon$.

Outline of Proof

The proof proceeds by strong induction (see Theorem 2-7-8) on the length of Υ.

1. We form the set H of all those numbers $z \in P$ such that $\mathrm{nl}(\mathrm{nr}(\Upsilon)) = \Upsilon$ for every proper numeral Υ of length z. Clearly the lemma is equivalent to the proposition that $H = P$.

2. Suppose Υ is any proper numeral of length 1; i.e., $\Upsilon = \langle b\rangle$ for some digit b. Then $\mathrm{nr}(\Upsilon) = b$, and $\mathrm{nl}(b) = \langle b\rangle$, by definitions of nr and nl respectively, and so $\mathrm{nl}(\mathrm{nr}(\Upsilon)) = \Upsilon$. This establishes that $1 \in H$.

3. Now let z be any element of H such that $u \in H$ for every $u \leq z$. We shall show that $z + 1$ is also in H. For this purpose we consider any proper numeral Υ of length $z + 1$, and wish to show that $\mathrm{nl}(\mathrm{nr}(\Upsilon)) = \Upsilon$.

4. Say $Y = \langle b_1, \ldots, b_{z+1}\rangle$. Then we have

$\mathrm{nr}(Y) = \sum \langle b_1, \ldots, b_{z+1}\rangle^*$; by the definition of nr.

$= \sum \langle b_1, b_2 \cdot T, \ldots, b_z \cdot T^{z-1}\rangle + b_{z+1} \cdot T^z$; by the definition of * and $\sum$.

$= \mathrm{nr}\langle b_1, \ldots, b_z\rangle + b_{z+1} \cdot T^z$; by the definition of nr.

Since $\mathrm{nr}\langle b_1, \ldots, b_z\rangle < T^z$ by Lemma 8-9-4.2, it follows from the definitions of quo and rem that

$$\begin{aligned}\mathrm{quo}\langle T^z, \mathrm{nr}(Y)\rangle &= b_{z+1}\\ &\neq 0 \text{ since } Y \text{ is proper,}\\ \mathrm{rem}\langle T^z, \mathrm{nr}(Y)\rangle &= \mathrm{nr}\langle b_1, \ldots, b_z\rangle.\end{aligned}$$

5. From the last equation, and the fact that $z \in H$ (step **3**), it follows that $\mathrm{nl}(\mathrm{rem}\langle T^z, \mathrm{nr}(Y)\rangle) = \langle b_1, \ldots, b_z\rangle$; by step (**1**). Hence by Part (**ii**) of the definition of nl and the second-from-last equation of step (**4**), we obtain

$$\begin{aligned}\mathrm{nl}(\mathrm{nr}(Y)) &= \langle b_1, \ldots, b_z, b_{z+1}\rangle\\ &= Y.\end{aligned}$$

Since Y was any proper numeral of length $z + 1$, this shows that $z + 1 \in H$, and hence complete the proof of Lemma 8-9-4.3 by strong induction.

As explained above, Lemma 8-9-4.3 leads directly to the result that if Y and Y_1 are proper numerals such that $\mathrm{nr}(Y) = x$ and $\mathrm{nr}(Y_1) = x$ (for some $x \in N$), then we must have $Y = Y_1$.

This completes our outline of the proof of Theorem 8-9-4.

Now we give in detail the rule for addition of numerals which is taught in grade school. As the reader will see, the full and precise statement of the rule is much too complicated for students in elementary school, and indeed it presupposes a large part of the theory of positive integers. It is remarkable that, in spite of this, most students master the use of the rule through imitating examples.

DEFINITION 8-9-5. *We define a binary operation $\oplus$ on Nu as follows:*

Case I. We first define $\oplus$ for those ordered pairs $\langle X, Y\rangle$ of numerals such that length X = length Y. The definition will be such that if X, Y both have length z, then $X \oplus Y$ will be of length $z + 1$. The definition proceeds by induction on the length of X.

(**i**) *Suppose X has length 1, say $X = \langle a\rangle$ and $Y = \langle b\rangle$. Then we define*

$$X \oplus Y = \langle \mathrm{rem}\langle T, a +_N b\rangle, \mathrm{quo}\langle T, a +_N b\rangle\rangle.$$

(**ii**) *Suppose z is any element of P and suppose that X is any numeral of length $z + 1$. Say $X = \langle a_1, \ldots, a_{z+1}\rangle$ and $Y = \langle b_1, \ldots, b_{z+1}\rangle$. Let $X' = \langle a_1, \ldots, a_z\rangle$ and $Y' = \langle b_1, \ldots, b_z\rangle$. If $X' \oplus Y' = \langle c_1, \ldots, c_{z+1}\rangle$, then we define $X \oplus Y = \langle c_1, \ldots, c_z, \mathrm{rem}\langle T, a_{z+1} +_N b_{z+1} +_N c_{z+1}\rangle, \mathrm{quo}\langle T, a_{z+1} +_N b_{z+1} +_N c_{z+1}\rangle\rangle$.*

Case II. Suppose X is any numeral of length x and Y is any numeral of length y. Suppose now that $x \neq y$. Then either $x < y$ or $y < x$.

Subcase 2.1. Suppose $x < y$. Then let X_1 be the numeral of length y such that for every $u \leq y$

$$X_1(u) = \begin{cases} X(u) \text{ if } u \leq x \\ 0 \text{ if } u > x. \end{cases}$$

Then we define $X \oplus Y = X_1 \oplus Y$. (The right member is defined by Case I.)

Subcase 2.2. Suppose $y < x$. Then let Y_1 be the numeral of length x such that for every $u \leq x$,

$$Y_1(u) = \begin{cases} Y(u) \text{ if } u \leq y \\ 0 \text{ if } u > y. \end{cases}$$

Then we define $X \oplus Y = X \oplus Y_1$. (The right member is defined by Case I.)

And now we state the fundamental theorem which associates the sum of two numerals with the sum of the corresponding numbers, thus justifying the method of adding numerals which is taught in grade school.

THEOREM 8-9-6. *For any numerals X and Y we have* $\text{nr}(X \oplus Y) = \text{nr}(X) +_N \text{nr}(Y)$.

We shall not give a proof of this theorem.

In principle we could go on from this point to define subtraction and multiplication of two numerals; we could then define division, and justify the process of long division with which we spent many a weary hour in the grades; and in this way we could retrace and justify most of the formal techniques of grade-school arithmetic up to junior-high level. The details would become quite complicated. We shall turn, instead, to a consideration of negative, rational, and real numbers—after an interruption to reexamine logic and the theory of sets.

EXERCISES

1. Show that if Y is a proper numeral and Z a numeral *other* than Y, then: $\text{nr}(Z) = \text{nr}(Y)$ if and only if [length (Z) > length (Y) and for every $u \leq$ length (Z)

$$Z(u) = \begin{cases} Y(u) \text{ if } u \leq \text{length}(Y) \\ 0 \text{ if } u > \text{length}(Y) \end{cases}].$$

2. Show that $x < T^x$ for every $x \in P$.
3.* Prove Lemma 8-9-4.2.

IX

The Theory of Sets

1. Introductory Remarks

We have indicated earlier that if mathematics were to be thought of as having a structure, such as a building, or a tree, we would find logic at the very lowest layer. All of mathematics rests upon logic. Although it is often quite difficult to find the thread of logic in most high-school mathematics courses, or even in many college courses, the reader who has come as far as this chapter should have a clear idea of the extent to which logic pervades the various branches of mathematics (such as the theory of numbers).

Immediately above logic in the structure of mathematics we find the theory of sets. Although the fact that logic plays an important part in the development of mathematics is very widely recognized, generally only the person who has studied mathematics fairly deeply recognizes the almost equally important role of set theory. Actually every branch of mathematics deals with sets.

Our reasons for delaying the study of sets until now were largely pedagogical. If we had approached the retracing of elementary mathematics from a strictly logical standpoint, without regard to pedagogical or psychological considerations, this chapter would have appeared as the second in the book. Chapter I, of course, would have developed the theory of logic.

The pedagogical principle which has prompted us to delay the study of set theory until this point is simply this: We believe that in order to appreciate the axiomatic development of any part of mathematics it is very desirable to have a considerable degree of intuitive acquaintance with the subject beforehand. Now everyone has had intuitive experience with the positive integers and with the extension we have made to the system of natural numbers. We trust the reader will agree that because of his grade-school experience with these numbers the material of Chapters II through VIII has had a much fuller meaning than if he had encountered these concepts here for the first time. But what experience has the reader had with sets? Most elementary courses in mathematics are usually presented in a fashion which completely avoids the concept. For this reason we have included in Chapter I, Section 3, a brief, informal, and intuitive discussion of sets, intended as an introduction to some of the basic concepts of set theory for readers with no prior knowledge of the subject. Subsequently, in our rigorous treatment of Peano models (Chapter III), we made more extensive use of ideas from set theory. We hope that by these means the reader's intuition of the subject has been built up so as to prepare the way for the axiomatic treatment which will be developed in this chapter.

Before commencing the axiomatic treatment, however, as a further aid to an intuitive handling of the concepts of set theory, it may be well to describe a pictorial, or geometric, interpretation often given for some of these concepts. Under this interpretation the abstract objects with which we deal as *elements* of sets are represented as "points" in a "plane," and the sets themselves are represented as "regions" of this plane—often circular regions or at any rate regions bounded by a closed curve. If such a region is taken to represent a set A, then the points of the plane on and inside the boundary represent those objects which are elements of the set A, and the points outside the boundary represent those objects which are not elements of A. Thus in Figure 1 we have a picture representing the two statements "$x \in A$" and "*not* ($y \in A$)." Such a picturization is generally known as a *Venn diagram.*

By this device it is possible to visualize many of the operations on sets, and relations among sets, which were introduced informally in earlier chapters. For example, recalling that the statement B *is a subset of* A (in symbols $B \subseteq A$), means that every element of B is also an element of A, we see that this relation between A and B can be portrayed as in Figure 2, since each point within the boundary of the region B is also inside the boundary of the region A. The set which is the *union* of two sets A and B (in symbols $A \cup B$), whose elements are all those objects which are elements of A or of B (or both), can be indicated by the shaded region in Figure 3. The *intersection* of the same two sets (in symbols $A \cap B$), whose elements are all those objects which are elements *both* of A and of B, is pictured as the cross-hatched region in Figure 3.

Of course, in the above illustrations such words as "point," "plane," "region," "closed curve," etc., have *not* been given precise definitions, and are certainly not a part of our axiomatic development. They are used solely in an intuitive sense.

The reader is cautioned that these Venn diagrams have no official status. They cannot be used in definitions, nor can they be used as arguments for the purpose of establishing theorems. But they *can* serve as aids to understanding, and to suggest possible theorems and methods of proof. In this respect their function is similar to that of diagrams which are often presented to illustrate theorems of elementary geometry.

Our development of set theory will be rigorous (i.e., axiomatic and

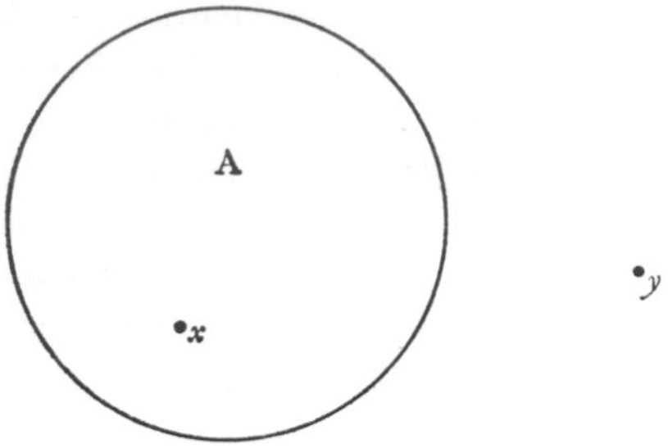

Figure 1

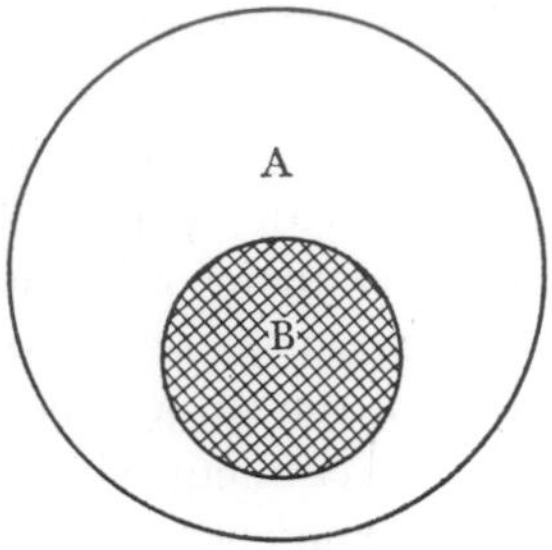

Figure 2

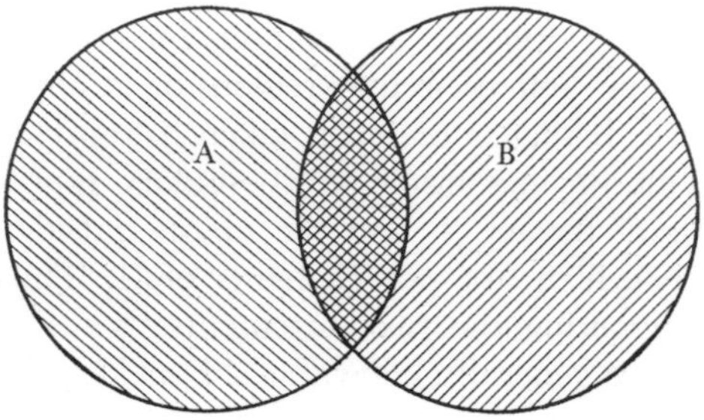

Figure 3

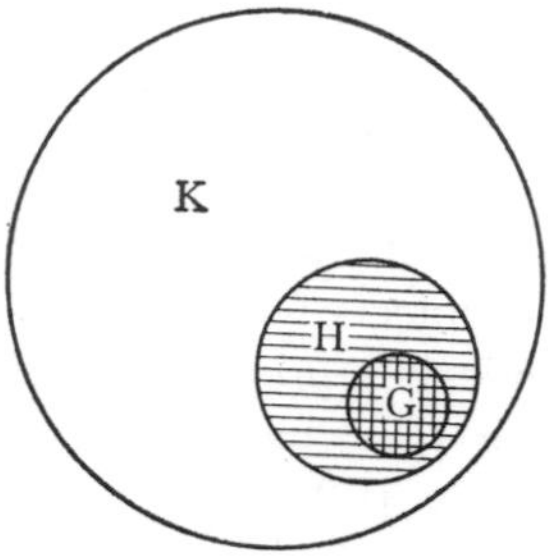

Figure 4

deductive in nature). As in any axiomatic theory we begin with a list of undefined terms and a list of axioms and then proceed to introduce definitions and prove theorems. However, there will be one major difference between our development of set theory and the axiomatic development of number theory which we have given: Whereas in number theory we relied on the reader's intuitive knowledge of set theory and logic in justifying the steps of the proofs of our theorems, in the present theory our justification for such steps will rely *only* on the reader's intuitive knowledge of logic. Naturally, the reader will find employment for his intuitive knowledge of set theory when seeking to guess what theorems can be proved, or in searching for proofs, just as the reader used his intuitive knowledge of numbers to help guess which theorems could be proved for Peano models, or how proofs could be constructed. But once a theorem is formulated and a proof found, the steps of the proof must be justified only by appeals to axioms, definitions, and intuitive use of the laws of logic.

Most elementary accounts of set theory start out by trying to indicate the meaning of the word "set". Some books give other words for "set" such as "collection", or "class", or "family", for example. These beginnings serve some intuitive purpose for those completely lacking in experience with the mathematical use of the word "set", but we are sufficiently familiar with the ways of axiomatic development to recognize that there must be some *undefined* terms at the beginning of such a development, and it turns out to be convenient in formulating the axiomatic theory of sets to take the term "set" itself as one of the undefined terms.

List of Undefined Terms

The term "*set*" shall be undefined. All we know is that certain things are called sets, but we do not try to specify *which* things they are.

The phrase "*is an element of*" (abbreviated by "ϵ") will also be used in our theory without definition. For any object x, and for any thing G which is a set, we suppose that it makes sense to say "x is an element of G"; that is, given x and G, the phrase "$x \in G$" is either true or false; in short, either $x \in G$ or $x \notin G$. But since "ϵ" is undefined, we do not attempt to specify for *which* x and G we have $x \in G$, or for *which* we have $x \notin G$. Objects which are elements of a set are also called *members* of that set.

The terms "set" and "ϵ" are the only undefined terms of our theory. So we proceed to list some axioms involving these terms, which state certain facts we shall assume about the unspecified sets and their members. Before doing so, however, we wish to remark on certain difficulties in formulating a list of axioms for set theory which were not present in the formulation of the axioms of number theory. It turns out that we shall need an *infinite number* of axioms in order to get an adequate theory of sets. This in itself is not an insurmountable difficulty, but it does necessitate finding a method of writing axioms by means other than listing them one by one. We shall see that this can be accomplished by grouping the axioms and describing all those which fall in one group by means of a single *schema*. Actually, we shall consider two different systems of axioms for the theory of sets, each of which is based upon the undefined concepts of *set* and ϵ. In Section 2 we shall present a system, associated with the name of the German mathematician Georg Cantor, representing what was historically the first comprehensive theory of sets. The second system, due to Ernest Zermelo (also a German), is described in Section 10 and corrects an important defect which will be pointed out in the Cantor system. We give the Cantor theory, despite its defective character, not only for historical reasons but also because it has a much simpler character than any other theory of sets.

Exercises

1. Let A, B, and C be sets such that: The elements of A are the numbers 1, 2, 3, 4, 5, 6, 7, 8; the elements of B are the numbers 2, 4, 6, 8; and the elements of C are the numbers 3, 5, 7, 9. Describe which objects are elements of each of

(a) $A \cap B$, (d) $A \cup (B \cup C)$,
(b) $A \cup C$, (e) $A \cap (B \cup C)$,
(c) $B \cap C$, (f) $A \cup (B \cap C)$.

2. For the sets A, B, C of problem **1**, which of the following statements are true:

(a) $B \subseteq A$,
(b) $C \subseteq A$,
(c) $B \cup C = C \cup B$,
(d) $A \cap (B \cup C) = (A \cap B) \cup (A \cap C)$,
(e) $A \cup (B \cap C) = (A \cup B) \cap (A \cup C)$?

3. By considering Venn diagrams try to guess which of the following statements are correct. For *any* sets A, B, C,

(a) $A \cap (B \cap C) = (A \cap B) \cup (A \cap C)$,
(b) $A \cap (B \cap C) = (A \cap B) \cap (A \cap C)$,
(c) $A \cup (B \cap C) = (A \cup B) \cap (A \cup C)$,
(d) If $A \subseteq B$ and $B \subseteq C$, then $A \subseteq C$,
(e) If $A \subseteq B$ and $B \subseteq A$, then $A = B$.

2. *Cantor's Development of the Theory of Sets*

In the 1870's the German mathematician Georg Cantor, following up ideas which he was led to develop in his efforts to solve a problem involving the system of real numbers, created the first version of the modern theory of sets. Cantor's treatment of the theory was not axiomatic, but a study of his work shows that it rests essentially on two fundamental principles. In this section we shall formulate these principles as axioms, and will indicate how the elementary development of Cantor's theory can be based upon them.

In addition to logical terminology our axioms will involve just the undefined terms, "*set*" and "*is an element of*", introduced in Section 1. For any object x, and for any thing G which is a set, the statement "x is an element of G" (abbreviated "$x \in G$") is either true or false.

Our first axiom will be a principle we have frequently used, on an intuitive basis, in our axiomatic development of the theory of positive integers.

AXIOM C1. THE AXIOM OF EXTENSIONALITY. *If G and H are any sets, and if for every object x we have $x \in G$ if and only if $x \in H$, then $G = H$.*

This axiom states that if G is a set and H is a set, and if the objects which are elements of G are exactly the same objects which are elements of H, then G and H are the same set. Put another way, whenever we have two different sets there must be an object which is an element of one of them but is not an element of the other. We sometimes express the content of this axiom by saying that a set is "completely determined" by the objects which are its elements.

Before we state the next axiom we wish to illustrate one of the notions from logic which we will need—that of a *sentential formula*. The phrase "x is a president of a republic" is one example of a sentential formula. We notice that if we replace the symbol "x" in this phrase by the name of a person we get a definite sentence which is either true or false. We shall use the notation "$S(x)$" to represent such a sentential formula. For another example consider the phrase "x is the president of the country y." This is a sentential formula with two variables. If we replace "x" and "y" by names of specific objects we again obtain a sentence which is either true or false.

We are now ready to state our second axiom. The reader will notice that it is not merely a single axiom but rather a scheme for writing infinitely many axioms, each axiom being determined by a sentential formula.

AXIOM C2. AXIOM SCHEMA OF SET-FORMATION. *Consider any sentential formula $S(x)$ which contains the letter "x" (and possibly others), but not the letter "G". Then the following shall be an axiom:*

There exists a set G such that for every object x we have $x \in G$ if and only if $S(x)$.

To illustrate the use of this axiom schema, we can infer from it that there is a set G such that for every object x we have $x \in G$ if and only if x is the president of a republic. That is, the schema permits us to write an axiom asserting the existence of a set whose members are all presidents of republics (and no others). As another example, there is a set G such that for every object x we have $x \in G$ if and only if x is the president of the country y. This instance of Axiom Schema C2 is intended to assert that for an arbitrary country y, there is a set whose members consist of all the presidents of that country.

These illustrations indicate one obvious way in which Axiom Schema C2 can be used to infer the existence of a set every element of which has a certain property. Yet it must not be assumed that all of the elements of a set must have a common property (other than being elements of the set). Consider, for example, the following sentential formula: "Either x is a purchaser of this book, or x is an air-borne B-52." Axiom Schema C2 asserts the existence of a set G which contains among its elements all of the buyers of this book, and in addition certain air-borne planes; yet there is probably very little in common between a plane in flight and the discriminating type of person who has bought this book.

For another example take $S(x)$ to be: "Either x is the city of Nanking or x is the Dodger baseball team or x is the planet Venus." Using this in Axiom Schema C2 we see that there is a set whose elements are just these three objects: Nanking, the Dodgers, and Venus. Clearly, in an analogous way any objects, however unrelated, may be brought together as objects of a single set.

Using the undefined terms "set" and "is an element of", the Axioms C1 and Schema C2 as given above, and the laws of logic, we now prove an important theorem which strengthens Axiom C2 by combining it with Axiom C1. This theorem, like C2, is actually a schema which permits us to obtain many different theorems, each one corresponding to a sentential formula.

THEOREM 9-2-1. *Suppose that* $S(x)$ *is any sentential formula containing the letter "*x*" (and possibly others), but not the letter "*G*". Then the following is a theorem: There exists one and only one set* G *such that for every object* x *we have* $x \in G$ *if and only if* $S(x)$.

That there exists *at least one* such set G follows immediately from Axiom C2, of course. That this is a unique set, however, requires proof. How should this be done? The basic idea is to consider *any two* such sets and to show that they must be the same.

Proof of Theorem 9-2-1

▶▶ **1.** Let $S(x)$ be a sentential formula.
▶▶ **2.** There is a set G such that for every object x we have $x \in G$ if and only if $S(x)$; by line **1** and Axiom Schema C2.
▶▶ **3.** Let H be *any* set such that for every x we have $x \in H$ if and only if $S(x)$.
▶ **4.** Let x be any object.
5. $x \in G$ if and only if $S(x)$; by lines **2** and **4**.
6. $x \in H$ if and only if $S(x)$; by lines **3** and **4**.
▶ **7.** $x \in G$ if and only if $x \in H$; by logic, applied to lines **5** and **6**. (The law of logic used here is a double-barreled application of the transitive property of implication, and may be stated as follows. From any two statements of the form "P if and only if Q" and "R if and only if Q," we may infer "P if and only if R.")
8. If x is any object, then $x \in G$ if and only if $x \in H$; by the Deduction Theorem applied to lines **4** through **7**.
▶▶ **9.** $G = H$; by line **8** and Axiom C1.
▶▶ **10.** If H is any set such that for all x we have $x \in H$ if and only if $S(x)$, then $G = H$; by the Deduction Theorem applied to lines **3** through **9**.
11. G is the only set such that for every object x we have $x \in G$ if and only if $S(x)$; by lines **2** and **10**.
12. For any sentential formula $S(x)$ there is one and only one set G such that for every object x we have $x \in G$ if and only if $S(x)$; by the Deduction Theorem applied to lines **1** through **11**.

Notation: The unique set G which corresponds to a given sentential formula $S(x)$, according to Theorem 9-2-1, will be symbolized by $\{x \mid S(x)\}$ and read "The set of all objects x such that $S(x)$."

As an application of the above theorem and notational convention, let us consider an example in which we take $S(x)$ to be the sentential formula: "x is an artificial satellite of the planet Earth." Axiom C2 above asserts that there exists a set having as its elements all those objects which are artificial satellites of Earth; but it leaves open the possibility that there is more than one such set. But Theorem 9-2-1 asserts not only that there is such a set, but that there is *only one*. According to our notational convention we use the expression "$\{x \mid x$ is an artificial satellite of the planet Earth$\}$" to denote this set. In common language, this is simply *the set of all artificial satellites of Earth*.

The following theorem schema combines Theorem 9-2-1 with our notational convention in a form useful for later reference.

THEOREM 9-2-2. *Let $S(x)$ be a sentential formula containing the letter "x" (and possibly others). Then the following is a theorem: For every object x we have $x \in \{x \mid S(x)\}$ if and only if $S(x)$.*

Proof

By the meaning of the notation $\{x \mid S(x)\}$ according to our convention, combined with Theorem 9-2-1.

As an instance of this theorem schema we see that for every object x we have $x \in \{x \mid x$ is a congressman$\}$ if and only if x is a congressman. This is hardly remarkable, since $\{x \mid x$ is a congressman$\}$ is our notation for the set of all objects x such that x is a congressman, i.e., for the set of all congressmen. Thus we are asserting nothing more than that an object x is an element of the set of all congressmen if and only if x is a congressman.

3. Subsets. The Null Set

So far we have not introduced any defined notions in our development of set theory. Now let us consider our first defined concept—that of a *subset*. We have used this idea frequently in earlier parts of the book, relying on the reader's intuitive understanding of sets. Here is a precise definition.

DEFINITION 9-3-1. *Let G and H be any sets. We say that G is a* **subset** *of H (Notation: $G \subseteq H$) if and only if, for all objects x, if $x \in G$ then also $x \in H$.*

As an illustration, suppose that H is the set of all positive integers from 1 to 100 inclusive, and that G is the set of all positive *odd* integers from 1 to 99 inclusive. Take any object x whatever. If $x \in G$ (i.e., if x is some odd integer from 1 to 99), then certainly $x \in H$. Hence $G \subseteq H$. Another illustration is given by the Venn diagram shown in Figure 2.

The notation which we have introduced to indicate the subset relation, $\subseteq$, is suggestive of the less-than-or-equal-to relation, $\leq$, familiar to us from the study of the number system. This may lead the reader to suspect that some of the properties of $\leq$ also hold for $\subseteq$. Let us consider, for example, the fundamental transitive property. Does it hold for $\subseteq$? Is it true, in other words, that whenever we have $G \subseteq H$ and $H \subseteq K$ then we must also have $G \subseteq K$? The Venn diagram of Figure 4, which pictures $G \subseteq H$ and $H \subseteq K$, would appear to indicate an affirmative answer. This indication can be justified by a rigorous proof within our axiomatic theory, and so we have the following important theorem.

THEOREM 9-3-2. THE TRANSITIVE LAW FOR $\subseteq$. *If G, H, K are any sets such that $G \subseteq H$ and $H \subseteq K$, then $G \subseteq K$.*

Proof

1. Let G, H, K be any sets such that $G \subseteq H$ and $H \subseteq K$.
2. For all x, if $x \in G$ then $x \in H$; and for all x, if $x \in H$ then $x \in K$; by line **1** and Definition 9-3-1.
3. For all x, if $x \in G$ then $x \in K$; by logic applied to line **2**.
4. $G \subseteq K$; by line **3** and Definition 9-3-1.
5. If G, H, K are any sets such that $G \subseteq H$ and $H \subseteq K$, then $G \subseteq K$; by the Deduction Theorem applied to lines **1** through **4**.

Remark: The law of logic used in passing from line **2** to line **3** is the transitive law for "if . . . then". This law states that from any sentences "if P then Q" and "if Q then R" we may infer the sentence "if P then R".

The reader will notice that our proofs so far (Theorems 9-2-1 and 9-3-2) have used only axioms or definitions of set theory, and rules of logic. But as a matter of fact, in our last proof we did not use *any* of the *axioms* of set theory—only Definition 9-3-1! This illustrates a point made earlier, namely, that definitions are just as important as axioms in producing theorems. Indeed, we see now that there are proofs in mathematics which do not use any of the axioms of the theory, but only the definitions.

The next theorem is one of the most useful in all of set theory. It is a very simple consequence of Axiom C1 and Definition 9-3-1, and the proof will be left as an exercise for the reader.

THEOREM 9-3-3. *If G and H are any sets such that $G \subseteq H$ and $H \subseteq G$, then $G = H$.*

Proof. See Exercise below.

In the theory of numbers it is useful to have a zero element. However, we developed a large portion of this theory before we introduced the number zero in Chapter VIII. In set theory there is a corresponding concept, that of a *null set*, and we choose to introduce the concept early.

DEFINITION 9-3-4. *The set* $\{x \mid x \neq x\}$, *i.e., the set of all those objects* x *such that* $x \neq x$, *is called the* **null set**. *We use the symbol* "$\varnothing$" *to denote this set:* $\varnothing = \{x \mid x \neq x\}$.

As we shall see later, the null set, $\varnothing$, plays much the same role in the algebra of sets as the number zero plays in our ordinary number system. However, the null set is actually something quite distinct from zero—it is a set, rather than a number. But the number of objects which are elements of the null set is zero—that is, the null set has *no* elements. This is the content of the next theorem, which we shall prove by contradiction.

THEOREM 9-3-5. *For every object* x *we have* $x \notin \varnothing$.

Proof

1. Suppose x is any object such that $x \in \varnothing$.
2. $x \in \varnothing$ if and only if $x \neq x$; by Definition 9-3-4 and Theorem Schema 9-2-2, taking $S(x)$ to be "$x \neq x$".
3. $x \neq x$; by lines **1** and **2**.
4. $x = x$; by E.
5. For any object x, if $x \in \varnothing$ then $x \neq x$ and $x = x$; by the Deduction Theorem applied to lines **1** through **3** and **4**.
6. For every object x we have $x \notin \varnothing$; by logic from line **5**.

The concepts of subset and null set are combined in the following theorem.

THEOREM 9-3-6. *If* G *is any set, then* $\varnothing \subseteq G$ *and* $G \subseteq G$.

Proof (of the first part of the theorem)

1. Let G be any set.
2. For any object x, $x \notin \varnothing$; by Theorem 9-3-5.
3. For any object x, if $x \in \varnothing$ then $x \in G$; by logic from line **2**.
4. $\varnothing \subseteq G$; by line **3** and Definition 9-3-1.
5. If G is any set than $\varnothing \subseteq G$; by the Deduction Theorem applied to lines **1** through **4**.

Remark on the proof of Theorem 9-3-6. The law of logic used to infer line **3** from line **2** is the following: The conditional sentence "If P then Q" is true whenever P, the antecedent sentence, is false. If we take P to be the sentence "$x \in \varnothing$" then we see that P is false from line **2**. Hence if we let Q be the statement "$x \in G$", the statement "If P than Q" is true, as asserted on line **3**.

EXERCISE

Prove Theorem 9-3-3.

4. Operations on Sets: Intersection, Union, and Complementation

We have already encountered the concept of *intersection* of sets in our informal use of set theory. We shall now introduce it formally into our development by means of a definition.

DEFINITION 9-4-1. *If H and K are any two sets we define the* **intersection** *of H and K (in symbols, $H \cap K$), to be the set $\{x \mid x \in H \text{ and } x \in K\}$.*

Referring to the meaning of the notation $\{x \mid S(x)\}$ (following Theorem 9-2-1), we see that an object x is an element of $H \cap K$ if and only if it is an element both of H and of K. This fact is expressed in the following theorem.

THEOREM 9-4-2. *If H and K are any sets, and if x is any object, then we have $x \in (H \cap K)$ if and only if $x \in H$ and $x \in K$.*

Proof

By Theorem 9-2-2 and Definition 9-4-1.

To illustrate this concept of intersection, let us consider several examples. Suppose that $H = \{x \mid x \text{ is a horse}\}$, i.e., H is the set of all horses. Suppose that $J = \{x \mid x \text{ has red hair}\}$, i.e., J is the set of all red-haired creatures. And suppose that $K = \{x \mid x \text{ is a woman}\}$, i.e., K is the set of all women. Then the intersection $H \cap J$ would be the set of all red-haired horses, the intersection $J \cap K$ would be the set of all red-haired women, and the intersection $H \cap K$ would be the null set, $\varnothing$.

From the definition of intersection we see that this operation is closely associated with the logical concept of conjunction (the "and" concept). Not so evident is the fact that there is also a connection between the intersection operation for sets and the multiplication operation for numbers. In fact, some authors use the multiplication symbol "$\cdot$" in place of the symbol "$\cap$" to indicate intersection. In the list of fundamental properties of the intersection operation which is given in the following theorem, each of the parts (**b**), (**c**), and (**d**) suggests a law of multiplication.

THEOREM 9-4-3. *For any sets H, K, J we have*

(**a**) $H \cap H = H$ (THE IDEMPOTENT LAW FOR $\cap$);
(**b**) $H \cap K = K \cap H$ (THE COMMUTATIVE LAW FOR $\cap$);
(**c**) $(H \cap K) \cap J = H \cap (K \cap J)$ (THE ASSOCIATIVE LAW FOR $\cap$);
(**d**) $H \cap \varnothing = \varnothing$.

We shall give a proof of Part (**b**) and leave the proofs of the remaining parts as exercises for the reader.

Proof of Part (**b**).

▶▶**1.** Let H, K be any two sets.

▶▶**2.** Let x be any object.

▶**3.** $x \in (H \cap K)$ if and only if $x \in H$ and $x \in K$; by lines **1** and **2** and Theorem 9-4-2.

▶**4.** $x \in (K \cap H)$ if and only if $x \in K$ and $x \in H$; by lines **1** and **2** and Theorem 9-4-2.

▶▶**5.** ($x \in H$ and $x \in K$) if and only if ($x \in K$ and $x \in H$); by logic (the commutative law for conjunction).

▶▶**6.** $x \in (H \cap K)$ if and only if $x \in (K \cap H)$; by lines **3**, **4**, and **5**.

7. For any object x, we have $x \in (H \cap K)$ if and only if $x \in (K \cap H)$; by the Deduction Theorem applied to lines **2** through **6**.

▶▶**8.** $H \cap K = K \cap H$; by line **7** and Axiom C1 (the Principle of Extensionality).

9. For any sets H, K, we have $H \cap K = K \cap H$; by the Deduction Theorem applied to lines **1** through **8**.

Note: The key step in the proof above is step **5**, the justification for which is the commutative law for conjunction (one of the elementary laws of logic). Similarly, in the proofs of each of the other parts of Theorem 9-4-3 the key step will be justified by one of the elementary laws of logic involving conjunction. For example, the key step in the proof of Part (**a**) will be justified by the "idempotent law of conjunction" which states that for all sentences P we have "(P and P) if and only if P".

The next step in developing our theory is to define a set-theoretic concept which is closely associated with the logical concept of disjunction (in the same way that intersection is associated with conjunction).

DEFINITION 9-4-4. *If H and K are any two sets we define the* **union** *of H and K (in symbols, $H \cup K$), to be the set $\{x \mid x \in H$ or $x \in K\}$.*

Recalling the meaning of the notation $\{x \mid S(x)\}$, we see that an object x is an element of $H \cup K$ if and only if it is an element of H or an element of K (or, of course, an element of both—since the word "or" is always used in its inclusive sense in mathematics). This fact is expressed in the following theorem.

THEOREM 9-4-5. *For any sets H, K and any object x we have $x \in (H \cup K)$ if and only if $x \in H$ or $x \in K$.*

Proof

By Theorem 9-2-2 and Definition 9-4-4.

To illustrate the concept, let us refer to the sets H and K given in the example following Theorem 9-4-2. Then the set $H \cup K$ is the set whose elements consist of all horses and all women (including, of course, any creatures who are both!). For another illustration take H to be the set of all people taller than 5 feet, and take K to be the set of all people shorter than 6 feet. Then $H \cup K$ is the set of all people.

It is worth noting that several of the properties of the operation of union for sets are suggestive of properties of the operation of addition for numbers. Indeed, we can think of the union of two sets, H and K, as the set obtained by "adding" the elements of H to those of K (except, of course, that we do not have to add those elements of H which are already in K). Some authors emphasize the similarity of the two operations by using the "+" symbol, rather than "$\cup$", to indicate union.

The next theorem lists the properties of union, which are entirely analogous to the properties of intersection listed in Theorem 9-4-3. Parts **b**, **c**, and **d** resemble laws of addition.

THEOREM 9-4-6. *For any sets H, J, K we have*

(**a**) $H \cup H = H$ (THE IDEMPOTENT LAW FOR $\cup$);
(**b**) $H \cup K = K \cup H$ (THE COMMUTATIVE LAW FOR $\cup$);
(**c**) $(H \cup K) \cup J = H \cup (K \cup J)$ (THE ASSOCIATIVE LAW FOR $\cup$);
(**d**) $H \cup \varnothing = H$.

The proof will be left as an exercise. The key step in the proof of each part of this theorem will be justified by the corresponding law for disjunction. For example, in proving (**c**) we use the law of logic which states that from a sentence of the form ((P or Q) or R) we may infer the sentence (P or (Q or R)).

The reader will recall that there are laws in the theory of numbers (such as the distributive law of $\cdot$ over $+$) which involve both of the operations $+$ and $\cdot$. Since intersection and union are operations on sets which we have already seen to resemble multiplication and addition, the reader will not be surprised to learn that there are laws which involve both intersection and union. The next theorem lists some of these fundamental laws.

THEOREM 9-4-7. *If H, J, K are any sets we have*

(**a**) $H \cap (H \cup J) = H$ *and* $H \cup (H \cap J) = H$ (*these are called* ABSORPTION LAWS);
(**b**) $H \cap (J \cup K) = (H \cap J) \cup (H \cap K)$ (*the* DISTRIBUTIVE LAW OF $\cap$ OVER $\cup$);
(**c**) $H \cup (J \cap K) = (H \cup J) \cap (H \cup K)$ (*the* DISTRIBUTIVE LAW OF $\cup$ OVER $\cap$).

Of the three parts of this theorem, only part (**b**) has an analogue in the theory of integers. We shall prove one of the two absorption laws given in part (**a**), leaving the remaining parts as an exercise.

Proof of the first Absorption Law

▶▶ **1.** Let H and J be any two sets.

▶▶ **2.** Let x be any object.

3. $x \in H \cup J$ if and only if either $x \in H$ or $x \in J$; by lines **1** and **2** and Theorem 9-4-5.

4. $x \in (H \cap (H \cup J))$ if and only if $x \in H$ and $x \in (H \cup J)$; by lines **1** and **2** and Theorem 9-4-2.

▶ **5.** $x \in (H \cap (H \cup J))$ if and only if $x \in H$ and either $x \in H$ or $x \in J$; by logic from lines **3** and **4**. [The law of logic used here states that from statements of the form (P if and only if Q and R), and (R if and only if S), we may infer (P if and only if Q and S).]

6. If $x \in H$, then either $x \in H$ or $x \in J$; by logic (based upon the inclusive use of the word "or").

7. If $x \in H$, then $x \in H$ and either $x \in H$ or $x \in J$; by logic from line **6**.

8. If $x \in H$ and either $x \in H$ or $x \in J$, then $x \in H$; by logic.

▶ **9.** $x \in H$ if and only if ($x \in H$ and either $x \in H$ or $x \in J$); by logic from lines **7** and **8**.

▶▶ **10.** $x \in (H \cap (H \cup J))$ if and only if $x \in H$; by logic from lines **5** and **9**.

11. For any object x we have $x \in (H \cap (H \cup J))$ if and only if $x \in H$; by the Deduction Theorem applied to lines **2** through **10**.

▶▶ **12.** $H \cap (H \cup J) = H$; by line **11** and Axiom C1 (the Principle of Extensionality).

13. If H and J are any sets then $H \cap (H \cup J) = H$; by the Deduction Theorem applied to lines **1** through **12**.

Note. It would have been possible to omit lines **6** through **8** of this proof, justifying line **9** directly by a law of logic. But since the law in question is not so familiar, we have preferred to insert the additional lines **6** through **8**. For a better understanding of the laws of logic used in proofs of this kind, the reader is referred to Chapter X.

To illustrate this Absorption Law, let us take H to be the set of all single-engine airplanes and J to be the set of all jet airplanes. Then $H \cup J$ is the set of all planes which have just one engine or which are jet propelled (or both, of course). By definition of intersection, and our choice of H, we see that $H \cap (H \cup J)$ has as its elements all those single-engine airplanes which are in the set $H \cup J$ just described. But these are nothing more or less than all single-engine airplanes. So $H \cap (H \cup J)$ is the same as H.

There are many places in mathematics where we encounter pairs of operations each of which is idempotent, commutative, associative, and which together satisfy the absorption laws. For example, the operations gcd and lcm of number theory are such a pair, as the reader can see by referring back to Chapter V. This has led mathematicians to study such pairs of operations abstractly, i.e., axiomatically. In other words, we consider a set of undefined objects and two undefined binary operations on this set, and we postulate the idempotent, commutative, associative, and absorption laws as axioms. Any model of these axioms is called a *lattice*. If, in addition to satisfying the axioms, a lattice satisfies the distributive laws, it is called a *distributive lattice*. Thus, in particular, the operations of union and intersection (together with the sets on which they act) constitute a distributive lattice as we see from Theorems 9-4-3, 9-4-6, and 9-4-7. In fact, so do the pair of operations gcd and lcm acting on P.

Now we shall state a theorem which ties up the notion of subset with those of union and intersection.

THEOREM 9-4-8.

(**a**) *For any sets H, K we have $H \subseteq K$ if and only if $H \cap K = H$.*
(**b**) *For any sets H, K we have $H \subseteq K$ if and only if $H \cup K = K$.*
(**c**) *For any sets H and K we have $H \subseteq H \cup K$ and $K \subseteq H \cup K$; and if J is **any** set such that $H \subseteq J$ and $K \subseteq J$, then $H \cup K \subseteq J$.*
(**d**) *For any sets H and K we have $H \cap K \subseteq H$ and $H \cap K \subseteq K$; and if J is **any** set such that $J \subseteq H$ and $J \subseteq K$, then $J \subseteq H \cap K$.*

As usual with theorems in this section, we shall prove only one part and leave the remaining parts—whose proofs all follow the same pattern—for the interested reader to try for himself. In this case we shall prove part (**d**). Before doing so, however, we remark that the first part of (**d**), the statement that $(H \cap K) \subseteq H$ and $(H \cap K) \subseteq K$, is sometimes expressed by saying that $H \cap K$ is a *lower bound* for the two sets H and K. Then the second part of (**d**) can be expressed by saying that if J is *any* lower bound for the two sets, then $J \subseteq (H \cap K)$; and *this* is sometimes expressed by saying that $H \cap K$ is the *greatest lower bound* for H and K. In a similar manner part (**c**) is sometimes expressed by saying that $H \cup K$ is the *least upper bound* for the two sets, H and K.

Proof of (**d**)

▶▶ **1.** Let H, K be *any* sets.
2. Suppose that x is any element of $H \cap K$.
3. $x \in H$ and $x \in K$; by line **2** and Theorem 9-4-2.
4. $x \in H$; by logic from line **3**.

▶ **5.** If x is any element of $H \cap K$, then also $x \in H$; by the Deduction Theorem applied to lines **2** through **4**.

▶▶ **6.** $(H \cap K) \subseteq H$; by line **5** and Definition 9-3-1.

▶▶ **7.** $(H \cap K) \subseteq K$; by reasoning similar to lines **4** through **6**.

▶▶ **8.** Let J be any set such that $J \subseteq H$ and $J \subseteq K$.

9. Suppose that y is any element of J.

10. $y \in H$ and $y \in K$; by lines **8** and **9** and Definition 9-3-1.

11. $y \in (H \cap K)$; by line **10** and Theorem 9-4-2.

▶ **12.** If y is any element of J, then also $y \in (H \cap K)$; by the Deduction Theorem applied to lines **9** through **11**.

▶▶ **13.** $J \subseteq (H \cap K)$; by line **12** and Definition 9-3-1.

14. If J is any set such that $J \subseteq H$ and $J \subseteq K$, then $J \subseteq (H \cap K)$; by the Deduction Theorem applied to lines **8** through **13**.

15. For any sets H and K we have $(H \cap K) \subseteq H$ and $(H \cap K) \subseteq K$; and if J is any set such that $J \subseteq H$ and $J \subseteq K$, then $J \subseteq (H \cap K)$; by the Deduction Theorem applied to lines **1** through **6**, **7**, and **14**.

In addition to the binary operations $\cap$ and $\cup$ on sets, a unary operation known as *complementation* is often considered. This is introduced in the following definition.

DEFINITION 9-4-9. *If H is any set we define the* **complement** *of H (in symbols, $\sim H$) to be the set $\{x \mid x \notin H\}$.*

Referring to the meaning of notation of the form $\{x \mid S(x)\}$ we see that an object x is in the complement of a set H if and only if x is not in H; that is, the elements of $\sim H$ are all and only those objects which are not in H. This is expressed in the following theorem.

THEOREM 9-4-10. *If H is any set and x any object, then $x \in \sim H$ if and only if $x \notin H$.*

Proof

By Theorem 9-2-2 and Definition 9-4-9.

The most elementary property of the operation of complementation is given in the next theorem.

THEOREM 9-4-11. *For any set H we have $\sim\sim H = H$.*

The key law of logic necessary for the proof of this theorem is the following: For any sentence P, we have "P if and only if *not* (*not* P)". This law is sometimes called the *Law of Double Negation*. We leave the reader to construct a detailed proof of Theorem 9-4-11.

There are various laws which connect the operation $\sim$ with the operations $\cap$ and $\cup$, and with the relation $\subseteq$. The most important of these are combined in the following theorem.

THEOREM 9-4-12. *For any sets H and K,*

(**a**) $\sim(H \cup K) = (\sim H) \cap (\sim K)$ *and* $\sim(H \cap K) = (\sim H) \cup (\sim K)$ (De Morgan's Law);

(**b**) $H \subseteq K$ *if and only if* $\sim K \subseteq \sim H$;

(**c**) $H \cap \sim H = \varnothing$, *and for every object x we have* $x \in (H \cup \sim H)$.

The several parts of this theorem can be established by the same basic pattern which has been used in proving other theorems of this section. However, by means of a "trick," the proof of part (**b**) can be brought to an end in a form rather different from the usual, and we show this below.

Proof of (**b**)

▶▶ **1.** Let H and K be any sets such that $H \subseteq K$.

▶ **2.** Suppose that x is any element of $\sim K$.

3. $x \notin K$; by line **2** and Theorem 9-4-10.

4. If $x \in H$ then $x \in K$; by line **1** and Definition 9-3-1.

5. $x \notin H$; by logic from lines **3** and **4**. [The law of logic used here states that from two statements of the form *If P then Q* and *not-Q*, we may infer *not-P*.]

▶ **6.** $x \in \sim H$; by line **5** and Theorem 9-4-10.

7. If x is any element of $\sim K$, then x is also an element of $\sim H$; by the Deduction Theorem applied to lines **2** through **8**.

▶▶ **8.** $\sim K \subseteq \sim H$; by line **7** and Definition 9-3-1.

9. If H and K are any sets such that $H \subseteq K$, then $\sim K \subseteq \sim H$; by the Deduction Theorem applied to lines **1** through **8**.

▶ **10.** If H and K are any sets such that $\sim K \subseteq \sim H$, then $\sim\sim H \subseteq \sim\sim K$; *by line* **9**! Since line **9** is a general statement which has been established for arbitrary sets, we may apply it to any particular case. In the application we require, the set H of line **9** is taken to be the set $\sim K$ in line **10**; and the K of line **9** is taken to be the set $\sim H$ in line **10**.

▶ **11.** For any sets H and K we have $\sim\sim H = H$ and $\sim\sim K = K$; by Theorem 9-4-11.

▶▶ **12.** If H and K are any sets such that $\sim K \subseteq \sim H$, then $H \subseteq K$; by E applied to lines **10** and **11**.

13. If H and K are any sets, then $H \subseteq K$ if and only if $\sim K \subseteq \sim H$; by lines **9** and **12**.

Recall that before formulating Theorem 9-4-8 we mentioned briefly the notion of a *lattice*, in the sense of modern abstract algebra, and more particularly a *distributive lattice*. In the study of lattice theory one often considers a distributive lattice which possesses a unary operation obeying the laws of complementation which are listed in Theorems 9-4-11 and 9-4-12. An algebraic structure of this kind is called a *Boolean Algebra*. (The name is derived from the English mathematician, George Boole, who was one of the first mathematicians to attack the problems of logic symbolically.)

EXERCISES

1. Prove the remaining parts of Theorem 9-4-3.
2. Prove Theorem 9-4-6.
3. Prove parts (**a**) and (**c**) of Theorem 9-4-7.
4. Prove parts (**a**), (**b**) and (**c**) of Theorem 9-4-8.
5. Prove Theorem 9-4-11.
6. Prove parts (**a**) and (**c**) of Theorem 9-4-12.

5. *Unit Sets and Pairs; Ordered Pairs*

The part of set theory which we have outlined so far is often called the "Boolean part" of set theory. Most elementary treatises on set theory contain this material. However, the theory of sets is much richer. In particular, two important concepts, those of *relation* and *function*, which in earlier theories were taken as primitive notions (i.e., undefined terms), can be introduced into set theory as defined notions. This possibility was discovered in 1920 by two mathematicians working quite independently: Casimir Kuratowski, of Poland, and Norbert Wiener, of the United States.

Before examining the method for bringing relations and functions into our theory we shall introduce the concepts of *unit set*, *pair*, and *ordered pair*, and shall consider some of their properties.

DEFINITION 9-5-1. *If y is any object, we define the* **unit set** *of y (in symbols, $\{y\}$) to be the set $\{x \mid x = y\}$. And if y and z are any objects, we define the* **pair** *of y and z to be the set $\{x \mid x = y$ or $x = z\}$. We denote this pair by $\{y, z\}$.*

The intuitive significance of unit sets and pairs is made evident in the following theorem.

THEOREM 9-5-2. *Suppose that y and z are any objects. Then:*

(**a**) $y \in \{y\}$;
(**b**) *the* **only** *element of $\{y\}$ is the object y;*
(**c**) $y \in \{y, z\}$ *and* $z \in \{y, z\}$;
(**d**) *the* **only** *elements of $\{y, z\}$ are the objects y and z.*

We shall give proofs for parts (**b**) and (**c**); the remaining parts may be proved similarly.

Proof of (**b**)

1. For any object x we have $x \in \{y\}$ if and only if $x = y$; by Definition 9-5-1 and Theorem 9-2-2.
2. If x is any element of $\{y\}$ then $x = y$; by logic from line **1**.
3. The *only* element of $\{y\}$ is the object y; by logic from line **2**.

Proof of (**c**)

1. For any object x we have $x \in \{y, z\}$ if and only if $x = y$ or $x = z$; by Definition 9-5-1 and Theorem 9-2-2.
2. $y \in \{y, z\}$ if and only if $y = y$ or $y = z$; by logic from line **1**.
3. $y = y$; by E.
4. $y = y$ or $y = z$; by logic from line **3**.
5. $y \in \{y, z\}$; by logic from lines **2** and **4**.
6. $z \in \{y, z\}$; by reasoning similar to lines **3** through **5**.

Several fundamental properties of unit sets and pairs are contained in the following theorem.

THEOREM 9-5-3. *Suppose that y, z, u, and v are any objects. Then:*

(**a**) $\{y, z\} = \{z, y\}$;
(**b**) $\{y\} \cup \{z\} = \{y, z\}$;
(**c**) $\{y, y\} = \{y\}$;
(**d**) *If* $\{y\} = \{z\}$ *then* $y = z$;
(**e**) *If* $\{y, z\} = \{u, v\}$ *then either* $y = u$ *and* $z = v$, *or* $y = v$ *and* $z = u$.

We shall give proofs for parts (**a**) and (**e**), leaving the remaining parts to the reader.

Proof of (**a**)

1. For any objects y, z we have $z \in \{z, y\}$ and $y \in \{z, y\}$; by Theorem 9-5-2(**c**). (Note that in this line the y of Theorem 9-5-3 is the z of Theorem 9-5-2, and vice-versa.)
2. y and z are the only elements of $\{y, z\}$; by Theorem 9-5-2(**d**).
3. For every object x, if $x \in \{y, z\}$ then $x \in \{z, y\}$; by lines **1** and **2**.
4. $\{y, z\} \subseteq \{z, y\}$; by line **3** and Definition 9-3-1.
5. $\{z, y\} \subseteq \{y, z\}$; by reasoning similar to lines **2** through **4**.
6. $\{y, z\} = \{z, y\}$; by lines **4** and **5** and Theorem 9-3-3.

Proof of (**e**)

▶▶ **1.** Suppose that y, z, u, v are any objects such that $\{y, z\} = \{u, v\}$.
2. $y \in \{y, z\}$ and $z \in \{y, z\}$; by Theorem 9-5-2.
3. $y \in \{u, v\}$ and $z \in \{u, v\}$; by E from lines **1** and **2**.
4. The only elements of $\{u, v\}$ are the objects u and v; by Theorem 9-5-2(**d**).

▶ **5.** Either $y = u$ or $y = v$ and either $z = u$ or $z = v$; by lines **3** and **4**.

▶ **6.** Either $u = y$ or $u = z$, and either $v = y$ or $v = z$; by reasoning similar to lines **2** through **5**.

7. *Suppose* that $y \neq u$.

8. $y = v$; by lines **7** and **5**.

9. $u = z$; by lines **6** and **7**.

▶ **10.** If $y \neq u$ then $y = v$ and $u = z$; by the Deduction Theorem applied to lines **7** through **8** and **9**.

▶ **11.** If $y \neq v$ then $y = u$ and $v = z$; by reasoning similar to lines **7** through **10**.

12. *Suppose* $y = u$ and $y = v$.

13. $u = v$; by E from line **12**.

14. $z = u$ or $z = u$; by E from lines **13** and **5**.

15. $y = v$ and $z = u$; by lines **12** and **14**.

▶ **16.** If $y = u$ and $y = v$, then $y = v$ and $z = u$; by the Deduction Theorem applied to lines **12** through **16**.

▶ **17.** Either $y \neq u$, or $y \neq v$, or else $y = u$ and $y = v$; by logic.

▶▶ **18.** Either $y = v$ and $z = u$, or $y = u$ and $z = v$; by line **17** and lines **10**, **11**, and **16**.

19. If y, z, u, v are any objects such that $\{y, z\} = \{u, v\}$, then either $y = v$ and $z = u$, or $y = u$ and $z = v$; by the Deduction Theorem applied to lines **1** through **18**.

A rather obvious and useful corollary to part (**e**) of the above theorem is as follows.

COROLLARY 9-5-3.1. *If y, z, and u are any objects such that $\{y, z\} = \{y, u\}$, then $z = u$.*

The proof of this corollary will be left as an exercise for the reader.

The notion of a pair, which we have been discussing in the context of our axiomatic theory of sets, is, of course, familiar to us from everyday affairs. For instance, we speak of a *pair* of socks, meaning essentially a set having just two objects as its elements—these objects being socks.

By contrast the notion of an *ordered pair*, which we shall introduce next, does not have a name in common language, although the concept itself is quite familiar. For instance, if we see the pair of digits 1 and 3 marked as the price of an item in a store, it is important to us to know which of these digits *comes first:* A price of 31 is very different from a price of 13.

If y and z are any objects, our notation for the ordered pair of these objects *in which y comes first* will be $\langle y, z\rangle$, and the ordered pair of the same objects *with z coming first* will be $\langle z, y\rangle$. As we have indicated, we expect that in general $\langle y, z\rangle \neq \langle z, y\rangle$. This is in contrast to the situation which holds for the pairs $\{y, z\}$ and $\{z, y\}$, as we see from Theorem 9-5-3.

Two ordered pairs are distinct unless they have the same first-members and the same second-members. In other words, if $\langle y, z\rangle = \langle u, v\rangle$ we must have $y = u$ and $z = v$. This property again contrasts with the weaker law which holds for the pairs $\{y, z\}$ and $\{u, v\}$, as we see from Theorem 9-5-3 (**e**).

It turns out that so far as mathematical use is concerned, the property of ordered pairs mentioned in the preceding paragraph is *the only thing we need to know about ordered pairs!* Furthermore, it turns out that the following definition of ordered pairs, which is certainly not in accordance with any intuitive notion of ordered pair derived from common experience, does have this property. This fact is the sole and sufficient justification for the definition.

DEFINITION 9-5-4. *For any objects y and z we define* **the ordered pair** $\langle y, z\rangle$ *to be the set* $\{\{y\}, \{y, z\}\}$.

Thus our definition identifies an ordered pair with a pair of objects, of which one is a unit set and the other is itself a pair. We proceed at once to show that this definition has the desired property.

THEOREM 9-5-5. *If* y, z, u, v *are any objects such that* $\langle y, z\rangle = \langle u, v\rangle$, *then* $y = u$ *and* $z = v$.

Proof

▶▶ **1.** Let y, z, u, v be any objects such that $\langle y, z\rangle = \langle u, v\rangle$.
▶▶ **2.** $\{\{y\}, \{y, z\}\} = \{\{u\}, \{u, v\}\}$; by line **1** and Definition 9-5-4.
▶▶ **3.** Either $\{y\} = \{u\}$ and $\{y, z\} = \{u, v\}$, or $\{y\} = \{u, v\}$ and $\{y, z\} = \{u\}$; by line **2** and Theorem 9-5-3(**e**).
4. $y \in \{y, z\}$ and $z \in \{y, z\}$; by Theorem 9-5-2(**c**).
5. If $\{y, z\} = \{u\}$ then $y \in \{u\}$ and $z \in \{u\}$; by E applied to line **4**.
6. The only element of $\{u\}$ is the object u; by Theorem 9-5-2.
▶ **7.** If $\{y, z\} = \{u\}$ then $y = u$ and $z = u$; by lines **5** and **6**.
▶ **8.** If $\{y\} = \{u\}$ then $y = u$; by Theorem 9-5-3(**d**).
9. Either $\{y\} = \{u\}$ or $\{y, z\} = \{u\}$; by line **3**.
▶▶ **10.** $y = u$; by lines **7** through **9**.
▶ **11.** $\{\{y\}, \{y, z\}\} = \{\{y\}, \{y, v\}\}$; by E from lines **2** and **10**.
▶ **12.** $\{y, z\} = \{y, v\}$; by line **11** and Corollary 9-5-3.1.
▶▶ **13.** $z = v$; by line **12** and Corollary 9-5-3.1.
14. If y, z, u, v are any objects such that $\langle y, z\rangle = \langle u, v\rangle$, then $y = u$ and $z = v$; by the Deduction Theorem applied to lines **1** through **10** and **13**.

EXERCISES

1. Prove parts (**a**) and (**d**) of Theorem 9-5-2.

2. Prove parts (**b**), (**c**) and (**d**) of Theorem 9-5-3.
3. Prove Corollary 9-5-3.1.

6. Relations

Having defined ordered pairs we are ready to introduce the concept of *relation* as one of the defined concepts of our theory. Before giving a precise definition, let us consider the matter intuitively.

Intuitively, a binary relation is something which "holds" between certain objects x and y, and fails to "hold" between others. For example, the relation *is the father of* holds between Adam and Abel (because Adam is the father of Abel), but not between Cain and Abel. Notice, however, that in determining whether a given relation holds between two objects it is important to specify these objects *in a given order*. For example, although the relation *is the father of* holds between Adam and Abel, it does *not* hold between Abel and Adam. We can express this fact by saying that the relation *is the father of* holds for the ordered pair ⟨Adam, Abel⟩, but not for ⟨Abel, Adam⟩. In general we may speak of a binary relation R as holding for certain ordered pairs $\langle x, y\rangle$, and not for others.

Given any binary relation R, we can thus associate with it a certain set, G_R, whose elements are all of those ordered pairs $\langle x, y\rangle$ for which the relation R holds. Conversely, given any set G such that all of its elements are ordered pairs, we can associate with it the binary relation R_G which holds for precisely those ordered pairs $\langle x, y\rangle$ which are elements of G.

Can we have two different relations, R_1 and R_2, which have the same associated set (i.e., such that $G_{R_1} = G_{R_2}$)? Consider, for example, two binary relations among people:

R_1: *is taller than*
R_2: *is closer to ten feet in height than.*

Due to the happenstance that no people are as tall as 10 feet, an ordered pair $\langle x, y\rangle$ will be in the set G_{R_1} if and only if it is in G_{R_2} (i.e., R_1 will hold for $\langle x, y\rangle$ if and only if R_2 holds for $\langle x, y\rangle$), and hence, by the principle of extensionality, $G_{R_1} = G_{R_2}$. Nevertheless the italicized phrases given above which define the relations R_1 and R_2, do not have exactly the same meaning, so we may wonder whether R_1 is the same relation and R_2. In mathematics we resolve this question by fiat. We simply declare that we shall not distinguish between two binary relations if each one holds for exactly the same ordered pairs as the other. We express this by saying that we regard relations *from the extensional point of view.*

Because of this viewpoint, and the remarks made above, we see that a binary relation R is completely determined by the associated set G_R, and that conversely each set G, all of whose elements are ordered pairs, completely determines a relation R_G. For all practical purposes we may, therefore, *identify* a relation R with its associated set of ordered pairs. This motivates the following definition.

DEFINITION 9-6-1. *By a* **binary relation** *we mean a set G such that every element of G is an ordered pair; i.e., for every $x \in G$ there exist objects y and z such that $x = \langle y, z \rangle$.*

Notation: We often use the letters Q, R, S, and T to denote sets which are binary relations, and we write $x \, R \, y$, $u \, Q \, v$, etc., in place of $\langle x, y \rangle \in R$, $\langle u, v \rangle \in Q$, etc.

Since relations are construed as special kinds of sets, we can at once extend the general Boolean theory of sets to relations. For example, we can speak of the union of two relations, the intersection of two relations, etc. However, there is a special theory of relations which goes beyond this Boolean theory, and which proceeds by introducing two new operations on relations which have no counterpart for arbitrary sets.

DEFINITION 9-6-2. *If R is any relation we define $R^{\cup}$ (the* **converse** *of R) to be the set $\{x \mid x = \langle y, z \rangle$ for some objects y and z such that $z \, R \, y\}$.*

The meaning of this definition is made clear by the following theorem and examples.

THEOREM 9-6-3. *If R is any binary relation then the set $R^{\cup}$ is also a binary relation, and for any objects u and v we have $u \, R^{\cup} \, v$ if and only if $v \, R \, u$.*

As familiar examples of relations and their converses we list these:

$$(\textit{is a parent of})^{\cup} = (\textit{is a child of})$$
$$(\textit{is taller than})^{\cup} = (\textit{is shorter than})$$
$$(\textit{owns})^{\cup} = (\textit{is owned by}).$$

Proof of Theorem 9-6-3

▶▶ **1.** Let R be any relation.

2. For any object x we have: $x \in R^{\cup}$ if and only if $x = \langle y, z \rangle$ for some objects y and z such that $z \, R \, y$; by Definition 9-6-2 and Theorem 9-2-2.

▶ **3.** If x is any element of $R^{\cup}$ then $x = \langle y, z \rangle$ for some objects y and z such that $z \, R \, y$; by logic from line **2**.

4. If x is any element of $R^{\cup}$ then $x = \langle y, z \rangle$ for some objects y and z; by line **3**.

▶▶ **5.** $R^{\cup}$ is a binary relation; by line **4** and Definition 9-6-1.

▶▶ **6.** Let u and v be any objects such that $u \, R^{\cup} \, v$.

▶ **7.** $\langle u, v \rangle \in R^{\cup}$; by line **6** and Definition 9-6-1.

8. $\langle u, v \rangle = \langle y, z \rangle$ for some y and z such that $z \, R \, y$; by line **7** and Definition 9-6-2.

9. $u = y$ and $v = z$ for some objects y and z such that $z\ R\ y$; by line **8** and Theorem 9-5-5.

▶▶**10.** $v\ R\ u$; by E applied to line **9**.

11. If u and v are any objects such that $u\ R^{\cup}\ v$, then $v\ R\ u$; by the Deduction Theorem applied to lines **6** through **10**.

12. If x is any object such that $x = \langle y, z\rangle$ for some objects y and z for which $z\ R\ y$, then $x \in R^{\cup}$; by logic from line **2**.

▶▶**13.** Let u, v be any objects such that $v\ R\ u$.

14. $\langle u, v\rangle = \langle y, z\rangle$ for some objects y and z such that $z\ R\ y$; by line **13** and Definition 9-6-1.

15. $\langle u, v\rangle \in R^{\cup}$; by lines **12** and **14**.

▶▶**16.** $u\ R^{\cup}\ v$; by line **15** and Definition 9-6-1.

17. If u, v are any objects such that $v\ R\ u$, then $u\ R^{\cup}\ v$; by the Deduction Theorem applied to lines **13** through **16**.

18. $R^{\cup}$ is a binary relation, and for any objects u and v we have $u\ R^{\cup}\ v$ if and only if $v\ R\ u$; by lines **5**, **11**, and **17**.

Among the general laws which hold for the converse operation are the following.

THEOREM 9-6-4. *For any relations R and T we have:*

(i) $R^{\cup\cup} = R$,
(ii) $(R \cup T)^{\cup} = R^{\cup} \cup T^{\cup}$, *and*
(iii) $(R \cap T)^{\cup} = R^{\cup} \cap T^{\cup}$.

The proof of this theorem is left to the reader.

Just as the operation of complementation can be applied to any set to yield another, so the operation of converse can be applied to any binary relation to yield another. And in analogy with the operations of intersection and union, we also have special operations which can be applied to *two* binary relations to yield another. Among these, the most important is that of *relative product.*

DEFINITION 9-6-5. *If Q and R are any binary relations, we define* $Q\ ;\ R$ (*the* **relative product** *of Q and R*), *to be the set* $\{x \mid$ *there exist objects u, v, and w such that* $u\ Q\ v$ *and* $v\ R\ w$, *and* $x = \langle u, w\rangle\}$.

The significance of this definition is made clear by the following theorem and examples.

THEOREM 9-6-6. *If Q and R are any binary relations, then* $Q\ ;\ R$ *is also a binary relation; and for any objects y and z we have* $y(Q\ ;\ R)z$ *if and only if there is an object t such that* $y\ Q\ t$ *and* $t\ R\ z$.

The proof of this theorem is basically like that of Theorem 9-6-3, and we leave the reader to formulate it in detail.

To gain an intuitive idea of the significance of the relative product of two relations, let R be the relation *is a parent of;* i.e., R is the set of all ordered pairs $\langle x, y\rangle$ such that x is a parent of y. Then it is easily seen that the relation *is a grandparent of* is the relation $R\,;\,R$, for by the preceding theorem we have $x(R\,;\,R)y$ if and only if: There is an object z such that x is a parent of z and z is a parent of y. As another example consider the relation T: *is a brother of*. Using R as above, it is not hard to see that the relation $T\,;\,R$ is the relation *is an uncle of*.

It is easily seen that the operation of relative product is not commutative. (To see this, compute $R\,;\,T$ in the above example.) But the operation *is* associative, as the first law in the following theorem indicates.

THEOREM 9-6-7. *For any relations R, T and W we have:*

(**a**) $(R\,;\,T)\,;\,W = R\,;\,(T\,;\,W)$,
(**b**) $(R\,;\,T)^{\cup} = (T^{\cup}\,;\,R^{\cup})$,
(**c**) $R\,;\,(T \cap W) \subseteq (R\,;\,T) \cap (R\,;\,W)$, *and*
(**d**) $R\,;\,(T \cup W) = (R\,;\,T) \cup (R\,;\,W)$.

We shall prove parts (**b**) and (**c**), leaving the remaining parts for the reader to try.

Proof of (**b**)

►► **1.** Let R and T be any binary relations.
► **2.** Let x be any element of $(R\,;\,T)^{\cup}$.
3. $x = \langle y, z\rangle$ for some objects y and z such that $z(R\,;\,T)y$; by line **2**, Definition 9-6-2, and Theorem 9-2-2.
4. There is an object t such that $z\,R\,t$ and $t\,T\,y$; by line **3** and Theorem 9-6-6.
5. $t\,R^{\cup}\,z$ and $y\,T^{\cup}\,t$; by line **4** and Theorem 9-6-3.
6. $y\,T^{\cup}\,t$ and $t\,R^{\cup}\,z$; by line **5**.
7. $y(T^{\cup}\,;\,R^{\cup})z$; by line **6** and Theorem 9-6-6.
8. $\langle y, z\rangle \in (T^{\cup}\,;\,R^{\cup})$; by line **5** and Definition 9-6-1.
► **9.** $x \in (T^{\cup}\,;\,R^{\cup})$; by E applied to lines **3** and **8**.
10. If x is any element of $(R\,;\,T)^{\cup}$, then $x \in (T^{\cup}\,;\,R^{\cup})$; by the Deduction Theorem applied to lines **2** through **9**.
►► **11.** $(R\,;\,T)^{\cup} \subseteq (T^{\cup}\,;\,R^{\cup})$; by line **10** and Definition 9-3-1.
► **12.** Let s be any element of $(T^{\cup}\,;\,R^{\cup})$.
13. There exist objects u, v, and w such that $u\,T^{\cup}\,v$ and $v\,R^{\cup}\,w$, and $s = \langle u, w\rangle$; by line **12**, Definition 9-6-5, and Theorem 9-2-2.
14. $v\,T\,u$ and $w\,R\,v$; by line **13** and Theorem 9-6-3.
15. $w\,R\,v$ and $v\,T\,u$; by line **14**.
16. $w(R\,;\,T)u$; by line **15** and Theorem 9-6-6.

17. $u(R\,;\,T)^{\cup}\,w$; by line **16** and Theorem 9-6-3.
18. $\langle u, w\rangle \in (R\,;\,T)^{\cup}$; by line **17** and Definition 9-6-1.
▶19. $s \in (R\,;\,T)^{\cup}$; by E applied to lines **18** and **13**.
20. If s is any element of $(T^{\cup}\,;\,R^{\cup})$ then $s \in (R\,;\,T)^{\cup}$; by the Deduction Theorem applied to lines **12** through **19**.
▶▶21. $(T^{\cup}\,;\,R^{\cup}) \subseteq (R\,;\,T)^{\cup}$; by line **20** and Definition 9-3-1.
▶▶22. $(R\,;\,T)^{\cup} = (T^{\cup}\,;\,R^{\cup})$; by lines **11** and **21**, and Theorem 9-3-3.
23. If R and T are any binary relations then $(R\,;\,T)^{\cup} = (T^{\cup}\,;\,R^{\cup})$; by the Deduction Theorem applied to lines **1** and **22**.

Proof of (**c**)

▶▶ 1. Let R, T, and W be any binary relations.
▶▶ 2. Let x be any element of $R\,;\,(T \cap W)$.
▶ 3. There exist objects u, v, and w such that $u\;R\;v$ and $v(T \cap W)w$, and $x = \langle u, w\rangle$; by line **2**, Definition 9-6-5, and Theorem 9-2-2.
4. $\langle v, w\rangle \in (T \cap W)$; by line **3** and Definition 9-6-1.
5. $\langle v, w\rangle \in T$ and $\langle v, w\rangle \in W$; by line **4** and Theorem 9-4-2.
6. $v\;T\;w$ and $v\;W\;w$; by line **5** and Definition 9-6-1.
7. $u\;R\;v$ and $v\;T\;w$, and also $u\;R\;v$ and $v\;W\;w$; by lines **3** and **6**.
8. $u(R\,;\,T)w$ and $u(R\,;\,W)w$; by line **7** and Theorem 9-6-6.
▶ 9. $\langle u, w\rangle \in (R\,;\,T)$ and $\langle u, w\rangle \in (R\,;\,W)$; by line **8** and Definition 9-6-1.
10. $\langle u, w\rangle \in (R\,;\,T) \cap (R\,;\,W)$; by line **9** and Theorem 9-4-2.
▶▶11. $x \in (R\,;\,T) \cap (R\,;\,W)$; by E applied to lines **3** and **10**.
12. If x is any element of $R\,;\,(T \cap W)$ then $x \in (R\,;\,T) \cap (R\,;\,W)$; by the Deduction Theorem applied to lines **2** through **11**.
13. $R\,;\,(T \cap W) \subseteq (R\,;\,T) \cap (R\,;\,W)$; by line **12** and Definition 9-3-1.
14. If R, T, and W are any binary relations, then $R\,;\,(T \cap W) \subseteq (R\,;\,T) \cap (R\,;\,W)$; by the Deduction Theorem applied to lines **1** through **13**.

To illustrate the parts of Theorem 9-6-7 which we have just proved, consider the example in which R is the relation *is a friend of*, T is the relation *is a brother of*, and W is the relation *is a classmate of*.

We see that $R\,;\,T$ is the relation *is a friend of a brother of*, whence $(R\,;\,T)^{\cup}$ is the relation *has a brother who is a friend of*. We see, too, that R is the same as $R^{\cup}$, the relation *is a friend of*, since if x is a friend of y then also y is a friend of x; while $T^{\cup}$ is the relation *has as a brother*. Hence $T^{\cup}; R^{\cup}$ is the relation *has as a brother a friend of*, and clearly this is the same relation as $(R\,;\,T)^{\cup}$ found above. This verifies part (**b**) of Theorem 9-6-7. Note, by the way, that $T^{\cup}$, *has as a brother*, is not the same as the relation *is a brother or sister of*, since two girls may stand in the latter relation.

To verify part (**c**), we observe that $R\,;\,W$ is the relation *is a friend of a classmate of*, so $(R\,;\,T) \cap (R\,;\,W)$ is the relation *is a friend of a brother and a friend of a classmate of*. On the other hand $T \cap W$ is the relation *is a brother and classmate of*, so that $R\,;\,(T \cap W)$ is the relation *is a friend of a brother-and-classmate of*. Clearly, then, we have $R\,;\,(T \cap W) \subseteq (R\,;\,T) \cap (R\,;\,W)$, since if x is a friend of a brother-and-classmate of y, then x is a friend of a brother and a friend of a classmate of y. On the other hand we do not have $(R\,;\,T) \cap (R\,;\,W) \subseteq R\,;\,(T \cap W)$, since it may well happen that x is a friend of a brother and a friend of a classmate of y, even though y has no brother who is a classmate (so that x cannot be a friend of a brother-and-classmate of y).

With any binary relation R we may associate a certain set, namely, the set of all those objects which bear the relation R to something. This set is called the *domain of* R. If we identify a relation with a set of ordered pairs (as we are here doing), then the domain of R is simply the set of all those objects which are first members of the ordered pairs of R. We formulate the definition precisely, as follows.

DEFINITION 9-6-8. *If R is any binary relation, we define the* **domain** *of R (notation: $D(R)$) to be the set $\{x \mid$ there is some object y such that $x\ R\ y\}$.*

We get at once:

THEOREM 9-6-9. *For any binary relation R, and any object x, we have $x \in D(R)$ if and only if there is an object y such that $x\ R\ y$.*

Proof

By Definition 9-6-8 and Theorem 9-2-2.

For example, the domain of the relation *is the mother of* is the set of all mothers. The domain of the *converse* of the relation *is a sister of* is the set of all those who have a sister.

If a relation is obtained from two other relations by means of one of the operations intersection, union, or relative product, then its domain is related to the domains of these other relations, as described in the following theorem.

THEOREM 9-6-10. *If R and T are any binary relations, then:*

(**a**) $D(R \cap T) \subseteq D(R) \cap D(T)$
(**b**) $D(R \cup T) = D(R) \cup D(T)$
(**c**) $D(R\,;\,T) \subseteq D(R)$.

The proof is left as an exercise.

EXERCISES

1. Show by an example that the relative product operation is not commutative.
2. Prove Theorem 9-6-4.
3. Prove Theorem 9-6-6.
4. Prove Parts (**a**) and (**d**) of Theorem 9-6-7.
5. Prove Theorem 9-6-10.

7. *Equivalence Relations*

In the preceding section we have given examples of some of the laws which hold in the theory of relations. Actually this theory is a very rich one, with many interesting laws. In the further development of this theory one usually defines and investigates properties of *transitive*, *reflexive*, *symmetric*, and other special kinds of relations which play an important part in mathematics. We shall not go into many of the details of this type of investigation here, but for the purposes of later chapters (in connection with further extensions of the number system), we must treat one special kind of relations, the so called *equivalence relations*.

DEFINITION 9-7-1. *Let G be any set and R any binary relation. Then we say that:*

(**i**) *R is* **reflexive** *on G if and only if $x\ R\ x$ for every $x \in G$;*
(**ii**) *R is* **symmetric** *on G if and only if for every $x, y \in G$ such that $x\ R\ y$ we have also $y\ R\ x$;*
(**iii**) *R is* **transitive** *on G if and only if for every $x, y, z \in G$ such that $x\ R\ y$ and $y\ R\ z$, we have also $x\ R\ z$;*
(**iv**) *R is* **an equivalence relation** *on G if and only if R is reflexive, symmetric, and transitive on G.*

Examples of relations of the kinds mentioned in this definition are plentiful. For example, if G is the set of all people then the relation *is a brother of* is neither symmetric, reflexive nor transitive on G (why?); the relation *stands next in line to* is symmetric on G (but not reflexive or transitive); the relation *is not taller than* is reflexive and transitive on G (but not symmetric on G); the relation *is an ancestor of* is transitive on G (but not reflexive or symmetric on G); the relation *is the same age as* is an equivalence relation on G.

Of particular importance in the theory of equivalence relations is their close connection with *partitions*, which we now proceed to define.

DEFINITION 9-7-2. *Let G be any set. By a* **partition** *of G we mean a set H such that:*

(**i**) *Every element U of H is a nonempty set such that $U \subseteq G$;*
(**ii**) *For every $y \in G$ there is one and only one $U \in H$ such that $y \in U$.*

For example, let G be the set of all people, let U be the set of all men and let V be the set of all women. Then the pair $\{U, V\}$ is a *partition* of G. For another partition of this same set G, consider any time-zone t and let U_t be the set of all people who were born in this zone; then the set H, whose elements are all of these sets U_t (for all zones t), is a *partition* of G.

The following theorem shows that every partition of a set G determines a certain equivalence relation on G.

THEOREM 9-7-3. *Let G be a set and H any partition of G. Then there is an equivalence relation R on G such that for every $y, z \in G$ we have $y\ R\ z$ if and only if there is some $U \in H$ for which we have $y \in U$ and $z \in U$.*

Proof

▶▶ **1.** Let G be a set and H any partition of G.

▶▶ **2.** Let R be the set $\{x |$ for some $U \in H$ there exist $y \in U$ and $z \in U$ such that $x = \langle y, z\rangle\}$.

▶▶ **3.** R is a set, and for every object x we have $x \in R$ if and only if for some $U \in H$ there exist $y, z \in U$ such that $x = \langle y, z\rangle$; by line **2** and Theorem 9-2-2.

4. R is a set, and for every $x \in R$ there exist objects y and z such that $x = \langle y, z\rangle$; by line **3**.

▶▶ **5.** R is a binary relation; by line **4** and Definition 9-6-1.

6. For all objects y and z we have $y\ R\ z$ if and only if for some $U \in H$ we have $y, z \in U$; by lines **5** and **3** and Definition 9-6-1.

▶ **7.** Let y be any element of G.

8. There is some $U \in H$ such that $y \in U$; by lines **7** and **1** and Definition 9-7-2(**ii**).

▶ **9.** $y\ R\ y$; by lines **6** and **8**.

10. If y is any element of G then $y\ R\ y$; by the Deduction Theorem applied to lines **7** through **9**.

▶▶ **11.** R is reflexive on G; by lines **5** and **10** and Definition 9-7-1(**i**).

▶ **12.** Let y and z be any elements of G such that $y\ R\ z$.

13. For some $U \in H$ we have both $y \in U$ and $z \in U$; by lines **6** and **12**.

14. For some $U \in H$ we have $z \in U$ and $y \in U$; by logic from line **13**.

▶ **15.** $z\ R\ y$; by lines **6** and **14**.

16. If y and z are any elements of G such that $y\ R\ z$, then also $z\ R\ y$; by the Deduction Theorem applied to lines **12** through **15**.

▶▶ **17.** R is symmetric on G; by lines **5** and **16** and Definition 9-7-1(**ii**).

▶ **18.** Let y, z and t be any elements of G such that $y\ R\ z$ and $z\ R\ t$.

19. There is some $U \in H$ such that both $y \in U$ and $z \in U$; by lines **6** and **18**.

20. There is some $V \in H$ such that both $z \in V$ and $t \in V$; by lines **6** and **18**.
21. $z \in U$ and $z \in V$; by lines **19** and **20**.
22. There is *only one* $W \in H$ such that $z \in W$; by Definition 9-7-2 (**ii**) and lines **1** and **18**.
23. $U = V$; by lines **21** and **22**.
24. $t \in U$; by E applied to lines **20** and **23**.
25. There is some $U \in H$ such that both $y \in U$ and $t \in U$; by lines **19** and **24**.
▶**26.** $y\ R\ t$; by lines **6** and **25**.
27. If y, z, and t are any elements of G such that $y\ R\ z$ and $z\ R\ t$, then also $y\ R\ t$; by the Deduction Theorem applied to lines **18** through **26**.
▶▶**28.** R is transitive on G; by lines **5** and **27** and Definition 9-7-1(**iii**).
▶▶**29.** R is an equivalence relation on G; by lines **11**, **17**, and **28** and Definition 9-7-1(**iv**).
30. Theorem 9-7-3 is now obtained by applying the Deduction Theorem to lines **1** through **6** and **29**.

In the theorem just established we have shown how, starting with a partition H of a set G, we can obtain a related equivalence relation, R, on G. We now show that the converse process is equally feasible.

THEOREM 9-7-4. *Let G be any set and R an equivalence relation on G. Then there is a partition H of G such that, for every* $y, z \in G$, *we have* $y\ R\ z$ *if and only if there is some* $U \in H$ *for which we have both* $y \in U$ *and* $z \in U$.

Proof

1. Let G be any set and R any equivalence relation on G.
2. For each $y \in G$ let U_y be the set $\{z \mid z \in G \text{ and } z\ R\ y\}$.
3. If y is any element of G then U_y is a set, and for every object z we have $z \in U_y$ if and only if $z \in G$ and $z\ R\ y$; by line **2** and Theorem 9-2-2.
4. If y is any element of G then $y\ R\ y$; by line **1** and Definitions 9-7-1 (**i**) and (**iv**).
5. If y is any element of G then $y \in U_y$; by lines **3** and **4**.
6. If y is any element of G then U_y is a nonempty set and $U_y \subseteq G$; by lines **3** and **5** and Definition 9-3-1.
7. Now suppose that y and z are any elements of G such that $y \in U_z$.
8. $y \in G$ and $y\ R\ z$; by lines **3** and **7**.
9. $z\ R\ y$; by lines **1** and **8** and Definitions 9-7-1 (**ii**) and (**iv**).
10. Let t be any element of U_z.
11. $t \in G$ and $t\ R\ z$; by line **3** and **10**.

12. $t \in G$ and $t\,R\,y$; by lines **1**, **9**, **11** and Definitions 9-7-1 (**iii**) and (**iv**).

13. $t \in U_y$; by lines **3** and **12**.

14. If t is any element of U_z then $t \in U_y$; by the Deduction Theorem applied to lines **10** through **13**.

15. $U_z \subseteq U_y$; by line **14** and Definition 9-3-1.

16. Let s be any element of U_y.

17. $s \in G$ and $s\,R\,y$; by lines **3** and **16**.

18. $s \in G$ and $s\,R\,z$; by lines **1**, **8**, and **17** and Definitions 9-7-1 (**iii**) and (**iv**).

19. $s \in U_z$; by lines **3** and **18**.

20. If s is any element of U_y, then also $s \in U_z$; by the Deduction Theorem applied to lines **16** through **19**.

21. $U_y \subseteq U_z$; by line **20** and Definition 9-3-1.

22. $U_y = U_z$; by lines **15** and **21** and Theorem 9-3-3.

23. If y and z are any elements of G such that $y \in U_z$, then $U_y = U_z$; by the Deduction Theorem applied to lines **7** through **22**.

24. Let H be the set $\{x|$ there is some $y \in G$ such that $x = U_y\}$.

25. H is a set, and for any object x we have $x \in H$ if and only if there is some $y \in G$ such that $x = U_y$; by line **24** and Theorem 9-2-2.

26. If x is any element of H then x is a nonempty set and $x \subseteq G$; by lines **6** and **25**.

27. If y is any element of G then there is an element x of H such that $y \in x$; by lines **5** and **25**.

28. If y is any element of G then there is *only one* element x of H (namely U_y) such that $y \in x$; by lines **23** and **25**.

29. H is a *partition* of G; by lines **26**, **27**, and **28** and Definition 9-7-1.

30. If y, $z \in G$ and $y\,R\,z$ then $y \in U_z$ and $z \in U_z$; by lines **3** and **5**.

31. If y, $z \in G$ and $y\,R\,z$, then there is an $x \in H$ such that $y \in x$ and $z \in x$; by lines **25** and **30**.

32. Suppose that y, $z \in G$ and that for some $x \in H$ we have $y \in x$ and $z \in x$.

33. y, $z \in G$, and for some $t \in G$ we have $y \in U_t$ and $z \in U_t$; by lines **25** and **32**.

34. y, $z \in G$ and $y\,R\,t$ and $z\,R\,t$; by lines **3** and **33**.

35. $t\,R\,z$; by lines **1** and **34** and Definitions 9-7-1 (**ii**) and (**iv**).

36. $y\,R\,z$; by lines **1**, **34**, and **35** and Definitions 9-7-1 (**iii**) and (**iv**).

37. If y, z are any elements of G such that for some $x \in H$ we have $y \in x$ and $z \in x$, then $y\,R\,z$; by the Deduction Theorem applied to lines **32** through **36**.

38. For any y, $z \in G$ we have $y\,R\,z$ if and only if there is some $x \in H$ such that $y \in x$ and $z \in x$; by lines **31** and **37**.

39. The theorem is now obtained by applying the Deduction Theorem to lines **1** through **29** and **38**.

EXERCISE

Select the key steps in the proof of Theorem 9-7-4.

8. *Functions*

Intuitively, we may think of a function as an abstract operation which converts certain things into others. The objects on which a function may act make up its *domain*, and the object produced by the action of a function on an object x of its domain is called the *value* of the function *corresponding to* x. At first sight this concept seems very different from the concept of a set. Nevertheless, it turns out to be possible to identify functions with certain sets (in fact, relations) of a special kind.

In order to see this, we observe first of all that given any function we can always associate with it a certain relation, namely, the relation which holds of an ordered pair $\langle x, y\rangle$ if and only if x is in the domain of the given function and y is the value of the function corresponding to x. It is clear that if R is a relation which is associated with some function in this way, then R must have the following property: For any object x, there is at most *one* object y such that $x\ R\ y$. (This object y will be *the* object into which x is converted by the action of the function.) Put another way, we can say that whenever $x\ R\ y$ and $x\ R\ z$ then we must have $y = z$.

Conversely, if we *start* with *any* relation R having the property described in the preceding sentence, then we can associate a certain function with it—namely the function whose domain is the domain of R, which, when it acts on any element x of this domain, converts it into the unique object y such that $x\ R\ y$.

These intuitive considerations suggest that we can simply *identify* a function with its associated relation, and we are thus led to the following definition.

DEFINITION 9-8-1. *We define a* **function** *to be a binary relation R such that whenever x, y, and z are objects for which $x\ R\ y$ and $x\ R\ z$, then $y = z$.*

For example, the relation *has as a mother* is a function, according to this definition, but the relations *has as a brother* and *is a mother of* are not.

The most basic fact about a function is contained in the following theorem.

THEOREM 9-8-2. *If R is any relation which is a function, and if x is any element of its domain, $D(R)$, then there is one and only one object y such that $x\ R\ y$.*

Proof

▶▶**1.** Let R be any relation which is a function.
▶▶**2.** Let x be any element of $D(R)$.
▶**3.** There is an object y such that $x\ R\ y$; by lines **1** and **2** and Theorem 9-6-9.

▶4. Suppose z is *any* object such that $x\ R\ z$.
5. $x\ R\ y$ and $x\ R\ z$; by lines **3** and **4**.
▶6. $z = y$; by lines **1** and **5** and Definition 9-8-1
7. If z is any object such that $x\ R\ z$, then $z = y$; by the Deduction Theorem applied to lines **4** through **6**.
▶▶8. There is one and only one object y such that $x\ R\ y$; by lines **3** and **7**.
9. If R is any relation which is a function, and if x is any element of $D(R)$, then there is one and only one object y such that $x\ R\ y$; by the Deduction Theorem applied to lines **1** and **2** through **8**.

As a matter of notation we often use the letters "f", "g", and "h" to denote functions. We follow this practice in formulating the following definition.

DEFINITION 9-8-3. *If f is any function, and if x is any element of its domain, $D(f)$, then the unique object y such that $x\ f\ y$ is called the* **value of f corresponding to x,** *and is denoted "$f(x)$" or "fx".*

When the operation of taking the relative product is performed on two relations which are functions, the resulting relation is again a function. This fact is part of the following theorem.

THEOREM 9-8-4. *If f and g are any functions, then $f\,;g$ is also a function. (This is often called the function* **composed** *of f and g.) Furthermore we have $D(f\,;g) \subseteq D(f)$.*

We leave the proof of this theorem to the reader.

The next theorem relates the values of a composed function to the values of the functions from which it is composed.

THEOREM 9-8-5. *If f and g are functions, and if $x \in D(f\,;g)$, then $f(x) \in D(g)$ and $g(f(x)) = (f\,;g)\,(x)$.*

As an illustration of these theorems, let f be the relation *has as a father* and let g be the relation *has as a mother*. Then both f and g are functions, and for any person x we have $f(x) =$ the father of x and $g(x) =$ the mother of x. The composed function (or relative product), $f\,;g$, is the relation *has as the mother of his father*, i.e., the relation *has as a paternal grandmother*, and for any person x we have $(f\,;g)\,(x) =$ the paternal grandmother of x. Clearly, if x is any person, $g(f(x)) = (f\,;g)\,(x)$.

Proof of Theorem 9-8-5

▶▶ 1. Let f and g be any functions.
▶ 2. The relation $f\,;g$ is a function; by line **1** and Theorem 9-8-4.
▶▶ 3. Let x be any element of $D(f\,;g)$.

▶ 4. There is one and only one object y such that $x(f\,;g)y$; by lines **2** and **3** and Theorem 9-8-2.

5. There is an object z such that $x\,f\,z$ and $z\,g\,y$; by lines **4** and **2** and Theorem 9-6-6.

▶ 6. $y = (f\,;g)\,(x)$; by line **4** and Definition 9-8-3.

7. $z \in D(g)$; by line **5** and Theorem 9-6-9.

8. $z = f(x)$ and $y = g(z)$; by lines **5** and **1** and Theorem 9-8-2 and Definition 9-8-3.

▶▶ 9. $f(x) \in D(g)$; by E applied to lines **7** and **8**.

▶ 10. $y = g(f(x)$; by E applied to line **8**.

▶▶ 11. $g(f(x)) = (f\,;g)\,(x)$; by E applied to lines **6** and **10**.

12. If f and g are any functions, and if x is any element of $D(f\,;g)$, then $f(x) \in D(g)$ and $g(f(x)) = (f\,;g)\,(x)$; by the Deduction Theorem applied to lines **1** and **3** through **9**, and **11**.

EXERCISES

1. Prove Theorem 9-8-4.

2. Let f be any function with a nonempty domain, G. Show that there is an equivalence relation R on G such that for every $y, z \in G$ we have $y\,R\,z$ if and only if $f(y) = f(z)$.

3. Let G be a set and R an equivalence relation on G. Show that there is a function f, having G as its domain, such that for every $y, z \in G$ we have $f(y) = f(z)$ if and only if $y\,R\,z$. (Such a function f is called a *representation function on G for the relation R*.)

9. *The Russell Paradox*

We now turn to an astonishing pair of theorems which can be derived within our system of axioms. These theorems concern a certain set, called the Russell set, defined as follows.

DEFINITION 9-9-1. *We define* **the Russell set,** *U, to be $\{x \mid x$ is a set and* **not** *$x \in x\}$.*

The nature of U is given in the following lemma.

LEMMA. *For any object x we have $x \in U$ if and only if: x is a set and* **not** *$x \in x$.*

Thus the elements of U are sets, and indeed all of those sets which are not elements of themselves. The proof of the lemma is immediate by Definition 9-9-1 and Theorem 9-2-2.

THEOREM 9-9-2. *U is not an element of itself. (I.e., not $U \in U$.)*

Proof

▶▶ 1. Suppose $U \in U$.

2. If x is any element of U, then *not* $x \in x$; by the Lemma above.

3. *Not* $U \in U$; by lines **1** and **2**.

▶▶4. $U \in U$ and *not* $U \in U$; by lines **1** and **3**.

5. If $U \in U$ then ($U \in U$ and *not* $U \in U$); by the Deduction Theorem applied to lines **1** through **4**.

▶▶6. *Not* $U \in U$; by logic from line **5**. (The law of logic used here is the "principle of contradiction," which allows us to infer *not-P* from a sentence of the form *If P then* (*Q and not-Q*).)

Having proved Theorem 9-9-2, we are now in a position to prove a closely related theorem.

THEOREM 9-9-3. $U \in U$.

Proof

1. U is a set; by Definition 9-9-1.
2. *Not* $U \in U$; by Theorem 9-9-2.
3. If x is any object such that x is a set and *not* $x \in x$, then $x \in U$; by the Lemma above.
4. $U \in U$; by lines **1**, **2**, and **3**.

The last two theorems together show that the laws of logic lead from our axioms to a pair of contradictory conclusions. We express this fact by saying that our system of axioms is *inconsistent*.

If the reader is surprised and disconcerted by this turn of events, imagine the reaction of "working mathematicians" when contradictions were first discovered in the theory of sets founded by Georg Cantor! The contradiction derived above was discovered by the English mathematician, logician, and philosopher, Bertrand Russell, and is known as the "Russell Paradox." But this was not the first contradiction to be found in Cantor's theory.

The first contradiction to be discovered, known as the "Burali-Forti Paradox," arose under the following circumstances. Cantor, in the course of developing his theory of sets, found it of interest to pick out certain sets which he called *ordinal numbers*. He defined an ordering relation for these numbers, and he published a proof that *there is no greatest ordinal number* (just as there is no greatest positive integer, for example). Soon afterward an Italian mathematician, Burali-Forti, published a paper in which he stated that Cantor had made a mistake in his proof, and as evidence *he* gave a proof that in fact there *was* a greatest ordinal number. But he did not point out where the error was in Cantor's proof!

Naturally mathematicians examined both of these proofs very carefully. When they could find no error of reasoning in *either* proof, they realized that there was something faulty at the foundation of Cantor's theory of sets. How this can be rectified will be indicated in the next section.

10. Zermelo's Theory of Sets

The discovery of contradictions in Cantor's theory of sets led mathematicians to reexamine the basic assumptions underlying this theory, and at the beginning of this century the first explicit *axiomatic* formulation was given by the German mathematician, Ernest Zermelo. Somewhat different axiomatic approaches were undertaken soon after by Bertrand Russell and Alfred Whitehead (whose work on the subject is known as the Theory of Types), and still later by the American logician, W. V. Quine.

In every case the aim of the proposed theory was to preserve those parts of Cantor's theory which seemed intuitively clear and were useful in applications, but to cut out those parts of Cantor's theory which led to contradictions. The basic idea of both Russell-Whitehead and Quine was to retain the axiom schema of set-formation, but to impose a restriction on the form of the sentential formula $S(x)$ which may be employed in applications of that schema. In particular, of course, the sentential formula "x is a set and $x \notin x$" was to be excluded, as this leads directly to the contradiction of the Russell paradox.

Zermelo's basic idea was somewhat different. Below we shall briefly survey his proposed axiom system in a form which incorporates various modifications and improvements suggested by later mathematicians—in particular by A. Fraenkel, of Israel, and T. Skolem, of Norway.

As in the case of Cantor's theory, we start with "set" and "ϵ" as our only undefined terms. The Axioms are as follows.

AXIOM Z1 (9-10-1) AXIOM OF EXTENSIONALITY. *If G and H are any sets, and if for every object x we have $x \in G$ if and only if $x \in H$, then $G = H$.*

This axiom is precisely the same as our Axiom C1 of Section 2.

The Axiom Schema of set formation (Axiom Schema C2 of Section 2) was the source of our derivation of contradiction in Cantor's theory. Zermelo's idea was to replace it with a schema of *subset* formulation.

AXIOM SCHEMA Z2 (9-10-2) AXIOM OF SUBSET FORMATION. *Let $S(x)$ be any sentential formula which contains the letter "x" (and possibly others), but not the letter G. Then the following shall be an axiom:*

> *If H is any set, then there is a set G such that for every x we have $x \in G$ if and only if ($x \in H$ and $S(x)$).*

Let us illustrate the use of Axiom Schema Z2 by an intuitive example. Take $S(x)$ to be the statement "x is an even number." Axiom Schema Z2 tells us that we have *as an axiom* the following: If H is any set, then there is a set G such that for every x, $x \in G$ if and only if $x \in H$ and x is an even number. Now let $H = \{1, 2, 3, 4, 5\}$. The above axiom asserts the existence of a set G made up of those objects which are both elements of H and even numbers. Clearly $G = \{2, 4\}$.

The essential difference between the schemas C2 and Z2 is that in the latter we need *both a sentential formula* $S(x)$ *and a set* H in order to form a set, whereas, in the original axiom schema we needed *only* a sentential formula. A set formed in Zermelo's theory by use of Axiom Schema Z2 is always a subset of a preexisting set H.

This modification of Axiom Schema C2 appears to eliminate all of the known paradoxes discovered in Cantor's theory—but not without some sacrifice. For example, it is impossible to guarantee the existence of the union of any two sets on the basis of Axioms Z1 and Z2 alone. To remedy this, so that the concept of the union of sets (and other familiar operations) could be introduced into his theory, Zermelo added three further axioms to his system, each of which is, in fact, an instance of Cantor's Schema C2.

AXIOM SCHEMA Z3 (9-10-3) AXIOM OF PAIRS. *If y and z are any objects, there is a set G such that for every object x we have $x \in G$ if and only if* $(x = y$ *or* $x = z)$.

As indicated by its name, this axiom can be used to introduce the concept of a *pair* into the theory.

AXIOM SCHEMA Z4 (9-10-4) AXIOM OF SUMS. *If H is any set, there is another set G such that for every object x we have $x \in G$ if and only if (there exists an object y such that y is a set and $x \in y$ and $y \in H$).*

When combined with Axiom Z3, this axiom can be used to introduce the concept of the *union* of two sets into the theory. This will be done later.

AXIOM SCHEMA Z5 (9-10-5) AXIOM OF POWER SETS. *If H is any set then there is a set G such that for every object x we have $x \in G$ if and only if (x is a set, and for every $y \in x$ we have $y \in H$).*

This axiom provides for the existence of a set whose elements are all of the subsets of a given set.

With the five axioms we have listed so far we can derive most of the basic material of Cantor's theory outlined above. In order to develop more advanced portions of set theory, however, certain additional axioms are needed. We shall first develop theory from Axioms Z1 through Z5, indicating what modifications are needed in order to obtain various results which were derived in Sections **2** through **8** from Axioms C1 and C2. And afterward we will describe the remaining axioms of Zermelos' system. Where proofs closely resemble those of preceding sections, we shall omit all details.

In the first place, we can combine Axioms Z1 and Z2 to obtain a fundamental theorem schema.

THEOREM 9-10-6. *Let $S(x)$ be any sentential formula containing the letter "x" (and possibly others), but not the letter "G." Then the following is a theorem:*

If H is any set, then there exists one and **only one** *set G such that for every object x we have $x \in G$ if and only if ($x \in H$ and $S(x)$).*

The proof is essentially the same as that given for Theorem 9-2-1.

We then introduce the following *notation:* The unique set G which corresponds to a given set H and a given sentential formula $S(x)$, according to theorem 9-10-6, will be symbolized by $\{x \in H \mid S(x)\}$, and read "the set of all elements x of H such that $S(x)$."

By combining this notational convention with Theorem 9-10-6 we obtain the following schema.

THEOREM 9-10-7. *Let $S(x)$ be a sentential function containing the letter "x" (and possibly others). Then the following is a theorem:*

For every object x we have $x \in \{x \in H \mid S(x)\}$ if and only if ($x \in H$ and $S(x)$).

This corresponds exactly to the Theorem 9-2-2 in our development of Cantor's Theory.

The introduction of the concept of subset, and the derivation of its fundamental properties, was accomplished in the previous section without any reference to Axiom C2. Hence we can transplant this material literally to the Zermelo theory; to facilitate reference we copy the relevant definition and theorems below (omitting proofs).

DEFINITION 9-10-8. *Let G and H be any sets. We say that G is a* **subset** *of H (notation: $G \subseteq H$) if and only if, for every object x, if $x \in G$ then also $x \in H$.*

THEOREM 9-10-9. *If G, H and K are any sets such that $G \subseteq H$ and $H \subseteq K$, then $G \subseteq K$.*

THEOREM 9-10-10. *If G and H are any sets such that $G \subseteq H$ and $H \subseteq G$, then $G = H$.*

The definition of the null set used in Section 3 depends upon Axiom C2, and so cannot be carried over to Zermelo's system, without justification. However, the necessary justification can be provided by the following theorem.

THEOREM 9-10-11. *There is one and only one set G such that for every object x we have $x \in G$ if and only if $x \neq x$.*

Proof

▶▶ **1.** There exists at least one set, say H; by Axiom Z3.

▶▶**2.** Let G be the set $\{x \in H \mid x \neq x\}$.

▶▶**3.** Let x be any object.

▶**4.** $x \in G$ if and only if $x \in H$ and $x \neq x$; by lines **2** and **3** and Theorem 9-10-7.

5. *Not* $x \neq x$; by E, the logic of equality.

6. *Not* ($x \in H$ and $x \neq x$); by logic from line **5.**

▶**7.** ($x \in H$ and $x \neq x$) if and only if $x \neq x$; by logic from lines **5** and **6.**

▶▶**8.** $x \in G$ if and only if $x \neq x$; by lines **4** and **7.**

9. For any object x we have $x \in G$ if and only if $x \neq x$; by the Deduction Theorem applied to lines **3** through **8.**

So far we have proved the existence of a set G of the kind mentioned in Theorem 9-10-11, and it remains to show that there is only one such set. But this is now easily accomplished with the aid of the Axiom of Extensionality (Axiom Z1), and so we shall leave the reader to finish the proof for himself.

DEFINITION 9-10-12. *The unique set G, such that for every object x we have $x \in G$ if and only if $x \neq x$, is called the* **null set,** *and is denoted by* $\varnothing$.

Of course this definition is justified by the preceding theorem. The fundamental properties of the null set now follow by the same arguments used in the Cantor theory; two of these properties are given in the following theorem.

THEOREM 9-10-13.

(i) *If x is any object, then* **not** $x \in \varnothing$.

(ii) *If G is any set, then* $\varnothing \subseteq G$.

This corresponds to Theorems 9-3-5 and 9-3-6 of the previous sections, and the proofs are substantially identical.

The introduction of the notion of the intersection of two sets can be accomplished in essentially the same manner as for Cantor's theory.

DEFINITION 9-10-14. *If H and K are any sets, we define the* **intersection** *of H and K (in symbols: $H \cap K$), to be the set* $\{x \in H \mid x \in K\}$.

Combining this definition with Theorem 9-10-7, we obtain at once:

THEOREM 9-10-15. *If H and K are any sets, and if x is any object, then $x \in H \cap K$ if and only if $x \in H$ and $x \in K$.*

This, of course, is identical with Theorem 9-4-2, and permits us in turn to derive the basic properties of intersection as formulated in Theorem 9-4-3. For reference purposes, we copy the theorem here.

THEOREM 9-10-16. *For any sets H, J, K we have*

(a) $H \cap H = H$,
(b) $H \cap K = K \cap H$,
(c) $(H \cap K) \cap J = H \cap (K \cap J)$,
(d) $H \cap \varnothing = \varnothing$.

The proofs are no different from those used in Cantor's theory.

After intersection, the next concept introduced in our development of Cantor's set theory was that of union. However, in the Zermelo theory it is necessary first to introduce the notion of a pair, and then to base the definition of union upon that of pair. (It was for this reason that we postulated Axioms Z3 and Z4.) The chain of ideas is sketched below.

THEOREM 9-10-17. *If y and z are any objects, there is one* **and only one** *set G such that, for every object x, we have $x \in G$ if and only if ($x = y$ or $x = z$).*

To prove this we simply combine Axioms Z1 and Z3. This theorem justifies the following definition.

DEFINITION 9-10-18. *If y and z are any objects, we define the* **pair** *of y and z to be the unique set G such that for every object x we have $x \in G$ if and only if ($x = y$ or $x = z$); and we denote this set $\{y, z\}$.*

From this definition we obtain easily the following basic theorem for pairs.

THEOREM 9-10-19. *If y and z are any objects, then*

(i) $y \in \{y, z\}$ *and* $z \in \{y, z\}$,
(ii) *the only objects which are elements of $\{y, z\}$ are y and z.*

For proof the reader should review Theorem 9-5-2 and *its* proof.

With Theorem 9-10-19 at hand we are ready to lay the groundwork for the definition of union by establishing the following theorem.

THEOREM 9-10-20. *If H and K are any sets then there is a unique set G such that, for every object x, we have $x \in G$ if and only if ($x \in H$ or $x \in K$).*

We shall give the details of the proof of existence of such a set G; the uniqueness is then easily obtained by Axiom Z1.

Proof

►► 1. Let H and K be any sets.
► 2. $\{H, K\}$ is a set; by Definition 9-10-18. (In applying this definition we take the objects y and z of 9-10-18 to be the sets H

and K of line **1**. If the reader doubts that sets qualify as objects in our system, he should review Section 1 of this chapter.)

▶▶ **3.** There is a set G such that for every object x we have $x \in G$ if and only if (there exists an object y such that y is a set and $x \in y$ and $y \in \{H, K\}$); by Axiom Z4, taking the H of that axiom to be the set $\{H, K\}$ of line **2**.

4. H is a set and $H \in \{H, K\}$; by line **1** and Theorem 9-10-19.

5. K is a set and $K \in \{H, K\}$; by line **1** and Theorem 9-10-19.

▶▶ **6.** Let x be any object.

7. If $x \in H$ or $x \in K$ then there exists an object y such that y is a set and $x \in y$ and $y \in \{H, K\}$; by lines **4**, **5**, and **6**.

▶▶ **8.** If $x \in H$ or $x \in K$ then $x \in G$; by lines **7** and **3**.

9. The only objects which are elements of $\{H, K\}$ are H and K; by Theorem 9-10-19.

10. If y is an object such that $x \in y$ and $y \in \{H, K\}$ then $x \in H$ or $x \in K$; by line **9**.

▶▶ **11.** If $x \in G$ then $x \in H$ or $x \in K$; by lines **3** and **10**.

12. $x \in G$ if and only if ($x \in H$ or $x \in K$); by lines **8** and **11**.

13. For every object x we have $x \in G$ if and only if ($x \in H$ or $x \in K$); by the Deduction Theorem applied to lines **6** through **12**.

With Theorem 9-10-20 at hand we are now justified in giving the following definition.

DEFINITION 9-10-21. *If H and K are any sets we define the* **union** *of H and K (in symbols: $H \cup K$) to be the unique set G such that for every object x we have $x \in G$ if and only if ($x \in H$ or $x \in K$).*

From this we obtain immediately

THEOREM 9-10-22. *For any sets H and K, and any object x, we have $x \in (H \cup K)$ if and only if ($x \in H$ or $x \in K$).*

This theorem is precisely the same as theorem 9-4-5, and hence we can use it to infer the various fundamental properties of union in the same way as was done in our treatment of Cantor's set theory. In fact, Theorems 9-4-6, 7, and 8 all go through without change, either in statement or proof. We list below, in a single theorem for ready reference, all of the properties mentioned in those theorems.

THEOREM 9-10-23. *The following properties of the operations $\cup$ and $\cap$, the set $\varnothing$, and the relation $\subseteq$, are true for arbitrary sets H, J, and K:*

(**a**) $H \cup H = H$
(**b**) $H \cup K = K \cup H$
(**c**) $(H \cup K) \cup J = H \cup (K \cup J)$

(d) $H \cup \varnothing = H$
(e) $H \cap (H \cup J) = H$ *and* $H \cup (H \cap J) = H$
(f) $H \cap (J \cup K) = (H \cap J) \cup (H \cap K)$
(g) $H \cup (J \cap K) = (H \cup J) \cap (H \cup K)$
(h) $H \subseteq K$ *if and only if* $H \cap K = H$
(i) $H \subseteq K$ *if and only if* $H \cup K = K$
(j) $H \subseteq H \cup K$ *and* $K \subseteq H \cup K$*; and if* J *is any set such that* $H \subseteq J$ *and* $K \subseteq J$*, then* $H \cup K \subseteq J$.
(k) $H \cap K \subseteq H$ *and* $H \cap K \subseteq K$*; and if* J *is any set such that* $J \subseteq H$ *and* $J \subseteq K$*, then* $J \subseteq H \cap K$.

If we try to develop Zermelo's system along the same lines as Cantor's, we would next seek to define the notion of the *complement* of a set (cf. Definition 9-4-9). Here, however, we find a radical difference between the two theories. For in Zermelo's system we can prove that there is not a single set which has a complement! In order to show this, we first show that there is no "universal set".

THEOREM 9-10-24. *There is no set* H *such that for every object* x *we have* $x \in H$.

The reader should note that the following proof is based upon exactly the same argument used to produce the Russell paradox in Cantor's theory (cf. Theorems 9-9-2 and 9-9-3).

Proof

▶▶ **1.** *Suppose* that there exists a set H such that for every object x we have $x \in H$.
▶ **2.** Let G be the set $\{x \in H \mid x$ is a set and *not* $x \in x\}$.
3. For every object x we have $x \in G$ if and only if $x \in H$ and x is a set and *not* $x \in x$; by line **2** and Theorem 9-10-7.
4. For every object x we have ($x \in H$ and x is a set and *not* $x \in x$) if and only if (x is a set and *not* $x \in x$); by logic from line **1**.
5. For every object x we have $x \in G$ if and only if (x is a set and *not* $x \in x$); by logic from lines **3** and **4**.
▶ **6.** $G \in G$ if and only if (G is a set and *not* $G \in G$); by logic from line **5**.
7. G is a set; by line **2**.
▶ **8.** (G is a set and *not* $G \in G$) if and only if *not* $G \in G$; by logic from line **7**.
9. $G \in G$ if and only if *not* $G \in G$; by lines **6** and **8**.
▶ **10.** It is *not* true that ($G \in G$ if and only if $G \in G$); by logic from line **9**. The law of logic used here allows us to infer *not* (P if and only if Q) from (P if and only if *not* Q).

▶11. $G \in G$ if and only if $G \in G$; by logic.

▶▶12. Lines **10** and **11** form a contradiction which has been inferred from the *supposition* of line **1**. Thus this supposition must be wrong: There is *no* set H such that for every object x we have $x \in H$.

We are now ready to show that no set can have a complement.

THEOREM 9-10-25. *Let K be any set. Then there is no set J such that for every object x we have $x \in J$ if and only if* **not** *$x \in K$.*

Proof

▶▶1. Let K be any set.

▶▶2. *Suppose* there is a set J such that for every object x we have $x \in J$ if and only if *not* $x \in K$.

3. For every object x we have $x \in (K \cup J)$ if and only if ($x \in K$ or $x \in J$); by Theorem 9-10-22.

4. For every object x we have $x \in (K \cup J)$ if and only if ($x \in K$ or *not* $x \in K$); by logic from lines **2** and **3**.

5. For every object x we have ($x \in K$ or *not* $x \in K$); by logic.

▶6. For every object x we have $x \in (K \cup J)$; by lines **4** and **5**.

▶7. It is *not* true that for every object x we have $x \in (K \cup J)$; by Theorem 9-10-24.

▶▶8. Lines **6** and **7** are a contradiction which results from the supposition of line **2**. Hence this supposition is wrong: There is *no* set J such that for every object x we have $x \in J$ if and only if *not* $x \in K$.

9. If K is any set, then there is *no* set J such that for every object x we have $x \in J$ if and only if *not* $x \in K$; by the Deduction Theorem applied to lines **1** through **8**.

While Theorem 9-10-25 shows that we cannot introduce the notion of the *complement* of a set in Zermelo's system, there is a closely related concept which for all practical purposes can take its place.

DEFINITION 9-10-26. *If J and K are any sets, we define the* **complement of K relative to J** *(in symbols: $J \sim K$) to be the set* $\{x \in J \mid \textbf{not } x \in K\}$.

As an illustration of this concept, consider the following sets:

$$J = \{1, 2, 3, 4, 5, 6, 7, 8, 9\}$$
$$K = \{1, 2, 3, 4, 5\}.$$

For these sets, the complement of K relative to J, $(J \sim K)$, is that set whose elements are *in* J, but are *not in* K. Here $J \sim K = \{6, 7, 8, 9\}$. What is $K \sim J$?

We get at once the following basic property of relative complements, from which all others are obtained.

THEOREM 9-10-27. *If J and K are any sets, and x any object, then we have $x \in J \sim K$ if and only if $x \in J$ and not $x \in K$.*

The proof is immediate by Definition 9-10-26 and Theorem 9-10-7.

In place of Theorem 9-4-11 for complements we get the following theorem for relative complements.

THEOREM 9-10-28. *If J and K are any sets, then $J \sim (J \sim K) = J \cap K$. If, in particular, $K \subseteq J$, then $J \sim (J \sim K) = K$.*

By Theorem 9-10-23, part **h**, we see that if $K \subseteq J$ then $J \cap K = K$; hence the second part of this theorem follows directly from the first part. The proof of the first part is left as an exercise.

In place of Theorem 9-4-12 for complements we have the following results for relative complements.

THEOREM 9-10-29 *For any sets J, H and K,*

(**a**) $J \sim (H \cup K) = (J \sim H) \cap (J \sim K)$ *and* $J \sim (H \cap K) = (J \sim H) \cup (J \sim K)$.
(**b**) *If* $H \subseteq K$ *then* $J \sim K \subseteq J \sim H$, *and if* $J \sim K \subseteq J \sim H$ *then* $J \cap H \subseteq J \cap K$
(**c**) $H \cap (J \sim H) = \varnothing$ *and* $J \subseteq H \cup (J \sim H)$.

The proofs of these statements closely resemble the corresponding proofs for Theorem 9-4-12, and will be omitted.

EXERCISES

1. Make up an example to illustrate Axiom Z4 (9-10-4).
2. Complete the proof of Theorem 9-10-11.
3. Prove Theorem 9-10-17.
4. Prove Theorem 9-10-19.
5. Prove the uniqueness of G in Theorem 9-10-20.
6. Make up examples to illustrate each of the properties listed in Theorem 9-10-23.
7. Prove Theorem 9-10-28.
8. Illustrate by examples the properties listed in Theorem 9-10-29.

11. Relations in Zermelo's Theory of Sets

Section 10 completed our discussion of the "Boolean part" of Zermelo's set theory, and we turn now to the treatment of relations. The notion of a pair having been already introduced (cf. Definition 9-10-18), we can proceed directly to define ordered pairs.

DEFINITION 9-11-1. *For any objects y and z we define the* **ordered pair** *of y and z (in symbols: $\langle y, z\rangle$) to be the set $\{\{y, y\}, \{y, z\}\}$.*

This definition is identical to Definition 9-5-4 except that we have used the pair $\{y, y\}$ in place of the unit set $\{y\}$. This difference is without significance, as the reader can see from Theorem 9-5-3, part (**c**), and is only introduced because we have not bothered to introduce the concept (and notation) of a unit set explicitly into our sketch of the Zermelo system.

THEOREM 9-11-2. *If y, z, u, v are any objects such that $\langle y, z\rangle = \langle u, v\rangle$, then $y = u$ and $z = v$.*

The proof is identical to that of Theorem 9-5-5. Of course the ground should be prepared by proving that Theorem 9-5-3, part (**e**), holds in the Zermelo system, even though we have not formulated this as a theorem of this section.

With ordered pairs at hand, the notion of a binary relation can be introduced exactly as in the Cantor theory.

DEFINITION 9-11-3. *We define a* **binary relation** *to be a set G such that for every object x, if $x \in G$ then x is an ordered pair, i.e., $x = \langle y, z\rangle$ for some objects y and z. Notation: We often use the letters Q, R, S and T to denote relations, and write $y\ R\ z$ in place of $\langle y, z\rangle \in R$, etc.*

The definition in Cantor's set theory of the *converse* of a relation (Definition 9-6-2) depended upon Axiom C2 and so is not available in the Zermelo system unless some special justification can be provided for it. It turns out that in order to furnish the required justification we must introduce the notions of the *power set* and the *sum set* of a given set. The definition of the first of these concepts is based upon the following theorem.

THEOREM 9-11-4. *If H is any set then there is one and only one set G such that for every object x we have $x \in G$ if and only if x is a set and $x \subseteq H$.*

This theorem asserts, for any given set H, the existence of a unique set G whose *elements* are all of the *subsets* of H. The existence of G is easily established by Axiom Z5 (9-10-5) and Definition 9-10-8, and the uniqueness by Axiom Z1; we shall omit a detailed proof.

DEFINITION 9-11-5. *If H is any set we define the* **power set** *of H (in symbols: $\mathbf{P}(H)$), to be the unique set G such that for every object x we have $x \in G$ if and only if x is a set and $x \subseteq H$.*

Of course this definition is justified by Theorem 9-11-4. From the definition we get at once:

THEOREM 9-11-6. *If H is any set and x any object, then $x \in \mathbf{P}(H)$ if and only if x is a set and $x \subseteq H$.*

Thus, if $H = \{1, 2, 3\}$, the power set of H, which has as its elements all of the subsets of H, is $\mathbf{P}(H) = \{\varnothing, \{1\}, \{2\}, \{3\}, \{1, 2\}, \{1, 3\}, \{2, 3\}, \{1, 2, 3\}\}$.

Turning to the concept of the *sum set* of a given set, we first provide a basis for the definition by the following theorem.

THEOREM 9-11-7. *If H is any set then there exists one and only one set G such that for every object x we have: $x \in G$ if and only if there is a set y such that $x \in y$ and $y \in H$.*

This theorem asserts, for any given set H, the existence of a unique set G obtained by lumping together the elements of all those sets (if any) which are elements of H. (Of course if no element of H happens to be a set then G is simply the null set, $\varnothing$.) A proof of this theorem is easily obtained by combining Axioms Z4 and Z1; we omit the details.

DEFINITION 9-11-8. *If H is any set we define the* **sum set** *of H (in symbols: $\sigma(H)$) to be the unique set G such that, for every object x, we have: $x \in G$ if and only if there is a set y such that $x \in y$ and $y \in H$.*

Of course this definition is justified by Theorem 9-11-7. From the definition we get at once:

THEOREM 9-11-9. *For any set H and any object x we have $x \in \sigma(H)$ if and only if there is some set y such that $x \in y$ and $y \in H$.*

As an illustration of the concept of sum set, consider the following example.

$$H = \{\{1\}, \{2\}, \{2, 3, 4\}, 5\}.$$

Here

$$\sigma(H) = \{1, 2, 3, 4\},$$

since each element of $\sigma(H)$ is an element of a set which is an element of H, and all such elements appear in $\{1, 2, 3, 4\}$.

Using the concepts of power set and sum set we can prepare the ground for the definition of the *converse* of a relation.

THEOREM 9-11-10. *If R is any binary relation, and if y and z are any objects such that $y \; R \; z$, then $y \in \sigma(\sigma(R))$ and $z \in \sigma(\sigma(R))$.*

Proof

▶▶ **1.** Let R be any binary relation, and let y and z be any elements such that $y \; R \; z$.

2. $\langle y, z\rangle \in R$; by line **1** and Definition 9-11-3.

3. $\langle y, z\rangle$ is a set and $\{y, z\} \in \langle y, z\rangle$; by Definition 9-11-1 and Theorem 9-10-19.

4. $\{y, z\} \in \sigma(R)$ if and only if there is some set w such that $\{y, z\} \in w$ and $w \in \langle y, z\rangle$; by Theorem 9-11-9.

▶ 5. $\{y, z\} \in \sigma(R)$; by lines **2**, **3**, and **4**.

▶ 6. $\{y, z\}$ is a set and $y \in \{y, z\}$ and $z \in \{y, z\}$; by Definition 9-10-18 and Theorem 9-10-19.

▶ 7. $y \in \sigma(\sigma(R))$ if and only if there is some set w such that $y \in w$ and $w \in \sigma(R)$; by Theorem 9-11-9.

▶▶ 8. $y \in \sigma(\sigma(R))$; by lines **5**, **6**, and **7**.

▶▶ 9. $z \in \sigma(\sigma(R))$; by reasoning similar to lines **7** and **8**.

10. If R is any binary relation, and if y and z are any objects such that $y\ R\ z$, then $y \in \sigma(\sigma(R))$ and $z \in \sigma(\sigma(R))$; by the Deduction Theorem applied to lines **1** through **8** and **9**.

The theorem just proved will be combined with the following.

THEOREM 9-11-11. *If K is any set and if y and z are any elements of K, then $\langle z, y\rangle \in \mathbf{P}(\mathbf{P}(K))$.*

Proof

▶▶ 1. Let K be any set and let y and z be any elements of K.

2. The *only* objects which are elements of $\{y, z\}$ are y and z; by Theorem 9-10-19.

3. For every object x, if $x \in \{y, z\}$ then also $x \in K$; by lines **1** and **2**.

▶ 4. $\{y, z\} \subseteq K$; by line **3** and Definition 9-10-8.

▶ 5. $\{z, z\} \subseteq K$; by reasoning similar to lines **2** to **4**.

▶▶ 6. $\{z, z\} \in \mathbf{P}(K)$ and $\{y, z\} \in \mathbf{P}(K)$; by lines **4** and **5** and Theorem 9-11-6.

7. The only objects which are elements of $\langle z, y\rangle$ are $\{z, z\}$ and $\{y, z\}$; by Definition 9-11-1 and Theorem 9-10-19.

8. For every object x, if $x \in \langle z, y\rangle$ then also $x \in \mathbf{P}(K)$; by lines **6** and **7**.

▶ 9. $\langle z, y\rangle \subseteq \mathbf{P}(K)$; by line **8** and Definition 9-10-8.

▶▶ 10. $\langle z, y\rangle \in \mathbf{P}(\mathbf{P}(K))$; by line **9** and Theorem 9-11-6.

11. If K is any set, and if y and z are any elements of K, then $\langle z, y\rangle \in \mathbf{P}(\mathbf{P}(K))$; by the Deduction Theorem applied to lines **1** through **10**.

Combining the last two theorems we get at once:

THEOREM 9-11-12. *If R is any binary relation, and if y and z are any objects such that $y\ R\ z$, then $\langle z, y\rangle \in \mathbf{P}(\mathbf{P}(\sigma(\sigma(R))))$.*

We are now ready to define the converse of a relation.

DEFINITION 9-11-13. *If R is any binary relation we define the* **converse** *of*

R (in symbols: $R^{\cup}$) to be the set $\{x \in \mathbf{P}(\mathbf{P}(\sigma(\sigma(R)))) \mid x = \langle z, y\rangle$ *for some objects y and z such that $y\ R\ z$*$\}$.

That this definition gives a concept of converse which is the same as that given in our development of Cantor's theory, is shown by the following theorem which is identical to Theorem 9-6-3.

THEOREM 9-11-14. *If R is any binary relation then $R^{\cup}$ is also a binary relation, and for any objects u and v we have $u\ R^{\cup}\ v$ if, and only if, $v\ R\ u$.*

The proof of this theorem begins as follows.

1. Let R be any binary relation.
2. For any object x we have: $x \in R^{\cup}$ if and only if $x \in \mathbf{P}(\mathbf{P}(\sigma(\sigma(R))))$ and $x = \langle z, y\rangle$ for some objects y and z such that $y\ R\ z$; by line **1**, Definition 9-11-13, and Theorem 9-10-7.
3. For any object x, if $x = \langle z, y\rangle$ for some objects y and z such that $y\ R\ z$, then $x \in \mathbf{P}(\mathbf{P}(\sigma(\sigma(R))))$; by logic from Theorem 9-11-12.
4. For any object x we have: $[x \in \mathbf{P}(\mathbf{P}(\sigma(\sigma(R))))$ and $x = \langle z, y\rangle$ for some objects y and z such that $y\ R\ z]$ if, and only if, $[x = \langle z, y\rangle$ for some objects y and z such that $y\ R\ z]$; by logic from line **3**. (The law of logic used here allows us to pass from a statement of the form *If P then Q*, to the statement (*Q and P*) *if and only if P*.)
5. For any object x we have: $x \in R^{\cup}$ if and only if $x = \langle z, y\rangle$ for some objects y and z such that $y\ R\ z$; by lines **2** and **4**.

Line **5** is identical (except for an interchange in the use of the letters "y" and "z") with line **2** of the proof of Theorem 9-6-3. Hence the remainder of that proof can be carried over verbatim to the present context, and results in the desired proof of Theorem 9-11-14.

The basic properties of the operation of converse, which were derived for Cantor's theory in Section 6, depended only on having Theorem 9-6-3 available. Since Theorem 9-11-14 is identical with Theorem 9-6-3, we can use the same proofs to establish the same properties in the Zermelo system. Thus we obtain:

THEOREM 9-11-15. *For any binary relations R and T we have*

(**a**) $R^{\cup\cup} = R$,
(**b**) $(R \cup T)^{\cup} = R^{\cup} \cup T^{\cup}$,
(**c**) $(R \cap T)^{\cup} = R^{\cup} \cap T^{\cup}$.

Continuing to seek a development of Zermelo's system which is parallel to that which we gave for Cantor's system, we turn next to the concept of the *relative product* of two binary relations. As in the case of the notion of converse, it is necessary to prepare the ground by establishing a preliminary theorem.

THEOREM 9-11-16. *If Q and R are relations, and if y, z, and t are any objects such that $y\ Q\ t$ and $t\ R\ z$, then* $\langle y, z\rangle \in \mathbf{P}(\mathbf{P}(\sigma(\sigma(Q \cup R))))$.

The proof is substantially like that of Theorem 9-11-12.

We are now ready to define the relative product of two relations.

DEFINITION 9-11-17. *If Q and R are any binary relations, we define the* **relative product** *of Q and R (in symbols: $Q\ ;R$) to be the set* $\{x \in \mathbf{P}(\mathbf{P}(\sigma(\sigma(Q \cup R)))) \mid$ *there exist objects u, v, and w such that $x = \langle u, w\rangle$ and $\langle u, v\rangle \in Q$ and $\langle v, w\rangle \in R$*$\}$.

That this definition gives a concept of relative product which is the same as that given in our development of Cantor's theory, is shown by the following theorem which is identical to Theorem 9-6-6.

THEOREM 9-11-18. *If Q and R are any binary relations, then $Q\ ;R$ is a binary relation; and for any objects y and z we have $y(Q\ ;R)z$ if and only if there is an object t such that $y\ Q\ t$ and $t\ R\ z$.*

To prove this theorem it is only necessary to modify the proof of Theorem 9-6-6 in the same way that the proof of Theorem 9-6-3 was modified to obtain a proof of Theorem 9-11-14. We omit the details.

With the aid of Theorem 9-11-18 we can go over the proof of Theorem 9-6-7 to obtain the basic properties of relative product, as formulated below.

THEOREM 9-11-19. *For any relations R, T, and W we have:*

(**a**) $(R\ ;T)\ ;W = R\ ;(T\ ;W)$,
(**b**) $(R\ ;T)^{\cup} = T^{\cup}\ ;R^{\cup}$,
(**c**) $R\ ;(T \cap W) \subseteq (R\ ;T) \cap (R\ ;W)$,
(**d**) $R\ ;(T \cup W) = (R\ ;T) \cup (R\ ;W)$.

The statement and proof of this theorem are identical to those of Theorem 9-6-7.

The definition of the *domain* of a binary relation must be modified from that given in the Cantor theory (Definition 9-6-8), since the latter depends on Axiom Schema C2, which is not available in the Zermelo theory. The required modification is as follows.

DEFINITION 9-11-20. *If R is any binary relation, we define the* **domain** *of R (in symbols: $D(R)$) to be the set* $\{x \in \sigma(\sigma(R)) \mid$ *there is some object y such that $x\ R\ y$*$\}$.

With the aid of Theorem 9-11-10 we can modify the proof of Theorem 9-6-9 to obtain the latter proposition in the Zermelo system. Thus,

THEOREM 9-11-21. *For any binary relation R, and any object x, we have* $x \in D(R)$ *if and only if there is some object y such that* $x\ R\ y$.

The fundamental properties of the concept of domain, and the introduction of the concept of function, can now be carried out within Zermelo's system in just the same manner as we employed for Cantor's system in Section 8. We shall not copy any of the details here.

However, the derivation of the Russell paradox, or some other well known contradiction such as the Burali-Forti paradox, can *not* be carried over from Cantor's system to Zermelo's—at least no one has ever been able, so far, to derive a contradiction from Zermelo's axioms.

As indicated after Axiom Z5, it is necessary to supplement Zermelo's first five axioms in order to carry out more advanced portions of the theory of sets, and we shall now list these further axioms with a few brief remarks.

It turns out that the system of Axioms Z1 through Z5 admits models in which every set is finite. In order to insure the existence of an infinite set we add the following Axiom.

AXIOM Z6 (9-11-22) AXIOM OF INFINITY. *There exists a set G such that*

(i) $\varnothing \in G$ *and*
(ii) *whenever x is any element of G then also* $\{x\} \in G$.

(Here $\{x\}$ stands for $\{x, x\}$, the unit set of x. See Definition 9-10-18.)

Intuitively, we can think of this postulate as follows. We know from (i) that $\varnothing \in G$. Then from (ii) we can infer that $\{\varnothing\} \in G$. Furthermore, we can show that $\varnothing \neq \{\varnothing\}$. Then, again by (ii), we obtain $\{\{\varnothing\}\} \in G$, and can show that $\{\{\varnothing\}\} \neq \{\varnothing\}$ and $\{\{\varnothing\}\} \neq \varnothing$. Repeated use of (ii) in this way generates an "infinity" of elements in G.

The following axiom is not really necessary for developing mathematics on the basis of set theory, but it is included because it simplifies certain proofs and definitions, and because it expresses a property of sets which appears intuitively very reasonable to many mathematicians.

AXIOM Z7 (9-11-23) AXIOM OF REGULARITY. *If G is a set other than the null set, and if all of the elements of G are themselves sets, then there must be an element K of G such that* $G \cap K = \varnothing$.

Although it is not evident from the form of this axiom, it is designed to insure that: If we start with any set G, and begin to form a sequence of sets $G_1, G_2, G_3, \ldots$ by picking $G_1 \in G$, then picking $G_2 \in G_1$, then $G_3 \in G_2$, etc., then eventually (after some finite number of steps) the sequence must terminate because we arrive at a set G_n which has no set as an element.

The following theorem gives a simple example of the kind of sets which are excluded by Axiom Z7.

THEOREM 9-11-24. *There is no set G such that $G \in G$.*

Proof

▶▶ **1.** Let G be any set.

2. $G \in \{G, G\}$, and the *only* object which is an element of $\{G, G\}$ is G; by Theorem 9-10-19.

3. $\{G, G\}$ is not the null set, and every element of $\{G, G\}$ is a set; by lines **1** and **2** and Theorem 9-10-13.

4. There is an element K of $\{G, G\}$ such that $\{G, G\} \cap K = \varnothing$; by line **3** and Axiom Z7.

5. $\{G, G\} \cap G = \varnothing$; by lines **2** and **4**.

▶▶ **6.** *Suppose* that $G \in G$.

7. $G \in \{G, G\} \cap G$; by lines **2** and **6** and Theorem 9-10-15.

▶ **8.** $G \in \varnothing$; by E from lines **5** and **7**.

▶ **9.** *Not* $G \in \varnothing$; by Theorem 9-10-13.

▶▶**10.** Lines **8** and **9** form a contradiction which has been inferred from the supposition on line **6**. Hence this supposition is wrong, and we must have *not* $G \in G$.

11. If G is any set, then *not* $G \in G$; by the Deduction Theorem applied to lines **1** through **10**.

For an application of this theorem see the discussion at the beginning of Chapter VIII.

A closely related theorem is the following.

THEOREM 9-11-25. *There are no sets G and K such that $G \in K$ and $K \in G$.*

We leave the proof of this theorem as an exercise, with the suggestion to modify the proof of Theorem 9-11-24 by considering the set $\{G, K\}$ in place of $\{G, G\}$.

Still another theorem of this kind is the following, which will find a use in Chapter XI when we consider a construction of the negative integers.

THEOREM 9-11-26. *If N is a set and x any object then $\langle x, N\rangle \notin N$.*

Outline of Proof

Let G be the set $\{N, \{x, N\}\} \cup \{N, \langle x, N\rangle\}$. It is easy to see that N, $\{x, N\}$, and $\langle x, N\rangle$ are elements of G, and that these are the *only* elements of G. Thus G is a set other than the null set, and all of the elements of G are themselves sets (N by hypothesis). It follows by Axiom Z7 that G contains an element K such that $G \cap K = \varnothing$.

Now K is not $\langle x, N\rangle$ since $\{x, N\} \in (G \cap \langle x, N\rangle)$, as we see by recalling that $\langle x, N\rangle = \{\{x, x\}, \{x, N\}\}$. Also K is not $\{x, N\}$, since $N \in (G \cap \{x, N\})$.

Hence we must have $K = N$. That is, $G \cap N = \varnothing$. But this shows that $\langle x, N \rangle \notin N$, since otherwise we would have $\langle x, N \rangle \in (G \cap N)$.

We come now to the last of our axioms—the so-called "axiom of choice." While the other axioms of Zermelo's system were universally acknowledged by mathematicians to be "correct," and indeed were well-known principles of the earlier system of Cantor's, the principle expressed by this axiom had gone entirely unrecognized until its formulation by Zermelo. And when he proposed it, it immediately became the center of strong controversy. Even today there are a few mathematicians who feel that its use is improper, although for the great majority it has become an indispensable and commonplace tool.

AXIOM Z8 (9-11-27) AXIOM OF CHOICE. *If G is any set whose elements are themselves sets other than $\varnothing$, then there is a function f, with domain G, such that for every $K \in G$ we have $f(K) \in K$.*

Intuitively, we can think of the function f in the above axiom as "choosing" an element from each set K in a given set G (whose elements are nonempty sets). One might think that such an axiom is unnecessary—that in the cases where one wished to "choose" an element from each such set K one could proceed by describing an explicit process for making this selection (using the previous axioms of set theory). But this is not so.

An incisive (but nonmathematical) example, which illustrates the difficulties of "choosing" an element from each set in a given class of sets, was given by Bertrand Russell. Suppose we think of a shoe store with infinitely many boxes each of which contains one pair of shoes. It is easy to describe a function f, having for its domain the set G of all boxes of shoes, and such that for any box B in G we have $f(B) \in B$. For example, for any box B we could take $f(B)$ to be the left shoe in that box. In this case the axiom of choice is not needed to guarantee the existence of such a function f. But, suppose the same shoe store has infinitely many boxes each containing one pair of *socks*. There is no right or left sock in a pair, so we cannot use the above means of choosing one sock from each box. In fact, there does not appear to be any explicit rule we can give which determines a definite sock in each pair. Yet, intuitively, we feel that there is such a function, and Axiom Z8 is a statement of our intuitive conviction in this case.

As a more mathematical example of the use of the Axiom of Choice, consider nonempty sets of positive integers. If we wish a function f which "chooses" an element from each of these sets we can select the function which acts on any one of these sets and produces the least element of the set: Again the Axiom of Choice is not necessary to guarantee the existence of such a function, since we have described one explicitly. But suppose we are dealing with the set of all nonempty sets of *real* numbers (instead of positive integers). There is no known way to describe a method for picking one number from each of these sets. Yet, in some branches of mathematics it is useful to have a function f which *does* choose one number from each nonempty set of real numbers; and the Axiom of Choice is used to guarantee the existence of such a function.

Our survey of the Zermelo axiom system is now complete. We have indicated in some detail how the elementary portions of set theory can be derived from Zermelo's axioms, and we have stated that no one has been able to derive the contradictions found in Cantor's theory from these axioms.

Of course the fact that no one has found such contradictions is no guarantee that they do not exist, and many mathematicians have sought for a *proof* that these axioms are free of contradiction. These efforts, however, were never successful. And the lack of success was explained when, in 1931, an Austrian mathematican, Kurt Gödel (now an American), gave a *proof* that *if* Zermelo's axioms *are* consistent, then it is impossible to give a *proof* of this fact!

EXERCISES

1. Give several examples of
  (a) Power sets of a set H,
  (b) Sum sets of a set H.

2. Prove Theorem 9-11-7.

3. Prove Theorem 9-11-16.

4. Prove Theorem 9-11-25.

5. Prove
  (a) $\sigma(K \cap H) \subseteq \sigma(K) \cap \sigma(H)$ (Does the opposite inclusion always hold?)
  (b) $\sigma(K \cup H) = \sigma(K) \cup \sigma(H)$
  (c) $\sigma(\{K, H\}) = K \cup H$
  (d) $\mathbf{P}(K) \cup \mathbf{P}(H) \subseteq \mathbf{P}(K \cup H)$
  (e) $\mathbf{P}(K \cap H) \subseteq \mathbf{P}(K) \cap \mathbf{P}(H)$
  (f) $K \subseteq \mathbf{P}(\sigma(K))$ if every element of K is a set
  (g) $K = \sigma(\mathbf{P}(K))$.

X

Mathematical Logic

1. Truth Tables and Sentential Laws of Logic

In the preceding chapters we have used laws of logic to help us provide theorems about numbers, sets, or other mathematical objects, but generally we have not specified explicitly what these rules of logic are. In this chapter we finally come to grips with this most fundamental problem of mathematics.

We have been able to come this far without explicitly setting down the logical rules because of our ability intuitively to recognize the correct application of these laws, based upon our intuitive knowledge of the meaning of certain key words which enter into their formulation. The most important of these key words are given in the following list: not, and, or, if then, only, is (equal to), any, each, all, every, there is, exists, some, such that. It would be well for the reader to review, at this time, our informal discussion of the mathematical use of these words as given in Chapter I, Section 2.

Let us first make the commonplace observation that the statements of the axioms, definitions, and theorems we have encountered, as well as the steps of the proofs, have been made up of *sentences*, either simple or compound. Examples of *simple* sentences are "It is raining," or "A is a subset of B." A *compound* sentence is a statement obtained from one or more simple sentences by the use of such *connectives* as "not," "and," "if . . . then," etc. Thus "If it is raining then A is a subset of B" is a compound sentence.

The fundamental property of *any* mathematical sentence is that it be either *true* or *false*, but not both. We shall not, like Pontius Pilate, ask the question "What is truth?" Instead, we shall assume simply that every sentence has associated with it a unique *truth value*—it is either true or false, but not both. In part, a study of the laws of logic is closely allied with a study of the relation between the truth values of various sentences.

In this chapter we shall confine our study to those laws of logic whose formulation involves only the following five words or phrases, which are called the *sentential connectives:* "not", "and", "or", "if . . . then", "if and only if". And to begin our study we shall introduce a special symbol for each of these connectives which will facilitate the construction of a mathematical theory involving them.

Sentential Connectives

English Phrase	*Special Symbol*
not	$\neg$
and	$\wedge$
or	$\vee$
if . . . then	$\rightarrow$
if and only if	$\leftrightarrow$

As noted in Chapter I, connectives are used to form compound sentences from given sentences (which may themselves be either simple—i.e., containing no connectives—or compound). Furthermore, if we know whether each of the given component sentences is true (T) or false(F), there is a rule for computing whether the compound sentence built from these components is true or false. For example, if P is any true sentence then $\neg P$ (not-P) is false; if Q and R are any false sentences then the compound sentence $Q \vee R$ (Q or R) is false. The full rules of computation, as described in Chapter I, are summarized in the following tables. In a sense, these tables specify the "meaning" of the different connectives.

P	$\neg P$
T	F
F	T

Table 1

P	Q	$P \wedge Q$	$P \vee Q$	$P \rightarrow Q$	$P \leftrightarrow Q$
T	T	T	T	T	T
T	F	F	T	F	F
F	T	F	T	T	F
F	F	F	F	T	T

Table 2

In the first column of Table 1 are listed the two possible "truth values," T and F, for a sentence P, and opposite each entry there is listed in the second column the corresponding truth value of the compound sentence $\neg P$. Similarly, in the first two columns of Table 2 are listed each of the four possible pairs of truth values for two sentences, P and Q, and opposite each such pair, in the last four columns, are listed the corresponding values of the compound sentences $P \wedge Q$, $P \vee Q$, $P \rightarrow Q$, and $P \leftrightarrow Q$. For example, from the third line we see that if P is a false sentence and Q a true one, then the compound sentence $P \leftrightarrow Q$ is false (according to the entry in the last column, third line).

With the aid of these tables we can compute a truth value for a compound sentence containing any number of connectives and any number of component sentences, as soon as we know the truth values of the components. For example, if P is true, Q false, and R true, then the compound sentence $(\neg Q \wedge (P \rightarrow R)) \leftrightarrow (\neg (P \vee R) \rightarrow Q)$ is true, as we see by the following computation:

$$\begin{aligned}(\neg \mathrm{F} \wedge (\mathrm{T} \rightarrow \mathrm{T})) \leftrightarrow (\neg (\mathrm{T} \vee \mathrm{T}) \rightarrow \mathrm{F}) &= (\mathrm{T} \wedge \mathrm{T}) \leftrightarrow (\neg \mathrm{T} \rightarrow \mathrm{F}) \\ &= \mathrm{T} \leftrightarrow (\mathrm{F} \rightarrow \mathrm{F}) \\ &= \mathrm{T} \leftrightarrow \mathrm{T} = \mathrm{T}.\end{aligned}$$

In this computation the first expression is obtained by replacing each component sentence of the given compound sentence by its truth value, and each succeeding line of the computation is obtained from its predecessor by use of Tables 1 and 2.

As the reader has noticed, in order to make assertions about arbitrary sentences we use letters such as "P", "Q", and "R"; letters used in this way are called *sentential variables*. And in order to describe a particular way of combining arbitrary sentences to form a compound sentence from them we have recourse to a formula, such as "$\neg P \rightarrow \neg (P \wedge Q)$", which is built up from sentential variables with the aid of connectives (and parentheses); such a formula is called a *sentential formula*. We may think of a sentential formula as indicating a "form of compound sentences."

Unlike a fixed compound sentence, a sentential formula does not have a definite truth value attached to it; but if we *assign* truth values (in any manner) to the sentential variables appearing in the formula, then we can compute a corresponding truth value for the formula (by repeated use of Tables 1 and 2). If we consider in turn *all possible* assignments of truth values to the variables of a formula, and if we compute the corresponding truth value of the formula for each of these assignments, then we obtain the so-called *truth table* for the formula.

For example, the truth table for the formula "$P \rightarrow \neg (Q \vee \neg (P \wedge R))$" is as follows:

P	Q	R	$P \rightarrow \neg (Q \vee \neg (P \wedge R))$
T	T	T	F
T	T	F	F
T	F	T	T
T	F	F	F
F	T	T	T
F	T	F	T
F	F	T	T
F	F	F	T

In the first three columns are listed all of the eight possible ways to assign truth values to the three sentential variables "P", "Q", and "R". The computation of the value of the given sentential formula corresponding to the assignment in the fourth line, for instance, is as follows:

$$\mathrm{T} \to \neg (\mathrm{F} \vee \neg (\mathrm{T} \wedge \mathrm{F})) = \mathrm{T} \to \neg (\mathrm{F} \vee \neg \mathrm{F}) = \mathrm{T} \to \neg (\mathrm{F} \vee \mathrm{T}) = \mathrm{T} \to \neg \mathrm{T} = \mathrm{T} \to \mathrm{F} = \mathrm{F}.$$

Act ıally, with a little experience one learns to avoid making the full computation for each line of a truth table by adopting various "short cuts." For example, we note from Table 2 that both $\mathrm{F} \to \mathrm{T} = \mathrm{T}$ and $\mathrm{F} \to \mathrm{F} = \mathrm{T}$; this enables us to say at once that the value of our formula (above) must be T in any line which assigns the value F to the variable P (i.e., in the last four lines).

For certain formulas we find that the value of the formula in *every* line of its truth table is T. Such a formula is called a *valid formula*, or *tautology*. Examples are "$P \to P$", "$P \vee \neg P$", "$P \to (Q \to P)$", "$(P \to \neg Q) \to (Q \to \neg P)$". As we shall see, tautologies are closely related to the "laws of logic."

And now we come to the central concept of logic: the notion of *consequence*. Suppose that we have several sentential formulas, say $A_1, A_2, \ldots, A_n$ (where n may be any positive integer). We say that a sentential formula B is a *sentential consequence* of the formulas $A_1, A_2, \ldots, A_n$ if *every assignment of truth values* (to the sentential variables appearing in the formulas $A_1, A_2, \ldots, A_n$, and B) *which produces a value* T *for each of the formulas* $A_1, A_2, \ldots, A_n$, *also produces a value* T *for the formula* B.

For example, the formula "$P \to R$" is a *sentential consequence* of the two formulas "$P \to Q$" and "$Q \to R$". To show this, we make a combined truth table for our three formulas, as follows.

P	Q	R	$P \to Q$	$Q \to R$	$P \to R$
T	T	T	T	T	T
T	T	F	T	F	F
T	F	T	F	T	T
T	F	F	F	T	F
F	T	T	T	T	T
F	T	F	T	F	T
F	F	T	T	T	T
F	F	F	T	T	T

By inspection, we see that the assignments of truth values to the sentential variables "P", "Q", and "R" which produce a value T for *each* of the formulas "$P \to Q$" and "$Q \to R$" are those on lines 1, 5, 7, and 8. And on every one of these lines we observe that "$P \to R$" has the value T. Hence we are entitled to say that "$P \to R$" is a *sentential consequence* of "$P \to Q$" and "$Q \to R$".

We shall use the notation

$$A_1, A_2, \ldots, A_n \Vdash B$$

to assert that a formula B is a sentential consequence of several formulas $A_1, A_2, \ldots, A_n$. Thus the observation of the previous paragraph can be expressed by writing $P \to Q, \quad Q \to R \Vdash P \to R$.

A statement of the form $A_1, A \ , \ldots, A_n \Vdash B$ we shall call a *sentential law of logic*. In connection with such a statement we say that the formulas $A_1, A_2, \ldots, A_n$ are the *premisses* of the law, and that the formula B is its *conclusion*. A few examples of sentential laws of logic are contained in the following theorem.

THEOREM 10-1-1.

(a) $P \Vdash Q \to P$

(b) $P \to Q, \quad P \to (Q \to R) \Vdash P \to R$

(c) $\neg P \to \neg Q \Vdash Q \to P$

(d) $P \vee Q \Vdash \neg P \to Q$

(e) $P \wedge Q \Vdash \neg (P \to \neg Q)$

(f) $P \to Q, \quad Q \to P \Vdash P \leftrightarrow Q$

(g) $\neg (P \vee Q) \Vdash \neg P \wedge \neg Q$

(h) $\neg (P \wedge Q) \Vdash \neg P \vee \neg Q$.

Proof

The proof of each part may be given by constructing an appropriate truth table. The details are left as an exercise.

In some cases we say that a sentential formula B may be obtained as a conclusion *without any premisses*, and we write simply $\Vdash B$. Referring to our definition of the relation of sentential consequence, $\Vdash$, we see that the natural meaning of an assertion of the form $\Vdash B$ is that *every possible assignment of truth values* (to the variables appearing in the formula B) *produces a value* T *for the formula B*. In other words we have $\Vdash B$ just in case B is a tautology.

While the assertion that a given formula is a tautology thus appears to be a special kind of sentential law of logic, there is a sense in which *every* law of logic can be expressed in this special form. We illustrate this for the case of laws having two premisses in the following theorem.

THEOREM 10-1-2. *Let A_1, A_2, and B be any sentential formulas.*

(i) *If $A_1, A_2 \Vdash B$, then $\Vdash (A_1 \wedge A_2) \to B$.*
(ii) *Conversely, if $\Vdash (A_1 \wedge A_2) \to B$, then $A_1, A_2 \Vdash B$.*

Proof

We shall present a proof of (i) in outline only.

Suppose that A_1, A_2, and B are sentential formulas such that $A_1, A_2 \Vdash B$. We consider *any* possible assignment of truth values (to the sentential variables appearing in the formulas A_1, A_2 and B), and we denote by $V(A_1)$ the corresponding truth value produced by this assignment for the formula A_1, by $V(A_1 \to B)$ the corresponding truth value produced by this assignment for the formula $A_1 \to B$, etc. Thus to show that $\Vdash (A_1 \wedge A_2) \to B$, and hence to establish (i), it suffices to prove that $V((A_1 \wedge A_2) \to B) = \text{T}$.

Now in case $V(A_1) = \text{F}$ we have $V(A_1 \wedge A_2) = \text{F}$ by Table 2, regardless whether $V(A_2) = \text{T}$ or $V(A_2) = \text{F}$. Hence, by a second application of Table 2, we have $V((A_1 \wedge A_2) \to B) = F \to V(B) = \text{T}$, regardless whether $V(B) = \text{T}$ or $V(B) = \text{F}$.

In the same way, we see that in case $V(A_2) = \text{F}$ we must have $V((A_1 \wedge A_2) \to B) = \text{T}$, regardless of the values $V(A_1)$ and $V(B)$.

Finally, in case *neither* $V(A_1) = \text{F}$ *nor* $V(A_2) = \text{F}$, we must have *both* $V(A_1) = \text{T}$ and $V(A_2) = \text{T}$. But then, from our hypothesis that $A_1, A_2 \Vdash \text{T}$ and our definition of $\Vdash$, it follows that we must have $V(B) = \text{T}$. Hence in this case we have $V((A_1 \wedge A_2) \to B) = (\text{T} \wedge \text{T}) \to \text{T} = \text{T} \to \text{T} = \text{T}$.

Thus in every case we come to the conclusion that $V((A_1 \wedge A_2) \to B) = \text{T}$, and this, as noted above, establishes (i).

We leave a proof of (ii) to the reader as an exercise.

EXERCISES

1–8. Prove parts (a) to (h) of Theorem 10-1-1.

9. Outline a proof of Theorem 10-1-2, part (ii).

10. Prove that the following formulas are tautologies:

(a) $P \to P$
(b) $P \vee \neg P$
(c) $P \to (Q \to P)$
(d) $(P \to \neg Q) \to (Q \to \neg P)$.

11. Which of the following formulas, if any, are tautologies:

(a) $P \wedge P$
(b) $(P \vee \neg P) \to P$
(c) $P \to (P \vee Q)$
(d) $P \to (P \vee \neg P)$
(e) $\neg (P \wedge \neg P)$?

2. *Axiomatic Logic*

In the previous section we have defined the notion of a sentential law of logic by means of truth tables. This definition provides a means whereby, given any particular sentential formulas $A_1, A_2, \ldots, A_n$ and B, we can decide by a finite table-computation whether or not we have $A_1, A_2, \ldots, A_n \Vdash B$. But the definition only permits us to establish a given sentential law of logic as an *isolated phenomenon*, so to speak. It does not furnish any information *relating* two different sentential laws of logic, and in particular it provides no means for *deriving* one such law from another. In order to accomplish this broader aim we shall seek an alternative formulation of the theory of sentential laws of logic which is *axiomatic* in character.

But a difficulty with this project at once suggests itself. For in every *other* axiomatic theory which we have encountered we were able to pass from axioms to theorems by applying laws of logic, already presumed known. However, since we are *now* trying to construct a theory in which the laws of logic are themselves to be established, it does not seem right to *use* these laws in order to justify steps in proving them.

The way in which modern logicians have been able to overcome this difficulty is to supply our axiomatic theory of logic not only with axioms, but also with what are called *formal rules of inference*. Roughly speaking, these are explicit rules which describe the conditions under which we may pass from one or more given lines of a proof in the axiomatic theory to another line; and the word *formal*, which is used to describe these rules of inference, signifies that they are to be so phrased that one can tell whether or not a rule applied simply by examining the *form* of the proposed lines of the proof, without regard to the *meaning* of the symbols involved.

In order to have a sound basis for the application of such formal rules of inference, it is desirable to precede them with a precise description, also in formal terms, of those arrays of symbols which may be used for asserting propositions of the theory, and hence which may appear as lines of proofs. This description is usually given in two parts: First, a list of the individual *symbols* which may be used, and second, a set of *formal rules of formation* which specify how the symbols are to be combined to obtain meaningful arrays.

Putting together the several concepts we have just mentioned, we are led to the notion of a *formal deductive system*, which is perhaps the central and most basic notion of modern logic. Any such system is defined by four components: A list of symbols, formal rules of formation, a list of axioms, and formal rules of inference. And within such a system we can introduce the notion of a *formal proof* and a *formal theorem*. We now illustrate these ideas by describing and developing a particular formal deductive system, $\mathcal{S}$, for the theory of sentential logic.

1. List of symbols in the system $\mathcal{S}$. (For ease in describing the formal rules of formation, below, we shall divide our list into several classes, and shall give a distinctive name to each such class.)

Sentential variables: P, Q, R.
Sentential connectives: $\neg$, $\wedge$, $\vee$, $\rightarrow$, $\leftrightarrow$.
Parentheses: (,).
Comma: , .
Consequence symbol: $\vdash$.

Thus our system $\mathcal{S}$ has 12 symbols altogether. In many systems of sentential logic one deals with more than three sentential variables—often an infinite number—but three will suffice for our illustrative purposes.

The reader will note, too, that the "consequence symbol" of our system $\mathcal{S}$ does not have the same shape as the symbol $\Vdash$ which we used to denote the consequence relation in Section 1. This has been done deliberately, to emphasize that the symbol $\vdash$ within the system $\mathcal{S}$ does not have the same meaning as the symbol $\Vdash$ —indeed, *it is to have no meaning whatever*! Like all symbols of the system $\mathcal{S}$, the symbol $\vdash$ is simply a shape to be combined and manipulated according to formal rules to be given below. And the fact that we call it a "consequence symbol" is of absolutely no significance for the system $\mathcal{S}$, but is simply done to help us (at a later stage) in relating the theorems of the system $\mathcal{S}$ to the sentential laws of logic as described in Section 1. Strictly speaking, it might have been preferable to alter all of the other symbols of the system $\mathcal{S}$ to distinguish them from symbols employed earlier; but as long as the reader keeps in mind that *within* $\mathcal{S}$ *no meaning is to be attached to any one of its twelve symbols*, there will be no confusion—and considerable help to the intuition—from using the symbols already familiar to us.

2. Formal rules of formation of the system $\mathcal{S}$. Among all possible strings of symbols of $\mathcal{S}$, i.e., among all possible finite rows of symbols of $\mathcal{S}$, we shall pick out certain ones to be called *assertion expressions* (AE's, for short). And as an aid in describing these, we shall first pick out certain strings to be called *formulas*, and others to be called *prefixes*.

RULE F1

(i) *A string consisting of a sentential variable standing alone is a* **formula.**

(ii) *A string obtained by taking any formula and placing the symbol* $\neg$ *immediately to its left, is again a* **formula**.

(iii) *A string obtained by taking any two formulas, placing any one of the symbols* $\wedge$, $\vee$, $\rightarrow$, *or* $\leftrightarrow$ *between them, then placing the symbol* (*immediately to the left of the result, and finally placing the symbol*) *immediately to the right of the string then resulting, is again a* **formula.**

The rule F1 is an example of what we call a *recursive rule*. Clause (**i**) of this rule picks out certain simple strings which are definitely to be called *formulas;* the other two clauses tell us how to build up complex formulas from simpler ones.

For example, we can use Rule F1 to show that the string $(\neg (P \wedge Q) \rightarrow \neg P)$ is a formula, as follows:

1. The strings P and Q are formulas; by clause (**i**) of Rule F1.
2. The string $\neg P$ is a formula; by line **1** above and clause (**ii**) of Rule F1.
3. The string $(P \wedge Q)$ is a formula; by line **1** above and clause (**iii**) of Rule F1.
4. The string $\neg (P \wedge Q)$ is a formula; by line **3** above and clause (**ii**) of Rule F1.
5. The string $(\neg (P \wedge Q) \rightarrow \neg P)$ is a formula; by lines **4** and **2** above, and clause (**iii**) of Rule F1.

The reader will note that in applying Rule F1 there is no need to attach any meaning to the symbols of $\mathcal{S}$. This is why we call Rule F1 a *formal rule.*

RULE F2. *A string of symbols of $\mathcal{S}$ is called a* **prefix** *if it consists of a single formula alone, or of several formulas separated by occurrences of the comma symbol.*

It would be possible to phrase Rule F2 as a recursive rule, specifying in clause (**i**) that a formula alone is a prefix, and in clause (**ii**) that a string obtained from a prefix by placing a comma to its left and a formula to the left of *that,* is also a prefix. However, we prefer the formulation given for its more intuitive character, even though in a certain sense the formulation of this rule involves more sophisticated notions than are needed in the recursive version.

As an example of the application of Rule F2, we can show that the string $(P \wedge Q), \neg P$ is a prefix by using lines **3** and **2** of the example following Rule F1.

RULE F3. *A string of symbols of $\mathcal{S}$ is called an* **assertion expression** (**AE,** *for short*), *if it consists of the symbol $\vdash$ followed by a formula, or else of a prefix followed by the symbol $\vdash$ and then followed by a formula.*

As an example, the string $(P \wedge Q), \neg P \vdash (\neg (P \wedge Q) \rightarrow \neg P)$ is an AE, as we see by Rule F3 and the examples following Rules F1 and F2.

The reader will note that Rules F2 and F3, like F1, are *formal* rules, in the sense that they can be applied without any need of meanings attached to the symbols of $\mathcal{S}$.

3. Axioms of the system $\mathcal{S}$. Among all possible AE's of $\mathcal{S}$ we select seven to be called the *formal axioms* of $\mathcal{S}$, as follows:

A1. $P \vdash P$
A2. $(\neg Q \rightarrow \neg P) \vdash (P \rightarrow Q)$
A3. $(P \rightarrow Q), (Q \rightarrow P) \vdash (P \leftrightarrow Q)$
A4. $(P \leftrightarrow Q) \vdash (P \rightarrow Q)$
A5. $(P \leftrightarrow Q) \vdash (Q \rightarrow P)$
A6. $\vdash ((P \vee Q) \leftrightarrow (\neg P \rightarrow Q))$
A7. $\vdash ((P \wedge Q) \leftrightarrow \neg (P \rightarrow \neg Q))$

Clearly there is no need to attach meanings to the symbols of $\mathcal{S}$ in order to decide whether or not a given AE is a formal axiom—we need only check the given formula against the list A1 through A7. It is again worthwhile to repeat that from the viewpoint of the system $\mathcal{S}$ itself the axioms are not meaningful sentences but merely particular rows of shapes without meaning.

The reader may wonder, quite justifiably, why this particular list of formal axioms was chosen. Why, for example, should A1 be $P \vdash P$ instead of $P \vdash \neg P$? The answer is that although these seven formal axioms are without meaning, they were selected in such a way that if and when conventional meanings are attached to each of the symbols, the axioms will be transformed into laws of logic in the sense of Section 1. However, in principle there is nothing to prevent us from adopting the AE $P \vdash \neg P$ as an axiom.

4. Formal rules of inference of the system $\mathcal{S}$. These are the rules which will allow us to construct *proofs* in the formal deductive system $\mathcal{S}$. We have four of them.

RULE I1. RULE OF ADDITIONAL AND REARRANGED HYPOTHESES. *Suppose that A is a formula and K a prefix. Suppose, too, that K' is another prefix with the property that every formula appearing in K appears also in K'. Then we may pass from the* AE

$$K \vdash A$$

to the AE

$$K' \vdash A.$$

Examples: We may pass from $P \vdash (Q \vee R)$ to $\neg Q, P, R \vdash (Q \vee R)$ by Rule I1. Also by this rule we may pass from $\neg Q, P \vdash (R \wedge P)$ to $P, \neg Q \vdash (R \wedge P)$.

RULE I2. RULE OF SUBSTITUTION. *We may pass from any* AE *to another one obtained from it by substituting arbitrary formulas for each of the variables occurring in it. (The same formula must be substituted for all occurrences of any one variable.)*

Examples: We may pass from $(P \rightarrow \neg Q) \vdash (Q \rightarrow \neg P)$ to $((P \wedge Q) \rightarrow \neg (P \vee R)) \vdash ((P \vee R) \rightarrow \neg (P \wedge Q))$ by Rule I2, substituting $(P \wedge Q)$ for P and $(P \vee R)$ for Q. Again, we may pass from $(P \rightarrow (Q \leftrightarrow R)) \vdash \neg (R \vee P)$ to $(Q \wedge R) \rightarrow (Q \leftrightarrow Q) \vdash \neg (Q \vee (Q \wedge R))$ by substituting $(Q \wedge R)$ for P, Q for Q, and Q for R.

RULE I3. RULE OF DETACHMENT. *If A and B are any formulas, and if K is any prefix, then we may pass from the two* AE's

$$K \vdash A$$

and

$$K \vdash (A \rightarrow B)$$

to the AE

$$K \vdash B.$$

(*Also, we may pass from the* AE's $\vdash A$ *and* $\vdash (A \rightarrow B)$ *to* $\vdash B$, *in the case of* AE's *which have no prefix.*)

Example: We may pass by Rule I3 from $(\neg P \leftrightarrow R) \vdash (P \rightarrow Q)$ and $(\neg P \leftrightarrow R) \vdash (P \rightarrow Q) \rightarrow (R \wedge Q)$ to $(\neg P \leftrightarrow R) \vdash (R \wedge Q)$.

RULE I4. RULE OF DEDUCTION. *Let K be any prefix, let A be any of the formulas of K, and let B be any formula whatever. Then we may pass from the* AE

$$K \vdash B$$

to the AE

$$K' \vdash (A \rightarrow B),$$

where K′ is the prefix obtained from K by deleting the formula A. Or if A is the only formula in the prefix K, we may pass from the AE

$$K \vdash B, \text{ (i.e., } A \vdash B)$$

to the AE

$$\vdash (A \rightarrow B).$$

Example: We may pass by Rule I4 from $(P \rightarrow \neg R), (Q \rightarrow R) \vdash \neg Q$ to $(P \rightarrow \neg R) \vdash ((Q \rightarrow R) \rightarrow \neg Q)$.

This concludes our list of formal rules of inference for the system S.

Now by a *formal proof* in the system S we mean a column of AE's, each of which is either a formal axiom of S or else is obtained from earlier lines of the column by one of the formal rules of inference of S. And by a *formal theorem* of S we mean any AE which can be obtained as the last line of some formal proof. These concepts are illustrated in the following theorems.

THEOREM 10-2-1. *The* AE $\vdash (P \rightarrow P)$ *is a formal theorem of* S.

Proof

The following two-line column of AE's is a formal proof:

1. $P \vdash P$
2. $\vdash (P \rightarrow P)$.

Indeed the first line is Axiom A1, and the second line is obtained from the first by applying Rule I4. Hence the last line of this column must be a formal theorem.

In the next theorem we shall present a more complicated formal proof.

THEOREM 10-2-2. *The* AE $(P \to Q), (Q \to R) \vdash (P \to R)$ *is a formal theorem of* $\mathcal{S}$.

Proof

We shall present a ten-line formal proof of $\mathcal{S}$ whose last line is the above indicated AE.

1. $P \vdash P$; Axiom A1.
2. $(P \to Q) \vdash (P \to Q)$; by Rule I2 applied to line **1** above, substituting $(P \to Q)$ for P.
3. $P, (P \to Q) \vdash P$; by Rule I1 applied to line **1**.
4. $P, (P \to Q) \vdash (P \to Q)$; by Rule I1 applied to line **2**.
5. $P, (P \to Q) \vdash Q$; by Rule I3 applied to lines **3** and **4**.
6. $(Q \to R) \vdash (Q \to R)$; by Rule I2 applied to line **1**, substituting $(Q \to R)$ for P.
7. $P, (P \to Q), (Q \to R) \vdash Q$; by Rule I1 applied to line **5**.
8. $P, (P \to Q), (Q \to R) \vdash (Q \to R)$; by Rule I1 applied to line **6**.
9. $P, (P \to Q), (Q \to R) \vdash R$; by Rule I3 applied to lines **7** and **8**.
10. $(P \to Q), (Q \to R) \vdash (P \to R)$; by Rule I4 applied to line **9**.

In the following theorem we describe a whole class of AE's which are formal theorems of $\mathcal{S}$.

THEOREM 10-2-3. *Suppose that K is any prefix and that A is any one of its formulas. Then the* AE $K \vdash A$ *is a formal theorem of* $\mathcal{S}$.

Proof

We shall show how, given any prefix K and any one of its formulas A we may construct a three-line formal proof whose last line is the AE $K \vdash A$.

1. $P \vdash P$; Axiom A1.
2. $A \vdash A$; by Rule I2 applied to line **1**, substituting the formula A for the variable P.
3. $K \vdash A$; by Rule I1 applied to line **2**. The rule may be applied in the indicated manner since we are supposing, in Theorem 10-2-3, that A is one of the formulas of the prefix K.

The formal theorems mentioned so far have involved only the connective $\to$. We now turn to some involving $\neg$ as well.

THEOREM 10-2-4. *The* AE $P, \neg P \vdash Q$ *is a formal theorem of* $\mathcal{S}$.

Proof

To write down a formal proof whose last line is the indicated AE would be rather lengthy. We shall, instead, give indications as to *how* to construct such a formal proof. For this purpose, consider the following column of formulas.

1. $P, \neg P, \neg Q \vdash \neg P$; this is a formal theorem of 7 by Theorem 10-2-3.
2. $P, \neg P \vdash (\neg Q \rightarrow \neg P)$; by applying Rule I4 to line **1** above.
3. $(\neg Q \rightarrow \neg P) \vdash (P \rightarrow Q)$; Axiom A2.
4. $\vdash ((\neg Q \rightarrow \neg P) \rightarrow (P \rightarrow Q))$; by applying Rule I4 to line **3**.
5. $P, \neg P \vdash ((\neg Q \rightarrow \neg P) \rightarrow (P \rightarrow Q))$; by applying Rule I1 to line **4**.
6. $P, \neg P \vdash (P \rightarrow Q)$; by applying Rule I3 to lines **2** and **5**.
7. $P, \neg P \vdash P$; this is a formal theorem of $\mathcal{S}$ by Theorem 10-2-3.
8. $P, \neg P \vdash Q$; by applying Rule I3 to lines **7** and **6**.

It will be observed that this column of eight lines does not qualify as a formal proof because two of its lines are neither formal axioms of $\mathcal{S}$ nor obtained from earlier lines of the column by means of formal rules of inference—these are lines **1** and **7**. However, as noted, both of these lines are formal theorems of $\mathcal{S}$. Hence we can obtain a formal proof of the AE $P, \neg P \vdash Q$ by first writing down a formal proof of line **1**, then continuing the column with a formal proof of line **7**, and finally writing the given eight-line column underneath. (Since in fact, lines **1** and **7** each has a three line formal proof, as we see from the proof of Theorem 10-2-3, that would make a fourteen line column altogether.) A little reflection will show that each line in the column so constructed must be either a formal axiom or else obtained from earlier lines of the column by one of the formal rules of inference.

In the remaining theorems of this chapter we shall permit ourselves freely to use already established formal theorems when indicating how to construct a formal proof, without each time giving the detailed explanation of the preceding paragraph.

THEOREM 10-2-5. *The* AE $\neg\neg P \vdash P$ *is a formal theorem of* $\mathcal{S}$.

Proof

1. $P, \neg P \vdash Q$; a formal theorem by Theorem 10-2-4.
2. $\neg P, \neg\neg P \vdash \neg (P \rightarrow P)$; by Rule I2 applied to line **1** above, substituting $\neg P$ for P and $\neg (P \rightarrow P)$ for Q.
3. $\neg\neg P \vdash (\neg P \rightarrow \neg (P \rightarrow P))$; by Rule I4 applied to line **2**.
4. $(\neg Q \rightarrow \neg P) \vdash (P \rightarrow Q)$; Axiom A2.

5. $(\neg P \to \neg (P \to P)) \vdash ((P \to P) \to P)$; by Rule I2 applied to line **4**, substituting P for Q and $(P \to P)$ for P.

6. $\vdash ((\neg P \to \neg (P \to P)) \to ((P \to P) \to P))$; by Rule I4 applied to line **5**.

7. $\neg\neg P \vdash ((\neg P \to \neg (P \to P)) \to ((P \to P) \to P))$; by Rule I1 applied to line **6**.

8. $\neg\neg P \vdash ((P \to P) \to P)$; by Rule I3 applied to lines **3** and **7**.

9. $\vdash (P \to P)$; this is a formal theorem by Theorem 10-2-1.

10. $\neg\neg P \vdash (P \to P)$; by Rule I1 applied to line **9**.

11. $\neg\neg P \vdash P$; by Rule I3 applied to lines **10** and **8**.

THEOREM 10-2-6. *The* AE $P \vdash \neg\neg P$ *is a formal theorem of* $\mathcal{S}$.

Proof

1. $\neg\neg P \vdash P$; this is a formal theorem by Theorem 10-2-5.

2. $\neg\neg\neg P \vdash \neg P$; by Rule I2 applied to line **1** above, substituting $\neg P$ for P.

3. $\vdash (\neg\neg\neg P \to \neg P)$; by Rule I4 applied to line **2**.

4. $(\neg Q \to \neg P) \vdash P \to Q$; Axiom A2.

5. $(\neg\neg\neg P \to \neg P) \vdash (P \to \neg\neg P)$; by Rule I2 applied to line **4**, substituting $\neg\neg P$ for Q and P for P.

6. $\vdash ((\neg\neg\neg P \to \neg P) \to (P \to \neg\neg P))$; by Rule I4 applied to line **5**.

7. $\vdash (P \to \neg\neg P)$; by Rule I3 applied to lines **3** and **6**.

8. $P \vdash (P \to \neg\neg P)$; by Rule I1 applied to line **7**.

9. $P \vdash P$; Axiom A1.

10. $P \vdash \neg\neg P$; by Rule I3 applied to lines **8** and **9**.

The formal theorems established in Theorems 10-2-5 and 10-2-6 are called the *formal laws of double negation.*

Before establishing further formal theorems in the system $\mathcal{S}$, it will save us considerable repetition to indicate a certain general pattern of procedure in the construction of formal proofs. This is embodied in the following theorem.

THEOREM 10-2-7.

(i) *Suppose that K is a prefix and that A and B are formulas. Then in constructing a formal proof we may always pass from lines $K \vdash A$ and $A \vdash B$ to the line $K \vdash B$.*

(ii) *Suppose that K_1 and K_2 are prefixes, and that A_1, A_2, and B are formulas. Then in constructing a formal proof we may always pass from lines $K_1 \vdash A_1$, $K_2 \vdash A_2$, and $A_1, A_2 \vdash B$, to the line $K \vdash B$, where K is any prefix which contains every formula appearing in K_1 as well as every formula appearing in K_2.*

Actually, the method of carrying out (**i**) above has already been illustrated in several of the proofs of previous theorems. For example, notice how in proving Theorem 10-2-4 we were able to pass from lines **2** and **3** to line **6**. The same technique was used in the proof of Theorem 10-2-5 to pass from lines **3** and **5** to line **8**. By describing this method in general terms the reader can obtain a proof of (**i**). (See Exercise 1.) Below we give a proof of (**ii**).

Proof of (**ii**)

Suppose that in the course of constructing a formal proof in the system $\mathcal{S}$ we have obtained three lines as follows:

(**a**) $K_1 \vdash A_1$
(**b**) $K_2 \vdash A_2$
(**c**) $A_1, A_2 \vdash B$.

Suppose, too, that K is a prefix which contains every formula appearing in K_1 as well as every formula appearing in K_2. Then we can proceed to obtain the line $K \vdash B$ as follows.

(**d**) $A_1 \vdash (A_2 \rightarrow B)$; by Rule I4 applied to line (**c**) above.
(**e**) $K_1 \vdash (A_2 \rightarrow B)$, by part (**i**) of Theorem 10-2-7, which we suppose already proved, applied to lines (**a**) and (**d**).
(**f**) $K \vdash A_2$; by Rule I1 applied to line (**b**), the rule being applicable because of our hypothesis about K.
(**g**) $K \vdash (A_2 \rightarrow B)$; by Rule I1 applied to line (**e**).
(**h**) $K \vdash B$; by Rule I3 applied to lines (**f**) and (**g**).

The form in which we have stated Theorem 10-2-7 resembles our formulation of the formal rules of inference, Rules I1 through I4. A theorem of this kind is often called a *derived rule of inference.*

THEOREM 10-2-8. *The* AE $(P \rightarrow Q), (P \rightarrow \neg Q) \vdash \neg P$ *is a formal theorem of* $\mathcal{S}$.

Proof

1. $\neg\neg P, (P \rightarrow Q), (P \rightarrow \neg Q) \vdash \neg\neg P$; this is a formal theorem by Theorem 10-2-3.
2. $\neg\neg P \vdash P$; by Theorem 10-2-5.
3. $\neg\neg P, (P \rightarrow Q), (P \rightarrow \neg Q) \vdash P$; by Theorem 10-2-7 (**i**) applied to lines **1** and **2**.
4. $\neg\neg P, (P \rightarrow Q), (P \rightarrow \neg Q) \vdash (P \rightarrow Q)$; by Theorem 10-2-3.
5. $\neg\neg P, (P \rightarrow Q), (P \rightarrow \neg Q) \vdash Q$; by Rule I3 applied to lines **3** and **4**.

6. $\neg\neg P, (P \rightarrow Q), (P \rightarrow \neg Q) \vdash (P \rightarrow \neg Q)$; by Theorem 10-2-3.

7. $\neg\neg P, (P \rightarrow Q), (P \rightarrow \neg Q) \vdash \neg Q$; by Rule **I3** applied to lines **3** and **6.**

8. $P, \neg P \vdash Q$; by Theorem 10-2-4.

9. $Q, \neg Q \vdash \neg (P \rightarrow P)$; by Rule **I2** applied to line **8**, substituting Q for P and $\neg (P \rightarrow P)$ for Q.

10. $\neg\neg P, (P \rightarrow Q), (P \rightarrow \neg Q) \vdash \neg (P \rightarrow P)$; by Theorem 10-2-7 (**ii**) applied to lines **5**, **7**, and **9.**

11. $(P \rightarrow Q), (P \rightarrow \neg Q) \vdash (\neg\neg P \rightarrow \neg (P \rightarrow P))$; by Rule I4 applied to line **10.**

12. $(\neg Q \rightarrow \neg P) \vdash (P \rightarrow Q)$; Axiom A2.

13. $(\neg\neg P \rightarrow \neg (P \rightarrow P)) \vdash ((P \rightarrow P) \rightarrow \neg P)$; by Rule I2 applied to line **12**, substituting $\neg P$ for Q and $(P \rightarrow P)$ for P.

14. $(P \rightarrow Q), (P \rightarrow \neg Q) \vdash ((P \rightarrow P) \rightarrow \neg P)$; by Theorem 10-2-7 (**i**) applied to lines **11** and **13.**

15. $\vdash (P \rightarrow P)$; by Theorem 10-2-1.

16. $(P \rightarrow Q), (P \rightarrow \neg Q) \vdash (P \rightarrow P)$; by Rule I1 applied to line **15.**

17. $(P \rightarrow Q), (P \rightarrow \neg Q) \vdash \neg P$; by Rule I3 applied to lines **14** and **16.**

The formal theorem of Theorem 10-2-8 is called the formal *law of contradiction.*

THEOREM 10-2-9. *The* AE $(P \rightarrow Q), (\neg P \rightarrow Q) \vdash Q$ *is a formal theorem of* $\mathcal{S}$.

This formal theorem is called the *law of proof by cases.* The proof is left to the reader. (See Exercise 3 for a suggestion.)

The formal theorems established thus far have involved only the connectives $\rightarrow$ and $\neg$. We now turn to a few which involve $\leftrightarrow$, $\wedge$, and $\vee$.

THEOREM 10-2-10. *The following* AE*'s are formal theorems of* $\mathcal{S}$*:*

(**i**) $\vdash (P \leftrightarrow P)$
(**ii**) $(P \leftrightarrow Q) \vdash (Q \leftrightarrow P)$
(**iii**) $(P \leftrightarrow Q), \ (Q \leftrightarrow R) \vdash (P \leftrightarrow R)$.

We shall prove part (**ii**), leaving the remaining parts as an exercise.

Proof of (**ii**)

1. $(P \leftrightarrow Q) \vdash (P \rightarrow Q)$: Axiom A4.

2. $(P \leftrightarrow Q) \vdash (Q \rightarrow P)$; Axiom A5.

3. $(P \rightarrow Q), \ (Q \rightarrow P) \vdash (P \leftrightarrow Q)$; Axiom A3.

4. $(Q \rightarrow P), (P \rightarrow Q) \vdash (Q \leftrightarrow P)$; by Rule I2 applied to line **3**, substituting Q for P and P for Q.

5. $(P \leftrightarrow Q) \vdash (Q \leftrightarrow P)$; by Theorem 10-2-7 (**ii**) applied to lines **1**, **2**, and **4**.

THEOREM 10-2-11. *The* AE $\vdash (P \vee \neg P)$ *is a formal theorem of* $\mathcal{S}$. This formal theorem is called the formal *law of excluded middle.*

Proof

1. $\vdash ((P \vee Q) \leftrightarrow (\neg P \rightarrow Q))$; Axiom A6.
2. $\vdash ((P \vee \neg P) \leftrightarrow (\neg P \rightarrow \neg P))$; by Rule I2 applied to line **1**, substituting P for P and $\neg P$ for Q.
3. $(P \leftrightarrow Q) \vdash (Q \rightarrow P)$; Axiom A5.
4. $\vdash ((P \leftrightarrow Q) \rightarrow (Q \rightarrow P))$; by Rule I4 applied to line **3**.
5. $\vdash (((P \vee \neg P) \leftrightarrow (\neg P \rightarrow \neg P)) \rightarrow ((\neg P \rightarrow \neg P) \rightarrow (P \vee \neg P)))$; by Rule I2 applied to line **4**, substituting $(P \vee \neg P)$ for P and $(\neg P \rightarrow \neg P)$ for Q.
6. $\vdash ((\neg P \rightarrow \neg P) \rightarrow (P \vee \neg P))$; by Rule I3 applied to lines **2** and **5**.
7. $\vdash (P \rightarrow P)$; by Theorem 10-2-1.
8. $\vdash (\neg P \rightarrow \neg P)$; by Rule I2 applied to line **7**, substituting $\neg P$ for P.
9. $\vdash (P \vee \neg P)$; by Rule I3 applied to lines **6** and **8**.

For other formal theorems involving the connective $\vee$, see Exercise 5.

Before establishing any formal theorems involving the connective $\wedge$, it will be useful to prove a theorem which, like Theorem 10-2-7, has the form of a "derived rule of inference."

THEOREM 10-2-12. *Suppose that A and B are **formulas**. Then in constructing a formal proof in $\mathcal{S}$ we may pass from the line $\vdash (A \leftrightarrow B)$ to the line $A \vdash B$ as well as to the line $B \vdash A$.*

Proof

Suppose that A and B are formulas, and that in constructing a formal proof we have reached a line

(**a**) $\vdash (A \leftrightarrow B)$.

Then we may proceed to obtain the line $A \vdash B$ as follows.

(**b**) $(P \leftrightarrow Q) \vdash (P \rightarrow Q)$; Axiom A4.
(**c**) $\vdash (P \leftrightarrow Q) \rightarrow (P \rightarrow Q)$; by Rule I4 applied to line (**b**).
(**d**) $\vdash (A \leftrightarrow B) \rightarrow (A \rightarrow B)$; by Rule I2 applied to line (**c**).
(**e**) $\vdash (A \rightarrow B)$; by Rule I3 applied to lines (**a**) and (**d**).
(**f**) $A \vdash (A \rightarrow B)$; by Rule I1 applied to line (**e**).
(**g**) $P \vdash P$; Axiom A1.
(**h**) $A \vdash A$; by Rule I2 applied to line (**g**).
(**i**) $A \vdash B$; by Rule I3 applied to lines (**f**) and (**h**).

We have shown above how to pass from $\vdash (A \leftrightarrow B)$ to $A \vdash B$. To show that we can also pass from $\vdash (A \leftrightarrow B)$ to $B \vdash A$ requires only a slight modification of the proof, principally the use of Axiom A5 instead of A4 on line (**b**). We leave the details to be supplied by the reader.

THEOREM 10-2-13. *The* AE $\vdash \neg (P \wedge \neg P)$ *is a formal theorem of* $\mathcal{S}$.

Proof

1. $\vdash ((P \wedge Q) \leftrightarrow \neg (P \rightarrow \neg Q))$; Axiom A7.
2. $(P \wedge Q) \vdash \neg (P \rightarrow \neg Q)$; by Theorem 10-2-12 applied to line **1**.
3. $(P \wedge \neg P) \vdash \neg (P \rightarrow \neg\neg P)$; by Rule I2 applied to line **2**, substituting P for P and $\neg P$ for Q.
4. $\neg\neg P \vdash P$; by Theorem 10-2-5.
5. $\neg\neg (P \wedge \neg P) \vdash (P \wedge \neg P)$; by Rule I2 applied to line **4**, substituting $(P \wedge \neg P)$ for P.
6. $\neg\neg (P \wedge \neg P) \vdash \neg (P \rightarrow \neg\neg P)$; by Theorem 10-2-7(**i**) applied to lines **3** and **5**.
7. $\vdash (\neg\neg (P \wedge \neg P) \rightarrow \neg (P \rightarrow \neg\neg P))$; by Rule I4 applied to line **6**.
8. $(\neg Q \rightarrow \neg P) \vdash (P \rightarrow Q)$; Axiom A2.
9. $\vdash (\neg Q \rightarrow \neg P) \rightarrow (P \rightarrow Q)$; by Rule I4 applied to line **8**.
10. $\vdash ((\neg\neg (P \wedge \neg P) \rightarrow \neg (P \rightarrow \neg\neg P)) \rightarrow ((P \rightarrow \neg\neg P) \rightarrow \neg (P \wedge \neg P)))$; by Rule I2 applied to line **9**, substituting $\neg (P \wedge \neg P)$ for Q and $(P \rightarrow \neg\neg P)$ for P.
11. $\vdash ((P \rightarrow \neg\neg P) \rightarrow \neg (P \wedge \neg P))$; by Rule I3 applied to lines **7** and **10**.
12. $P \vdash \neg\neg P$; by Theorem 10-2-6.
13. $\vdash (P \rightarrow \neg\neg P)$; by Rule I4 applied to line **12**.
14. $\vdash \neg (P \wedge \neg P)$; by Rule I3 applied to lines **11** and **13**.

This is as far as we shall carry the formal development of the system $\mathcal{S}$.

The reader is reminded that this is a formal deductive system in which formal rules have been applied to meaningless symbols. Just how can the theorems which we have obtained be interpreted—how can they be used? This problem will be considered in the following section.

EXERCISES

1. Prove Theorem 10-2-7, part (**i**). For a suggestion as to how to proceed, see paragraph following the statement of this theorem.

2. Show that the following AE's are formal theorems of $\mathcal{S}$:

(**i**) $Q \vdash (P \rightarrow Q)$
(**ii**) $\neg P \vdash (P \rightarrow Q)$
(**iii**) $(P \rightarrow \neg Q) \vdash (Q \rightarrow \neg P)$
(**iv**) $(\neg P \rightarrow Q) \vdash (\neg Q \rightarrow P)$
(**v**) $(P \rightarrow Q) \vdash (\neg Q \rightarrow \neg P)$.

Suggestions: For **(i)**, use Theorem 10-2-3; for **(ii)** use Theorem 10-2-4; for **(iii)** use (i) and Theorem 10-2-8.

3. Prove Theorem 10-2-9. *Suggestion*: Use Exercise 2 [parts **(iv)** and **(v)**].

4. Prove Theorem 10-2-10, parts **(i)** and **(iii)**.

5. Show that the following AE's are formal theorems of $\mathcal{S}$:

(i) $Q \vdash (P \vee Q)$

(ii) $(P \vee Q) \vdash (Q \vee P)$.

(iii) $(P \vee Q), \neg P \vdash Q$.

Suggestions: For **(i)** use Axiom A6, Exercise 2 **(i)**; for **(ii)** use Axiom A6, Exercise 2 **(iv)**.

6. Show that the following AE's are formal theorems of $\mathcal{S}$:

(i) $P, \neg Q \vdash \neg (P \rightarrow Q)$

(ii) $\neg (P \rightarrow Q) \vdash P$

(iii) $\neg (P \rightarrow Q) \vdash \neg Q$.

7. Show that the following AE's are formal theorems of $\mathcal{S}$:

(i) $P, Q \vdash (P \wedge Q)$

(ii) $(P \wedge Q) \vdash P$

(iii) $(P \wedge Q) \vdash Q$

(iv) $(P \wedge Q) \vdash (Q \wedge P)$

(v) $((P \wedge Q) \wedge R) \vdash (P \wedge (Q \wedge R))$.

Suggestions: For **(i)**, **(ii)**, **(iii)** use Exercise 6; for **(iv)** and **(v)** use **(i)**, **(ii)**, and **(iii)**.

3. *Interpretation and Application of Axiomatic Logic*

In developing the formal deductive system $\mathcal{S}$ of the preceding section we have seen that the derivation of formal theorems can be carried out by means of formal rules, without attaching any meanings to the symbols, formulas, or AE's of the system. What, then, have we accomplished when these meaningless strings of symbols have been established?

The answer is one which is applicable to any axiomatic theory whatever. Namely, we have shown that *if* we can find an interpretation for the symbols, formulas, and AE's of $\mathcal{S}$ which makes the axioms true, and for which the rules of inference preserve truth, *then* all of the theorems of the system will express true propositions under this interpretation. Actually, there are *many* such interpretations which are possible, so that the axiomatic theory serves simultaneously to give us information about many different domains. For discussion of this point the reader should compare Chapter III, on models of axiomatic theories.

In the *primary* interpretation of the symbolism of $\mathcal{S}$ we interpret each AE as an assertion about the relation of *sentential consequence* described in section 1 of this chapter. Namely, we interpret any AE of the form $K \vdash A$ (where K is a *prefix* and A a *formula*), as asserting that $K \Vdash A$ (i.e., that A is a sentential consequence of the formulas listed in K). *When so interpreted*, each AE becomes *true* or *false*. In a more extensive treatment of logic it could be shown that *every AE which is a formal theorem is true* under this interpretation, and that conversely *every AE which is true under this interpretation is a formal theorem of* $\mathcal{S}$. Thus if we take any formal theorem, and replace the symbol $\vdash$ by the symbol $\Vdash$, we get a sentential law of logic; and furthermore, every sentential law of logic can be obtained this way.

In the previous paragraph we have spoken of the *primary* interpretation of the symbolism of S. To investigate other interpretations would lead us into the theory of *Boolean Algebras*, which is beyond the scope of this book.

Finally, now that we have seen how to establish sentential laws of logic both by the method of truth-tables and by the axiomatic method within a formal deductive system, we wish to give a brief indication of how these laws can be used in constructing proofs within axiomatic theories of various branches of mathematics. The simplest way is to examine one of the proofs from an earlier chapter of the book.

To take a very simple example, consider the proof of Theorem 9-4-12 (**b**). Let P be the sentence "$x \in H$", and let Q be the sentence "$y \in K$". Then we can abbreviate line **3** of the proof, "$x \notin K$", as $\neg Q$, and line **4**, "If $x \in H$ then $x \in K$", as $P \rightarrow Q$. In line **5** we concluded from lines **3** and **4** that $x \notin H$ (i.e., $\neg P$). What sentential law of logic is involved in reaching this conclusion? Nothing more or less than the law $\neg Q, P \rightarrow Q \Vdash \neg P$.

In the same way, laws of logic are used *whenever* we pass from one (or several) lines of a proof, to another line. Of course these laws are not always laws of *sentential* logic—they may be laws of the *logic of identity*, or of the *logic of quantifiers* (which deal with words like "all" and "some"). To study all of these laws would, of course, require a book in itself.

Exercises

Consider the proofs of the following theorems. In each case formulate the laws of sentential logic used and establish these laws by truth tables.

1. Theorem 9-4-3 (**b**).
2. Theorem 9-4-7 (**a**).
3. Theorem 2-7-7.

XI

Negative Integers—A Further Extension of the Number System

1. Introductory Remarks

We have thus far made one extension in the development of our number system—from the system of positive integers $\langle P, +, \cdot \rangle$ to the system of natural numbers $\langle N, +_N, \cdot_N \rangle$. Essentially this consisted in adding the number zero to our number system. Formally, we introduced a new element z such that $z +_N 1 = 1$ and then found that more generally, $z +_N a = a$ for all $a \in N$.

We are of course aware, from early studies, of the existence of numbers other than the natural numbers, e.g., negative integers (such as -1, -20) and rational numbers (such as $\frac{1}{2}$, $\frac{2}{3}$). Why do we want such numbers? And assuming that we do want them, how can we extend our number system in a mathematically precise way so as to obtain them?

As we shall see, there is good reason for wanting both negative and rational numbers. But we shall carry out the extension in two separate steps. It turns out that it is possible to introduce the positive rational numbers first (as is done in the elementary grades), and then the negative numbers, or else to introduce the negative integers before the rational numbers. We have chosen to adopt the second of these procedures—in part because it enables us to discuss certain related algebraic matters in a more natural way.

As we have seen in the previous chapter, the subtraction function $-_N$ does not operate on *all* ordered pairs $\langle a, b \rangle$ of N but only on those pairs $\langle a, b \rangle$ for which $a \geq_N b$. Similarly, the division function $\div$ operates only on the ordered pairs $\langle a, b \rangle$ for which $b \mid a$. Basically, it is to eliminate these restrictions on the use of the subtraction and the division functions that one introduces respectively the negative and the rational numbers. In line with our previous approach, therefore, we shall first seek a system of numbers in which all *additive* equations, i.e., all equations of the form $x + a = b$, have a solution; and then we shall seek a second system in which *multiplicative* equations, i.e., equations of the form $a \cdot x = b$ (for $a \neq 0$), have a solution as well. We shall postpone the second of these problems until the following chapter and consider only the first one here.

To begin, let us turn from what may appear at first to be the rather difficult task of finding a system in which *all* equations of the form $x + a = b$ have a solution, to the more modest task of finding a system in which the *single* equation $x + 1 = 0$ has a solution. Since, for any *natural* number x, we know that $x + 1$ is a positive integer, and hence not zero, this equation certainly does *not* have a solution *in* $\mathcal{N}$. Thus to obtain a solution it is necessary to add at least one new number to $\mathcal{N}$.

Now in our previous extension, from the positive integers to the natural numbers, we also had as our problem the solution of a single equation, namely, $x + 1 = 1$; and in that case the solution was achieved by adding just a single new element (zero) to the positive integers. At first glance, therefore, we might expect to be able to solve our present problem also by adjoining just one new element (intuitively, the number -1) to the set $\mathcal{N}$. However, in addition to having a root of $x + 1 = 0$ we shall require that our new number system have certain basic properties possessed by the earlier systems $\mathcal{P}$ and $\mathfrak{N}$, that is, the commutative, associative, distributive and cancellation properties. And if we restrict ourselves to the set $\mathcal{N} \cup \{-1\}$ it turns out to be impossible to satisfy these. Actually, as we shall see from Theorem 11-3-1, it becomes necessary to add many new elements to our system—intuitively, all of the negative integers. And then we discover a remarkable thing: Although we only set out to construct an extension of $\mathfrak{N}$ which contains a solution of a *single* equation of the form $x + a = b$, our new number system turns out to contain a solution of *every* such equation!

Now let us formulate our problem in detail.

Problem $\mathcal{J}$. Can we find a number system $\langle \mathcal{J}, +_J, \cdot_J \rangle$, consisting of a set of elements, $\mathcal{J}$, and two binary operations, $+_J$ and $\cdot_J$, satisfying the following three conditions:

- **(i)** The system shall be an extension of $\langle \mathcal{N}, +_N, \cdot_N \rangle$ (i.e., $\mathcal{N} \subseteq \mathcal{J}$, and whenever $x, y \in \mathcal{N}$ then $x +_J y = x +_N y$ and $x \cdot_J y = x \cdot_N y$);
- **(ii)** The operations $+_J$ and $\cdot_J$ shall be associative and commutative, $\cdot_J$ shall be distributive over $+_J$, and $+_J$ shall obey the cancellation law;
- **(iii)** $\mathcal{J}$ shall contain a number x such that $x +_J 1 = 0$?

Before tackling problem $\mathcal{J}$ let us take a moment to discuss a matter of notation. We have introduced the symbols "$+_J$" and "$\cdot_J$" to represent "addition" and "multiplication," respectively, in our new system. The symbols "$+$" and "$\cdot$" were used originally to represent the corresponding operations on the set P, and when we extended our number system to include zero we used the symbols "$+_N$" and "$\cdot_N$" for addition and multiplication on the resulting set $\mathcal{N}$. Now that we contemplate a further extension of the domain on which our operations act, to the set we call $\mathcal{J}$, we need still other symbols, for we are in effect defining new operations.

Of course the domain $\mathcal{J}$ of the new operations is to include $\mathcal{N}$. If a and b are both elements of $\mathcal{N}$, then we want $a +_J b$ to be the same as $a +_N b$, but if either a or b is *not* an element of $\mathcal{N}$, we cannot very well say that $a +_J b = a +_N b$, since in this case $a +_N b$ has no meaning—the operation $+_N$ being defined *only* for ordered pairs of elements *in* $\mathcal{N}$.

Although it is important to distinguish between the operations $+_N$ and $+_J$, or between $\cdot_N$ and $\cdot_J$, while discussing the extension from $\mathcal{N}$ to $\mathcal{J}$, there is no longer any purpose in distinguishing between the notation "$+$" and "$+_N$," or "$\cdot$" and "$\cdot_N$." In fact, now that "$+_N$" and "$\cdot_N$" are firmly established, there is never any need to use "$+$" and "$\cdot$," for whenever we wish to write "$a + b$" to refer to the element obtained by applying $+$ to elements a and b of P, we can equally well write "$a +_N b$" because $+_N$ can also be applied to a and b and yields the same result. Since, however, the notation "$+$" is so much simpler and more natural than "$+_N$," it is customary to keep the former and discard the latter—*however, using* "$+$" *in the sequel to denote the operation* $+_N$ *on* $\mathcal{N}$. Similarly, we use "$\cdot$" in place of "$\cdot_N$" from now on. And we shall also drop the subscript "$\mathcal{N}$" from "$-_N$", "$<_N$", etc.

Having agreed to this notational simplification, let us return to Problem $\mathcal{J}$ and see how it may be solved.

2. *The System* $\langle \mathcal{J}, +_J, \cdot_J \rangle$

On the basis of our school experience we know that an answer to problem $\mathcal{J}$ can be obtained by adding to $\mathcal{N}$ a set of numbers, each of which is the "negative" of an element in P. In the following we give a mathematically precise description of such a system, relying on previous knowledge of negative numbers to guide us in formulating our definition of the extended operations (but not to justify any steps of construction or of proof).

To construct our new number system we shall require a one-one mapping ν (*cf.* Chapter I, Section 5) of the elements of P onto the elements of another set, which we shall call P^-, no element of which is in $\mathcal{N}$.[1] (That is, we require P^- and $\mathcal{N}$ to be *disjoint*.) As we shall see, the precise natures of the function ν and of the new elements of P^- are entirely immaterial for our purposes, but it may occur to us to wonder whether logically we can be sure of finding such new elements and such a mapping. To show that this can be done we shall exhibit one possible set P^- and one possible function ν. Thus, consider the set P^- of all ordered pairs $\langle x, \mathcal{N} \rangle$ for all $x \in P$, and let ν be the function, with domain P, such that for every $x \in P$ we have $\nu(x) = \langle x, \mathcal{N} \rangle$. By the basic axioms of set theory it can be shown that no ordered pair whose second member is $\mathcal{N}$ can itself be an element of $\mathcal{N}$, so that P^- and $\mathcal{N}$ are disjoint (see Theorem 9-11-26). The function ν is one-one, for if x and y are elements

[1] The symbol "ν" is the Greek letter nu.

of P such that $x \neq y$, then also $\langle x, \mathcal{N}\rangle \neq \langle y, \mathcal{N}\rangle$ (i.e., $\nu(x) \neq \nu(y)$) by Theorem 9-5-5. Finally, ν maps P onto P^-, for if $\langle x, \mathcal{N}\rangle$ is *any* element of P^-, we have $\nu(x) = \langle x, \mathcal{N}\rangle$ and hence $\langle x, \mathcal{N}\rangle$ is a value of the function ν. Needless to say, we have given only *one* example of how P^- and ν might be constructed, but many others are possible. As indicated above, there is no need to choose among these possibilities for they each lead to essentially the same number system.

Before plunging into the definition of the system $\langle \mathcal{J}, +_J, \cdot_J\rangle$ the reader should bear in mind the relationship between the rules of the proposed system and the rules of algebra with which he is familiar. Briefly, if x and y are elements of P (i.e., positive integers), then $\nu(x)$ and $\nu(y)$, elements of P^-, will play the role of the negative integers $-x$ and $-y$. Thus we will take $P^- \cup \mathcal{N}$ for our set $\mathcal{J}$, and this will be the set of *all* integers—negative, zero, and positive. The operations $+_J$ and $\cdot_J$, which may act on any elements of the set $\mathcal{J}$, are to be defined in such a way that the familiar rules for adding and multiplying signed numbers will apply. For example, since we know from rules of high-school algebra that $(-2) + (-3) = -(2 + 3)$, and that $(-2) \cdot (-3) = 2 \cdot 3$, we want our operations to be defined in such a way that $\nu(2) +_J \nu(3) = \nu(2 +_J 3)$ and $\nu(2) \cdot_J \nu(3) = 2 \cdot_J 3$. As long as the reader keeps the familiar "laws" for operating on signed numbers in mind he will have no difficulty in understanding the motivation for the following definitions.

DEFINITION 11-2-1. *The number system* $\mathcal{G} = \langle \mathcal{J}, +_J, \cdot_J\rangle$ *is to be obtained by choosing a set* $\mathcal{J}$ *and operations* $+_J$ *and* $\cdot_J$ *as follows:*

I. *Definition of* $\mathcal{J}$. *Select in any way a set* P^- *and a function* ν *such that* P^- *is disjoint from* $\mathcal{N}$ *and* ν *is a one-one mapping of* P *onto* P^-. *Let* $\mathcal{J} = \mathcal{N} \cup P^-$. *Clearly* $\mathcal{N} \subseteq \mathcal{J}$. *We call the elements of* P^- **negative integers** *and the elements of* $\mathcal{J}$ **integers.**

II. *Definition of the operation* $+_J$. *The binary operation* $+_J$ *on* $\mathcal{J}$ *is defined as follows:*

(i) *For any* $x, y \in P$:

(a) $x +_J y = x + y$; (*I.e., the addition operation in the new number system, when applied to positive integers, is to consist simply in applying the old operation of addition to these numbers.*)

(b) $\nu(x) +_J \nu(y) = \nu(x + y)$;

(c) $$x +_J \nu(y) = \begin{cases} x - y \text{ if } y < x, \\ \nu(y - x) \text{ if } x < y, \\ 0 \text{ if } x = y; \end{cases}$$

(d) $$\nu(x) +_J y = \begin{cases} \nu(x - y) \text{ if } y < x, \\ y - x \text{ if } x < y \\ 0 \text{ if } x = y. \end{cases}$$

(ii) *For any* $z \in \mathcal{J}$;
(a) $z +_J 0 = z$;
(b) $0 +_J z = z$.

III. *Definition of the operation* $\cdot_J$. *The binary operation* $\cdot_J$ *on* $\mathcal{J}$ *is defined as follows:*

(i) *For any* $x, y \in P$:
(a) $x \cdot_J y = x \cdot y$;
(b) $\nu(x) \cdot_J \nu(y) = x \cdot y$;
(c) $x \cdot_J \nu(y) = \nu(x \cdot y)$;
(d) $\nu(x) \cdot_J y = \nu(x \cdot y)$.

(ii) *For any* $z \in \mathcal{J}$:
(a) $z \cdot_J 0 = 0$
(b) $0 \cdot_J z = 0$.

This is a rather long and involved definition, in which we seemed to rely heavily on our previous knowledge of negative numbers. It is natural to wonder whether we could have used some other simpler definition of $+_J$ and $\cdot_J$ which would solve Problem $\mathcal{J}$ equally well. But as the reader will see below, in Theorem 11-3-1, Definition 11-2-1 provides what is essentially *the only* way to solve Problem $\mathcal{J}$. Further, Theorem 11-3-1 does not depend on the theorems which precede it—it could be proved *before* giving Definition 11-2-1, and indeed in seeking a formulation and a proof of Theorem 11-3-1 one would be led naturally to discover this definition even if one had no previous acquaintance with negative numbers.

In order to see that part II provides an adequate definition of an operation $+_J$ on $\mathcal{J}$, we must be sure that to any pair of elements a and b of $\mathcal{J}$ there is assigned *one* and *only one* element $a +_J b$ by this definition; and a similar problem arises in connection with the definition III of $\cdot_J$. But this is not a difficult matter. For by part I of Definition 11-2-1 we see that any element a of $\mathcal{J}$ must be in P or in P^- or must be zero—and it cannot simultaneously satisfy more than one of these conditions; and of course the same considerations apply to the element b. Hence we can divide the possibilities into nine exclusive cases: (**1**) $a \in P$ and $b \in P$; (**2**) $a \in P^-$ and $b \in P^-$; (**3**) $a \in P$ and $b \in P^-$; (**4**) $a \in P^-$ and $b \in P$; (**5**) $a \in P$ and $b = 0$; (**6**) $a \in P^-$ and $b = 0$; (**7**) $a = 0$ and $b \in P$; (**8**) $a = 0$ and $b \in P^-$; (**9**) $a = 0$ and $b = 0$.

Now it is clear that in case (**1**) above a value $a +_J b$ can be obtained by using part II (**i**) (**a**) of the definition and by no other part: similarly, cases (**2**), (**3**), and (**4**) above are handled respectively by parts (**i**) (**b**), (**i**) (**c**), and (**i**) (**d**) of the definition, cases (**5**) and (**6**) are handled by part (**ii**) (**a**) of the definition, and cases (**7**) and (**8**) are handled by part (**ii**) (**b**) of the definition. The last case, (**9**), unlike the others, can be handled under either of two different parts of the definition—(**ii**) (**a**) or (**ii**) (**b**); fortunately however, the same result is obtained for $a +_J b$ whichever of these parts is used.

We still must make sure that in any of the cases (**1**) through (**8**) the unique part of the definition which can be used to supply a value for $a +_J b$ (or for $a \cdot_J b$) will supply *only one* such value. Consider case (**3**), for instance, where $a \in P$ and $b \in P^-$. Suppose that we wish to determine the value $a +_J b$ by using part (**i**) (**c**) of II in Definition 11-2-1. Because ν maps P *onto* P^- we know that we can find an element $y \in P$ such that $\nu(y) = b$; and because ν is *one-one*, we know that there is *only one* such element y. Hence there is only one way in which we can apply part (**i**) (**c**) of the definition to compute $a +_J b$, and the result which is obtained—which depends on whether $y < a$, $a < y$, or $a = y$—is unique by Theorem 2-5-3. Similar considerations apply in the other cases (**1**) through (**8**).

Now that we have satisfied ourselves that Definition 11-2-1 really defines a unique number system $\langle \mathcal{J}, +_J, \cdot_J \rangle$ we can begin to study its properties. In the following theorems we show that the system $\langle \mathcal{J}, +_J, \cdot_J \rangle$ as described by Definition 11-2-1 does actually solve Problem $\mathcal{J}$.

THEOREM 11-2-2. *The system* $\langle \mathcal{J}, +_J, \cdot_J \rangle$ *is an extension of* $\langle \mathcal{N}, +, \cdot \rangle$.

Proof

By our definition of the word "extension" the system $\langle \mathcal{J}, +_J, \cdot_J \rangle$ is considered an extension of $\langle \mathcal{N}, +, \cdot \rangle$ if and only if the following three conditions hold:

(**i**) $\mathcal{N} \subseteq \mathcal{J}$,
(**ii**) $x +_J y = x + y$ *for any* $x, y \in \mathcal{N}$,
(**iii**) $x \cdot_J y = x \cdot y$ *for any* $x, y \in \mathcal{N}$.

From Definition 11-2-1, part I, it is clear that (**i**) holds. Statement (**ii**) follows readily from part II of Definition 11-2-1, since if $x, y \in P$ we know that $x +_J y = x + y$ by (**i**) (**a**), while if x, y are elements of $\mathcal{N}$ which are not both in P then at least one of them must be zero and so (by Definition 11-2-1 (II) (**ii**) and Definition 8-2-1) we see that $x +_J y = x + y$ in this case too. Similarly, statement (**iii**) can be established by part III of Definition 11-2-1.

In Chapter VIII we found that the system $\langle \mathcal{N}, +, \cdot \rangle$ satisfied certain commutative, associative and distributive laws. Do these continue to hold for our new extended system? That they do is established in the following theorem.

THEOREM 11-2-3. *If* x, y, z *are any elements of* $\mathcal{J}$, *then:*

(**i**) $x +_J y = y +_J x$ (*the Commutative Law for* $+_J$),

(ii) $x \cdot_J y = y \cdot_J x$ (*the Commutative Law for* $\cdot_J$),
(iii) $(x +_J y) +_J z = x +_J (y +_J z)$ (*the Associative Law of* $+_J$),
(iv) $(x \cdot_J y) \cdot_J z = x \cdot_J (y \cdot_J z)$ (*the Associative Law of* $\cdot_J$),
(v) $z \cdot_J (x +_J y) = z \cdot_J x +_J z \cdot_J y$ (*the Left Distributive Law for* $\cdot_J$ *over* $+_J$),
(vi) $(x +_J y) \cdot_J z = x \cdot_J z +_J y \cdot_J z$ (*the Right Distributive Law for* $\cdot_J$ *over* $+_J$),
(vii) $x \cdot_J 1 = x$.

Proof

We shall outline the proof for (i) only; the method of proof used here can be applied to the other parts of the theorem. The essential idea is to use Definition 11-2-1, all possible cases for x, y, and z (as to whether each lies in P or P^- or is zero), and to combine the definition with the known laws for the systems $\mathcal{P}$ and $\mathfrak{N}$.

Case I. Suppose $x, y \in P$. By Definition 11-2-1, $x +_J y = x + y$ and $y +_J x = y + x$. Since $+$ is a commutative operation in the system $\langle P, +, \cdot \rangle$ (Theorem 2-4-2), we have $x + y = y + x$ and it follows by the logic of identity that $x +_J y = y +_J x$.

Case II. Suppose $x \in P$, $y \in P^-$. Then there exists a unique element $y' \in P$ such that $y = \nu(y')$. Since $x, y' \in P$, we have by Definition 11-2-1,

$$x +_J \nu(y') = \begin{cases} x - y', & \text{if } y' < x, \\ \nu(y' - x), & \text{if } x < y', \\ 0, & \text{if } x = y', \end{cases}$$

while

$$\nu(y') +_J x = \begin{cases} x - y', & \text{if } y' < x, \\ \nu(y' - x), & \text{if } x < y', \\ 0, & \text{if } y' = x. \end{cases}$$

Clearly we have $x +_J \nu(y') = \nu(y') +_J x$ in each possible case, and hence $x +_J y = y +_J x$.

Case III. Suppose $x \in P^-$, $y \in P$. This case is similar to Case II, the roles of x and y being interchanged.

Case IV. Suppose $x, y \in P^-$. Then there exist unique elements x' and y' in P such that $x = \nu(x')$, $y = \nu(y')$. By Definition 11-2-1,

$$x +_J y = \nu(x') +_J \nu(y') = \nu(x' + y')$$

and

$$y +_J x = \nu(y') +_J \nu(x') = \nu(y' + x').$$

Since $x' + y' = y' + x'$ (Theorem 2-4-2), we get $\nu(x' + y') = \nu(y' + x')$ by the logic of identity, and hence $x +_J y = y +_J x$.

Case V. Suppose $x \in \mathcal{J}$, $y = 0$. By Definition 11-2-1,

$$x +_J 0 = x \text{ and } 0 +_J x = x,$$

and hence $x +_J 0 = 0 +_J x$.

Case VI. Suppose $x = 0$, $y \in \mathcal{J}$. This case is treated just as Case V.

Cases I through VI exhaust the possibilities for x and y. In every case the operation $+_J$ has been proved to be commutative. Hence we can state the commutative law for the system $\mathcal{G}$ in full generality.

The proofs of the remaining parts of Theorem 11-2-3, which are time (and paper) consuming but not difficult, will be left to the reader in the form of exercises.

In Chapter VIII we obtained certain cancellation laws for the operations $+$ and $\cdot$ of the system $\mathfrak{N}$. Do similar laws hold for our new system? The following theorem asserts that they do.

THEOREM 11-2-4. *For any* $x, y, z \in \mathcal{J}$,

(**i**) *if* $x +_J z = y +_J z$, *then* $x = y$ (*the Right Cancellation Law for* $+_J$);
(**ii**) *if* $z +_J x = z +_J y$, *then* $x = y$ (*the Left Cancellation Law for* $+_J$).

For any $x, y \in \mathcal{J}$, *and for any* $z \in P \cup P^-$ (*i.e., any* $z \in \mathcal{J}$ *such that* $z \neq 0$),

(**iii**) *if* $x \cdot_J z = y \cdot_J z$, *then* $x = y$ (*the Right Cancellation Law for* $\cdot_J$);
(**iv**) *if* $z \cdot_J x = z \cdot_J y$, *then* $x = y$ (*the Left Cancellation Law for* $\cdot_J$).

Proof

Parts (**ii**) and (**iv**) of this theorem follow immediately from parts (**i**) and (**iii**) respectively, together with the commutative laws (Theorem 11-2-3, parts (**i**) and (**ii**)). The proof of (**i**), which is outlined below, is by cases. The proof of (**iii**) will be left as an exercise.

Case I. Suppose $z \in P$. If $x +_J z = y +_J z$, it follows by E that $(x +_J z) +_J \nu(z) = (y +_J z) +_J \nu(z)$, and hence, using the associative law for $+_J$ (Theorem 11-2-3), $x +_J (z +_J \nu(z)) = y +_J (z +_J \nu(z))$. But, by Definition 11-2-1, $z +_J \nu(z) = 0$, and so $x +_J 0 = y +_J 0$, or $x = y$ (by Definition 11-2-1).

Case II. Suppose $z \in P^-$. Let z' be the unique element of P such that $z = \nu(z')$. If $x +_J z = y +_J z$, i.e., if $x +_J \nu(z') = y +_J \nu(z')$, then by E we have $(x +_J \nu(z')) +_J z' = (y +_J \nu(z')) +_J z'$ and by the associative law for $+_J$ (Theorem 11-2-3), $x +_J (\nu(z') +_J z') = y +_J (\nu(z') +_J z')$. Just as in the previous case we obtain $x = y$ by applying the law $\nu(z') +_J z' = 0$ (Definition 11-2-1).

Case III. Suppose $z = 0$. Clearly, if $x +_J 0 = y +_J 0$, then $x = y$ directly by Definition 11-2-1.

By comparing Theorems 11-2-3 and 11-2-4 with Problem $\mathcal{J}$, we observe that in order to complete the solution of this problem it remains only to show that for some element x of $\mathcal{J}$ we have $x +_J 1 = 0$. This is a simple matter, of course, since $\nu(1) +_J 1 = 0$ directly by Definition 11-2-1. Actually, however, something much more is true: In the next theorem we shall show that for *any* a, b *in* $\mathcal{J}$ (and hence, in particular, for any a, b *in* $\mathcal{N}$), there exists a unique element x of $\mathcal{J}$ which is a root of the equation $x +_J b = a$.

THEOREM 11-2-5. *Let a and b be any elements of $\mathcal{J}$. Then there exists a unique element $x \in \mathcal{J}$ such that $x +_J b = a$.*

Before proving this theorem we shall first state and prove the following lemma.

LEMMA 11-2-5.1. *For any element $b \in \mathcal{J}$ there exists an element $x \in \mathcal{J}$ such that $x +_J b = 0$.*

Proof outline

Case I. Suppose $b \in P$. Then by Definition 11-2-1 $\nu(b) +_J b = 0$.

Case II. Suppose $b \in P^-$. Then by Definition 11-2-1 there exists an element $b' \in P$ such that $\nu(b') = b$. Furthermore, $b' +_J b = b' +_J \nu(b') = 0$ by E and Definition 11-2-1.

Case III. Suppose $b = 0$. Then $0 +_J b = 0 +_J 0 = 0$ by E and Definition 11-2-1.

These three cases exhaust all possibilities for b and in each case we see that there exists $x \in \mathcal{J}$ such that $x +_J b = 0$.

Proof of Theorem 11-2-5 *outlined*

Let a, b be any elements in $\mathcal{J}$. Then by Lemma 11-2-5.1 there exists $b^- \in \mathcal{J}$ such that $b^- +_J b = 0$. Now

$$(1) \qquad (a +_J b^-) +_J b = a +_J (b^- +_J b)$$

by the associative law for $+_J$ (Theorem 11-2-3 (**iii**)). Since $b^- +_J b = 0$, we have

(**2**) $$a +_J (b^- +_J b) = a +_J 0, \text{ by E,}$$
$$= a, \text{ by Definition 11-2-1.}$$

Hence, by applying E to (**1**) and (**2**), we obtain

$$(a +_J b^-) +_J b = a.$$

Thus we see that there is at least one element $x \in \mathcal{J}$ such that $x +_J b = a$.

It remains to show that x is unique. Suppose, therefore, that x and x' are *both* elements in $\mathcal{J}$ such that $x +_J b = a$ and $x' +_J b = a$. Then $x +_J b = x' +_J b$ by E, and so by the right cancellation law for $+_J$ (Theorem 11-2-4) we get $x = x'$. This argument shows that we cannot have two *different* elements, x and x', both of which satisfy the equation $x +_J b = a$. The proof of Theorem 11-2-5 is now complete.

EXERCISES

1. Prove Theorem 11-2-3, parts (**ii**) through (**vii**).
2. Prove Theorem 11-2-4, part (**iii**).
3. Show that for any $x, y \in \mathcal{J}$ such that $x \neq 0$ and $y \neq 0$ we have $x \cdot_J y \neq 0$.
4. Generalize the Associative Laws for $+_J$ and $\cdot_J$ to four elements of $\mathcal{J}$.

3. *Other Solutions of Problem* $\mathcal{G}$

We have seen that in constructing $\mathcal{J}$, and in defining the operations $+_J$ and $\cdot_J$ on $\mathcal{J}$, we were motivated by our previous knowledge of the negative numbers. How might we proceed if we had no such prior knowledge? Might one not find other number systems, quite different from the system $\mathcal{G}$, which would do as well for solving Problem $\mathcal{J}$?

A rather natural way of attacking the problem would be to seek for properties which *any* number system must necessarily have if it is to provide a solution to Problem $\mathcal{J}$. That is, we assume we have an arbitrary number system which solves the problem, and then we seek to discover and establish some of its properties. By proceeding in this way we discover Theorem 11-3-1, below, which says in effect that Definition 11-2-1 provides essentially the *only* way of solving Problem $\mathcal{J}$. Thus, in seeking a formulation and proof of Theorem 11-3-1, one is naturally led to discover Definition 11-2-1 even if he has no previous acquaintance with negative numbers. The fact that Theorem 11-3-1 would be naturally discovered *before* Definition 11-2-1, even though it is presented *afterwards* in our theory, is only one more example of what we have observed on several earlier occasions, namely, that psychological processes and logical methods are two entirely different things.

As we shall see, Theorem 11-3-1 states that if $\mathfrak{Q} = \langle Q, +_Q, \cdot_Q \rangle$ is any number system which solves Problem $\mathcal{J}$, then $\mathfrak{Q}$ has a part which is just like $\mathfrak{J}$. By this we mean that: There is a subset R of Q which is disjoint from N, and another subset J' of Q which is $N \cup R$; there is a one-one mapping μ of P onto R;[1] and the operations $+_Q$ of "addition" and $\cdot_Q$ "multiplication" of the system $\mathfrak{Q}$, when acting on elements of J', obey the rules given in Definition 11-2-1 (except that P^- is replaced by R and ν by μ). Since, in our construction of $\mathcal{J}$, we emphasized that the precise nature of P^- and of ν was irrelevant as long as P^- was disjoint from N and ν mapped P onto P^- in a one-one manner, we see that R and μ could just as well have been chosen for P^- and ν respectively.

In mathematical terminology, the fact that there exists in the extension $\mathfrak{Q}$ of $\mathfrak{N}$ a part $\mathfrak{J}'$ which is just like the extension $\mathfrak{J}$ of $\mathfrak{N}$, would be expressed by saying that there is an *isomorphism* h of $\mathfrak{J}$ into $\mathfrak{Q}$, such that h maps J onto J' and leaves each element of N fixed. In other words, there is a one-one mapping h of J onto J' such that

$$\begin{aligned} h(x +_J y) &= h(x) +_Q h(y) \text{ for all } x, y \in J, \\ h(x \cdot_J y) &= h(x) \cdot_Q h(y) \text{ for all } x, y \in J, \\ h(x) &= x \text{ for all } x \in N. \end{aligned}$$

These results form the content of our next two theorems.

THEOREM 11-3-1. *Let $\mathfrak{Q} = \langle Q, +_Q, \cdot_Q \rangle$ be any number system such that:*

(**a**) *$\mathfrak{Q}$ is an extension of $\mathfrak{N} = \langle N, +, \cdot \rangle$;*
(**b**) *there is an element $m \in Q$ such that $m +_Q 1 = 0$;*
(**c**) *the associative and commutative laws hold for $+_Q$ and $\cdot_Q$;*
(**d**) *the left and right distributive laws hold for $\cdot_Q$ over $+_Q$; and*
(**e**) *the left and right cancellation laws hold for $+_Q$.*

Then we can find a subset R of Q, and a function μ mapping P onto R, such that the following are true:

(**i**) *R is disjoint from N, i.e., $R \cap N = \varnothing$;*
(**ii**) *μ is a one-one mapping of P onto R;*
(**iii**) *for any $x, y \in P$ we have*

$$x +_Q y = x + y,$$
$$\mu(x) +_Q \mu(y) = \mu(x + y),$$
$$x +_Q \mu(y) = \begin{cases} x - y \text{ if } y < x, \\ \mu(y - x) \text{ if } x < y, \\ 0 \text{ if } x = y, \end{cases}$$
$$\mu(x) +_Q y = \begin{cases} y - x \text{ if } x < y, \\ \mu(x - y) \text{ if } y < x, \\ 0 \text{ if } x = y, \end{cases}$$

[1] The symbol "μ" is the Greek letter mu.

and for any $z \in Q$ *we have*

$$z +_Q 0 = z \text{ and } 0 +_Q z = z;$$

(iv) *for any* $x, y \in P$ *we have*

$$\begin{aligned} x \cdot_Q y &= x \cdot y, \\ \mu(x) \cdot_Q \mu(y) &= x \cdot y, \\ x \cdot_Q \mu(y) &= \mu(x \cdot y), \\ \mu(x) \cdot_Q y &= \mu(x \cdot y), \end{aligned}$$

and for any $z \in Q$ *we have*

$$z \cdot_Q 0 = 0 \text{ and } 0 \cdot_Q z = 0.$$

Proof

We take μ to be the function with domain P, such that for any $x \in P$ we have $\mu(x) = m \cdot_Q x$ (where m is the element mentioned in hypothesis (**b**)). And we take R to be the range of this function μ, so that the elements of R are all those elements of Q which are products $m \cdot_Q x$ for some $x \in P$. Clearly R is a subset of Q and μ is a function mapping P onto R.

Before proving the parts (**i**) through (**iv**) of the theorem, we give two lemmas. The first lemma is actually a part of the theorem, but since it will be needed throughout the proof of the other parts it is presented first.

LEMMA 11-3-1.1. *For all* $z \in Q$, $z +_Q 0 = z$ *and* $0 +_Q z = z$; $z \cdot_Q 0 = 0$ *and* $0 \cdot_Q z = 0$.

Proof

▶▶ **1.** Let z be any element of Q.
▶ **2.** $0 +_Q 0 = 0$; by Definition 8-2-1, since $0 \in \mathcal{N}$ and $\mathbb{Q}$ is an extension of $\mathfrak{N}$ (hypothesis (**a**)).
3. $z +_Q (0 +_Q 0) = z +_Q 0$; from line **2** by E.
4. $(z +_Q 0) +_Q 0 = z +_Q 0$; from line **3** by E and the associative law for $+_Q$ (hypothesis (**c**)).
▶ **5.** $z +_Q 0 = z$; from line **4** by the right cancellation law for $+_Q$ (hypothesis (**e**)).
6. $0 +_Q z = z +_Q 0$; by the commutative law for $+_Q$ (hypothesis (**c**)).
▶ **7.** $0 +_Q z = z$; from lines **5** and **6** by E.
▶▶ **8.** For all $z \in Q$, $z +_Q 0 = z$ and $0 +_Q z = z$; by the Deduction Theorem applied to lines **1** through **5** and **7**.
▶ **9.** $z \cdot_Q (0 +_Q 0) = z \cdot_Q 0$; from line **2** by E.
10. $z \cdot_Q 0 = z \cdot_Q 0 +_Q 0$; by line **8**.
11. $z \cdot_Q (0 +_Q 0) = z \cdot_Q 0 +_Q z \cdot_Q 0$; by the distributive law of $\cdot_Q$ over $+_Q$ (hypothesis (**d**)).

12. $z \cdot_Q 0 +_Q z \cdot_Q 0 = z \cdot_Q 0 +_Q 0$; from lines **9**, **10**, and **11** by E.

▶**13.** $z \cdot_Q 0 = 0$; from line **12** by the left cancellation law for $+_Q$ (hypothesis (**e**)).

14. $0 \cdot_Q z = z \cdot_Q 0$; by the commutative law of $\cdot_Q$ (hypothesis (**c**)).

▶**15.** $0 \cdot_Q z = 0$; from lines **13** and **14** by E.

▶▶**16.** For all $z \in Q$, $z \cdot_Q 0 = 0$ and $0 \cdot_Q z = 0$; by the Deduction Theorem applied to lines **1** through **13** and **15**.

Lines **8** and **16** prove the lemma. In connection with line **10**, it must be borne in mind that we obtain it by applying line **8** not to the element z chosen in line **1**, but to the element $z \cdot_Q 0$. Since line **8** tells us that $z +_Q 0 = 0$ for *all* elements z of Q, this equation will, in particular, be true for the element $z \cdot_Q 0$ (where z is the element chosen in line **1**); and this gives line **10**.

LEMMA 11-3-1.2.

(**i**) $m \cdot_Q 1 = m$.
(**ii**) $m \cdot_Q m = 1$.
(**iii**) *For all* $x \in \mathcal{N}$, $m \cdot_Q x +_Q x = 0$.

Proof of (**i**)

▶▶**1.** $m +_Q 1 = 0$; by hypothesis (**b**).

▶**2.** $(m +_Q 1) \cdot_Q 1 = 0 \cdot_Q 1$; from line **1** by E.

3. $0 \cdot_Q 1 = 0$; by Lemma 11-3-1.1.

4. $(m +_Q 1) \cdot_Q 1 = m \cdot_Q 1 +_Q 1 \cdot_Q 1$; by the distributive law of $\cdot_Q$ over $+_Q$ (hypothesis (**d**)).

5. $1 \cdot_Q 1 = 1$; by Theorem 8-2-1, since $1 \in \mathcal{N}$ and $\mathfrak{Q}$ is an extension of $\mathfrak{N}$ (hypothesis (**a**)).

6. $(m +_Q 1) \cdot_Q 1 = m \cdot_Q 1 +_Q 1$; from lines **4** and **5** by E.

▶**7.** $m \cdot_Q 1 +_Q 1 = 0$; from lines **6**, **2**, and **3** by E.

▶**8.** $m \cdot_Q 1 +_Q 1 = m +_Q 1$; from lines **1** and **7** by E.

▶▶**9.** $m \cdot_Q 1 = m$; from line **8** by the right cancellation law for $+_Q$ (hypothesis (**e**)).

Proof of (**ii**)

▶▶**1.** $m +_Q 1 = 0$; by hypothesis (**b**).

▶**2.** $m \cdot_Q (m +_Q 1) = m \cdot_Q 0$; from line **1** by E.

3. $= 0$; by Lemma 11-3-1.1.

4. $m \cdot_Q (m +_Q 1) = m \cdot_Q m +_Q m \cdot_Q 1$; by the distributive law of $\cdot_Q$ over $+_Q$ (hypothesis (**d**)).

5. $= m \cdot_Q m +_Q m$; from part (**i**) by E.

6. $m \cdot_Q m +_Q m = 0$; from lines **2** through **5** by E.

▶7. $1 +_Q m = 0$; from line **1** by the commutative law for $+_Q$ (hypothesis (**c**)).
▶8. $m \cdot_Q m +_Q m = 1 +_Q m$; from lines **6** and **7** by E.
▶▶9. $m \cdot_Q m = 1$; from line **8** and the right cancellation law of $+_Q$ (hypothesis (**e**)).

Proof of (**iii**)

▶▶1. Let x be any element of $\mathcal{N}$.
▶▶2. $m +_Q 1 = 0$; by hypothesis (**b**).
▶3. $(m +_Q 1) \cdot_Q x = 0 \cdot_Q x$; from lines **1** and **2** by E.
4. $= 0$; by Lemma 11-3-1.1.
5. $(m +_Q 1) \cdot_Q x = m \cdot_Q x +_Q 1 \cdot_Q x$; by the right distributive law of $\cdot_Q$ over $+_Q$ (hypothesis (**d**)).
6. $= m \cdot_Q x +_Q x$; by line **1**, Theorem 8-2-3 (**vii**), hypothesis (**a**), and E.
▶▶7. $m \cdot_Q x +_Q x = 0$; by E, lines **3**, **4**, **5**, and **6**.

We now proceed to the proof of the several parts of Theorem **11-3-1.**

Proof of (**i**) *of Theorem* 11-3-1.

▶▶ 1. Suppose that there is an element y such that both $y \in R$ and $y \in \mathcal{N}$.
▶ 2. $y = \mu(x)$ for some $x \in P$; by the definition of R and line **1**.
3. $y = m \cdot_Q x$; by line **2** and the definition of μ.
4. $y +_Q x = m \cdot_Q x +_Q x$; by E from line **3**.
5. $m \cdot_Q x +_Q x = 0$; by line **2** and Lemma 11-3-1.2.
6. $y +_Q x = 0$; from lines **4** and **5** by E.
7. $y +_Q x = y + x$; by lines **1**, **2**, and hypothesis (**a**).
▶ 8. $y + x = 0$; from lines **6** and **7** by E.
▶ 9. $y + x \neq 0$; from lines **1**, **2**, and Definition 8-2-1.
10. If y is an element in both R and $\mathcal{N}$ then $y + x = 0$ for some $x \in P$ and $y + x \neq 0$; by the Deduction Theorem applied to lines **1** and **2** through **8** and **9**.
▶▶11. There is no element y such that $y \in R$ and $y \in \mathcal{N}$; by line **10**.
12. R and $\mathcal{N}$ are disjoint; by line **11**.

Proof of (**ii**)

Since we have observed, in defining R, that μ is a mapping of P onto R, we need only show that μ is one-one.

▶▶ 1. Let x, y be any elements of P such that $\mu(x) = \mu(y)$.
▶ 2. $m \cdot_Q x = m \cdot_Q y$; by line **1** and the definition of μ.
3. $m \cdot_Q x +_Q x = m \cdot_Q y +_Q x$; by line **2** by E.
4. $m \cdot_Q x +_Q x = 0$; by line **1** and Lemma 11-3-1.2 (**iii**).
5. $m \cdot_Q y +_Q x = 0$; from lines **3** and **4** by E.

6. $m \cdot_Q y +_Q y = 0$; by line **1** and Lemma 11-3-1.2.
▶ 7. $m \cdot_Q y +_Q x = m \cdot_Q y +_Q y$; from lines **5** and **6** by E.
▶▶ 8. $x = y$; by line **7** and the left cancellation law for $+_Q$ (hypothesis (**e**)).
9. For all $x, y \in P$, if $\mu(x) = \mu(y)$ then $x = y$; from lines **1** through **8** by the Deduction Theorem.
10. μ is one-one; by line **9**.

Proof of (**iii**)

▶▶ 1. Let x, y be any elements of P.
▶▶ 2. $x +_Q y = x + y$; by line **1** since $\mathfrak{Q}$ is an extension of $\mathfrak{N}$ (hypothesis (**a**)).

▶ 3. $\mu(x) +_Q \mu(y) = m \cdot_Q x +_Q m \cdot_Q y$; by the definition of μ.
4. $= m \cdot_Q (x +_Q y)$; by the left distributive law of $\cdot_Q$ over $+_Q$ (hypothesis (**d**)).
5. $= m \cdot_Q (x + y)$; from line **2** by E.
6. $= \mu(x + y)$; by the definition of μ.
▶▶ 7. $\mu(x) +_Q \mu(y) = \mu(x + y)$; from lines **3**, **4**, **5**, and **6** by E.

▶ 8. $x +_Q \mu(y) = x +_Q m \cdot_Q y$; by the definition of μ and E.

▶ 9. *Case I.* Suppose $y < x$.
10. $x = y + (x - y)$; from line **9** by Theorem 2-6-3.
11. $x = y +_Q (x - y)$; from line **10** and E since $\mathfrak{Q}$ is an extension of $\mathfrak{N}$ (hypothesis (**a**)).
12. $x +_Q m \cdot_Q y = (y +_Q (x - y)) +_Q m \cdot_Q y$; from line **11** by E.
13. $= (m \cdot_Q y +_Q y) +_Q (x - y)$; by the associative and commutative laws of $+_Q$ (hypothesis (**c**)).
14. $= x - y$; by Lemma 11-3-1.1 and 11-3-1.2.
▶ 15. $x +_Q \mu(y) = x - y$; by E from lines **8**, **12**, **13**, and **14**.
▶▶ 16. If $y < x$ then $x +_Q \mu(y) = x - y$; by the Deduction Theorem applied to lines **9** through **15**.

▶ 17. *Case II.* Suppose $x < y$.
18. $y = x + (y - x)$; from line **17** by Theorem 2-6-3.
19. $y = x +_Q (y - x)$; by line **18** since $\mathfrak{Q}$ is an extension of $\mathfrak{N}$ (hypothesis (**a**)).
20. $x +_Q m \cdot_Q y = x +_Q m \cdot_Q (x +_Q (y - x))$; from line **19** by E.
21. $= (x +_Q m \cdot_Q x) +_Q m \cdot_Q (y - x)$; by the distributive and associative laws (hypotheses (**c**) and (**d**)).

22. $= 0 +_Q m \cdot_Q (y - x)$; by Lemma 11-3-1.2, E, and the commutative law of $+_Q$.
23. $= m \cdot_Q (y - x)$; by Lemma 11-3-1.1.
▶24. $x +_Q \mu(y) = \mu(y - x)$; by E from lines **20** to **23** and the definition of μ.
▶▶25. If $x < y$ then $x +_Q \mu(y) = \mu(y - x)$; by the Deduction Theorem applied to lines **17** through **24**.

▶26. *Case III.* Suppose $x = y$.
27. $x +_Q m \cdot_Q y = y +_Q m \cdot_Q y$; from line **26** by E.
28. $= 0$; by Lemma 11-3-1.2.
▶29. $x +_Q \mu(y) = 0$; by lines **8, 27,** and **28.**
▶▶30. If $x = y$ then $x +_Q \mu(y) = 0$; by the deduction Theorem applied to lines **26** through **29**.

31. For any $x, y \in P$,

$$x +_Q \mu(y) = \begin{cases} x - y \text{ if } y < x, \\ \mu(y - x) \text{ if } x < y, \\ 0 \text{ if } x = y; \end{cases}$$

by lines **1, 16, 25,** and **30.**

32. $\mu(x) +_Q y = y +_Q \mu(x)$; by the commutative law of $+_Q$ (hypothesis (**c**)).

▶▶33.
$$= \begin{cases} y - x \text{ if } x < y, \\ \mu(x - y) \text{ if } y < x, \\ 0 \text{ if } y = x; \end{cases}$$ by lines **1** and **31.**

34.
$$\mu(x) +_Q y = \begin{cases} y - x \text{ if } x < y, \\ \mu(x - y) \text{ if } y < x, \\ 0 \text{ if } x = y; \end{cases}$$ by lines **32** and **33** and E.

35. Lines **1, 2, 7, 31,** and **34** together with Lemma 11-3-1.1 summarize part (**iii**).

Proof of (**iv**)

▶▶ 1. Let x, y be any elements of P.
▶▶ 2. $x \cdot_Q y = x \cdot y$; by line **1** since Q is an extension of N (hypothesis (**a**)).

▶ 3. $\mu(x) \cdot_Q \mu(y) = (m \cdot_Q x) \cdot_Q (m \cdot_Q y)$; by the definition of μ and E.
4. $= (m \cdot_Q m) \cdot_Q (x \cdot_Q y)$; by the associative and commutative laws for $\cdot_Q$ (hypothesis (**c**)).

5. $= 1 \cdot_Q (x \cdot_Q y)$; by Lemma 11-3-1.2 and E.
6. $= x \cdot y$; by line **1** since $\mathbb{Q}$ is an extension of $\mathfrak{N}$ (hypothesis (**a**)).

►► 7. $\mu(x) \cdot_Q \mu(y) = x \cdot y$; from lines **3** through **6** by E.

► 8. $x \cdot_Q \mu(y) = x \cdot_Q (m \cdot_Q y)$; by the definition of μ and E.
9. $= m \cdot_Q (x \cdot_Q y)$; by the associative and commutative laws for $\cdot_Q$ (hypothesis (**c**)).
10. $= m \cdot_Q (x \cdot y)$; by line **1** since $\mathbb{Q}$ is an extension of $\mathfrak{N}$ (hypothesis (**a**)) and E.
11. $= \mu(x \cdot y)$; by the definition of μ.

►► 12. $x \cdot_Q \mu(y) = \mu(x \cdot y)$; by lines **8** through **11** and E.
13. For all $x, y \in P$, $x \cdot_Q \mu(y) = \mu(x \cdot y)$; by the Deduction Theorem applied to lines **1** through **12**.

► 14. $\mu(x) \cdot_Q y = y \cdot_Q \mu(x)$; by the commutative law of $\cdot_Q$.
15. $= \mu(y \cdot x)$; by lines **1** and **13**.

►► 16. $\mu(x) \cdot_Q y = \mu(x \cdot y)$; by lines **14**, **15**, the commutative law of $\cdot$, and E.

17. Lines **1**, **2**, **7**, **13**, and **16** together with Lemma 11-3-1.1 summarize Part (**iv**).

THEOREM 11-3-2. *Let $\mathbb{Q} = \langle Q, +_Q, \cdot_Q\rangle$ be any number system such that*

(**a**) *$\mathbb{Q}$ is an extension of $\mathfrak{N}$;*
(**b**) *Q contains an element m such that $m +_Q 1 = 0$;*
(**c**) *the associative and commutative laws hold for $+_Q$ and $\cdot_Q$;*
(**d**) *the left and right distributive laws hold for $\cdot_Q$ over $+_Q$; and*
(**e**) *the left and right cancellation laws hold for $+_Q$.*

Then there is an isomorphism of the system $\mathcal{J}$ into $\mathbb{Q}$. That is, there exists a one-one mapping h of $\mathcal{J}$ into Q such that

$$h(x +_J y) = h(x) +_Q h(y)$$
$$h(x \cdot_J y) = h(x) \cdot_Q h(y)$$

for all $x, y \in \mathcal{J}$. Furthermore, for any $x \in N$ we have $h(x) = x$.

Proof

The proof of this theorem is rather lengthy, and will be found in the appendix.

In Theorems 11-2-4 and 11-2-5 we have seen that (**A**) if x, y, z are any elements of $\mathcal{J}$ such that $x \cdot_J y = x \cdot_J z$ and $x \neq 0$, then $y = z$, and (**B**) for any elements a, b of $\mathcal{J}$ there is a unique element x in $\mathcal{J}$ such that $x +_J a = b$.

Another law which follows readily from Definition 11-2-1 is this: (**C**) For all $z \in \mathcal{J}$, $z \cdot_J 1 = z$. Now if Q is an arbitrary number system satisfying the hypotheses of Theorems 11-3-1 and 11-3-2 we know that there is an isomorphism of $\mathfrak{J}$ into $\mathfrak{Q}$ which maps $\mathcal{J}$ onto a certain part $\mathcal{J}'$ of Q which is thus just like $\mathcal{J}$; and from this it is easy to show that the properties (**A**), (**B**), and (**C**) are enjoyed by $\mathcal{J}'$ as well as by $\mathcal{J}$. In the case of (**C**), for example, this means that $z \cdot_Q 1 = z$ *for all* z *in* $\mathcal{J}'$.

It is natural to ask, then, whether properties (**A**), (**B**), and (**C**) hold *throughout* Q; e.g., in the case of (**C**) we may wonder whether in any number system Q satisfying the hypotheses of Theorem 11-3-2 we must have $z \cdot_Q 1 = z$ *for all* $z \in Q$. This possibility is suggested, for example, by Lemma 11-3-1.1, which shows that laws like $z \cdot_Q 0 = 0$ and $z +_Q 0 = z$ hold not only for all $z \in \mathcal{J}'$, but indeed for all $z \in Q$.

Of course there *are* systems $\mathfrak{Q}$, satisfying the hypotheses of Theorem 11-3-1 and 11-3-2, where the laws (**A**), (**B**), and (**C**) do hold throughout Q. For example, $\mathfrak{J}$ itself is such a system! But the following system $\mathfrak{K} = \langle K, +_K, \cdot_K \rangle$ is an example where none of the laws (**A**), (**B**), and (**C**) hold for all elements, even though the system satisfies the hypotheses of Theorems 11-3-1 and 11-3-2.

To construct the system $\mathfrak{K}$, we let M be the set of all ordered pairs $\langle x, 2 \cdot y \rangle$, for all $x \in \mathcal{J}$ and $y \in P$, and we take $K = \mathcal{J} \cup M$. Define the operations $+_K$ and $\cdot_K$ on K as follows:

$$\langle x, 2 \cdot z \rangle +_K \langle y, 2 \cdot w \rangle = \langle x +_J y, 2 \cdot (z + w) > \text{ for } x, y \in \mathcal{J} \text{ and } z, w \in P.$$
$$\langle x, 2 \cdot z \rangle \cdot_K \langle y, 2 \cdot w \rangle = \langle x \cdot_J y, 4 \cdot (z \cdot w) \rangle \text{ for } x, y \in \mathcal{J} \text{ and } z, w \in P.$$
$$x +_K \langle y, 2 \cdot w \rangle = \langle y, 2 \cdot w \rangle +_K x = \langle x +_J y, 2 \cdot w \rangle \text{ for } x, y \in \mathcal{J}, \quad w \in P.$$
$$x \cdot_K \langle y, 2 \cdot w \rangle = \langle y, 2 \cdot w \rangle \cdot_K x = x \cdot_J y \text{ for } x, y \in \mathcal{J}, \quad w \in P.$$
$$x +_K y = x +_J y \text{ for } x, y \in \mathcal{J}.$$
$$x \cdot_K y = x \cdot_J y \text{ for } x, y \in \mathcal{J}.$$

The reader can readily show that $\mathfrak{K} = \langle K, +_K, \cdot_K \rangle$ is an extension of $\mathfrak{J}$ (and hence of $\mathfrak{N}$), and satisfies all of the hypotheses (**b**) through (**e**) of Theorem 11-3-2, but does not satisfy any of the laws (**A**), (**B**), or (**C**) above.

EXERCISES

1. If $\mathfrak{Q}$ is any system satisfying the hypotheses of Theorems 11-3-1 and 11-3-2, and if $\mathcal{J}'$ is the part of Q just like $\mathcal{J}$, prove that

(**a**) If $x, y, z \in \mathcal{J}'$, $x \cdot_Q y = x \cdot_Q z$, and $x \neq 0$, then $y = z$;

(**b**) For any elements a, b in $\mathcal{J}'$ there is a unique solution x in $\mathcal{J}'$ of the equation $x +_Q a = b$; and

(**c**) For any $z \in \mathcal{J}'$, $z \cdot_Q 1 = z$.

2. (**i**) Prove that the system $\mathfrak{K}$ constructed in the last paragraph is an extension of $\mathfrak{J}$ (and hence of $\mathfrak{N}$), and indeed satisfies all of the hypotheses of Theorem 11-3-2.

(**ii**) Show that (**A**) does not hold throughout K.

(iii) Show that law (**B**) does not hold throughout K.

(iv) Show that if $a \in \mathfrak{F}$, $b \in P$, then $1 \cdot_K \langle a, 2 \cdot b \rangle z \neq z \langle a, 2 \cdot b \rangle$, so that law (**C**) does not hold throughout K.

4. *Subtraction: "Signed" Numbers*

In the preceding sections we have seen how the problem of finding a solution to the equation $x + 1 = 0$ led us to the definition of an extended number system $\langle \mathcal{J}, +_J, \cdot_J \rangle$ as given in Definition 11-2-1, and we have seen that this is essentially the only way in which the problem can be solved. We shall now develop the theory of the number system $\langle \mathcal{J}, +_J, \cdot_J \rangle$ in the same spirit in which we developed the system $\mathcal{P}$ of positive integers and the system $\mathfrak{N}$ of natural numbers. Indeed, many of our theorems will be simply restatements of earlier theorems concerning the system $\mathfrak{N}$, only now the theorems will apply more generally to elements of the system $\langle \mathcal{J}, +_J, \cdot_J \rangle$. Our treatment will be largely parallel to the earlier development, and we will permit ourselves to be less detailed.

We begin our discussion of the properties of integers by defining the operation of *subtraction*, and considering some of the elementary rules concerning subtraction.

DEFINITION 11-4-1. *The* **subtraction operation** $-_J$ *is a binary operation on* $\mathcal{J}$ *whose value, for any ordered pair* $\langle x, y \rangle$ *of elements* $x, y \in \mathcal{J}$, *is the unique integer* z *such that* $z +_J y = x$. (*The existence and uniqueness of such an element is established in Theorem* 11-2-5.) *As in the case of the earlier systems* $\mathcal{P}$ *and* $\mathfrak{N}$ *we use the notation* $x -_J y$ *for the value of* $-_J$ *when applied to* $\langle x, y \rangle$, *in preference to the notation* $-_J \langle x, y \rangle$.

We observe that when subtraction was defined for the system $\mathcal{P}$ of *positive integers* it was defined as a *function* whose domain was merely the set of *those* ordered pairs $\langle x, y \rangle$ of elements x, y of P *for which* $y < x$. (See Definition 2-6-2.) A similar remark applies to the subtraction function $-_N$ (see Definition 8-5-1), where the domain consists of all ordered pairs $\langle x, y \rangle$ such that $x, y \in N$ and $y < x$. Hence $-$ and $-_N$ cannot be called operations, for a binary *operation* on a set is a function which has as its domain *all* ordered pairs of elements of the set. However, we see that $-_J$ can rightfully be called a binary operation on $\mathcal{J}$. Doubtless it will be a relief to the reader finally to be able to speak of the "operation of subtraction"!

Some of the important properties of $-_J$ are given in the next theorem.

THEOREM 11-4-2.

(a) $-_J$ *is an extension of* $-$. *In other words, whenever* $x, y \in N$ *and* $y \leq x$, *then* $x -_J y = x - y$.

(b) *For all* $x \in \mathcal{J}$, $x -_J 0 = x$.

(c) *For all* $x \in \mathcal{J}$, $x -_J x = 0$.
(d) *For all* $x, y \in \mathcal{J}$, $x +_J (y -_J x) = y$.
(e) *For all* $x, y, z \in \mathcal{J}$, $(x +_J y) -_J z = x +_J (y -_J z)$.
(f) *For all* $x, y, z \in \mathcal{J}$, $x \cdot_J (y -_J z) = (x \cdot_J y) -_J (x \cdot_J z)$.
(g) *For all* $x, y, z \in \mathcal{J}$, $x +_J y = z$ *if and only if* $y = z -_J x$.
(h) *For all* $x, y, z \in \mathcal{J}$, *if* $x -_J z = y -_J z$ *then* $x = y$.
(i) *For all* $x, y, z \in \mathcal{J}$, *if* $z -_J x = z -_J y$ *then* $x = y$.

We shall prove part (**e**) and leave the proofs of the other parts as exercises for the reader.

Proof of (**e**)

▶▶ **1.** Let x, y, z be any elements of $\mathcal{J}$.
▶ **2.** Let $q = (x +_J y) -_J z$.
3. $q +_J z = x +_J y$; by line **2** and Definition 11-4-1.
▶ **4.** Let $r = y -_J z$.
5. $r +_J z = y$; by line **4** and Definition 11-4-1.
6. $x +_J r = x +_J (y -_J z)$; by E from line **4**.
7. $(x +_J r) +_J z = x +_J y$; by E and the associative law for $+_J$ (Theorem 11-2-3) from line **5**.
8. $(x +_J r) +_J z = q +_J z$; by E from lines **3** and **7**.
▶ **9.** $x +_J r = q$; by line **8** and the right cancellation law of $+_J$ (Theorem 11-2-5).
▶▶ **10.** $(x +_J y) -_J z = x +_J (y -_J z)$; by E from lines **2**, **4**, and **9**.
11. For all $x, y, z \in \mathcal{J}$, $(x +_J y) -_J z = x +_J (y -_J z)$; by the Deduction Theorem applied to lines **1** through **10**.

The reader is familiar from his early algebraic experience with the symbol "$-$" used in expressions such as "-3", "$-x$", etc. We had occasion in section 1 of this chapter to refer to such numbers. And indeed our familiarity with the "laws of signs" served to help us in formulating Definition 11-2-1. But what is the precise meaning of expressions like "-3" or "$-x$"? From the position of the sign "$-$" in these expressions it appears that "$-$" denotes a function which is being applied to the number 3 or the element x; and yet we have seen that the operation $-$ is to be applied to *ordered pairs* of numbers.

The fact is that the minus sign is used in two different ways in elementary algebra: sometimes it denotes a *binary operation*, to be applied to pairs of numbers, and sometimes a *unary operation*, to be applied to single numbers. Because these two operations are closely related it is actually rather convenient to use the same symbol to denote these two different things. However, such ambiguous usage tends to obscure the logical status of our statements. Accordingly, we shall here use a heavy minus "**—**", for the unary operation, which we introduce in the following definition.

DEFINITION 11-4-3. *The* **negation operation** $-$ *has* $\mathcal{J}$ *as its domain, and for any* $x \in \mathcal{J}$ *we define* $-x = 0 -_J x$.

Such familiar laws of elementary algebra as $a + (-b) = a - b$ will appear in our notation as $a +_J (-b) = a -_J b$, and of course they require proof. However, before coming to this, let us consider a theorem which connects the operation $-$ with the function ν which was used to define the system $\mathcal{J}$.

THEOREM 11-4-4. *For any* $x \in P$, $\nu(x) = -x$.

Proof

1. Let x be any element of P.
2. $\nu(x) +_J x = 0$; by Definition 11-2-1.
3. $\nu(x) = 0 -_J x$; by line **2** and Definition 11-4-1.
4. $\nu(x) = -x$; by line **3** and Definition 11-4-3.

Thus we see that the operation $-$ is an *extension* of the function ν. The former may operate on *any* element of $\mathcal{J}$, the latter *only on elements of* P; but for elements in P, the two functions give the same value. For this reason there is no longer any need to use the function ν. However, in first defining the system $\mathcal{J}$, it would have been quite confusing to use $-$ instead of ν.

THEOREM 11-4-5. *For all* $x, y \in \mathcal{J}$,

(a) $x -_J y = x +_J (-y)$.
(b) $-x = (-1) \cdot_J x$.
(c) $(-x) \cdot_J (-y) = x \cdot_J y$.
(d) $-(-x) = x$.
(e) $-(x \cdot_J y) = (-x) \cdot_J y = x \cdot_J (-y)$.
(f) $-(x +_J y) = (-x) -_J y$.
(g) $-(x -_J y) = y -_J x$.
(h) $-0 = 0$.

Proof of Part (**a**)

▶▶**1.** Let x and y be any integers.
▶**2.** $x +_J (-y) = x +_J (0 -_J y)$; by E and Definition 11-4-3.
3. $x +_J (0 -_J y) = (x +_J 0) -_J y$; by Theorem 11-4-2 (**e**).
4. $x +_J 0 = x$; by definition of $+_J$ (Definition 11-2-1).
▶▶**5.** $x +_J (-y) = x -_J y$; by E from lines **2**, **3**, and **4**.

Proof of Part (**b**)

▶▶ **1.** Let x be any integer.
2. $x +_J (-1) \cdot_J x = 1 \cdot_J x +_J (-1) \cdot_J x$; by E and Theorem 11-2-3 (**vii**).

3. $1 \cdot_J x +_J (-1) \cdot_J x = [1 +_J (-1)] \cdot_J x$; by the right distributive law of $\cdot_J$ over $+_J$.
4. $1 +_J (-1) = 1 -_J 1$; by Part (**a**).
5. $= 0$; by Theorem 11-4-2 (**c**).
6. $x +_J (-1) \cdot_J x = 0 \cdot_J x$; by lines **2**, **3**, **4**, and **5** and E.
7. $= 0$; by the definition of $\cdot_J$ (Definition 11-2-1).

▶▶ 8. $x +_J (-1) \cdot_J x = 0$; by E applied to lines **6** and **7**.

9. $(-1) \cdot_J x = 0 -_J x$; by line **8** and Theorem 11-4-2.
10. $= -x$; by Definition 11-4-3.

▶▶ 11. $(-1) \cdot_J x = -x$; by lines **9** and **10**, and E.

Before proving the remaining parts of the theorem we shall state the following lemma:

LEMMA 11-4-5.1. $(-1) \cdot_J (-1) = 1$.

The proof of this lemma duplicates that of Lemma 11-3-1.2 Part (**b**), with appropriate notational changes, and will be left as an exercise for the reader.

Proof of Part (**c**)

▶▶ 1. Let x and y be any integers.

▶ 2. $(-x) \cdot_J (-y) = [(-1) \cdot_J x] \cdot_J [(-1) \cdot_J y]$; by E and Part (**b**).

3. $= [(-1) \cdot_J (-1)] \cdot_J (x \cdot_J y)$; by the commutative law and the associative law of $\cdot_J$ (Theorem 11-2-3).

▶ 4. $= 1 \cdot_J (x \cdot_J y)$; by E and Lemma 11-4-5.1.

5. $= x \cdot_J y$; by Theorem 11-2-3.

▶▶ 6. $(-x) \cdot_J (-y) = x \cdot_J y$; by E applied to lines **2** through **5**.

The proofs of the remaining parts are left as exercises for the reader.

EXERCISES

1. Prove part (**a**) of Theorem 11-4-2.
2. Prove part (**b**) of Theorem 11-4-2.
3. Prove part (**c**) of Theorem 11-4-2.
4. Prove part (**d**) of Theorem 11-4-2.
5. Prove part (**f**) of Theorem 11-4-2.
6. Prove part (**g**) of Theorem 11-4-2.
7. Prove part (**d**) of Theorem 11-4-5.
8. Prove part (**e**) of Theorem 11-4-5.
9. Prove part (**f**) of Theorem 11-4-5.
10. Prove part (**g**) of Theorem 11-4-5.
11. Prove part (**h**) of Theorem 11-4-5.
12. Show that for any $x, y \in \mathcal{J}$ we have $(x +_J y) \cdot_J (x -_J y) = x \cdot_J x -_J y \cdot_J y$.

5. *Order*

In our development of the positive integers the relation $<$ was defined (Definition 2-5-1) and many of its basic properties were derived. This notion was extended later to the set of natural numbers when $<_N$ was defined (Definition 8-4-1) and its properties discussed. We now extend this relation further to $\mathcal{J}$.

Actually, there are several equivalent but different ways in which we can define an extension $<_J$ for $<_N$. However, as we shall see below, if we wish the relation to obey certain laws similar to those which hold for $<$, there is only one relation which will serve.

One way in which we might try to define $<_J$ would be by imitating Definition 2-5-1. This might at first suggest the following: For any $x, y \in \mathcal{J}$, let $x <_J y$ hold if and only if there is an element $z \in \mathcal{J}$ such that $x +_J z = y$. However, by Theorem 11-2-5 (and 11-2-3) we see that for *any* $x, y \in \mathcal{J}$ there is an element $z \in \mathcal{J}$ such that $x +_J z = y$; hence if we used such a definition of $<_J$ we would find that *any* element of $\mathcal{J}$ is *less than any other*—which of course is not what we wish. However, we can modify the proposed definition in a manner suggested by Theorem 8-4-2 (**f**). Namely, we can specify that for any $x, y \in \mathcal{J}$ the relation $x <_J y$ should hold if and only if there is an element $z \in P$ such that $x +_J z = y$. This form of definition proves to be satisfactory. Of course in view of Theorem 11-4-2 (**g**) the unique element z of $\mathcal{J}$ such that $x +_J z = y$ is $y -_J x$, so an equivalent form of our definition is to specify that $x <_J y$ if and only if $(y -_J x) \in P$.

DEFINITION 11-5-1. *We let $<_J$ be the binary relation on $\mathcal{J}$ such that for all $x, y \in \mathcal{J}$, $x <_J y$ if and only if $y -_J x \in P$.*

We will now state and prove some of the interesting properties of $<_J$.

THEOREM 11-5-2.

(**a**) *$<_J$ is an extension of $<_N$. In other words, for all $x, y \in \mathcal{N}$ we have $x <_J y$ if and only if $x <_N y$.*

(**b**) *For all $x, y \in P$ we have $x <_J y$ if and only if $\nu(y) <_J \nu(x)$.*

(**c**) *For any $x \in \mathcal{N}$ and $y \in P$ we have $\nu(y) <_J x$.*

(**d**) *For no $x \in \mathcal{N}$ and $y \in P$ do we have $x <_J \nu(y)$.*

Before proving this theorem we note that the parts (**a**), (**b**), (**c**), and (**d**) effectively divide all ordered pairs of elements of $\mathcal{J}$ into four classes, and the theorem states, for each of these classes, exactly which of the ordered pairs are in the relation $<_J$. Thus part (**a**) states that an ordered pair of elements of $\mathcal{N}$ is in the relation $<_J$ just in case it is in the relation $<_N$; part (**b**) states the conditions under which an ordered pair of elements of P^- is in the relation $<_J$; parts (**c**) and (**d**) deal with ordered pairs of which one member is in N and the other in P^-. Actually, these four parts together could be used as an alternative form of definition of the relation $<_J$. This would provide a definition in the style of Definition 8-4-1 which was used for the relation $<_N$.

Proof of part (**a**).

▶▶ **1.** Let x, y be any two numbers in N such that $x <_J y$.
2. $y -_J x \in P$; by Definition 11-5-1 and line **1**.
▶ **3.** $y = x +_J u$ for some $u \in P$; by line **2** and Definition 11-4-1.
▶ **4.** $y = x +_N u$ for some $u \in P$; by lines **1** and **3** and the fact that $+_J$ is an extension of $+_N$ (Theorem 11-2-2).
▶▶ **5.** $x <_N y$; by line **4** and Theorem 8-4-2 (**f**).
6. If x, y are any elements of N such that $x <_J y$, then $x <_N y$; by the Deduction Theorem applied to lines **1** through **5**.

▶▶ **7.** Conversely, suppose x, y are elements of $\mathcal{J}$ such that $x <_N y$.
▶ **8.** $y = x +_N u$ for some $u \in P$; by line **7** and Theorem 8-4-2 (**f**).
9. $y = x +_J u$ for some $u \in P$; by line **8** and the fact that $+_J$ is an extension of $+_N$ (Theorem 11-2-2).
10. $y -_J x = u$; by line **9** and Theorem 11-4-2.
▶ **11.** $y -_J x \in P$; by lines **8** and **10**.
▶▶ **12.** $x <_J y$; by line **11** and Definition 11-5-1.
13. If x, y are elements of $\mathcal{J}$ such that $x <_N y$, then $x <_J y$; by the Deduction Theorem applied to lines **7** through **12**.
14. For any $x, y \in N$, $x <_J y$ if and only if $x <_N y$; by lines **6** and **13**.

We note that in view of Theorem 11-4-4, part (**b**) is a special case of Theorem 11-5-3 (**c**) below. Similarly, the proofs of parts (**c**) and (**d**) are obtained easily by combining part (**a**) with Theorem 11-5-3 below. Hence we shall not furnish separate proofs for parts (**b**), (**c**), and (**d**).

In the next theorem we collect some basic facts about the relation $<_J$.

THEOREM 11-5-3.

(**a**) *For all* $x, y, z \in \mathcal{J}$, $x +_J z <_J y +_J z$ *if and only if* $x <_J y$ (*the Additive Law for* $<_J$).
(**b**) *For all* $x, y, z \in \mathcal{J}$, $x -_J z <_J y -_J z$ *if and only if* $x <_J y$.
(**c**) *For all* $x, y \in \mathcal{J}$, $x <_J y$ *if and only if* $-y <_J -x$.
(**d**) *For all* $x, y, z \in \mathcal{J}$, *if* $x <_J y$ *and* $y <_J z$ *then* $x <_J z$ (*the Transitive Law of* $<_J$).
(**e**) *For all* $x, y, z \in \mathcal{J}$, *if* $0 <_J z$ *and* $x <_J y$ *then* $x \cdot_J z <_J y \cdot_J z$.

(**f**) *For all* $x, y, z \in J$, *if* $z <_J 0$ *and* $x <_J y$ *then* $y \cdot_J z <_J x \cdot_J z$.
(**g**) *For any* $x, y \in J$ *one and only one of the following relations holds:* $x <_J y$, *or* $x = y$, *or* $y <_J x$ *(the Trichotomy Law for* $<_J$*)*.

Proof of Part (**f**)

▶▶ **1.** Let x, y, z be any numbers in J such that $z <_J 0$ and $x <_J y$.
2. $y -_J x \in P$ and $0 -_J z \in P$; by line **1** and Definition 11-5-1.
3. $-z \in P$; by E, line **2**, and Definition 11-4-3.
▶ **4.** $(-z) \cdot_J (y -_J x) \in P$; by lines **2** and **3** since $\cdot_J$ is an extension of $\cdot$ (Definition 11-2-1).
5. $(-z) \cdot_J (y -_J x) = (-z) \cdot_J y -_J (-z) \cdot_J x$; by Theorem 11-4-2 (**f**).
6. $= -(z \cdot_J y) +_J \{-[-(z \cdot_J x)]\}$; by Theorem 11-4-5 (**a**) and (**e**).
7. $= -(z \cdot_J y) +_J (z \cdot_J x)$; by Theorem 11-4-5 (**d**).
8. $= (z \cdot_J x) -_J (z \cdot_J y)$; by the commutative law of $+_J$ (Theorem 11-2-3) and Theorem 11-4-5 (**a**).
▶ **9.** $(z \cdot_J x) -_J (z \cdot_J y) \in P$; by E from lines **4** to **8**.
▶▶ **10.** $y \cdot_J z <_J x \cdot_J z$; by line **9**, Definition 11-5-1, and the commutative law of $\cdot_J$ (Theorem 11-2-3).
11. For all $x, y, z \in J$, if $z <_J 0$ and $x <_J y$ then $y \cdot_J z <_J x \cdot_J z$; by the Deduction Theorem applied to lines **1** through **10**.

The proofs of the remaining parts will be left as exercises for the reader.

In the next theorem we show that $<_J$ is the only binary relation on J which is an extension of $<_N$ and satisfies condition 11-5-3 (**a**).

THEOREM 11-5-4. *Let* $<'$ *be any binary relation on* J *such that:*

(**a**) *For all* $x, y \in N$ *we have* $x <' y$ *if and only if* $x <_N y$;
(**b**) *For all* $x, y, z \in J$, *if* $x <' y$ *then* $x +_J z <' y +_J z$.

Then $<' = <_J$; *i.e., for all* $x, y \in J$, *we have* $x <' y$ *if and only if* $x <_J y$.

Proof

▶▶ **1.** Let x, y be any elements of J such that $x <_J y$.
2. $y -_J x \in P$; by line **1** and Definition 11-5-1.
3. $0 <_N y -_J x$; by line **2** and Definition 8-4-1.
4. $0 <' y -_J x$; by line **3** and (**a**).
5. $0 +_J x <' (y -_J x) +_J x$; by line **4** and (**b**).
▶▶ **6.** $x <' y$; by E from line **5**, Definition 11-2-1, and Theorems 11-4-2 (**d**) and 11-2-3.
7. If x, y are any elements of J such that $x <_J y$, then $x <' y$; by the Deduction Theorem applied to lines **1** through **6**.

▶▶ 8. Now let x, y be any elements of $\mathcal{J}$ such that $x <' y$.

9. $x +_J (-x) <' y +_J (-x)$;   by line 8 and (b).

10. $0 <' y -_J x$;   by line 9 and Theorems 11-4-5 (a) and 11-4-2 (c).

▶ 11. $y -_J x \in \mathcal{J}$;   by line 8 and Definition 11-4-1.

▶ 12. Either $y -_J x = 0$ or $y -_J x \in P$ or $y -_J x \in P^-$;   by line 11 and Definitions 8-2-1 and 11-2-1.

▶ 13. *Suppose* $y -_J x = 0$.

14. $0 <' 0$;   by E and lines 10 and 13.

15. $0 <_N 0$;   by line 14 and (a).

16. If $y -_J x = 0$ then $0 <_N 0$;   by the Deduction Theorem applied to lines 13 through 15.

17. *Not* $0 <_N 0$;   by Definition 8-4-1.

▶ 18. $y -_J x \neq 0$;   by lines 16 and 17.

▶ 19. *Suppose* $y -_J x \in P^-$.

20. $y -_J x = \nu(z)$ for some $z \in P$;   by line 19 and Definition 11-2-1.

21. $0 <' \nu(z)$;   by E applied to lines 10 and 20.

22. $0 +_J z <' \nu(z) +_J z$;   by line 21 and (b).

23. $z <' 0$;   by E, line 22, and Definition 11-2-1.

24. $z <_N 0$;   by lines 23 and 20 and (a).

25. If $y -_J x \in P^-$ then $z <_N 0$ for some $z \in P$;   by the Deduction Theorem applied to lines 19 through 20 and 24.

26. There is no $z \in P$ such that $z <_N 0$;   by Definition 8-4-1.

▶ 27. $y -_J x \notin P^-$;   by lines 25 and 26.

▶ 28. $y -_J x \in P$;   by lines 12, 18, and 27.

▶▶ 29. $x <_J y$;   by line 28 and Definition 11-5-1.

30. If x, y are any elements of $\mathcal{J}$ such that $x <' y$, then $x <_J y$;   by the Deduction Theorem applied to lines 8 through 29.

31. For all $x, y \in \mathcal{J}$ we have $x <' y$ if and only if $x <_J y$;   by lines 7 and 30.

EXERCISES

1. Prove part (a) of Theorem 11-5-3.

2. Prove part (b) of Theorem 11-5-3.

3. Prove part (c) of Theorem 11-5-3.

4. Prove part (d) of Theorem 11-5-3.

5. Prove part (e) of Theorem 11-5-3.

6. Prove part (g) of Theorem 11-5-3.

7.* Find some combination of conditions 11-5-3 (b) through 11-5-3 (g) for which you can show that $<_J$ is the only extension of $<_N$ (to a binary relation on $\mathcal{J}$) which satisfies these conditions.

6. Groups

So far in this chapter we have been largely concerned with a particular number system, $\mathcal{J}$, and have sought to discover and establish laws which express general propositions about the elements of this system. As in the case of our study of the number systems $\mathfrak{N}$ and $\mathcal{P}$, however, we wish to consider briefly the totality of different number systems which share some of these properties. In this way (as noted earlier) we are led to a more abstract, and hence more general, mathematical theory, with a much wider domain of application than the theory of the particular system $\mathcal{J}$.

Consider first, systems $\mathcal{G}$ of the form $\langle G, +_G\rangle$, where G may be any (non-empty) set of elements and $+_G$ any binary operation on G. Such a system $\mathcal{G}$ is called a *group* (cf. the informal discussion of a group in Chapter III, Section 3) if it satisfies the conditions given in the following definition.

DEFINITION 11-6-1. *A system $\langle G, +_G\rangle$ is a* **group** *if and only if*

(a) *For all $x, y, z \in G$ we have $(x +_G y) +_G z = x +_G (y +_G z)$, and*
(b) *For every $a, b \in G$ there is one and only one $x \in G$ such that $x +_G b = a$, and there is one and only one $y \in G$ such that $b +_G y = a$.*

The group $\langle G, +_G\rangle$ is called an **abelian** *group if $x +_G y = y +_G x$ for all $x, y \in G$.*

We see at once, by combining theorems 11-2-3 and 11-2-5, that the system obtained from $\mathcal{J}$ by "ignoring" the multiplication operation, i.e., the system $\langle \mathcal{J}, +_J\rangle$, is an example of a group—and indeed an abelian group. We shall state this in the following theorem, leaving the formal proof to the reader.

THEOREM 11-6-2. *The system $\langle \mathcal{J}, +_J\rangle$ is an abelian group.*

The system $\langle \mathcal{J}, +_J\rangle$ is but one example of a group. There are many other groups known to mathematicians, some of which are not at all "number systems" in the ordinary sense.

For example, consider a disk which can rotate in its plane about its center. Let R be the set of all possible rotations of the disk, and let $+_R$ be the binary operation on R defined as follows: If x, y are any elements of R, then $x +_R y$ is the rotation of the disk obtained by first carrying out the rotation x and then following it by the rotation y. Thus, if x is the clockwise rotation through 410° and y is the counterclockwise rotation through 680°, then $x +_R y$ is the counterclockwise rotation through 270°. It can easily be seen that the system $\langle R, +_R\rangle$ is an abelian group.

For another example, consider a sphere which is free to rotate in 3-dimensional space about its center. Let $\overline{R}$ be the set of all *these* rotations, and let $+_{\overline{R}}$ be the binary operation on $\overline{R}$ defined in a way completely analogous to the definition of $+_R$. Again it can be shown that the system $\langle R, +_{\overline{R}}\rangle$ is a group—but this time it is *not* abelian. To see that $+_{\overline{R}}$ is not commutative, consider two mutually perpendicular diameters of the sphere, which for convenience we shall call the N–S axis and the E–W axis. Now let x be a rotation of 180° about the N–S axis, and let y be a rotation of 90° about the

E–W axis. We claim that $x +_{\bar{R}} y \neq y +_{\bar{R}} x$. To see this, consider the "equator" to be the great circle (on the surface sphere) whose plane is perpendicular to the N–S axis, and let P be a point on the equator which is midway between the ends of the E–W axis. Then under the rotation $x +_{\bar{R}} y$ the point P is moved to one end of the N–S axis, but under the rotation $y +_{\bar{R}} x$ it is moved to the other end. Hence $x +_{\bar{R}} y$ and $y +_{\bar{R}} x$ cannot be the same rotation.

By comparing Definitions 11-6-1 and 3-3-1 we see that every group is a semi-group; but of course the converse is not true, for we know that the semi-group $\langle P, +\rangle$ is not a group (because there is no $x \in P$ such that $x + 1 = 1$, and so condition (**b**) of Definition 11-6-1 fails for the system $\langle P, +\rangle$). On the other hand we see that the semi-group $\langle P, +\rangle$ can be extended to the group $\langle \mathcal{J}, +_J\rangle$.

It may occur to us to wonder whether *every* semi-group can be extended to a group. That this is not so can be inferred from the following theorem.

THEOREM 11-6-3. *Every group is a cancellation semi-group. That is, if $\langle G, +_G\rangle$ is any group, then the left and right cancellation laws hold for $+_G$: For all $x, y, z \in G$,*

(**a**) *if $x +_G z = y +_G z$ then $x = y$; and*
(**b**) *if $z +_G x = z +_G y$ then $x = y$.*

Proof

The proofs of parts (**a**) and (**b**) are entirely similar, so we confine ourselves to the former.

1. Let $\langle G, +_G\rangle$ be a group and let x, y, z be any elements of G such that $x +_G z = y +_G z$.
2. $y +_G z = y +_G z$; by E.
3. There is one, and only one, $w \in G$, such that $w +_G z = y +_G z$; by line **1** and Definition 11-6-1 (**b**).
4. $x = y$; by lines **1**, **2**, and **3**.
5. If $\langle G, +_G\rangle$ is a group, and x, y, z are any elements of G such that $x +_G z = y +_G z$, then $x = y$; by the Deduction Theorem applied to lines **1** through **4**.

Let us reassure the reader that, in considering such general properties of groups as those stated in the above theorem (11-6-3), we have not abandoned our discussion of $\mathcal{J}$. *Any* properties of all groups will perforce be properties of the system $\langle \mathcal{J}, +_J\rangle$ (although the properties of $\langle \mathcal{J}, +_J\rangle$ are not necessarily shared by all groups). Thus it would be possible to give the following proof of part (**h**) of Theorem 11-4-2:

1. Let x, y, z be any elements of $\mathcal{J}$ such that $x -_J z = y -_J z$.

2. $x -_J z = x +_J (-z)$ and $y -_J z = y +_J (-z)$; by Theorem 11-4-5 (**a**).
3. $x +_J (-z) = y +_J (-z)$; by E from lines **1** and **2**.
4. $x = y$; by line **3** and Theorem 11-6-3 (**a**), since $\langle \mathcal{J}, +_J \rangle$ is a group.

This proof might suggest to us that there is much to be gained by considering general group properties. In further extensions of the number system we shall encounter other systems which are groups. Once the group property is established, we shall have at once a list of further properties which such a system must possess.

It follows from Theorem 11-6-3 that if we have any semi-group in which one of the cancellation laws fails, it cannot be extended to a group. For example, if $\oplus$ is the operation on P such that $x \oplus y = 1$ for all $y, x \in P$, then (as we have seen in Chapter III) the system $\langle P, \oplus \rangle$ is a semi-group; but it cannot be extended to a group, because in any extension of this system we will have the elements 1 and 2 such that $1 \oplus 1 = 1$ and $1 \oplus 2 = 1$ but $1 \neq 2$, so that condition (**b**) of Definition 11-6-1 will fail for this extension.

Having found that semi-groups which do not satisfy the cancellation laws cannot be extended to groups, we may wonder if every *cancellation* semi-group *can* be extended to a group. The answer, it turns out, is affirmative. But we shall have to wait until the next chapter before developing methods by which we can show this.

In the next theorem we establish the existence of certain kinds of elements in every group.

THEOREM 11-6-4. *In every group $\langle G, +_G \rangle$ there is a unique element e, called the* **null element** *of G, such that:*

(**a**) *$x +_G e = x$ and $e +_G x = x$ for all $x \in G$, and*

(**b**) *For every $y \in G$ there is a unique element $y' \in G$, called the* **inverse** *of y, such that $y' +_G y = e$ and $y +_G y' = e$.*

Proof

We give the proof of part (**a**) and leave the proof of part (**b**) as an exercise.

▶▶ 1. Let $\langle G, +_G \rangle$ be any group, and let a be any element of G.

▶▶ 2. There is an element e in G such that $e +_G a = a$; by line **1** and Definition 11-6-1 (**b**).

▶▶ 3. Let x be any element of G.

4. $(x +_G e) +_G a = x +_G (e +_G a)$; by line **1** and Definition 11-6-1 (**a**).

5. $(x +_G e) +_G a = x +_G a$; by E from lines **2** and **4**.

▶▶ 6. $x +_G e = x$; by lines **1** and **5** and Theorem 11-6-3.

7. There is an element $y \in G$ such that $a +_G y = x$; by line **1** and Definition 11-6-1 (**b**).

8. $e +_G x = e +_G (a +_G y)$; by E and line **7**.

9. $= (e +_G a) +_G y$; by line **1** and Definition 11-6-1 (**a**).

10. $= a +_G y$; by E and line **2**.

11. $= x$; by line **7**.

▶▶**12.** $e +_G x = x$; by E from lines **8** through **11**.

13. If x is any element of G, then $x +_G e = x$ and $e +_G x = x$; by the Deduction Theorem applied to lines **3** through **6** and **12**.

▶▶**14.** Suppose f is *any* element of G such that $x +_G f = x$ and $f +_G x = x$ for all $x \in G$.

15. $e +_G f = e$; by lines **13** and **14**.

16. $e +_G f = f$; by lines **13** and **14**.

▶▶**17.** $e = f$; by E and lines **15** and **16**.

18. If f is any element of G such that $x +_G f = x$ and $f +_G x = x$ for all $x \in G$, then $f = e$; by the Deduction Theorem applied to lines **14** through **17**.

19. There is one and only one element e of G such that $x +_G e = x$ and $e +_G x = x$ for all $x \in G$; by lines **13** and **18**.

It is not hard to show that any semi-group which contains an element e satisfying conditions (**a**) and (**b**) of Theorem 11-6-4 must be a group. We shall list this below as an exercise.

DEFINITION 11-6-5. *By an* **ordering** *for a group* $\langle G, +_G \rangle$ *we mean a binary relation* $<_G$ *on* G *such that:*

(**a**) *If* $x, y, z \in G$ *and* $x <_G y$ *and* $y <_G z$, *then* $x <_G z$.

(**b**) *For any* $x, y \in G$ *exactly one of the relations* $x <_G y$, $x = y$, $y <_G x$ *holds.*

(**c**) *For any* $x, y, z \in G$, *whenever* $x <_G y$, *then also* $x +_G z <_G y +_G z$ *and* $z +_G x <_G z +_G y$.

If $<_G$ *is an ordering relation for a group* $\langle G, +_G \rangle$ *and if* e *is the null element (cf. Theorem* 11-6-4) *of the group, we say that an element* x *is* **positive** *(with respect to* $<_G$) *if* $e <_G x$, *and* **negative** *if* $x <_G e$.

We see by Theorem 11-5-2 that $<_J$ is an ordering of the group $\langle \mathcal{J}, +_J \rangle$ and that the elements of P are the positive elements with respect to $<_J$.

The following theorem lists the basic properties of the set of positive elements of any group.

THEOREM 11-6-6. *Let* $\langle G, +_G \rangle$ *be any group, let* e *be its null element, and for each* $x \in G$ *let* x' *be the inverse of* x *(cf. Theorem* 11-6-4). *Suppose that* $<_G$ *is an ordering of G, and that H is the set of all elements of G which are positive with respect to* $<_G$. *Then*

(**a**) $e \notin H$;
(**b**) *if* $x, y \in H$ *then also* $x +_G y \in H$;
(**c**) *if x is any element of G other than e we have* $x \in H$ *if and only if* $x' \notin H$.

Outline of Proof

(**a**) If we had $e \in H$ then, by Definition 11-6-5, we would have $e <_G e$. But also $e = e$. This contradicts Definition 11-6-5 (**b**), and hence we cannot have $e \in H$.

(**b**) Suppose $x, y \in H$, so that $e <_G x$ and $e <_G y$. Combining the first of these inequalities with 11-6-5 (**c**) we get $e +_G y <_G x +_G y$; but $e +_G y = y$ (Theorem 11-6-4), and so $y <_G x +_G y$ by E. Now combining the last inequality with $e <_G y$, we see that $e <_G x +_G y$ (by 11-6-5 (**a**)), so that $x +_G y \in H$.

(**c**) Suppose x is any element of H. If x' were also in H then by part (**b**), just proved, we would have $x +_G x' \in H$. But $x +_G x' = e$ (11-6-4 (**b**)), so we would have $e \in H$. This contradicts part (**a**) proved above, and shows that if $x \in H$ then we cannot have $x' \in H$; i.e., if x $\in H$ then $x' \notin H$.

Now suppose that x is an element of G other than e, and that $x \notin H$. Then by 11-6-5 (**b**) we must have $x <_G e$. Hence $x +_G x' <_G e +_G x'$, by 11-6-5 (**c**). But $x +_G x' = e$ and $e +_G x' = x'$ (11-6-4), so we have $e <_G x'$, and this means that $x' \in H$. In other words, we have shown that if x is any element of G other than e, and if $x \notin H$, then $x' \in H$. It follows that if $x' \notin H$ then $x \in H$. Since we have shown above that if $x \in H$ then $x' \notin H$, the sketch of our proof of Theorem 11-6-6 is completed.

As we shall see in Exercise 5 below, whenever we find a group containing a set H of elements which satisfies conditions (**a**), (**b**), (**c**) of Theorem 11-6-6, we can always find an ordering of the group with respect to which the set of positive elements coincides with H.

EXERCISES

1. Does the system $\langle \mathcal{J}, \cdot_J \rangle$ form a group? Why, or why not?
2. Prove Theorem 11-6-2.
3. Prove Theorem 11-6-4 (**b**).
4.* Prove that the only orderings of the group $\langle \mathcal{J}, +_J \rangle$ are $<_J$ and $>_J$.
5.* Suppose that $\langle G, +_G \rangle$ is a group, and that H is a subset of G satisfying conditions (**a**), (**b**), and (**c**) of Theorem 11-6-6. Show that there is an ordering $<_G$ of this group such that an element $x \in G$ is positive (with respect to $<_G$) if and only if $x \in H$.

7. Rings

In considering the group properties of the system $\langle \mathcal{J}, +_J \rangle$, as we have in the last section, we have obviously disregarded one of the basic operations of $\mathcal{J}$, namely, the multiplication operation $\cdot_J$. Might there be some extension of the group concept to an abstract system involving *two* operations? In this section we shall consider such systems, known as *rings*, which share certain fundamental properties with our system $\mathcal{J}$. The precise definition of ring follows.

DEFINITION 11-7-1.   *Let G be any nonempty set and let $+_G$ and $\cdot_G$ be any binary operations on G. The system $\langle G, +_G, \cdot_G \rangle$ is called a* **ring** *if and only if the following conditions are satisfied:*

(a) $\langle G, +_G \rangle$ *is an abelian group.* (*See Definition* 11-6-1.)

(b) *The operation $\cdot_G$ is associative: For all $x, y, z \in G$, $(x \cdot_G y) \cdot_G z = x \cdot_G (y \cdot_G z)$.*

(c) *The operation $\cdot_G$ is left- and right-distributive over $+_G$: For all $x, y, z \in G$,*
$x \cdot_G (y +_G z) = x \cdot_G y +_G x \cdot_G z$ *and* $(y +_G z) \cdot_G x = y \cdot_G x +_G z \cdot_G x$.

The system $\langle G, +_G \rangle$ is called the **additive group** *of the ring $\langle G, +_G, \cdot_G \rangle$. The ring is called* **commutative** *if the operation $\cdot_G$ obeys the commutative law: For all $x, y \in G$, $x \cdot_G y = y \cdot_G x$. An element i of a ring is called an* **identity element** *if $x = i \cdot_G x = x \cdot_G i$ for all $x \in G$. A commutative ring with an identity element is called an* **integral domain** *if, whenever x, y are elements of G each different from the null element e of its additive group, then also $x \cdot_G y \neq e$.*

From Theorems 11-2-3 and 11-2-5 we see that our system $\langle \mathcal{J}, +_J, \cdot_J \rangle$ is a ring, and indeed a commutative ring; and from Definition 11-2-1 we see furthermore that $\mathcal{J}$ is an integral domain. The identity element is the number 1. For reference purposes we shall state this fact in the following theorem, leaving the formal proof for the reader.

THEOREM 11-7-2.   *The system $\mathcal{J} = \langle \mathcal{J}, +_J, \cdot_J \rangle$ is an integral domain (and thus a commutative ring). The null element of the additive group $\langle \mathcal{J}, +_J \rangle$ of this ring is the number* 0. *The identity element of the ring is the number* 1.

An example of a commutative ring without identity element is obtained by considering the set of all *even* integers (positive, negative, and 0), with the usual operations of addition and multiplication. An example of a commutative ring which has an identity element but which is not an integral domain may be obtained as follows. Take G to be the set of all ordered pairs $\langle x, y \rangle$ for all $x, y \in \mathcal{J}$. Let $+_G$ and $\cdot_G$ be the operations on G defined by the rules

$$\langle x_1, y_1 \rangle +_G \langle x_2, y_2 \rangle = \langle x_1 +_J x_2, \ y_1 +_J y_2 \rangle$$
$$\langle x_1, y_1 \rangle \cdot_G \langle x_2, y_2 \rangle = \langle x_1 \cdot_J x_2, \ y_1 \cdot_J y_2 \rangle$$

for all $x_1, y_1, x_2, y_2 \in \mathcal{J}$. Then it can be seen that $\langle G, +_G, \cdot_G\rangle$ is a commutative ring with the identity element $\langle 1, 1\rangle$, that $\langle 0, 0\rangle$ is the null element e of its additive group, but that the ring does not qualify as an integral domain because $\langle 0, 1\rangle \neq e$, $\langle 1, 0\rangle \neq e$, but $\langle 0, 1\rangle \cdot_G \langle 1, 0\rangle = e$.

There are many examples of noncommutative rings in mathematics, but the interesting ones are a little complicated to describe and so we shall not give such examples here in detail. However, for the reader who is familiar with matrix algebra we mention one example of a noncommutative ring. One can easily verify that if G is the set of $n \times n$ matrices with elements in $\mathcal{J}$, if $+_G$ is matrix addition and $\cdot_G$ is matrix multiplication, then the system $\mathfrak{M} = \langle G, +_G, \cdot_G\rangle$ is a ring with identity element. For example, if $n = 2$, the matrix $I_2 = \begin{bmatrix} 1 & 0 \\ 0 & 1 \end{bmatrix}$ is the identity element and $E_2 = \begin{bmatrix} 0 & 0 \\ 0 & 0 \end{bmatrix}$ is the null element. Furthermore, we see that $\cdot_G$ is not commutative, for if $A = \begin{bmatrix} 1 & 1 \\ 1 & 0 \end{bmatrix}$ and $B = \begin{bmatrix} 0 & 1 \\ 1 & 1 \end{bmatrix}$, then $A \cdot_G B = \begin{bmatrix} 1 & 2 \\ 0 & 1 \end{bmatrix}$, but $B \cdot_G A = \begin{bmatrix} 1 & 0 \\ 2 & 1 \end{bmatrix}$. Thus $A \cdot_G B \neq B \cdot_G A$. $\mathfrak{M}$ is *not* an integral domain, not only because it is noncommutative, but because $\begin{bmatrix} 0 & 1 \\ 0 & 0 \end{bmatrix} \cdot_G \begin{bmatrix} 0 & 1 \\ 0 & 0 \end{bmatrix} = E_2$ while $\begin{bmatrix} 0 & 1 \\ 0 & 0 \end{bmatrix} \neq E_2$.

We shall now consider some of the fundamental properties of rings—bearing in mind that these properties hold for *all* rings. Thus they hold not only for the ring $\langle \mathcal{J}, +_J, \cdot_J\rangle$ (actually many of these properties have already been established for this particular system), but also for further extensions of the number system which we shall encounter in the following chapters.

THEOREM 11-7-3. *Let $\mathcal{G} = \langle G, +_G, \cdot_G\rangle$ be any ring and let e be the null element of its additive group. Then:*

(a) *$x \cdot_G e = e$ and $e \cdot_G x = e$ for all $x \in G$.*

(b) *There can be at most one identity element in G.*

(c) *If the left cancellation law for $\cdot_G$ holds in $\mathcal{G}$, then whenever $x \neq e$ and $y \neq e$ we have $x \cdot_G y \neq e$; and conversely.*

Proof of Part **(a)**

▶▶ **1.** Let x be any element in G.

▶ **2.** $x \cdot_G e +_G x \cdot_G x = x \cdot_G (e +_G x)$; by line **1** and Definition 11-7-1 (**c**).

3. $= x \cdot_G x$; by Definition 11-7-1 (**a**) and Theorem 11-6-4 (**a**).

4. $= e +_G x \cdot_G x$; by Theorem 11-6-4 (**a**).

▶ **5.** $x \cdot_G e +_G x \cdot_G x = e +_G x \cdot_G x$; by E from lines **2**, **3**, and **4**.

▶▶ **6.** $x \cdot_G e = e$; from line **5** by Theorem 11-6-3 (**a**).
▶ **7.** $e \cdot_G x +_G x \cdot_G x = (e +_G x) \cdot_G x$; by line **1** and Definition 11-7-1 (**c**).
8. $= x \cdot_G x$; by Definition 11-7-1 (**a**), and E.
9. $= e +_G x \cdot_G x$; by Theorem 11-6-4 (**a**).
▶**10.** $e \cdot_G x +_G x \cdot_G x = e +_G x \cdot_G x$; by E from lines **7**, **8**, and **9**.
▶▶**11.** $e \cdot_G x = e$; from line **10** by Theorem 11-6-3 (**a**).
12. $x \cdot_G e = e$ and $e \cdot_G x = e$ for all $x \in G$; by the Deduction Theorem applied to lines **1** through **6** and **11**.

Proof of Part (**b**)

▶▶ **1.** Let i and j be any identity elements of G.
2. $i \cdot_G j = i$; by Definition 11-7-1 and line **1**
3. $i \cdot_G j = j$; by Definition 11-7-1 and line **1**.
▶▶ **4.** $i = j$; by E from lines **2** and **3**.
5. If i and j are any identity elements of G then $i = j$; by the Deduction Theorem applied to lines **1** through **4**.
6. There can be at most one identity element in G; from line **5**.

Proof of Part (**c**)

▶▶ **1.** Suppose the left cancellation law for $\cdot_G$ holds in G and $x \neq e$ and $y \neq e$.
▶ **2.** *Assume* that $x \cdot_G y = e$.
3. $x \cdot_G e = e$; by part (**a**).
4. $x \cdot_G y = x \cdot_G e$; by E from lines **2** and **3**.
5. $y = e$; from lines **1** and **4**.
6. $y \neq e$; by line **1**.
▶ **7.** If $x \cdot_G y = e$ then $y = e$ and $y \neq e$; by the Deduction Theorem applied to lines **2** through **5** and **6**.
▶ **8.** *Not* ($y = e$ and $y \neq e$); by E.
▶▶ **9.** $x \cdot_G y \neq e$; from lines **7** and **8**.
10. If the left cancellation law for $\cdot_G$ holds in G and $x \neq e$ and $y \neq e$, then $x \cdot_G y \neq e$; by the Deduction Theorem applied to lines **1** through **9**.

▶▶**11.** Suppose, conversely, that whenever $x \neq e$ and $y \neq e$ then $x \cdot_G y \neq e$.
▶▶**12.** Let x, y, z be any elements such that $x \neq e$ and $x \cdot_G y = x \cdot_G z$.
▶**13.** $x \cdot_G y +_G x \cdot_G y' = x \cdot_G z +_G x \cdot_G y'$; from line **12** by E.
14. $x \cdot_G (y +_G y') = x \cdot_G (z +_G y')$; from line **13** by Definition 11-7-1 (**c**).
15. $x \cdot_G (y +_G y') = x \cdot_G e$; by Theorem 11-6-4, and E.
16. $= e$; by Theorem 11-7-3, part (**a**).

▶17. $x \cdot_G (z +_G y') = e$; by E applied to lines **14, 15,** and **16.**
18. If $z +_G y' \neq e$ then $x \cdot_G (z +_G y') \neq e$; by lines **11** and **12.**
▶19. $z +_G y' = e$; by lines **17** and **18.**
20. $(z +_G y') +_G y = e +_G y$; by E applied to line **19.**
▶21. $= y$; by Theorem 11-6-4 (**a**).
22. $(z +_G y') +_G y = y$; by E applied to lines **20** and **21.**
23. $(z +_G y') +_G y = z +_G (y' +_G y)$; by Definition 11-6-1.
▶24. $= z$; by Theorem 11-6-4.
▶▶25. $y = z$; by E applied to lines **22, 23,** and **24.**
26. If x, y, z are any elements of G such that $x \neq e$ and $x \cdot_G y = x \cdot_G z$ then $y = z$; by the Deduction Theorem applied to lines **12** through **25.**
▶▶27. If for every $x, y \in G$ such that $x \neq e$ and $y \neq e$ we have $x \cdot_G y \neq e$, then the left cancellation law holds for $\cdot_G$; by the Deduction Theorem applied to lines **11** through **26.**

28. If the left cancellation law for $\cdot_G$ holds in $\mathcal{G}$, then whenever $x \neq e$ and $y \neq e$ we have $x \cdot_G y \neq e$; and conversely. By lines **10** and **27.**

We now turn to the concept of order in an arbitrary ring.

DEFINITION 11-7-4. *Let* $\mathcal{G} = \langle G, +_G, \cdot_G \rangle$ *be any ring, and let* e *be the null element of its additive group. By an* **ordering** *of* $\mathcal{G}$ *we mean a binary relation* $<_G$ *on* G *such that:*

(**a**) $<_G$ *is an ordering of the additive group* $\langle G, +_G \rangle$; (*See Definition* 11-6-5)
(**b**) *if* $x <_G y$ *and* $e <_G z$ *then* $x \cdot_G z <_G y \cdot_G z$ *and* $z \cdot_G x <_G z \cdot_G y$.

An element x *of* G *is called* **positive** *with respect to* $<_G$ *if* $e <_G x$; **negative** *if* $x <_G e$.

Another concept, and one which we shall use repeatedly in the following chapters, is that of *subtraction in a ring*. We shall define the subtraction operation (in the usual way) in terms of the (undefined) addition operation of the ring.

DEFINITION 11-7-5. *Let* $\mathcal{G} = \langle G, +_G, \cdot_G \rangle$ *be any ring having the additive group* $\langle G, +_G \rangle$. *We define* **subtraction in the ring** $\mathcal{G}$ (*in symbols* $-_G$) *to be the binary operation on* G *whose value for any ordered pair* $\langle x, y \rangle$ *of elements* x, y *of* G *is the unique element* $z \in G$ *such that* $z +_G y = x$. *We use the notation* $-_G \langle x, y \rangle = x -_G y$.

This definition must be justified by showing that there exists a unique element z having this property. That this is the case is immediately evident from the definition of a group (Definition 11-6-1 (**b**)).

The subtraction function in the ring $\mathcal{G}$ has been defined as a *binary* operation. However, just as we did in discussing subtraction in $\mathcal{J}$, we find it convenient to introduce a *negation operation* which acts on *single* elements of G (cf. Definition 11-4-3).

DEFINITION 11-7-6. *Let $\mathcal{G} = \langle G, +_G, \cdot_G \rangle$ be a ring, and let e be the null element of its additive group $\langle G, +_G \rangle$. The* **negation operation** $-_G$ *has G as its domain, and for any $x \in G$ we define $-_G x$ to be $e -_G x$.*

We shall now state a number of properties for rings which involve the subtraction and negation operations, as well as arbitrary ordering relations $<_G$.

THEOREM 11-7-7. *Let $\mathcal{G} = \langle G, +_G, \cdot_G \rangle$ be any ring, and let e be the null element of its additive group $\langle G, +_G \rangle$. Then, for any $x, y, z \in G$, we have:*

(a) $x -_G e = x$,
(b) $x -_G x = e$,
(c) $x +_G (y -_G x) = y$,
(d) $(x +_G y) -_G z = x +_G (y -_G z)$,
(e) $(x -_G y) +_G z = x -_G (y -_G z)$,
(f) $(x -_G y) -_G z = x -_G (y +_G z)$,
(g) $x \cdot_G (y -_G z) = x \cdot_G y -_G x \cdot_G z$;
$(y -_G z) \cdot_G x = y \cdot_G x -_G z \cdot_G x$,
(h) $x +_G y = z$ *if and only if* $y = z -_G x$,
(i) *If* $x -_G z = y -_G z$ *then* $x = y$,
(j) *If* $z -_G x = z -_G y$ *then* $x = y$,
(k) $-_G x$ *is the additive inverse of* x,
(l) $x -_G y = x +_G (-_G y)$,
(m) $(-_G x) \cdot_G (-_G y) = x \cdot_G y$,
(n) $(-_G x) \cdot_G y = x \cdot_G (-_G y) = -_G (x \cdot_G y)$,
(o) $-_G (-_G x) = x$,
(p) $-_G (x +_G y) = (-_G x) +_G (-_G y)$,
(q) $-_G (x -_G y) = y -_G x$,
(r) $-_G e = e$,
(s) $x +_G (-_G x) = e$.

THEOREM 11-7-8. *Let $\mathcal{G} = \langle G, +_G, \cdot_G \rangle$ be any ring with an identity element,* 1. *Then*

(a) $(-_G 1) \cdot_G (-_G 1) = 1$,
(b) *For any* $x \in G$, $(-_G x) = (-_G 1) \cdot_G x = x \cdot_G (-_G 1)$.

THEOREM 11-7-9. *Let $\mathcal{G} = \langle G, +_G, \cdot_G \rangle$ be any ring having an ordering $<_G$. Then for all $x, y, z \in G$,*

(**a**) *$x <_G y$ if and only if $-_G y <_G -_G x$.*
(**b**) *$x <_G y$ if and only if $x -_G z <_G y -_G z$.*
(**c**) *$x <_G y$ if and only if $z -_G y <_G z -_G x$.*
(**d**) *If x and y are both positive (i.e., $e <_G x$ and $e <_G y$, where e is the null element) or both negative (i.e., $x <_G e$ and $y <_G e$) then $x \cdot_G y$ is positive.*
(**e**) *If x is positive and y is negative, or vice versa, then $x \cdot_G y$ is negative.*

The proofs of many of the parts of these three theorems are completely similar to the corresponding parts of Theorems 11-4-2, 11-4-5, 11-4-5.1, and 11-5-3 and involve only notational changes. We shall present only the proof of Theorem 11-7-9 (**d**).

Proof

▶▶ **1.** Let $<_G$ be an ordering of a ring and let x, y both be positive with respect to $<_G$.
2. $e <_G x$ and $e <_G y$; by line **1** and Definition 11-7-4.
▶ **3.** $e \cdot_G y <_G x \cdot_G y$; by line **2** and Definition 11-7-4 (**b**).
4. $e \cdot_G y = e$; by Theorem 11-7-3 (**a**).
▶▶ **5.** $e <_G x \cdot_G y$; by E from lines **3** and **4**.
6. $x \cdot_G y$ is positive; by line **5** and Definition 11-7-4.
7. If x, y are both positive then $x \cdot_G y$ is positive; by the Deduction Theorem applied to lines **1** through **6**.
▶▶ **8.** Suppose x and y are both negative.
▶ **9.** x' and y' are both positive; by Theorem 11-6-6.
10. $x' \cdot_G y'$ is positive; by lines **1** and **7**.
11. $x' \cdot_G y' = x \cdot_G y$; by Theorem 11-7-7, parts (**k**) and (**m**).
▶▶ **12.** $x \cdot_G y$ is positive; by E from lines **10** and **11**.
13. If x, y are both negative then $x \cdot_G y$ is positive; by the Deduction Theorem applied to lines **8** through **12**.
14. If x, y are both positive or both negative then $x \cdot_G y$ is positive; by lines **7** and **13**.
15. If $<_G$ is an ordering of a ring, and if x, y are both positive, or both negative, with respect to $<_G$, then $x \cdot_G y$ is positive; by the Deduction Theorem applied to lines **1** through **14**.

Since $\mathcal{J}$ is a ring having both an identity element and an ordering relation $<_J$, the hypotheses for Theorems 11-7-7, 11-7-8 and 11-7-9 are met, and the system $\mathcal{J}$ must possess the properties listed in all three of these theorems.

EXERCISES

1. If a ring has an identity element it must be positive with respect to any ordering.
2.* The only ordering of the ring $\langle \mathcal{J}, +_J, \cdot_J \rangle$ is $<_J$.
3. If H is a set of elements of a ring satisfying 11-6-6 (**a**), (**b**), (**c**), and if the product of any two elements of H is also in H, then there is an ordering of the ring whose positive elements are exactly the elements of H.

4. An element w of a ring with identity element u is a *unit* if $w \cdot t = u$ for some t in the ring. Show that the set of all units form a (multiplicative) group.

5. Let G be any nonempty set and let $+_G$ and $\cdot_G$ be any binary operations on G. The system $\langle G, +_G, \cdot_G\rangle$ is called a *semi-ring* if and only if: (**a**) $\langle G, +_G\rangle$ is an abelian semi-group with a null element e (cf. Definitions 3-3-2 and 4-3-1), (**b**) the operation $\cdot_G$ is associative, and (**c**) the operation $\cdot_G$ is right and left distributive over $+_G$. Define the concept of an ordering for semi-rings.

6.* (**a**) Suppose $\langle G, +_G\rangle$ is a semi-group with a null element, e. (See Definition 4-3-1.) Suppose that $<_G$ is an ordering of this semi-group (see Definition 3-3-4) such that for all $x \in G$ other than $x = e$ we have $e <_G x$. Then the system $\langle G, +_G\rangle$ can be extended to a group $\langle G', +_G'\rangle$, and $<_G$ can be extended to an ordering $<_G'$ on this group. If $+_G$ is commutative, then so is $+_G'$.

(**b**) Similarly, suppose that $\mathcal{G} = \langle G, +_G, \cdot_G\rangle$ is a semi-ring, and that e is a null element for its additive semi-group (cf. Exercise 5, above). If $<_G$ is an ordering of this $\mathcal{G}$ semi-ring such that $e <_G x$ for all $x \in G$ except $x = e$, then $\mathcal{G}$ can be extended to a ring $\mathcal{G}' = \langle G', +_G', \cdot_G'\rangle$, and $<_G$ can be extended to an ordering of $\mathcal{G}'$. If $\mathcal{G}$ is commutative, so is $\mathcal{G}'$. (This problem may be solved along the lines of Definition 11-2-1 and Theorems 11-2-2 through 11-2-5.)

XII

Rational Numbers

1. Further Remarks on Integral Domains

Our motivation in extending the number system, first from $\mathcal{P} = \langle P, +, \cdot \rangle$ to $\mathcal{N} = \langle N, +_N, \cdot_N \rangle$ and, secondly, from $\mathcal{N}$ to $\mathcal{J} = \langle J, +_J, \cdot_J \rangle$, was in each case to produce a root of an equation whose coefficients lie in the system at hand, but which can not be solved in that system. In each of the extended systems we have seen that the equation which led us to make the extension becomes solvable, and in the second case we gained even more, finding that *every equation in $\mathcal{J}$ which involves addition* (but not multiplication) can be solved in $\mathcal{J}$.

In this chapter we shall extend the system $\mathcal{J}$ to a new system, $\mathcal{R}$, after observing that there are equations involving multiplication whose coefficients lie in $\mathcal{J}$, but which cannot be solved in $\mathcal{J}$. Before continuing, however, let us agree to drop the subscript "J" from the symbols "$+_J$" and "$\cdot_J$"; henceforth we will write simply "+" for the operation $+_J$ and "·" for the operation $\cdot_J$. Thus, for example, we shall write $\mathcal{J} = \langle J, +, \cdot \rangle$ for what heretofore has been designated by $\langle J, +_J, \cdot_J \rangle$. Since the operations $+_J$ and $\cdot_J$ in the system $\langle J, +_J, \cdot_J \rangle$ are actually extensions of the operations $+$ and $\cdot$ in $\langle N, +, \cdot \rangle$, and since there will be few references back to $\langle N, +, \cdot \rangle$ in this and future chapters, there will be little possibility for ambiguous interpretation of our new notation. Similarly we shall remove the subscript "J" from the symbols "$-_J$", "$<_J$" and "$\boldsymbol{-}_J$".

We have already seen that the system $\mathcal{J} = \langle J, +, \cdot \rangle$ is an example of a kind of number systems which algebraists call *integral domains.* (See Definition 11-7-1 and the observation which follows it.) Integral domains have been studied *abstractly* by mathematicians, and many interesting properties which hold for every one of them have been discovered. To say that integral domains have been studied abstractly means simply that the whole study is founded on the definition of integral domains (such as our Definition 11-7-1), without specifying any *particular* number system of this kind as basic, so that the theorems which are established hold for *all* integral domains. Of course, *not every integral domain has all the properties of our particular number system* $\mathcal{J} = \langle J, +, \cdot \rangle$. We can be assured only that an integral domain has *those* properties which are given in Definition 11-7-1, and those further properties which are derived solely from this definition (such as the cancellation laws of Theorem 11-6-3).

For example, if D is the set $\{0, 1, 2\}$, and if $+_D$ and $\cdot_D$ are the binary operations on D whose values are given by the tables

$+_D$	0	1	2
0	0	1	2
1	1	2	0
2	2	0	1

$\cdot_D$	0	1	2
0	0	0	0
1	0	1	2
2	0	2	1

then it can be shown, by checking the conditions in Definition 11-7-1, that the system $\mathfrak{D} = \langle D, +_D, \cdot_D \rangle$ is indeed an integral domain. Yet it can also be shown (See Exercise 1 below) that any attempt to define a relation $<_D$ on D, having properties of $<_J$ such as are given in Theorem 11-5-3, will fail, so that $\mathfrak{D}$ *does not* share with $\mathcal{J}$ the important property that *it can be ordered*. It is important, therefore, in dealing with integral domains, to remember both that $\langle J, +, \cdot \rangle$ is such a number system, and that there are many others, some of which are very different from $\mathcal{J}$ and have quite different properties.

EXERCISE

Show that $<_J$ (Definition 11-5-1) is an ordering of $\mathcal{J}$ (Definition 11-7-4) but that there is *no* ordering of $\mathfrak{D} = \langle D, +_D, \cdot_D \rangle$. Suggestion: *Assume* that there *is* an ordering relation $<_D$ for $\mathfrak{D}$, and derive a contradiction from this assumption by demonstrating that $0 <_D 0$ and *not* $0 <_D 0$.

2. *Fields*

Which equations, with coefficients in J, have solutions in J? We know that every *additive* equation of the form $a + x = b$, where a and b are any elements of J, has a unique solution x in J (Theorem 11-2-5). But what about *multiplicative* equations, of the form $a \cdot x = b$?

If $a = 0$, then *every* element of J will be a solution of $a \cdot x = b$ if $b = 0$, and *no* element of J will be a solution if $b \neq 0$. These facts follow immediately from Definition 11-2-1, and lead us to call equations of the form $0 \cdot x = b$, for any $b \in J$, *degenerate* multiplicative equations.

What about the *nondegenerate* multiplicative equations? Of course many of these have solutions in J. For example, we know that for every $b \in J$ the equation $1 \cdot x = b$ has a solution in J, namely, b. On the other hand many such equations do *not* have solutions in J; the following theorem provides an example.

THEOREM 12-2-1. *There is no $x \in \mathcal{J}$ such that $2 \cdot x = 1$.*

Proof

▶▶ **1.** Let x be any element in $\mathcal{J}$.
▶▶ **2.** Either $x \in P$ or $x = 0$, or $x \in P^-$; by line **1** and Definitions 11-2-1 and 8-2-1.

▶ **3.** *Case I. Suppose* $x \in P$.
▶ **4.** $2 \cdot x \neq 1$; by line **3** and Exercise 14, Chapter IV, Section 1.
5. If $x \in P$ then $2 \cdot x \neq 1$; by the Deduction Theorem applied to lines **3** and **4**.

▶ **6.** *Case II.* Suppose $x = 0$.
7. $2 \cdot x = 2 \cdot 0$; by E from line **6**.
8. $= 0$; by Definition 11-2-1.
9. $2 \cdot x = 0$; by E from lines **8** and **7**.
10. $0 \neq 1$; by Definition 8-2-1.
▶ **11.** $2 \cdot x \neq 1$; by E from lines **9** and **10**.
12. If $x = 0$ then $2 \cdot x \neq 1$; by the Deduction Theorem applied to lines **6** through **11**.

▶ **13.** *Case III.* Suppose $x \in P^-$.
14. There is some number $u \in P$ such that $x = \nu(u)$; by line **13** and Definition 11-2-1.
15. $2 \cdot x = 2 \cdot \nu(u)$; by E from line **14**.
16. $= \nu(2 \cdot u)$; by Definition 11-2-1.
17. $2 \cdot x = \nu(2 \cdot u)$; by E from lines **16** and **15**.
18. $\nu(2 \cdot u) \in P^-$; by line **14** and Definition 11-2-1.
19. $2 \cdot x \in P^-$; by E from lines **17** and **18**.
20. $1 \notin P^-$; by Definition 11-2-1.
▶ **21.** $2 \cdot x \neq 1$; by E from lines **19** and **20**.
22. If $x \in P^-$ then $2 \cdot x \neq 1$; by the Deduction Theorem applied to lines **13** through **21**.

▶▶ **23.** For all $x \in \mathcal{J}$ we have $2 \cdot x \neq 1$; by lines **1**, **2**, **5**, **12**, and **22**.
24. There is no $x \in \mathcal{J}$ such that $2 \cdot x = 1$; by line **23**.

One question is immediately suggested by Theorem 12-2-1: Is it possible to *extend* $\mathcal{G}$ to some new number system $\mathcal{R} = \langle R, +_R, \cdot_R \rangle$ which, like $\mathcal{G}$, obeys all the laws required of an integral domain, but such that the equation $2 \cdot x = 1$ has a solution in $\mathcal{R}$, and more generally such that *every* nondegenerate multiplicative equation $a \cdot_R x = b$ has a solution in $\mathcal{R}$? Since the reader has already survived two extensions in which the answer to such questions was "yes," he will suspect that our question is loaded—and he will be right. Indeed, as we shall see, such an extension can be found.

Any integral domain $\mathcal{R}$ in which all nondegenerate multiplicative equations have solutions is called a *field*, and such number systems have been studied abstractly, and in great detail, by modern algebraists.

A precise definition of fields follows.

DEFINITION 12-2-2. *By a* **field** *we mean a number system* $\mathcal{Q} = \langle Q, +_Q, \cdot_Q \rangle$ *such that:*

(i) *$\mathcal{Q}$ is an integral domain, and*

(ii) *If a, b are any elements of Q such that $a \neq e$, where e is the null element of the additive group $\langle Q, +_Q \rangle$, then there is an element x in Q such that $a \cdot_Q x = b$.*

(For terms employed in this definition see Chapter XI, Definition 11-7-1.)

In addition to such familiar fields as the rational number system studied in grade school, the reader can easily verify that the system $\langle D, +_D, \cdot_D \rangle$ of the previous section is a field—and indeed there are many other examples known which are quite different from the number systems usually studied in school.

What we are about to undertake is an extension of our particular integral domain $\mathcal{J}$ to a system $\mathcal{R} = \langle R, +_R, \cdot_R \rangle$ which will turn out to be a field. In so doing we shall not use any properties of $\mathcal{J}$ except those properties, listed in Definition 11-7-1 and Theorems 11-7-3, 11-7-7 and 11-7-8, which hold for *every* integral domain. Hence, in effect, we shall be showing how, starting from *any* integral domain, we can construct an extension which is a field.

In each extension of a number system which we have undertaken so far, we have relied heavily on our intuitive knowledge of the extension undertaken in order to obtain our definitions of the extended operations. But we also pointed out that, even if we had had no prior intuitive knowledge of the system we were constructing, we would have been led to define the same operations by the nature of the problem. While we could follow a similar pattern in the present case, we shall in fact *not* rely on our intuitive idea of the rational numbers acquired in grade school or in high school. Instead we will analyse the properties which an *arbitrary* number system must have in order to solve our problem, and then we will use this information to construct the desired extension of $\mathcal{J}$. Thus there will first be an analysis and then a synthesis.

EXERCISES

1. Show that if a is an element of J such that $a \neq 1, -1$, then the equation $a \cdot x = 1$ has no solution $x \in J$.

2. Let a, b be any elements of J. Show that we have $a + y = b$ or $b + y = a$ for some $y \in N$.

3. *Analysis of the Problem*

The question which concerns us is this: Is it possible to extend $\mathcal{J}$ to some new number system $\mathcal{R} = \langle R, +_R, \cdot_R \rangle$ which is an integral domain, and in which every equation $a \cdot_R x = b$, where $a, b \in R$ and $a \neq 0$, has a solution? In view of the definition of a field (12-2-2), this problem may be formulated concisely as:

PROBLEM R. *Can we find a field $\mathcal{R}$ which is an extension of $\mathcal{J}$?*

In order to answer this question let us begin by supposing that we have somehow found a system $\mathcal{Q}$ with many of the required properties, and let us see what information we can obtain about the way in which one calculates with its operations.

HYPOTHESIS Q (HQ): *Let us* ***assume*** *that $\mathcal{Q} = \langle Q, +_Q, \cdot_Q \rangle$ is a number system such that*

HQ(i) *$\mathcal{Q}$ is an extension of $\mathcal{J}$, (cf. Chapter VIII, Section 1)*

HQ(ii) *the operation $\cdot_Q$ is associative and commutative, and is left distributive over $+_Q$;*

HQ(iii) *if we have $a \in J$, $x, y \in Q$, and $a \neq 0$, and if $a \cdot_Q x = a \cdot_Q y$, then we must have $x = y$;*

HQ(iv) *for every $a, b \in J$ such that $a \neq 0$ there is an $x \in Q$ such that $a \cdot_Q x = b$.*

Notice that $\mathcal{Q}$ is not assumed to be a field (and hence is not assumed to be a solution of problem R) for three reasons. First, the system $\langle Q, +_Q \rangle$ is not assumed to be a commutative group, since we have not supposed that $+_Q$ is commutative or associative, or that every additive equation has a solution in Q—unique or otherwise. (These properties are subsumed under Definition 12-2-2 (**i**).) Second, the modified cancellation law for $\cdot_Q$ is not assumed in full generality, for we assume that only nonzero *elements of J* may be "cancelled" (HQ(**iii**)). (To satisfy Definition 12-2-2 (**i**), every nonzero *element of Q* would have to be "cancellable.") And third, we have not assumed that for *every* $a, b \in Q$ such that $a \neq 0$ there is a unique solution of $a \cdot_Q x = b$ in Q, but only for $a, b \in J$ (HQ(**iv**)).

Nevertheless, despite the fact that $\mathcal{Q}$ itself is not assumed to be a solution to problem R, we shall see that we can find out enough about how to compute with its operations to enable us to construct a number system which *does* solve Problem R.

To begin with, we notice that from HQ(**iii**) and (**iv**) we can infer that for every $a, b \in \mathcal{J}$ such that $a \neq 0$ there is a *unique* $x \in Q$ satisfying $a \cdot_Q x = b$. For if we have both $a \cdot_Q x_1 = b$ and $a \cdot_Q x_2 = b$ then of course $a \cdot_Q x_1 = a \cdot_Q x_2$ by E, and so by **(iii)** we get $x_1 = x_2$. Thus we have shown:

PROPOSITION Q1. *For every $a, b \in \mathcal{J}$ such that $a \neq 0$ there is a unique $x \in Q$ satisfying $a \cdot_Q x = b$.*

The following definition is now justified.

DEFINITION Q2. *We shall denote by $\rho(a, b)$ the unique x in Q such that $a \cdot_Q x = b$, where a, b are any given elements in $\mathcal{J}$ such that $a \neq 0$.[1] Also we shall let Q^* be the set of **all** elements $\rho(a, b)$ of Q, for **all** $a, b \in \mathcal{J}$ such that $a \neq 0$.*

We now continue our analysis by investigating the properties of the operations $+_Q$ and $\cdot_Q$ *when restricted to elements of Q^**. We shall find that from this restricted investigation we can get enough clues for the contruction of the sought-for solution to Problem R.

Now, although we are not relying on intuitive knowledge of the rational numbers, it is difficult to keep a reader who has such knowledge from using it. Thus $\rho(a, b)$, the unique solution of $a \cdot_Q x = b$, certainly suggests b/a. Hence most readers will anticipate what is coming. However, it is of interest to keep in mind that a sufficiently intelligent being from outer (or inner!) space, who might not possess this intuitive knowledge, would be able to carry on our analysis and discover these properties in a purely logical manner.

Let us start by asking ourselves under what conditions two multiplicative equations have the *same* solution: I.e., we ask under what conditions will the solutions of $a \cdot_Q x = b$ and $c \cdot_Q x = d$ be equal? We assume here, of course, that $a, b, c, d \in \mathcal{J}$ and that $a, c \neq 0$. Thus another way of phrasing our question is simply this: Under what conditions does $\rho(a, b) = \rho(c, d)$?

Let $x = \rho(a, b)$ and $y = \rho(c, d)$. Then we have $a \cdot_Q x = b$ and $c \cdot_Q y = d$, from the definition of ρ (Definition Q2), and it follows by E that

$$c \cdot_Q (a \cdot_Q x) = c \cdot_Q b$$

and

$$a \cdot_Q (c \cdot_Q y) = a \cdot_Q d.$$

Now, on using the associative and commutative properties of $\cdot_Q$ assumed in HQ(**ii**), we infer that $(a \cdot_Q c) \cdot_Q x = b \cdot_Q c$ and $(a \cdot_Q c) \cdot_Q y = a \cdot_Q d$; and since $a, b, c, d \in \mathcal{J}$ we see by HQ(**i**) that $a \cdot_Q c = a \cdot c$, $b \cdot_Q c = b \cdot c$, and $a \cdot_Q d = a \cdot d$, so that we can write our equations in the form

$$(*) \qquad \begin{aligned} (a \cdot c) \cdot_Q x &= b \cdot c \\ (a \cdot c) \cdot_Q y &= a \cdot d. \end{aligned}$$

[1] The symbol "ρ" is the Greek letter rho.

Now if $\rho(a, b) = \rho(c, d)$, i.e., if $x = y$, we see from equations (*) that $a \cdot d = b \cdot c$. Conversely, if $a \cdot d = b \cdot c$ we obtain $(a \cdot c) \cdot_Q x = (a \cdot c) \cdot_Q y$ from (*), and hence $x = y$ by HQ(**iii**). (We can apply HQ(**iii**) since $a \cdot c \neq 0$, as follows from our assumption that a and $c \neq 0$, and from the definition of $\cdot$ (Definition 11-2-1)). Thus we have outlined a proof of the following result.

PROPOSITION Q3. *If a, b, c, d are any elements of $\mathcal{J}$ such that $a, c \neq 0$, then $\rho(a, b) = \rho(c, d)$ if and only if $a \cdot d = b \cdot c$.*

It is perhaps worthwhile to give also a detailed proof of this proposition.

Proof of Proposition Q3

▶▶ **1.** Let a, b, c, d be any elements of $\mathcal{J}$ such that $a, c \neq 0$.

▶ **2.** There exist unique elements $x, y \in Q$ such that $a \cdot_Q x = b$ and $c \cdot_Q y = d$; by line **1** and Proposition Q1.

▶ **3.** $x = \rho(a, b)$ and $y = \rho(c, d)$; by line **2** and the definition of ρ (Definition Q2).

4. $c \cdot_Q (a \cdot_Q x) = c \cdot_Q b$ and $a \cdot_Q (c \cdot_Q y) = a \cdot_Q d$; by E from line **2**.

5. $(a \cdot_Q c) \cdot_Q x = b \cdot_Q c$ and $(a \cdot_Q c) \cdot_Q y = a \cdot_Q d$; by E and by HQ(**ii**) from line **4**.

6. $a \cdot_Q c = a \cdot c$, $b \cdot_Q c = b \cdot c$, and $a \cdot_Q d = a \cdot d$; by line **1** and HQ(**i**).

▶ **7.** $(a \cdot c) \cdot_Q x = b \cdot c$ and $(a \cdot c) \cdot_Q y = a \cdot d$; by E from lines **5** and **6**.

▶▶ **8.** Suppose $\rho(a, b) = \rho(c, d)$.

9. $x = y$; by E, from lines **3** and **8**.

10. $(a \cdot c) \cdot_Q x = (a \cdot c) \cdot_Q y$; by E from line **9**.

▶▶ **11.** $a \cdot d = b \cdot c$; by E from lines **7** and **10**.

12. If $\rho(a, b) = \rho(c, d)$ then $a \cdot d = b \cdot c$; by the Deduction Theorem applied to lines **8** through **11**.

▶▶ **13.** Suppose $a \cdot d = b \cdot c$.

14. $(a \cdot c) \cdot_Q x = (a \cdot c) \cdot_Q y$; by E from lines **7** and **13**.

15. $(a \cdot c) \in \mathcal{J}$ and $a \cdot c \neq 0$; by line **1** and the definition of $\cdot$ (Definition 11-2-1).

16. $x = y$; by lines **14**, **15**, and HQ(**iii**).

▶▶ **17.** $\rho(a, b) = \rho(c, d)$; by E from lines **3** and **16**.

18. If $a \cdot d = b \cdot c$, then $\rho(a, b) = \rho(c, d)$; by the Deduction Theorem applied to lines **13** through **17**.

19. $\rho(a, b) = \rho(c, d)$ if and only if $a \cdot d = b \cdot c$; by logic from lines **12** and **18**.

20. Proposition Q3 now follows by applying the Deduction Theorem to lines **1** through **19**.

What Proposition Q3 accomplishes is to reduce the problem of determining the equality of any two given objects *in* Q^*, to the problem of determining whether a certain pair of objects *in* J are equal.

Now let us tackle the problem of learning how to compute with $\cdot_Q$ in Q^*. Specifically, if $x = \rho(a, b)$ and $y = \rho(c, d)$ what is $x \cdot_Q y$? To answer this, we must somehow proceed from $a \cdot_Q x = b$ and $c \cdot_Q x = d$, which hold by our choice of x, y and our definition of ρ, to an equation of the form $p \cdot_Q (x \cdot_Q y) = q$, where $p, q \in J$ and $p \neq 0$; for then we will know that $x \cdot_Q y = \rho(p, q)$ by another appeal to the definition of ρ.

The procedure is evident. By combining $a \cdot_Q x = b$ and $c \cdot_Q y = d$ we get $(a \cdot_Q c) \cdot_Q (x \cdot_Q y) = b \cdot_Q d$, using property HQ(**ii**); and then from HQ(**i**) we obtain $(a \cdot c) \cdot_Q (x \cdot_Q y) = b \cdot d$. As in the proof of Proposition Q3 we infer from our assumptions $a \neq 0$ and $c \neq 0$, and from Definition 11-2-1, that $a \cdot c \neq 0$; and thus, by definition of ρ (Definition Q2), we see that $x \cdot_Q y = \rho(a \cdot c, b \cdot d)$. Recalling what x and y are, we observe that we have indicated how to establish

PROPOSITION Q4. *For any* $a, b, c, d \in J$ *such that* $a, c \neq 0$ *we have* $\rho(a, b) \cdot_Q \rho(c, d) = \rho(a \cdot c, b \cdot d)$.

Again, let us give a detailed proof of this proposition.

Proof

▶▶ **1.** Let a, b, c, d be any elements of J such that $a, c \neq 0$.

▶ **2.** There exist unique elements $x, y \in Q$ such that $a \cdot_Q x = b$ and $c \cdot_Q y = d$; by Proposition Q1.

▶ **3.** $x = \rho(a, b)$ and $y = \rho(c, d)$; by the definition of ρ (Definition Q2).

▶ **4.** $(a \cdot_Q x) \cdot_Q (c \cdot_Q y) = b \cdot_Q d$; by E from line **2**.

5. $(a \cdot_Q c) \cdot_Q (x \cdot_Q y) = b \cdot_Q d$; from line **4** by E and HQ(**ii**).

6. $a \cdot_Q c = a \cdot c$ and $b \cdot_Q d = b \cdot d$; by HQ(**i**).

▶ **7.** $(a \cdot c) \cdot_Q (x \cdot_Q y) = b \cdot d$; by E from lines **5** and **6**.

8. $(a \cdot c) \in J$ and $a \cdot c \neq 0$; by line **1** and the definition of $\cdot$ (Definition 11-2-1).

▶ **9.** $x \cdot_Q y = \rho(a \cdot c, b \cdot d)$; by lines **7** and **8** and Definition Q2.

▶▶ **10.** $\rho(a, b) \cdot_Q \rho(c, d) = \rho(a \cdot c, b \cdot d)$; by E from lines **3** and **9**.

11. The proposition now follows by applying the Deduction Theorem to lines **1** through **10**.

Having learned, from Proposition Q4, how to multiply any two elements $\rho(a, b)$ and $\rho(c, d)$ of Q^*, we turn now to the question of adding such elements. In order to discover a rule for computing $\rho(a, b) +_Q \rho(c, d)$ we must seek to obtain an equation of the form $p \cdot_Q (x +_Q y) = q$ from given equations $a \cdot_Q x = b$ and $c \cdot_Q y = d$. This can be done by first deriving

$(a \cdot c) \cdot_Q x = b \cdot c$ and $(a \cdot c) \cdot_Q y = a \cdot d$, as in the proof of Proposition Q3, and then "adding these equations," as we may by properties HQ (**i**) and (**ii**), to get $(a \cdot c) \cdot_Q (x +_Q y) = a \cdot d + b \cdot c$. As before, $a \cdot c \neq 0$, and so $x +_Q y = \rho(a \cdot c, a \cdot d + b \cdot c)$. The argument thus sketched indicates that the following rule holds in Q^*.

PROPOSITION Q5. *For any* $a, b, c, d \in \mathcal{J}$ *such that* $a, c \neq 0$ *we have* $\rho(a, b) +_Q \rho(c, d) = \rho(a \cdot c, a \cdot d + b \cdot c)$.

We have outlined a proof of this proposition. Only outlines of proofs for this and the remaining propositions of this section will be given. The reader will be asked to furnish detailed proofs as exercises.

Notice that Propositions Q4 and Q5 together show that Q^* is *closed* under $+_Q$ and $\cdot_Q$. That is, whenever we apply one of these two operations to *elements of* Q the resulting element of Q is also in Q^*.

Now by Theorem 12-2-1 we know that not *all* equations of the form $a \cdot x = b$, where $a, b \in \mathcal{J}$, and $a \neq 0$, have a solution x which is in $\mathcal{J}$. On the other hand we have observed that *certain* ones do; in particular, any equation of the form $1 \cdot x = b$ has the unique solution b. The latter observation, when combined with the definition of ρ (Definition Q2), establishes the following rule of computation for Q^*.

PROPOSITION Q6. *For any* $b \in \mathcal{J}$ *we have* $\rho(1, b) = b$.

From Proposition Q6 and Definition Q2 we see that $\mathcal{J}$ is a subset of Q^*, since every element b of $\mathcal{J}$ is one of the elements $\rho(a, b)$ which were put into Q^*. Furthermore, by HQ(**i**) we know that $+_Q$ and $\cdot_Q$ are extensions of the operations $+$ and $\cdot$ respectively. Thus, if we denote by "$+_{Q^*}$" and "$\cdot_{Q^*}$" the restrictions of the operations $+_Q$ and $\cdot_Q$, respectively, to the subset Q^* of Q, we see that $+_{Q^*}$ and $\cdot_{Q^*}$ will themselves be extensions of $+$ and $\cdot$. Hence we get the following result.

PROPOSITION Q7. *The number system* $\langle Q^*, +_{Q^*}, \cdot_{Q^*}\rangle$ *is an extension of the system* $\mathfrak{J} = \langle \mathcal{J}, +, \cdot\rangle$.

Which algebraic laws do the operations $+_{Q^*}$ and $\cdot_{Q^*}$ satisfy? It turns out that all of the laws we have been studying for these operations hold. For example, we have

PROPOSITION Q8. *Both* $+_{Q^*}$ *and* $\cdot_{Q^*}$ *are commutative and associative, and the latter distributes over the former.*

Of course the three laws involving $\cdot_{Q^*}$ follow immediately from HQ(**ii**) and the definition of $\cdot_{Q^*}$. Each of the other two laws may be proved simply from the known properties of the system $\mathfrak{Q}$, by using Proposition Q5. For example, to establish the associative law for $+_{Q^*}$, let $\rho(x, y)$, $\rho(z, t)$, and $\rho(u, v)$ be any elements of Q^*, so that $x, y, z, t, u, v \in \mathcal{J}$ and $x, z, u \neq 0$. Then we find:

$$\rho(x, y) +_{Q^*} \rho(z, t) = \rho(x \cdot z,\ x \cdot t + y \cdot z); \quad \text{by Proposition Q5}$$

and so

$$(\dagger) \qquad [\rho(x, y) +_{Q^*} \rho(z, t)] +_{Q^*} \rho(u, v) = \rho((x \cdot z) \cdot u,\ (x \cdot z) \cdot v + (x \cdot t + y \cdot z) \cdot u),$$

by a second application of Proposition Q5. Similarly, we find that

$$(\dagger\dagger) \qquad \rho(x, y) +_{Q^*} [\rho(z, t) +_{Q^*} \rho(u, v)] = \rho(x \cdot (z \cdot u),\ x \cdot (z \cdot v + t \cdot u) + y \cdot (z \cdot u)).$$

By comparing equations (†) and (††) we see that in order to infer the desired equation

$$[\rho(x, y) +_{Q^*} \rho(z, t)] +_{Q^*} \rho(u, v) = \rho(x, y) +_{Q^*} [\rho(z, t) +_{Q^*} \rho(u, v)],$$

it suffices to show that

$$(x \cdot z) \cdot u = x \cdot (z \cdot u)$$

and

$$(x \cdot z) \cdot v + (x \cdot t + y \cdot z) \cdot u = x \cdot (z \cdot v + t \cdot u) + y \cdot (z \cdot u).$$

But these are immediate from Theorem 11-2-3.

PROPOSITION Q9. *The system* $\mathcal{Q}^* = \langle Q^*, +_{Q^*}, \cdot_{Q^*} \rangle$ *is a commutative ring.*

By comparing Proposition Q8 with Definition 11-7-1 we see that to establish Proposition Q9 it remains only to show that every additive equation with coefficients in Q^* has a unique solution in Q^*. To show this, let $\rho(a, b)$ and $\rho(c, d)$ be any elements of Q^*, so that $a, b, c, d \in \mathcal{J}$ and $a, c \neq 0$. Our object is to show that there is one and only one element $\rho(x, y)$ of Q^* which satisfies the equation

$$\rho(x, y) +_{Q^*} \rho(a, b) = \rho(c, d).$$

Using Proposition Q5 we see that this is equivalent to showing that there is one and only one $\rho(x, y) \in Q^*$ such that

$$\rho(x \cdot a,\ x \cdot b + y \cdot a) = \rho(c, d),$$

or equivalently, by Proposition Q3, such that

$$(x \cdot a) \cdot d = (x \cdot b + y \cdot a) \cdot c.$$

Finally, using Theorems 11-2-3 and 11-4-2 we see that we must show the existence of a unique $\rho(x, y) \in Q^*$ such that

$$x \cdot (a \cdot d - b \cdot c) = y \cdot (a \cdot c).$$

Now to obtain *one* such $\rho(x,y)$ is easy: We simply take $x_0 = a \cdot c$ and $y_0 = a \cdot d - b \cdot c$, and obtain the desired equation $x_0 \cdot (a \cdot d - b \cdot c) = y_0 \cdot (a \cdot c)$ by the commutative law for $\cdot$ (Theorem 11-2-3). (Notice that $x_0 \neq 0$ by our hypothesis that $a, c \neq 0$, so that $\rho(x_0, y_0)$ is defined.)

To see that there is *only one* such $\rho(x,y)$, we observe that if $\rho(x,y)$ is *any* element of Q^* such that $x \cdot (a \cdot d - b \cdot c) = y \cdot (a \cdot c)$ then by Proposition Q3 we have

$$\rho(x,y) = \rho(a \cdot c,\ a \cdot d - b \cdot c),$$

and hence $\rho(x,y) = \rho(x_0, y_0)$ by choice of x_0 and y_0 above.

PROPOSITION Q10. *The system* $\mathfrak{Q}^* = \langle Q^*, +_{Q^*}, \cdot_{Q^*}\rangle$ *is an integral domain.*

By comparing Proposition Q9 with Definition 11-7-1 we see that to establish Proposition Q10 we need only show that the commutative ring $\langle Q^*, +_{Q^*}, \cdot_{Q^*}\rangle$ possesses an identity element, that 0 is the null element of Q^*, and that if $\rho(a, b)$ and $\rho(c, d)$ are any elements of Q each different from 0, then $\rho(a, b) \cdot_{Q^*} \rho(c, d) \neq 0$.

In fact, we shall show that the element 1 is an identity element for Q^*. By Proposition Q6 we have that $1 = \rho(1, 1)$. Hence if $\rho(x, y)$ is any element of Q^*, we have $\rho(x,y) \cdot_Q 1 = \rho(x,y) \cdot_{Q^*} \rho(1, 1) = \rho(x \cdot 1, y \cdot 1) = \rho(x, y)$ by Proposition Q4 and Theorem 11-2-3. Similarly it can be shown that $1 \cdot_{Q^*} \rho(x,y) = \rho(x,y)$. Hence 1 is an identity element of Q^* (Definition 11-7-1), as claimed above.

Now by Proposition Q6 we have $0 = \rho(1, 0)$, and hence for any $\rho(x,y) \in Q^*$ we have $\rho(x,y) +_{Q^*} 0 = \rho(x,y) +_{Q^*} \rho(1, 0) = \rho(x \cdot 1, x \cdot 0 + y \cdot 1) = \rho(x,y)$. (We leave it to the reader to furnish the details of justification for this last chain of equalities.) Similarly, it can be shown that $0 +_{Q^*} \rho(x,y) = \rho(x,y)$. Thus 0 is the unique null element of the ring $\langle Q^*, +_{Q^*}, \cdot_{Q^*}\rangle$ (Theorem 11-6-4 and Definition 11-7-1) as claimed above.

Finally, suppose that $\rho(a, b)$ and $\rho(c, d)$ are any elements of Q^* such that $\rho(a, b) \cdot_{Q^*} \rho(c, d) = 0$. Then by Propositions Q4 and Q6 we have $\rho(a \cdot c,\ b \cdot d) = \rho(1, 0)$, and hence $(b \cdot d) \cdot 1 = (a \cdot c) \cdot 0$ by Proposition Q3. By Definition 11-2-1 and Theorem 11-2-3 we can then conclude that $b \cdot d = 0$. Now since we know that $\mathcal{J}$ is an integral domain by 11-7-3 (**i**) we see that either $b = 0$ or $d = 0$. But if $b = 0$, then $\rho(a, b) = \rho(a, 0) = \rho(1, 0) = 0$ by Propositions Q3 and Q6, and similarly, if $d = 0$ we get $\rho(c, d) = 0$. Thus we have shown that either $\rho(a, b) = 0$ or $\rho(c, d) = 0$, starting from the assumption that $\rho(a, b) \cdot_{Q^*} \rho(c, d) = 0$. It follows that if we know both $\rho(a, b) \neq 0$ and $\rho(c, d) \neq 0$ then we must have $\rho(a, b) \cdot_{Q^*} \rho(c, d) \neq 0$.

This concludes our outline of a proof of Proposition Q10.

PROPOSITION Q11. *The system*: $\mathfrak{Q}^* = \langle Q^*, +_{Q^*}, \cdot_{Q^*}\rangle$ *is a field.*

By comparing Proposition Q10 with Definition 12-2-2 we see that we need only show that every non-degenerate multiplicative equation with coefficients in Q^* possesses a root in Q^*. Thus let $\rho(a, b)$ and $\rho(c, d)$ be any elements of Q^* such that $\rho(a, b) \neq 0$. We wish to find an element $\rho(x, y) \in Q^*$ such that $\rho(a, b) \cdot_{Q^*} \rho(x, y) = \rho(c, d)$.

By Proposition Q4 our problem is equivalent to finding an element $\rho(x, y)$ in Q such that $\rho(a \cdot x, b \cdot y) = \rho(c, d)$ or, equivalently (by Proposition Q3), such that

$$(a \cdot x) \cdot d = (b \cdot y) \cdot c.$$

It is clear, by Theorem 11-2-3, that we can obtain elements x, y satisfying this equation by taking $x = b \cdot c$ and $y = a \cdot d$; and hence we will have the desired element $\rho(x, y)$—*providing* we know that ρ is defined for the pair (x, y), i.e., that $x \neq 0$, or that $b \cdot c \neq 0$. Of course we know that $c \neq 0$, since $\rho(c, d) \in Q^*$. Thus, (since $\mathcal{J}$ is an integral domain by Theorem 11-7-2) it remains only to show that $b \neq 0$. But this must be so, for if we had $b = 0$ then

$$\begin{aligned} \rho(a, b) &= \rho(a, 0) \\ &= \rho(1, 0) \text{ by Proposition Q3} \\ &= 0 \text{ by Proposition Q6,} \end{aligned}$$

and this contradicts our hypothesis that $\rho(a, b) \neq 0$.

Let us now sum up the results of the analysis carried out in this section.

THEOREM 12-3-1. *Let $\mathfrak{Q} = \langle Q, +_Q, \cdot_Q \rangle$ be any number system such that:*

(i) *$\mathfrak{Q}$ is an extension of $\mathcal{J}$;*
(ii) *the operation $\cdot_Q$ is associative and commutative, and is left distributive over $+_Q$;*
(iii) *whenever $a \in J$ and $a \neq 0$, $x, y \in Q$ and $a \cdot_Q x = a \cdot_Q y$, then $x = y$;*
(iv) *for every $a, b \in J$ such that $a \neq 0$, there is an $x \in Q$ such that $a \cdot_Q x = b$.*

It follows that for every $a, b \in J$ such that $a \neq 0$ there is a ***unique*** *$x \in Q$ satisfying the equation $a \cdot_Q x = b$, which we call $\rho(a, b)$. We let Q^* be the set of all elements $\rho(a, b)$ of Q, for all $a, b \in J$ such that $a \neq 0$; and we let $+_{Q^*}$, $\cdot_{Q^*}$ be the operations obtained by restricting $+_Q$ and $\cdot_Q$ to Q^*.*

Conclusion: The number system $\mathfrak{Q}^* = \langle Q^*, +_{Q^*}, \cdot_{Q^*} \rangle$ is a field, and an extension of the system $\mathcal{J}$. Furthermore, computation with the operations $+_{Q^*}$ and $\cdot_{Q^*}$ can be reduced to the rules of computation for $+$ and $\cdot$ by the following equations:

1. $\rho(a, b) = \rho(c, d)$ *if and only if* $a \cdot d = b \cdot c$.
2. $\rho(a, b) \cdot_{Q^*} \rho(c, d) = \rho(a \cdot c, b \cdot d)$

3. $\rho(a, b) +_{Q^*} \rho(c, d) = \rho(a \cdot c,\ a \cdot d + b \cdot c)$
4. $\rho(1, b) = b.$

At first sight it may seem as if Theorem 12-3-1 solves Problem R, since it seems to produce a field Q^* which is an extension of $\mathcal{J}$. Actually, however, Theorem 12-3-1 only shows how to produce such a system Q^* *providing* we have, to begin with, a system $\mathfrak{Q}$ satisfying the hypotheses (**i**) through (**iv**). But for all we have shown so far, there *may be no such system!*

EXERCISES

1. Prove in detail Proposition Q5.
2. Prove in detail Proposition Q7.
3. Prove in detail Proposition Q8.
4. Prove in detail Proposition Q9.
5. Prove in detail Proposition Q10.
6. Prove in detail Proposition Q11.
7. Show that in a field there is only *one* solution to any non-degenerate multiplicative equation.
8. Show that a commutative ring Q with an identity element u, in which for each $a \neq 0$ there is a unique x such that $a \cdot_Q x = u$, must be a field.
9. Generalize Theorem 12-3-1 by observing that throughout this section we can replace the particular integral domain $\mathcal{J} = \langle J, +, \cdot \rangle$ by an arbitrary integral domain $\mathfrak{D} = \langle D, +_D, \cdot_D \rangle$.

4. *Construction of the Rationals*

We shall now use the information gained about Q^* in the preceding section, which is summarized in Theorem 12-3-1, to *construct* a field with the properties of Q^*, starting only with the number system $\mathcal{J}$. Equation **1** of Theorem 12-3-1 suggests that in order to construct a field with the properties of Q^* we must associate with *each* ordered pair $\langle a, b \rangle$, where $a, b \in J$ and $a \neq 0$, some object—let us call it $\sigma(a, b)$—in such a way that $\sigma(a, b) = \sigma(c, d)$ if and only if $a \cdot d = b \cdot c$. Using the terminology of set theory we may express this suggestion by saying that we seek to define a *function*, σ, which maps the set of ordered pairs $\langle a, b \rangle$ described above onto some set of objects in such a way that $\sigma(a, b) = \sigma(c, d)$ if and only if $a \cdot d = b \cdot c$. As we shall see, the *nature* of the objects $\sigma(a, b)$ is largely immaterial for our purpose; the important thing is that the objects be associated with the ordered pairs $\langle a, b \rangle$ by a function σ in the manner indicated. To accomplish our aim we shall form a *partition* of our set of ordered pairs by first defining an *equivalence relation* on it. (For terminology see Chapter IX, Section 2: Definitions 9-7-2 and 9-7-1.)

DEFINITION 12-4-1. *Let F be the set of all ordered pairs $\langle a, b \rangle$ for all elements $a, b \in J$ such that $a \neq 0$. We define $\stackrel{r}{=}$ to be the binary relation on F such* *that, for any elements* $\langle a, b\rangle$ *and* $\langle c, d\rangle$ *of* F, *we have* $\langle a, b\rangle \overset{r}{=} \langle c, d\rangle$ *if and only if* $a \cdot d = b \cdot c$.

Note: In the notation of Chapter IX we take F to be the set $\{x \mid$ for some $a, b \in \mathcal{J}$ we have $a \neq 0$ and $x = \langle a, b\rangle\}$ (cf. Theorem 9-2-2); and we take $\overset{r}{=}$ to be the set $\{x \mid$ for some $a, b, c, d \in \mathcal{J}$ we have $a \neq 0$ and $c \neq 0$ and $a \cdot d = b \cdot c$ and $x = \langle\langle a, b\rangle, \langle c, d\rangle\rangle\}$, which is easily seen to be a binary relation (cf. Definition 9-6-1).

THEOREM 12-4-2. *The relation* $\overset{r}{=}$ *is an equivalence relation on* F; *i.e.*, $\overset{r}{=}$ *is reflexive, symmetric, and transitive on* F.

Proof

▶▶ **1.** Let $\langle a, b\rangle$ be any element in F.
2. $a \cdot b = b \cdot a$; by line **1**, Definition 12-4-1, and Theorem 11-2-3.
▶▶ **3.** $\langle a, b\rangle \overset{r}{=} \langle a, b\rangle$; by line **2** and Definition 12-4-1.
4. For any $\langle a, b\rangle \in F$ we have $\langle a, b\rangle \overset{r}{=} \langle a, b\rangle$; by the Deduction Theorem applied to lines **1** through **3**.
5. The relation $\overset{r}{=}$ is reflexive on F; by Definition 9-7-1 (**i**) from line **4**.

▶▶ **6.** Let $\langle a, b\rangle$ and $\langle c, d\rangle$ be any elements of F such that $\langle a, b\rangle \overset{r}{=} \langle c, d\rangle$.
7. $a \cdot d = b \cdot c$; from line **6** and Definition 12-4-1.
8. $c \cdot b = d \cdot a$; by E from line **7** and the commutative law for $\cdot$ (Theorem 11-2-3).
▶▶ **9.** $\langle c, d\rangle \overset{r}{=} \langle a, b\rangle$; by line **8** and Definition 12-4-1.
10. If $\langle a, b\rangle$ and $\langle c, d\rangle$ are any elements of F such that $\langle a, b\rangle \overset{r}{=} \langle c, d\rangle$ then $\langle c, d\rangle \overset{r}{=} \langle a, b\rangle$; by the Deduction Theorem applied to lines **6** through **9**.
11. The relation $\overset{r}{=}$ is symmetric on F; from line **10** by Definition 9-7-1 (**ii**).

▶▶ **12.** Let $\langle a, b\rangle$, $\langle c, d\rangle$, and $\langle e, f\rangle$ be any elements in F such that $\langle a, b\rangle \overset{r}{=} \langle c, d\rangle$ and $\langle c, d\rangle \overset{r}{=} \langle e, f\rangle$.
13. $a \cdot d = b \cdot c$ and $c \cdot f = d \cdot e$; by line **12** and Definition 12-4-1.
14. $(a \cdot d) \cdot e = (b \cdot c) \cdot e$ and $a \cdot (c \cdot f) = a \cdot (d \cdot e)$; by E from line **13**.
15. $a \cdot (c \cdot f) = (b \cdot c) \cdot e$; by E and the associative law of $\cdot$ (Theorem 11-2-3) from line **14**.
16. $c \cdot (a \cdot f) = c \cdot (b \cdot e)$; by line **15** and the associative and commutative laws for $\cdot$ (Theorem 11-2-3).
17. $c \neq 0$; by line **12** and Definition 12-4-1.
18. $a \cdot f = b \cdot e$; by lines **16** and **17** and Theorem 11-2-4.
▶▶ **19.** $\langle a, b\rangle \overset{r}{=} \langle e, f\rangle$; by line **18** and Definition 12-4-1.
20. If $\langle a, b\rangle$, $\langle c, d\rangle$, and $\langle e, f\rangle$ are any elements in F such that

$\langle a, b\rangle \overset{r}{=} \langle c, d\rangle$ and $\langle c, d\rangle \overset{r}{=} \langle e, f\rangle$ then $\langle a, b\rangle \overset{r}{=} \langle e, f\rangle$; by the Deduction Theorem applied to lines **12** through **19**.

21. The relation $\overset{r}{=}$ is transitive on F; by line **20** and Definition 9-7-1 **(iii)**.

22. The relation $\overset{r}{=}$ is an equivalence relation on F; by lines **5**, **11**, and **21** and Definition 9-7-1 **(iv)**

The following fact about the equivalence relation $\overset{r}{=}$ will be of use in connection with a subsequent construction.

THEOREM 12-4-3. *Suppose that $\langle a, b\rangle \in F$ and that c and d are elements of $\mathcal{J}$ such that $\langle a, b\rangle \overset{r}{=} \langle 1, c\rangle$ and $\langle a, b\rangle \overset{r}{=} \langle 1, d\rangle$. Then we must have $c = d$.*

Proof

▶▶**1.** Suppose that $\langle a, b\rangle \in F$, that $c, d \in \mathcal{J}$, and that $\langle a, b\rangle \overset{r}{=} \langle 1, c\rangle$ and $\langle a, b\rangle = \langle 1, d\rangle$.

▶**2.** $a \cdot c = b \cdot 1$ and $a \cdot d = b \cdot 1$; by line **1** and Definition 12-4-1.

3. $a \cdot c = a \cdot d$; by E applied to line **2**.

4. $a \neq 0$; by line **1** and Definition 12-4-1.

▶▶**5.** $c = d$; by lines **3** and **4**, and Theorem 11-2-4.

6. The theorem is now obtained by applying the Deduction Theorem to lines **1** and **5**.

In general, if we are given a set G and an equivalence relation T on G, we can define (in many ways) a function h, having G as its domain, such that for all $x, y \in G$ we have $h(x) = h(y)$ if, and only if, $x\ T\ y$. (Compare Exercises 2 and 3 at the end of Chapter IX, Section 8.) Such a function h we call a *representation function* on the set G for the relation T.

In view of Theorem 12-4-2, and our assertion of the previous paragraph, we see that there exist representation functions on the set F for the relation $\overset{r}{=}$. In our construction of the rational number system we shall require such a representation function, and we shall need one which possesses the additional property that its value for any element $\langle 1, c\rangle$ of F is the element c of $\mathcal{J}$. That there exist such functions is shown in the following theorem.

THEOREM 12-4-4. *There exists a function σ with the following properties:*[1]

(i) *The domain of σ is the set F of Definition 12-4-1;*

(ii) *For any elements $\langle a, b\rangle$ and $\langle c, d\rangle$ of F we have $\sigma(a, b) = \sigma(c, d)$ if and only if $a \cdot d = b \cdot c$;*

(iii) *For any $c \in \mathcal{J}$ we have $\sigma(1, c) = c$;*

(iv) *For any $\langle a, b\rangle \in F$, and any element k of $\mathcal{J}$ such that $k \neq 0$, we have $\sigma(a, b) = \sigma(k \cdot a, k \cdot b)$.*

We note that **(i)** *and* **(ii)** *together entitle us to say that σ is a representation function on F for the relation $\overset{r}{=}$.*

[1] The symbol "σ" is the Greek letter sigma.

Proof

We give only an outline of this proof.

1. There is a partition H of F such that for any elements $\langle a, b\rangle$ and $\langle c, d\rangle$ of F we have $\langle a, b\rangle \overset{r}{=} \langle c, d\rangle$ if and only if there is some $u \in H$ such that both $\langle a, b\rangle \in u$ and $\langle c, d\rangle \in u$; by Theorems 12-4-2 and 9-7-3.
2. We divide the elements of F into two classes. We let F_1 be the subset of F consisting of all those $\langle a, b\rangle \in F$ such that $\langle a, b\rangle \overset{r}{=} \langle 1, c\rangle$ for some $c \in \mathcal{J}$; and we let F_2 be the subset of F consisting of all the *remaining* elements of F (i.e., those not in F_1).
3. Now we let σ be the function, with domain F, whose values are defined by the following rule:

   If $\langle a, b\rangle \in F_1$ then there exists an element $c \in \mathcal{J}$ such that $\langle a, b\rangle \overset{r}{=} \langle 1, c\rangle$ (by line **2**), and there is *only one* such c, (by Theorem 12-4-3), and in this case we set $\sigma(a, b) = c$; if $\langle a, b\rangle \in F_2$, then let u be the unique element of H such that $\langle a, b\rangle \in u$ (which exists by line **1** and Definition 9-7-2) and in this case we set $\sigma(a, b) = \langle u, \mathcal{J}\rangle$.
4. Now suppose that $\langle a_1, b_1\rangle \overset{r}{=} \langle a_2, b_2\rangle$ and that $\langle a_1, b_1\rangle \in F_1$. If for some $c \in \mathcal{J}$ we have $c = \sigma(a_1, b_1)$, then by line **3** we have $\langle a_1, b_1\rangle = \langle 1, c\rangle$, and since $\overset{r}{=}$ is symmetric and transitive we can then infer from our supposition that also $\langle a_2, b_2\rangle \overset{r}{=} \langle 1, c\rangle$. But this shows that $\langle a_2, b_2\rangle \in F_1$ (by line **2**) and that $\sigma(a_2, b_2) = c$ (by line **3**). Hence in this case we have $\sigma(a_1, b_1) = \sigma(a_2, b_2)$.
5. In a manner entirely similar to that used in line **4**, we show that if $\langle a_1, b_1\rangle \overset{r}{=} \langle a_2, b_2\rangle$ and $\langle a_2, b_2\rangle \in F_1$, then we must have $\sigma(a_1, b_1) = \sigma(a_2, b_2)$.
6. Suppose, next, that $\langle a_1, b_1\rangle \overset{r}{=} \langle a_2, b_2\rangle$ and that *both* $\langle a_1, b_1\rangle$ and $\langle a_2, b_2\rangle$ are in F_2. From line **1** we infer that there is some $u \in H$ such that both $\langle a_1, b_1\rangle$ and $\langle a_2, b_2\rangle$ are in u, and then from line **3** we see that for this u we have both $\sigma(a_1, b_1) = \langle u, \mathcal{J}\rangle$ and $\sigma(a_2, b_2) = \langle u, \mathcal{J}\rangle$. Hence in this case, too, we get $\sigma(a_1, b_1) = \sigma(a_2, b_2)$.
7. Lines **4**, **5**, and **6** together show (by virtue of line **2**) that if $\langle a_1, b_1\rangle$ and $\langle a_2, b_2\rangle$ are *any* elements of F such that $\langle a_1, b_1\rangle = \langle a_2, b_2\rangle$, then $\sigma(a_1, b_1) = \sigma(a_2, b_2)$.
8. We next seek to prove the converse of line **7**, so as to obtain Theorem 12-4-4 (**ii**). As a preliminary we note that if c is any element of $\mathcal{J}$, and if u is any element of H, then $c \neq \langle u, \mathcal{J}\rangle$. This follows from one of the fundamental axioms of set theory (cf. Theorem 9-11-26).
9. It follows from line **8** that if one of the elements $\langle a_1, b_1\rangle$ and $\langle a_2, b_2\rangle$ is in F_1 and the other is in F_2, then we must have $\sigma(a_1, b_1) \neq \sigma(a_2, b_2)$; for by line 3, one of the objects $\sigma(a_1, b_1)$ and $\sigma(a_2, b_2)$ will be an element c of $\mathcal{J}$, and the other will be an ordered pair $\langle u, \mathcal{J}\rangle$ for some $u \in H$.

10. If $\langle a_1, b_1\rangle$ and $\langle a_2, b_2\rangle$ are any elements of F such that $\sigma(a_1, b_1) = \sigma(a_2, b_2)$, then either $\langle a_1, b_1\rangle$ and $\langle a_2, b_2\rangle$ are both in F_1, or they are both in F_2. This is simply a reformulation of line **9**.

11. If $\sigma(a_1, b_1) = \sigma(a_2, b_2)$ and both $\langle a_1, b_1\rangle$ and $\langle a_2, b_2\rangle$ are in F_1, then by line **3** there is an element c of $\mathcal{J}$ (the common value of $\sigma(a_1, b_1)$ and $\sigma(a_2, b_2)$) such that $\langle a_1, b_1\rangle \stackrel{r}{=} \langle 1, c\rangle$ and $\langle a_2, b_2\rangle \stackrel{r}{=} \langle 1, c\rangle$. Since $=$ is symmetric and transitive it then easily follows that $\langle a_1, b_1\rangle \stackrel{r}{=} \langle a_2, b_2\rangle$ in this case.

12. If $\sigma(a_1, b_1) = \sigma(a_2, b_2)$ and both $\langle a_1, b_1\rangle$ and $\langle a_2, b_2\rangle$ are in F_2, then by line **3** the common value of $\sigma(a_1, b_1)$ and $\sigma(a_2, b_2)$ is an ordered pair $\langle u, \mathcal{J}\rangle$, where u is an element of H such that both $\langle a_1, b_1\rangle \in u$ and $\langle a_2, b_2\rangle \in u$. But from these relations we infer by line **1** that we must have $\langle a_1, b_1\rangle \stackrel{r}{=} \langle a_2, b_2\rangle$ in this case also.

13. By combining lines **10**, **11**, and **12** we see that if $\langle a_1, b_1\rangle$ and $\langle a_2, b_2\rangle$ are *any* elements of F such that $\sigma(a_1, b_1) = \sigma(a_2, b_2)$, then $\langle a_1, b_1\rangle \stackrel{r}{=} \langle a_2, b_2\rangle$.

14. Lines **7** and **13** together show that for all elements $\langle a_1, b_1\rangle$ and $\langle a_2, b_2\rangle$ of F we have $\sigma(a_1, b_1) = \sigma(a_2, b_2)$ if and only if $\langle a_1, b_1\rangle \stackrel{r}{=} \langle a_2, b_2\rangle$.

15. In view of the definition of $\stackrel{r}{=}$ (Definition 12-4-1), we see that line **14** is equivalent to the statement that condition (**ii**) of Theorem 12-4-4 holds for our function σ. Conditions (**i**) and (**iii**) are immediate from the definition of σ (line **3**). Thus it remains only to show that condition (**iv**) is satisfied.

16. But condition (**iv**) is a simple consequence of condition (**ii**). For if $\langle a, b\rangle \in F$ then $a \stackrel{r}{\neq} 0$ (by Definition 12-4-1); and so if k is an element of $\mathcal{J}$ other than 0 we have $k \cdot a \neq 0$, whence $\langle k \cdot a,\ k \cdot b\rangle \in F$. But clearly $a \cdot (k \cdot b) = b \cdot (k \cdot a)$, whence by (**ii**) we get $\sigma(a, b) = \sigma(k \cdot a,\quad k \cdot b)$, as claimed.

17. Lines **15** and **16** together complete the proof of the theorem.

In our proof of Theorem 12-4-4 we have shown how to construct a *particular* function σ of the kind described in the *statement* of the theorem. Actually, there are many other functions with the same properties (**i**) through (**iv**) of this theorem.

Let us suppose, now, that we choose an *arbitrary* function σ satisfying condition (**i**) through (**iv**) of Theorem 12-4-4. Let R be the *range* of σ, i.e., the set of all objects $\sigma(a, b)$ for all $\langle a, b\rangle \in F$. In the sequel we shall show that, by defining suitable operations $+_R$ and $\cdot_R$ on this set R, we can obtain a number system $\langle R, +_R, \cdot_R\rangle$ which solves Problem R of section 3—and hence which may be identified with the field of rational numbers.

Propositions Q4 and Q5 give us clues for the definitions of the operations $+_R$ and $\cdot_R$ on the set R. They suggest that we define these to be the binary operations such that, for any $\sigma(a, b)$ and $\sigma(c, d)$ in R, we have:

(*) $$\sigma(a, b) \cdot_R \sigma(c, d) = \sigma(a \cdot c,\ b \cdot d)$$

and

(**) $$\sigma(a, b) +_R \sigma(c, d) = \sigma(a \cdot c,\ a \cdot d + b \cdot c).$$

But are these valid definitions?

To see why we raise this question consider two different elements $\langle a_1, b_1\rangle$ and $\langle a_2, b_2\rangle$ of F which have the same representative in R, i.e., such that $\sigma(a_1, b_1) = \sigma(a_2, b_2)$; and similarly suppose that $\langle c_1, d_1\rangle$ and $\langle c_2, d_2\rangle$ have the same representative: $\sigma(c_1, d_1) = \sigma(c_2, d_2)$. *If* the equation (*) could be used as a definition of $\cdot_R$ we would have

$$\sigma(a_1, b_1) \cdot_R \sigma(c_1, d_1) = \sigma(a_1 \cdot c_1,\ b_1 \cdot d_1)$$

and

$$\sigma(a_2, b_2) \cdot_R \sigma(c_2, d_2) = \sigma(a_2 \cdot c_2,\ b_2 \cdot d_2)$$

and hence by E, and the way in which we chose $\langle a_1, b_1\rangle$, $\langle a_2, b_2\rangle$, $\langle c_1, d_1\rangle$, and $\langle c_2, d_2\rangle$, we would get

(***) $$\sigma(a_1 \cdot c_1,\ b_1 \cdot d_1) = \sigma(a_2 \cdot c_2,\ b_2 \cdot d_2).$$

But how do we know that in fact this last equation *does* hold? The selection of σ was made *before* we set out to define $\cdot_R$; and if σ happens to assign two *different* representatives to the elements $\langle a_1 \cdot c_1,\ b_1 \cdot d_1\rangle$ and $\langle a_2 \cdot c_2,\ b_2 \cdot d_2\rangle$ of F, then we see that (*) would lead us to the *false* conclusion (***) and so could not be used as a definition of $\cdot_R$. In the same way we would regard (**) as a defective definition if σ assigned representatives in such a way that

$$\sigma(a_1 \cdot c_1,\ a_1 \cdot d_1 + b_1 \cdot c_1) \neq \sigma(a_2 \cdot c_2,\ a_2 \cdot d_2 + b_2 \cdot c_2).$$

These considerations show that before we can use equations (*) and (**) to define our operations we must be sure of the following: Whenever $\langle a_1, b_1\rangle$, $\langle a_2, b_2\rangle$, $\langle c_1, d_1\rangle$, and $\langle c_2, d_2\rangle$ are elements of F such that $\sigma(a_1, b_1) = \sigma(a_2, b_2)$ and $\sigma(c_1, d_1) = \sigma(c_2, d_2)$ then we will have

$$\sigma(a_1 \cdot c_1,\ b_1 \cdot d_1) = \sigma(a_2 \cdot c_2,\ b_2 \cdot d_2)$$

and

$$\sigma(a_1 \cdot c_1,\ a_1 \cdot d_1 + b_1 \cdot c_1) = \sigma(a_2 \cdot c_2,\ a_2 \cdot d_2 + b_2 \cdot c_2).$$

That this is indeed the case is the content of the following theorem.

THEOREM 12-4-5. *For any* $\langle a_1, b_1\rangle$, $\langle a_2, b_2\rangle$, $\langle c_1, d_1\rangle$, and $\langle c_2, d_2\rangle \in F$ *such that* $\sigma(a_1, b_1) = \sigma(a_2, b_2)$ *and* $\sigma(c_1, d_1) = \sigma(c_2, d_2)$, *we have also* $\sigma(a_1 \cdot c_1,\ b_1 \cdot d_1) = \sigma(a_2 \cdot c_2,\ b_2 \cdot d_2)$ *and* $\sigma(a_1 \cdot c_1,\ a_1 \cdot d_1 + b_1 \cdot c_1) = \sigma(a_2 \cdot c_2,\ a_2 \cdot d_2 + b_2 \cdot c_2)$.

Proof

►► 1. Let $\langle a_1, b_1\rangle$, $\langle a_2, b_2\rangle$, $\langle c_1, d_1\rangle$, and $\langle c_2, d_2\rangle$ be any elements in F such that $\sigma(a_1, b_1) = \sigma(a_2, b_2)$ and $\sigma(c_1, d_1) = \sigma(c_2, d_2)$.

▶ **2.** $a_1 \cdot b_2 = b_1 \cdot a_2$ and $c_1 \cdot d_2 = d_1 \cdot c_2$; by line **1** and Theorem 12-4-4 (**ii**).

3. $(a_1 \cdot b_2) \cdot (c_1 \cdot d_2) = (b_1 \cdot a_2) \cdot (d_1 \cdot c_2)$; by E from line **2**.

▶ **4.** $(a_1 \cdot c_1) \cdot (b_2 \cdot d_2) = (b_1 \cdot d_1) \cdot (a_2 \cdot c_2)$; from line **3** by E and the commutative and associative laws for $\cdot$.

5. $a_1 \neq 0$, $a_2 \neq 0$, $c_1 \neq 0$, and $c_2 \neq 0$; by line **1** and Definition 12-4-1.

▶ **6.** $a_1 \cdot c_1 \neq 0$ and $a_2 \cdot c_2 \neq 0$; by line **5** and the definition of $\cdot$ (Definition 11-2-1).

7. $\langle a_1 \cdot c_1, \ b_1 \cdot d_1\rangle$ and $\langle a_2 \cdot c_2, \ b_2 \cdot d_2\rangle$ are in F; by lines **1**, **6** and Definition 12-4-1.

▶▶ **8.** $\sigma(a_1 \cdot c_1, \ b_1 \cdot d_1) = \sigma(a_2 \cdot c_2, \ b_2 \cdot d_2)$; by lines **4** and **7** and Theorem 12-4-4 (**ii**).

▶ **9.** $(a_1 \cdot a_2) \cdot (c_1 \cdot d_2) = (a_1 \cdot a_2) \cdot (d_1 \cdot c_2)$ and $(c_1 \cdot c_2) \cdot (a_1 \cdot b_2) = (c_1 \cdot c_2) \cdot (b_1 \cdot a_2)$; by E from line **2**.

10. $(a_1 \cdot c_1) \cdot (a_2 \cdot d_2) = (a_1 \cdot d_1) \cdot (a_2 \cdot c_2)$ and $(a_1 \cdot c_1) \cdot (b_2 \cdot c_2) = (b_1 \cdot c_1) \cdot (a_2 \cdot c_2)$; from line **9** by E and the associative and commutative laws for $\cdot$ (Theorem 11-2-3).

▶ **11.** $(a_1 \cdot c_1) \cdot (a_2 \cdot d_2 + b_2 \cdot c_2) = (a_1 \cdot d_1 + b_1 \cdot c_1) \cdot (a_2 \cdot c_2)$; by E from line **10** and the distributive laws of $\cdot$ over $+$ (Theorem 11-2-3).

▶▶ **12.** $\sigma(a_1 \cdot c_1, \ a_1 \cdot d_1 + b_1 \cdot c_1) = \sigma(a_2 \cdot c_2, \ a_2 \cdot d_2 + b_2 \cdot c_2)$; from lines **6** and **11** and Theorem 12-4-4 (**ii**).

13. For any $\langle a_1, b_1\rangle$, $\langle a_2, b_2\rangle$, $\langle c_1, d_1\rangle$, and $\langle c_2, d_2\rangle \in F$ such that $\sigma(a_1, b_1) = \sigma(a_2, b_2)$ and $\sigma(c_1, d_1) = \sigma(c_2, d_2)$ we have $\sigma(a_1 \cdot c_1, \ b_1 \cdot d_1) = \sigma(a_2 \cdot c_2, \ b_2 \cdot d_2)$ and $\sigma(a_1 \cdot c_1, \ a_1 \cdot d_1 + b_1 \cdot c_1) = \sigma(a_2 \cdot c_2, \ a_2 \cdot d_2 + b_2 \cdot c_2)$; by the Deduction Theorem applied to lines **1** through **8** and **12**.

As we have seen from the discussion preceding Theorem 12-4-5 we are now justified in using equations (*) and (**) to define operations $+_R$ and $\cdot_R$. This is done in the next definition.

DEFINITION 12-4-6. *We define the binary operations* $\cdot_R$ *and* $+_R$ *as follows: For any elements* $\sigma(a, b)$ *and* $\sigma(c, d)$ *of R we set* $\sigma(a, b) \cdot_R \sigma(c, d) = \sigma(a \cdot c, b \cdot d)$ *and* $\sigma(a, b) +_R \sigma(a, d) = \sigma(a \cdot c, \ a \cdot d + b \cdot c)$.

And we now formally introduce the term "rational number" into our theory.

DEFINITION 12-4-7. *If* σ *is any function satisfying conditions* (**i**) *through* (**iv**) *of Theorem* 12-4-4, *if R is the range of* σ, *and if* $+_R$ *and* $\cdot_R$ *are the operations on R which are specified in Definition* 12-4-6, *then the system* $\mathcal{R} = \langle R, +_R, \cdot_R\rangle$ *is* *called a* **rational number system** *and the elements of R are called* **rational numbers.**

Theorems 12-4-4 and 12-4-5 assure us that there are indeed rational number systems. The reader should keep in mind that we are seeking a solution to Problem R, i.e., the problem of constructing a *field* which is an extension of $\mathcal{J}$. As we shall see, any system $\mathcal{R}$ of the kind specified in Definition 12-4-7 furnishes a solution of the problem.

THEOREM 12-4-8. *Any rational number system* $\mathcal{R} = \langle R, +_R, \cdot_R \rangle$ *is an extension of the system* $\mathcal{J} = \langle J, +, \cdot \rangle$.

Proof

▶▶ **1.** Let x be any element in J.

2. $x = \sigma(1, x)$; by line **1**, Definition 12-4-7, and Theorem 12-4-4 (**iii**).

▶ **3.** $x \in R$; by E from line **2** and Definition 12-4-7.

4. If x is any element of J then $x \in R$; by the Deduction Theorem applied to lines **1** through **3**.

▶▶ **5.** $J \subseteq R$; by line **4** and Definition of $\subseteq$ (Definition 9-3-1).

▶▶ **6.** Let x, y be any elements in J.

▶ **7.** $x +_R y = \sigma(1, x) +_R \sigma(1, y)$; by E, Definition 12-4-7, and Theorem 12-4-4 (**iii**).

8. $= \sigma(1 \cdot 1, \ 1 \cdot y + x \cdot 1)$; by Definition 12-4-6.

9. $= \sigma(1, \ y + x)$; by E from Theorem 11-2-3.

▶ **10.** $= \sigma(1, \ x + y)$; by E from Theorem 11-2-3.

11. $= x + y$; by Definition 12-4-7 and Theorem 12-4-4 (**iii**).

▶▶ **12.** $x +_R y = x + y$; by E from lines **7** to **11**.

▶ **13.** $x \cdot_R y = \sigma(1, x) \cdot_R \sigma(1, y)$; by E and Definition 12-4-7, and Theorem 12-4-4 (**iii**).

14. $= \sigma(1 \cdot 1, \ x \cdot y)$; by Definition 12-4-6.

▶ **15.** $= \sigma(1, x \cdot y)$; by E and Theorem 11-2-3.

16. $= x \cdot y$; by Definition 12-4-7 and Theorem 12-4-4 (**iii**).

▶▶ **17.** $x \cdot_R y = x \cdot y$; by E from lines **13** to **16**.

18. For any $x, y \in J$ we have $x +_R y = x + y$ and $x \cdot_R y = x \cdot y$; by lines **6, 12,** and **17** and the Deduction Theorem.

▶▶ **19.** $\mathcal{R}$ is an extension of $\mathcal{J}$; by lines **5** and **18** and the definition of *extension* (cf. Chapter VIII, Section 1).

We next show that our system $\mathcal{R}$ satisfies various algebraic identities.

THEOREM 12-4-9. *If $\sigma(a, b)$, $\sigma(c, d)$ and $\sigma(e, f)$ are any elements of R, then:*

(**i**) $\sigma(a, b) \cdot_R \sigma(c, d) = \sigma(c, d) \cdot_R \sigma(a, b)$ (*The Commutative Law for* $\cdot_R$);
(**ii**) $[\sigma(a, b) \cdot_R \sigma(c, d)] \cdot_R \sigma(e, f) = \sigma(a, b) \cdot_R [\sigma(c, d) \cdot_R \sigma(e, f)]$ (*The Associative Law for* $\cdot_R$);
(**iii**) $\sigma(a, b) \cdot_R [\sigma(c, d) +_R \sigma(e, f)] = \sigma(a, b) \cdot_R \sigma(c, d) +_R \sigma(a, b) \cdot_R \sigma(c, d)$ (*The Left Distributive Law of* $\cdot_R$ *over* $+_R$).

Proof

We shall prove part (**iii**) and leave the proofs of the other parts as exercises.

▶▶ **1.** Let $\sigma(a, b)$, $\sigma(c, d)$, and $\sigma(e, f)$ be any elements of R.
2. $\sigma(a, b) \cdot_R [\sigma(c, d) +_R \sigma(e, f)] = \sigma(a, b) \cdot_R \sigma(c \cdot e,\ c \cdot f + d \cdot e)$; by E from Definition 12-4-6.
3. $= \sigma(a \cdot (c \cdot e),\ b \cdot (c \cdot f + d \cdot e))$; by Definition 12-4-6.
▶ **4.** $\sigma(a, b) \cdot_R [\sigma(c, d) +_R \sigma(e, f)] = \sigma(a \cdot (c \cdot e),\ b \cdot (c \cdot f + d \cdot e))$; by E from lines **2** and **3**.
5. $\sigma(a, b) \cdot_R \sigma(c, d) +_R \sigma(a, b) \cdot_R \sigma(e, f) = \sigma(a \cdot c,\ b \cdot d) +_R \sigma(a \cdot e,\ b \cdot f)$; by E from Definition 12-4-6.
6. $= \sigma[(a \cdot c) \cdot (a \cdot e),\ (a \cdot c) \cdot (b \cdot f) + (b \cdot d) \cdot (a \cdot e)]$; by Definition 12-4-6.
7. $= \sigma[a \cdot (a \cdot (c \cdot e)),\ a \cdot (b \cdot (c \cdot f + d \cdot e))]$; by the commutative, associative, and distributive laws of $\cdot$ (Theorem 11-2-3).
8. $= \sigma[a \cdot (c \cdot e),\ b \cdot (c \cdot f + d \cdot e)]$; by Theorem 12-4-4 (**iv**).
▶ **9.** $\sigma(a, b) \cdot_R \sigma(c, d) +_R \sigma(a, b) \cdot_R \sigma(e, f) = \sigma[a \cdot (c \cdot e),\ b \cdot (c \cdot f + d \cdot e)]$; by E from lines **5** to **8**.
▶▶ **10.** For all $\sigma(a, b)$, $\sigma(c, d)$, and $\sigma(e, f) \in R$ we have $\sigma(a, b) \cdot_R [\sigma(c, d) +_R \sigma(e, f)] = \sigma(a, b) \cdot_R \sigma(c, d) +_R \sigma(a, b) \cdot_R \sigma(e, f)$; by E and the Deduction Theorem applied to lines **1** through **4** and **9**.

Having shown in Theorem 12-4-8 that $\mathcal{R}$ is an extension of $\mathcal{J}$, we next wish to show that $\mathcal{R}$ is a field: This will complete the verification that $\mathcal{R}$ constitutes a solution of Problem R (Section 3). A part of this task has been accomplished by Theorem 12-4-9; the next three theorems will complete the demonstration.

THEOREM 12-4-10. *If $a \in J$ and $a \neq 0$, if $\sigma(b_1, c_1)$, $\sigma(b_2, c_2) \in R$, and if $a \cdot_R \sigma(b_1, c_1) = a \cdot_R \sigma(b_2, c_2)$, then $\sigma(b_1, c_1) = \sigma(b_2, c_2)$.*

Proof

▶▶ **1.** Let a be any element in $\mathcal{J}$ such that $a \neq 0$, and let $\sigma(b_1, c_1)$ and $\sigma(b_2, c_2)$ be any elements in R such that $a \cdot_R \sigma(b_1, c_1) = a \cdot_R \sigma(b_2, c_2)$.

2. $a = \sigma(1, a)$; by line **1**, Definition 12-4-7, and Theorem 12-4-4 (**iii**).

3. $\sigma(1, a) \cdot_R \sigma(b_1, c_1) = \sigma(1, a) \cdot_R \sigma(b_2, c_2)$; from lines **1** and **2** by E.

4. $\langle a, 1 \rangle \in F$; by line **1** and Definition 12-4-1.

5. $\sigma(a, 1) \cdot_R [\sigma(1, a) \cdot_R \sigma(b_1, c_1)] = \sigma(a, 1) \cdot_R [\sigma(1, a) \cdot_R \sigma(b_2, c_2)]$; by line **4** and by E from line **3**.

6. $[\sigma(a, 1) \cdot_R \sigma(1, a)] \cdot_R \sigma(b_1, c_1) = [\sigma(a, 1) \cdot_R \sigma(1, a)] \cdot_R \sigma(b_2, c_2)$; by E, line **5** and the Associative Law of $\cdot_R$ (Theorem 12-4-9 (**ii**)).

7. $\sigma(a \cdot 1,\ 1 \cdot a) \cdot_R \sigma(b_1, c_1) = \sigma(a \cdot 1,\ 1 \cdot a) \cdot_R \sigma(b_2, c_2)$; by line **6**, E, and Definition 12-4-6.

8. $\sigma(a, a) \cdot_R \sigma(b_1, c_1) = \sigma(a, a) \cdot_R \sigma(b_2, c_2)$; by E from line **7** and Theorem 11-2-3.

▶ **9.** $\sigma(a \cdot b_1,\ a \cdot c_1) = \sigma(a \cdot b_2,\ a \cdot c_2)$; by E from line **8** and Definition 12-4-6.

▶ **10.** $\sigma(a \cdot b_1,\ a \cdot c_1) = \sigma(b_1, c_1)$ and $\sigma(a \cdot b_2,\ a \cdot c_2) = \sigma(b_2, c_2)$; by line **1** and Theorem 12-4-4 (**iv**).

▶▶ **11.** $\sigma(b_1, c_1) = \sigma(b_2, c_2)$; by E from lines **9** and **10**.

12. If $a \in \mathcal{J}$ and $a \neq 0$, if $\sigma(b_1, c_1), \sigma(b_2, c_2) \in R$, and if $a \cdot_R \sigma(b_1, c_1) = a \cdot_R \sigma(b_2, c_2)$, then $\sigma(b_1, c_1) = \sigma(b_2, c_2)$; by the Deduction Theorem applied to lines **1** through **11**.

THEOREM 12-4-11. *For every $a, b \in \mathcal{J}$ such that $a \neq 0$ we have $a \cdot_R \sigma(a, b) = b$.*

The proof of this theorem is left as an exercise for the reader.

THEOREM 12-4-12. *The system $\mathfrak{R} = \langle R, +_R, \cdot_R \rangle$ is a field.*

The proof of this theorem may be given by first using the four theorems 12-4-8 through 12-4-11 to show that the hypotheses of Theorem 12-3-1 are satisfied when we take the system $\mathfrak{Q}$ of that theorem to be our system $\mathfrak{R}$. Then it is easy to show that in this application the set Q^* of Theorem 12-3-1 is, in fact, simply the set R, and hence that the system $\mathfrak{R}$ is a field. The details of the proof are left for the reader.

By comparing Theorems 12-4-8 and 12-4-12 with *Problem R* we see that Definition 12-4-7 in effect supplies a solution to this problem.

EXERCISES

1. Prove parts (i) and (ii) of Theorem 12-4-9.

2. Prove Theorem 12-4-11.

3. Give a detailed proof of Theorem 12-4-12.

4. *The method of Sections 3 and 4 of this chapter can be used to construct the system $\mathcal{J}$ of integers in a way quite different from that employed in Chapter XI. In fact, this method can effect the construction of $\mathcal{J}$ directly as an extension of the number system $\mathcal{P}$, without recourse to the intermediate number system $\mathcal{N}$. Below we sketch an outline, first (A) of the analysis corresponding to Section 3, and then (B) of the construction corresponding to Section 4. And we leave the reader to carry through the details.

A. Suppose that $\mathcal{I} = \langle I, +_I, \cdot_I \rangle$ is an extension of the number system $\mathcal{P} = \langle P, +, \cdot \rangle$, which obeys various of the common algebraic laws which have been discussed, and which, for each $a, b \in P$, contains an element x such that $a +_I x = b$. If one of the laws holding in $\mathcal{I}$ is the left cancellation law for $+_I$, it can be shown that for each $a, b \in P$ there is one *and only one* element $x \in I$ such that $a +_I x = b$. Let us denote this unique element x by $\mu(a, b)$, so that we have $a +_I \mu(a, b) = b$ for all $a, b \in P$. Then we can show: (i) $\mu(a, b) = \mu(c, d)$ if, and only if $a + d = b + c$; (ii) $\mu(a, b) +_I \mu(c, d) = \mu(a + c, b + d)$; and (iii) $\mu(a, b) \cdot_I \mu(c, d) = \mu(a \cdot d + b \cdot c, a \cdot c + b \cdot d)$. Let I^* be the set of all elements $\mu(a, b)$, for all $a, b \in P$, and let $+_I{}^*$ and $\cdot_I{}^*$ be the restrictions to I^* of the operations $+_I$ and $\cdot_I$ respectively. Then the system $\mathcal{I}^* = \langle I^*, +_I{}^*, \cdot_I{}^* \rangle$ is an integral domain and an extension of $\mathcal{P}$.

B. Let G be the set of all ordered pairs $\langle a, b \rangle$ for all $a, b \in P$, and let $\stackrel{t}{=}$ be the binary relation such that for all $\langle a, b \rangle$ and $\langle c, d \rangle$ of G we have $\langle a, b \rangle \stackrel{t}{=} \langle c, d \rangle$ if and only if $a + c = b + d$. Then $\stackrel{t}{=}$ is an equivalence relation on G. We can, therefore, define a function λ such that:[1] (i) The domain of λ is G; (ii) for all $\langle a, b \rangle$ and $\langle c, d \rangle$ of G we have $\lambda(a, b) = \lambda(c, d)$ if and only if $a + c = b + d$, (iii) for all $b \in P$ we have $\lambda(0, b) = b$; and (iv) for all $a, b, c \in P$ we have $\lambda(a, b) = \lambda(a + c, b + c)$. Choose such a function λ, and let T be its range. Then it is possible to define operations $+_T$ and $\cdot_T$ on T by the rules: $\lambda(a, b) +_T \lambda(c, d) = \lambda(a + c, \ b + d)$ and $\lambda(a, b) \cdot_T \lambda(c, d) = \lambda(a \cdot d + b \cdot c, \ \ a \cdot c + b \cdot d)$. The resulting system $\mathfrak{I} = \langle T, +_T, \cdot_T \rangle$ is an integral domain and an extension of $\mathcal{P}$.

5. Show how to define an isomorphism of the system $\mathcal{J}$ onto the system $\mathfrak{I}$.

6. Since the system $\mathcal{R} = \langle R, +_R, \cdot_R \rangle$ is a field (Theorem 12-4-12), it is certainly a ring (see Definitions 12-2-2 and 11-7-1) and hence must possess properties shared by all rings. Introduce the *subtraction* and *negation operations* for $\mathcal{R}$ by restating Definitions 11-7-5 and 11-7-6. Observe that Theorems 11-7-7 and 11-7-8 hold for elements of R.

7. Prove that, for any $a \in R$,

(a) $a \cdot_R 0 = 0 \cdot_R a = 0$,

(b) $a +_R 0 = 0 +_R a = a$.

8. Prove that, if a and b are any elements of R such that $a \cdot_R b = 0$, then either $a = 0$ or $b = 0$ (or both).

[1] The symbol "λ" is the Greek lambda.

5. Uniqueness of Our Solution

Having obtained a solution to Problem R through Definition 12-4-7 and Theorems 12-4-8 and 12-4-12, the question naturally arises: Are there *other* solutions? On each of the two previous occasions where such a question was raised, i.e., in the case of our extensions of the system $\mathcal{P}$ and the system $\mathfrak{N}$, we found that our solution was essentially unique. (See Theorems 8-3-1 and 11-3-2.) In the present case a similar answer is obtained, and in fact this has largely been established already by Theorem 12-3-1. We make this clear in the following theorem which is largely a rewording of Theorem 12-3-1.

THEOREM 12-5-1. *Let* $\mathcal{Q} = \langle Q, +_Q, \cdot_Q \rangle$ *be any number system such that:*

(i) $\mathcal{Q}$ *is an extension of* $\mathcal{J}$;
(ii) *the operation* $\cdot_Q$ *is associative and commutative, and distributive over* $+_Q$;
(iii) *if* $a \in J$ *and* $a \neq 0$, *if* $x, y \in Q$, *and if* $a \cdot_Q x = a \cdot_Q y$, *then* $x = y$;
(iv) *for every* $a, b \in J$ *such that* $a \neq 0$, *there is an* $x \in Q$ *such that* $a \cdot_Q x = b$.

Then the system $\mathcal{Q} = \langle Q, +_Q, \cdot_Q \rangle$ *is an extension of some system* $\mathcal{Q}^* = \langle Q^*, +_{Q^*}, \cdot_{Q^*} \rangle$ *which is a field, which is an extension of* $\mathcal{J}$, *and which is isomorphic to* $\mathcal{R}$.

To prove this we take the given system $\mathcal{Q}$, we form the system $\mathcal{Q}^*$ from it as described in Theorem 12-3-1, and we let f be the function which maps Q^* onto R as follows: For any $\rho(a, b) \in Q^*$, let $f[\rho(a, b)] = \sigma(a, b)$. This definition is justified because whenever $\langle a_1, b_1 \rangle$ and $\langle a_2, b_2 \rangle$ are elements of F such that $\rho(a_1, b_1) = \rho(a_2, b_2)$ we must have $\sigma(a_1, b_1) = \sigma(a_2, b_2)$, as see from Proposition Q3 (Section 3) and Theorem 12-4-4 (**ii**). By Theorem 12-3-1 [parts (**i**) and (**ii**)] and Definition 12-4-6, it is then easy to show that f is an isomorphism of Q onto R. (See Exercise below.)

EXERCISE

*Give a detailed proof of Theorem 12-5-1.

6. Quotients in a Field

The reader may wonder what connection there is between the numbers $\sigma(a, b)$ of a rational number system $\mathcal{R}$ (Definition 12-4-7), and the familiar numbers b/a which he is accustomed to calling rational numbers and which he is used to calling "quotients of integers." As we shall see, after we formally introduce the symbol "/" into our theory, $\sigma(a, b)$ and b/a are one and the same number when a and b are any integers such that $a \neq 0$. Why then, did we not use the familiar notation "b/a" instead of "$\sigma(a, b)$"? The answer is simply that we want the symbol "/" to have the broader meaning that it actually has in mathematics—advanced or elementary. In ordinary mathematics, "/" is used to form not only the "quotient" of two *integers*, but also, for example, the "quotient" of any two rational numbers, $(a/b)/(c/d)$.

By Definition 12-2-2 we know that if $\mathfrak{F} = \langle F, +_F, \cdot_F\rangle$ is any field, and if x and y are any elements of F such that $y \neq e$, where e is the null element of the additive group $\langle F, +_F\rangle$, then there exists a unique element $z \in F$ such that $y \cdot_F z = x$. Hence the following definition is justified.

DEFINITION 12-6-1. *Let $\mathfrak{F} = \langle F, +_F, \cdot_F\rangle$ be any field, and let e be the null element of its additive group $\langle F, +_F\rangle$. We define $/_F$ to be the function whose domain is the set of ordered pairs $\langle x, y\rangle$ for all $x, y \in F$ such that $y \neq e$, and whose value for any such $\langle x, y\rangle$ is that unique element z of F such that $y \cdot_F z = x$. Thus, for any $x, y \in F$ such that $y \neq e$ we have $y \cdot_F (x/_F y) = x$. We shall call $x/_F y$* **the quotient of x divided by y.**

The following theorem indicates the most fundamental properties of quotients which are employed in computing with them.

THEOREM 12-6-2. *For any quotients $x_1/_F y_1$ and $x_2/_F y_2$ of a field $\mathfrak{F} = \langle F, +_F, \cdot_F\rangle$ we have*

(i) $x_1/_F y_1 = x_2/_F y_2$ *if and only if* $x_1 \cdot_F y_2 = y_1 \cdot_F x_2$;
(ii) $x_1/_F y_1 \cdot_F x_2/_F y_2 = (x_1 \cdot_F x_2)/_F (y_1 \cdot_F y_2)$;
(iii) $x_1/_F y_1 +_F x_2/_F y_2 = (x_1 \cdot_F y_2 +_F y_1 \cdot_F x_2)/_F (y_1 \cdot_F y_2)$.

These rules of computation are essentially identical to equations 1, 2, and 3 of Theorem 12-3-1. Hence it is not surprising that for a proof of this theorem we can refer back to section 3 of this chapter and to the observation made in Exercise 9 at the end of that section. Since $\mathfrak{F}$ is a field it is certainly an integral domain (Definition 12-2-2). Hence Propositions Q3, Q4, and Q5 of Section 3 hold if the system $\mathfrak{J}$ and the function ρ of those propositions are replaced by the given field and the function $/_F$ respectively.

THEOREM 12-6-3. *Let $\mathfrak{F} = \langle F, +_F, \cdot_F\rangle$ be any field and let i be the identity element of $\mathfrak{F}$. Then:*

(i) *For any $x \in F$ we have $x/_F i = x$;*
(ii) *For any quotient $x/_F y$ of $\mathfrak{F}$, and for any element t of F such that $t \neq e$, we have $(t \cdot_F x)/_F (t \cdot_F y) = x/_F y$;*
(iii) *For any $y \in F$ such that $y \neq e$ we have $e/_F y = e$ and $y/_F y = i$.*

Part **(i)** can easily be proved directly by using Definition 12-6-1 and the definition of a field (Definition 12-2-2), or else by making use of Proposition Q4 of Section 3 together with the observation of Exercise 9, Section 3.

The proofs of parts **(ii)** and **(iii)** are left as exercises for the reader without further comment.

For purposes of later reference we shall combine the results of the last two theorems into a single theorem expressed for the particular field, $\mathcal{R} = \langle R, +_R, \cdot_R \rangle$.

THEOREM 12-6-4. *Let us write "/" (instead of "$/_R$") to designate the quotient function for the field $\mathcal{R} = \langle R, +_R, \cdot_R \rangle$. Then for any quotients x_1/y_1 and x_2/y_2 of $\mathcal{R}$ we have:*

A. **(i)** $x_1/y_1 = x_2/y_2$ *if and only if* $x_1 \cdot_R y_2 = y_1 \cdot_R x_2$;
(ii) $x_1/y_1 \cdot_R x_2/y_2 = (x_1 \cdot_R x_2)/(y_1 \cdot_R y_2)$;
(iii) $x_1/y_1 +_R x_2/y_2 = (x_1 \cdot_R y_2 +_R y_1 \cdot_R x_2)/(y_1 \cdot_R y_2)$.
B. **(i)** *For any* $x \in R$ *we have* $x/1 = x$;
(ii) *for any quotient* x/y *of* $\mathcal{R}$, *and for any element* t *of* R *such that* $t \neq 0$, *we have* $(t \cdot_R x)/(t \cdot_R y) = x/y$; *and*
(iii) *for any* $y \in R$ *such that* $y \neq 0$ *we have* $0/y = 0$ *and* $y/y = 1$.

And now we are ready to see that indeed *rational numbers are quotients of integers.*

THEOREM 12-6-5.

(i) *For any* $a, b \in \mathcal{J}$ *such that* $b \neq 0$ *we have* $a/b = \sigma(b, a)$.
(ii) *For any* $x \in R$ *there exist* $a, b \in \mathcal{J}$ *such that* $b \neq 0$ *and* $x = a/b$.

Proof

▶▶**1.** Let a and b be any elements in $\mathcal{J}$ such that $b \neq 0$.
2. a and b are in R; since $\mathcal{R}$ is an extension of $\mathcal{G}$ (Theorem 12-4-8).
3. $b \cdot_R \sigma(b, a) = a$; by line **1** and Theorem 12-4-11.
▶▶**4.** $\sigma(b, a) = a/b$; by line **3** and Definition 12-6-1 (using the notation of Theorem 12-6-4).
5. For any $a, b \in \mathcal{J}$ such that $b \neq 0$ we have $a/b = \sigma(b, a)$; by the Deduction Theorem applied to lines **1** through **4**.
▶▶**6.** Let x be any element of R.
7. There exist elements a, b of $\mathcal{J}$ such that $b \neq 0$ and $x = \sigma(b, a)$; by line **6** and Definition 12-4-7.
▶▶**8.** There exist elements a, b of $\mathcal{J}$ such that $b \neq 0$ and $x = a/b$; by lines **5** and **7**.
9. For any $x \in R$ there exist $a, b \in \mathcal{J}$ such that $b \neq 0$ and $x = a/b$; by the Deduction Theorem applied to lines **6** through **8**.

EXERCISES

1. Prove that for any field $\mathfrak{F} = \langle F, +_F, \cdot_F \rangle$ and any quotients $a/_F\, b$ and $c/_F\, d$ of $\mathfrak{F}$ such that $c \neq 0$ we have $(a/_F\, b)/_F(c/_F\, d) = (a \cdot_F d)/(b \cdot_F c)$.

2. Prove parts **(ii)** and **(iii)** of Theorem 12-6-3.

7. *Ordering of the Rational Field*

By combining Definitions 11-7-4 and 11-6-5 we see that for a given ring $\mathcal{G} = \langle G, +_G, \cdot_G \rangle$, a binary relation $<_G$ on G will be an *ordering* of $\mathcal{G}$ if and only if the following conditions hold.

OP(**i**). If $x, y, z \in G$ and $x <_G y$ and $y <_G z$ then $x <_G z$. (The Transitive Property of $<_G$.)

OP(**ii**). For any $x, y \in G$ exactly one of the relations $x <_G y$, $x = y$, $y <_G x$ holds. (The Trichotomy Property of $<_G$.)

OP(**iii**). Whenever $x <_G y$ then also $x +_G z <_G y +_G z$. (The Additive Property of G.)

OP(**iv**). If $x <_G y$ and $e <_G z$ then $x \cdot_G z <_G y \cdot_G z$ and $z \cdot_G x <_G z \cdot_G y$. (The Multiplicative Property of G. Recall that e is the null element of the additive group of $\mathcal{G}$, i.e., the element such that $x + e = x$ for all $x \in G$. See Definition 11-7-4.)

We have listed these defining properties of an ordering relation here for ready reference in the statements and proofs of the theorems of this section.

We have seen, also, that the ring of *integers* $\mathcal{J} = \langle J, +, \cdot \rangle$ has a *unique* ordering. (See Exercise 2, Section 7, Chapter XI.) A natural question to ask is whether there is an ordering of the field $\mathcal{R} = \langle R, +_R, \cdot_R \rangle$ which is an extension of $<_J$. Indeed, as we shall see, there *is* such an ordering, and there is only *one* such ordering of $\mathcal{R}$; and in fact, *this is the only ordering of* $\mathcal{R}$.

Before stating the definition of this ordering we recall our agreement to drop the subscript "J" from such symbols as "$+_J$", "$\cdot_J$", and "$<_J$"; this convention is used frequently in what follows. At this point we shall find it convenient, also, to write "pq" for "$p \cdot q$", "$rs \cdot uv$" for "$(r \cdot s) \cdot (u \cdot v)$", etc. Finally, we recall (Exercise 4, Chapter XI, Section 2) that for any integers a, b, c, d we have $(a \cdot b) \cdot (c \cdot d) = [a \cdot (b \cdot c)] \cdot d = [(a \cdot b) \cdot c] \cdot d = a \cdot [(b \cdot c) \cdot d] = a \cdot [b \cdot (c \cdot d)]$, so that whenever we write "$a \cdot b \cdot c \cdot d$" it may be interpreted as standing for any one of these products.

DEFINITION 12-7-1. *We define* $<_R$ *to be the binary relation on* R *such that for any integers* a, b, c, d *for which* $b, d \neq 0$, *we have* $a/b <_R c/d$ *if and only if* $ab \cdot dd < cd \cdot bb$.

Thus our ordering of $\mathcal{R}$ is defined in terms of the ordering of $\mathcal{J}$ already introduced. Of course it is not hard to see, informally, how one arrives at such a definition as this. One would like to introduce an ordering between quotients $a/b <_R c/d$, in terms of the ordering $<$ between integers which we already have in our number system. One's first thought is to "cross-multiply," passing from $a/b <_R c/d$ to $ad < bc$; but then we recall from high school algebra that an inequality must be reversed when we multiply through by a negative number, and of course either b or d (or both) may be negative integers. One possible definition, then, would be to say that $a/b <_R c/d$ should hold if and only if: $ad < bc$ and b, d are both positive or both negative, or $bc < ad$ and one of b, d is positive while the other is negative. Logically speaking this is a perfectly possible form of definition, and would lead to a correct theory. (See Exercise 12-7-1.) However, it is a *clumsy* definition which would considerably increase the length of the proofs necessary to establish the fundamental properties of the relation $<_R$. To get a simpler looking definition we rewrite our given quotients using the relations $a/b = ab/bb$ and $c/d = cd/dd$, the advantage being that in the new form the quotients have positive denominators and so there is no question about reversing the direction of the inequality. When we "cross-multiply" the quotients in the new form we arrive at Definition 12-7-1.

However, while the discussion above makes evident how one *arrives* at our definition, it is important to note that from the logical point of view *our definition requires justification*. For if, in addition to a, b, c, and d we have four *other* integers a', b', c', d' (with $b', d' \neq 0$), and if $a/b = a'/b'$ and $c/d = c'/d'$, then from $a/b <_R c/d$ we could infer (by E) that $a'/b' <_R c'/d'$, and so according to Definition 12-7-1 we should have $a'b' \cdot d'd' < c'd' \cdot b'b'$. If it should turn out, however, that $ab \cdot dd < cd \cdot bb$ but *not* $a'b' \cdot d'd' < c'd' \cdot b'b'$, this would show that the proposed Definition 12-7-1 leads to a contradiction, and hence we would reject it as a faulty definition. Thus to justify our definition we need the following:

LEMMA. *Suppose that $a, b, c, d, a', b', c', d'$ are integers in J with $b, d, b', d' \neq 0$, such that $a/b = a'/b'$ and $c/d = c'/d'$. Then if $ab \cdot dd < cd \cdot bb$ we must have also $a'b' \cdot d'd' < c'd' \cdot b'b'$.*

Proof

▶▶ **1.** Let $a, b, c, d, a', b', c', d'$ be integers with $b, d, b', d' \neq 0$.

▶▶ **2.** Suppose $a/b = a'/b'$ and $c/d = c'/d'$.

3. $ab' = a'b$ and $cd' = c'd$; by line **2** and Theorem 12-6-4.

4. $0 < bb$, $0 < dd$, $0 < b'b'$, and $0 < d'd'$; by line **1** and Theorem 11-7-9 (**d**).

▶▶ **5.** *Assume* $ab \cdot dd < cd \cdot bb$.

▶ **6.** $ab \cdot dd \cdot b'b' \cdot d'd' < cd \cdot bb \cdot b'b' \cdot d'd'$; by lines **4** and **5** and Theorem 11-5-3 (**e**).

7. $ab \cdot dd \cdot b'b' \cdot d'd' = ab' \cdot b'b \cdot dd \cdot d'd'$ and $cd \cdot bb \cdot b'b' \cdot d'd' = cd' \cdot d'd \cdot bb \cdot b'b'$; by the commutative and associative laws for $\cdot$ (Theorem 11-2-3).

8. $ab' \cdot b'b \cdot dd \cdot d'd' < cd' \cdot d'd \cdot bb \cdot b'b'$; by E from lines **6** and **7**.

9. $a'b \cdot b'b \cdot dd \cdot d'd' < c'd \cdot d'd \cdot bb \cdot b'b'$; by E from lines **3** and **8**.

10. $a'b \cdot b'b \cdot dd \cdot d'd' = a'b' \cdot d'd' \cdot bb \cdot dd$ and $c'd \cdot d'd \cdot bb \cdot b'b' = c'd' \cdot b'b' \cdot bb \cdot dd$; by the commutative and associative laws for $\cdot$ (Theorem 11-2-3).

▶**11.** $a'b' \cdot d'd' \cdot bb \cdot dd < c'd' \cdot b'b' \cdot bb \cdot dd$; by E from lines **9** and **10**.

▶▶**12.** $a'b' \cdot d'd' < c'd' \cdot b'b'$; by lines **11**, **4**, and Theorem 4-1-9.

13. If $ab \cdot dd < cd \cdot bb$ then $a'b' \cdot d'd' < c'd' \cdot b'b'$; by the Deduction Theorem applied to lines **5** through **12**.

14. The lemma is now obtained by applying the Deduction Theorem to lines **1** and **2** through **13**.

Now that we have justified our definition of the relation $<_R$ (through this lemma), we proceed to show that it has the properties for which it was designed, i.e., that it is indeed an ordering of the system $\mathfrak{R}$.

THEOREM 12-7-2. *The relation* $<_R$ *is an ordering of the ring* $\mathfrak{R} = \langle R, +_R, \cdot_R \rangle$.

To prove this theorem we must show that the relation $<_R$ has the properties OP(**i**) through OP(**iv**) listed at the beginning of this section.

Proof

Part (**i**): The relation $<_R$ satisfies OP(**i**).

Before examining a finished proof of Part (**i**), let us see informally what it is that has to be proved, and how one might go about looking for a proof.

We wish to show that the relation $<_R$ obeys the transitive law. This means that we consider any three quotients a/b, c/d, and e/f such that $a/b <_R c/d$ and $c/d <_R e/f$, and we seek to show that we must have $a/b <_R e/f$. How do we begin?

The first step is to use Definition 12-7-1 to "translate" what we are given, and what we must prove, into terms involving the relation $<$ whose theory has already been largely worked out. When we do this we see that we are *given* $ab \cdot dd < cd \cdot bb$ and $cd \cdot ff < ef \cdot dd$, and we wish *to show* that $ab \cdot ff < ef \cdot bb$. At this point there is no automatic method of proceeding; we need an idea. And here it may occur to us that since we are seeking to prove the transitive law for the new relation $<_R$, perhaps we can *use* the transitive law which we already know holds for the old relation $<$. At first sight, however, it does not seem that we can apply this law to the two inequalities which are "given," since the given inequalities involve four different terms instead of three. But then it may occur to us that if each of the given inequalities is "multiplied through" by a suitable quantity we can arrive at two new inequalities which involve a total of only three terms.

Upon inspection we observe that the necessary multipliers are positive, and hence the multiplications are justified. We thus pass from the "given" inequalities to the "new" ones $ab \cdot dd \cdot ff < cd \cdot bb \cdot ff$ and $cd \cdot ff \cdot bb < ef \cdot dd \cdot bb$, and then, by the transitive law of $<$, to $ab \cdot dd \cdot ff < ef \cdot dd \cdot bb$. Now can we pass from *this* inequality to the one we need to show? Inspection shows that an application of the cancellation law for the relation $<$ would do the trick. Is the application justified? Yes, since the cancelled term is positive! Well then, we have found our proof. Now let us see how we write it up in finished form.

▶▶ **1.** Let x, y, z be any elements of R such that $x <_R y$ and $y <_R z$.

▶▶ **2.** There are integers a, b, c, d, e, f in J, with $b, d, f \neq 0$, such that $x = a/b$, $y = c/d$, $z = e/f$; by line **1** and Theorem 12-6-5 (**ii**).

3. $a/b <_R c/d$ and $c/d <_R e/f$; by E from lines **1** and **2**.

▶ **4.** $ab \cdot dd < cd \cdot bb$ and $cd \cdot ff < ef \cdot dd$; by line **3** and the definition of $<_R$ (Definition 12-7-1).

5. $0 < bb$, $0 < dd$, and $0 < ff$; by line **2** and Theorem 11-7-9 (**d**).

▶ **6.** $ab \cdot dd \cdot ff < cd \cdot bb \cdot ff$ and $cd \cdot ff \cdot bb < ef \cdot dd \cdot bb$; by lines **4** and **5** and Theorem 11-5-3 (**e**).

7. $ab \cdot dd \cdot ff = ab \cdot ff \cdot dd$, $ef \cdot dd \cdot bb = ef \cdot bb \cdot dd$, and $ed \cdot bb \cdot ff = cd \cdot ff \cdot bb$; by the commutative and associative laws for $\cdot$ (Theorem 11-2-3).

8. $ab \cdot ff \cdot dd < cd \cdot bb \cdot ff$ and $cd \cdot bb \cdot ff < ef \cdot bb \cdot dd$; by E from lines **6** and **7**.

▶ **9.** $ab \cdot ff \cdot dd < ef \cdot bb \cdot dd$; by line **8** and the transitive law for $<$ (Theorem 11-5-3 (**d**)).

▶ **10.** $ab \cdot ff < ef \cdot bb$; by lines **5** and **9** and the cancellation law for $<$ (Theorem 4-1-9).

▶▶ **11.** $a/b <_R e/f$; by line **10** and the definition of $<_R$ (Definition 12-7-1).

12. $x <_R z$; by E from lines **2** and **11**.

13. If x, y, z are any elements of R such that $x <_R y$ and $y <_R z$ then $x <_R z$; by the Deduction Theorem applied to lines **1** through **12**.

Thus the transitive law holds for $<_R$.

Part (**ii**): The relation $<_R$ satisfies OP(**ii**).

▶▶ **1.** Let x, y be any elements of R.

▶▶ **2.** There are integers a, b, c, d in J, with $b, d \neq 0$, such that $x = a/b$ and $y = c/d$; by line **1** and Theorem 12-6-5 (**ii**).

▶ **3.** $a/b = c/d$ if and only if $ad = bc$; by line **2** and Theorem 12-6-4.

4. $bd \neq 0$; by line **2** and Exercise 11-2-3.

5. If $ad = bc$ then $ad \cdot bd = bc \cdot bd$; by E.

6. If $ad \cdot bd = bc \cdot bd$ then $ad = bc$; by line **4** and the cancellation law for $\cdot$ [Theorem 11-2-4 (**iii**)].

▶ 7. $a/b = c/d$ if and only if $ad \cdot bd = bc \cdot bd$; by logic from lines **3** and **6**.

8. $ad \cdot bd = ab \cdot dd$ and $bc \cdot bd = cd \cdot bb$; by the commutative and associative laws for $\cdot$ (Theorem 11-2-3).

▶ 9. $a/b = c/d$ if and only if $ab \cdot dd = cd \cdot bb$; by E from lines **7** and **8**.

▶ 10. $a/b <_R c/d$ if and only if $ab \cdot dd < cd \cdot bb$; by line **2** and Definition 12-7-1.

▶ 11. $c/d <_R a/b$ if and only if $cd \cdot bb < ab \cdot dd$; by line **2** and Definition 12-7-1.

▶▶ 12. One and only one of the following holds: $ab \cdot dd < cd \cdot bb$, $ab \cdot dd = cd \cdot bb$, $cd \cdot bb < ab \cdot dd$; by the Trichotomy Law for $<$ [Theorem 11-5-3 (**g**)].

▶▶ 13. One and only one of the following holds: $a/b <_R c/d$, $a/b = c/d$, $c/d <_R a/b$; by logic from lines **9**, **10**, **11**, and **12**.

14. One and only one of the following holds: $x <_R y$, $x = y$, $y <_R x$; by E from lines **2** and **13**.

15. The Trichotomy Law for $<_R$ now follows by applying the Deduction Theorem to lines **1** through **14**.

Part (**iii**): The relation $<_R$ satisfies OP(**iii**).

▶▶ 1. Let x, y be any elements of R such that $x <_R y$, and let z be any element of R whatever.

▶▶ 2. There are integers a, b, c, d, e, f in $\mathcal{J}$, with $b, d, f \neq 0$, such that $x = a/b$, $y = c/d$, $z = e/f$; by line **1** and Theorem 12-6-5 (**ii**).

3. $a/b <_R c/d$; by E from lines **1** and **2**.

4. $ab \cdot dd < cd \cdot bb$; by line **3** and Definition 12-7-1.

▶▶ 5. $x +_R z = a/b +_R e/f$ and $y +_R z = c/d +_R e/f$; by E from line **2**.

▶▶ 6. $a/b +_R e/f = (af + eb)/bf$ and $(c/d +_R e/f) = (cf + ed)/df$; by line **2** and Theorem 12-6-4.

▶ 7. $ab \cdot dd \cdot ff \cdot ff < cd \cdot bb \cdot ff \cdot ff$; by E from line **4**.

8. $ab \cdot dd \cdot ff \cdot ff = af \cdot bf \cdot df \cdot df$ and $cd \cdot bb \cdot ff \cdot ff = cf \cdot df \cdot bf \cdot bf$; by the commutative and associative laws for $\cdot$ (Theorem 11-2-3).

9. $af \cdot bf \cdot df \cdot df < cf \cdot df \cdot bf \cdot bf$; by E from lines **7** and **8**.

10. $eb \cdot bf \cdot df \cdot df = ed \cdot df \cdot bf \cdot bf$; by the commutative and associative laws for $\cdot$ (Theorem 11-2-3).

11. $af \cdot bf \cdot df \cdot df + eb \cdot bf \cdot df \cdot df < cf \cdot df \cdot bf \cdot bf + ed \cdot df \cdot bf \cdot bf$;

by lines **9** and **10** and the additive law for $<$ (Theorem 11-5-3 (**a**)).

▶**12.** $(af + eb) \cdot bf \cdot df \cdot df < (cf + ed) \cdot df \cdot bf \cdot bf$; by linc **11** and the distributive law for $\cdot$ (Theorem 11-2-3).

▶▶**13.** $(af + eb)/bf <_R (cf + ed)/df$; by line **12** and the definition of $<_R$ (Definition 12-7-1).

▶▶**14.** $x +_R z <_R y +_R z$; by E from lines **5**, **6**, and **13**.

15. The Additive Law for $<_R$ is now obtained by applying the Deduction Theorem to lines **1** through **14**.

Part (**iv**): The relation $<_R$ satisfies OP(**iv**).

▶▶ **1.** Let x, y, z be any elements of R such that $x <_R y$ and $0 <_R z$.

▶▶ **2.** There are integers a, b, c, d, e, f in J, with $b, d, f \neq 0$, such that $x = a/b$, $y = c/d$, $z = e/f$; by line **1** and Theorem 12-6-5 (**ii**).

3. $0 = 0/1$; by Theorem 12-6-4.

4. $a/b <_R c/d$ and $0/1 <_R e/f$; by E from lines **1**, **2**, and **3**.

5. $ab \cdot dd < cd \cdot bb$ and $0 \cdot 1 \cdot ff < e \cdot f \cdot 1 \cdot 1$; by line **4** and the definition of $<_R$ (Definition 12-7-1).

▶▶ **6.** $x \cdot_R z = a/b \cdot_R e/f$ and $y \cdot_R z = c/d \cdot_R e/f$; by E from line **2**.

▶▶ **7.** $a/b \cdot_R e/f = ae/bf$ and $c/d \cdot_R e/f = ce/df$; by line **2** and Theorem 12-6-4.

8. $0 \cdot 1 \cdot f \cdot f = 0$ and $e \cdot f \cdot 1 \cdot 1 = ef$; by Definition 11-2-1 and Theorem 11-2-3.

9. $0 < ef$; by E from lines **5** and **8**.

10. $0 < ff$; by line **2** and Theorem 11-7-9 (**d**).

▶**11.** $ab \cdot dd \cdot ef \cdot ff < cd \cdot bb \cdot ef \cdot ff$; by lines **5**, **9**, **10** and the multiplicative property of $<$ (Theorem 11-5-3).

12. $ab \cdot dd \cdot ef \cdot ff = ae \cdot bf \cdot df \cdot df$ and $cd \cdot bb \cdot ef \cdot ff = ce \cdot df \cdot bf \cdot bf$; by the commutative and associative laws for $\cdot$ (Theorem 11-2-3).

▶**13.** $ae \cdot bf \cdot df \cdot df < ce \cdot df \cdot bf \cdot bf$; by E from lines **11** and **12**.

▶▶**14.** $ae/bf <_R ce/df$; by line **13** and the definition of $<_R$ (Definition 12-7-1).

▶▶**15.** $x \cdot_R z <_R y \cdot_R z$; by E from lines **6**, **7**, and **14**.

16. The Multiplicative Law for $<_R$ now follows by applying the Deduction Theorem to lines **1** through **15**.

Parts (**i**) through (**iv**) together establish Theorem 12-7-2.

Now that we know the relation $<_R$ is an ordering of the system $\mathcal{R} = \langle R, +_R, \cdot_R \rangle$, we wish to show that it is an extension of the ordering relation $<$ of the system $\mathcal{J} = \langle J, +, \cdot \rangle$ (of which $\mathcal{R}$ is an extension by Theorem 12-4-8).

THEOREM 12-7-3. *The relation $<_R$ is an extension of the relation $<$, i.e., for any $a, b \in \mathcal{J}$ we have $a <_R b$ if and only if $a < b$.*

Proof

▶▶1. Let a, b be any integers in $\mathcal{J}$.

2. $a = a/1$ and $b = b/1$; by line **1** and Theorems 12-4-8, 12-6-4.

▶3. $a <_R b$ if and only if $a/1 <_R b/1$; by E from line **2**.

▶4. $a/1 <_R b/1$ if and only if $a \cdot 1 \cdot 1 \cdot 1 < b \cdot 1 \cdot 1 \cdot 1$; by the definition of $<_R$ (Definition 12-7-1).

5. $a \cdot 1 \cdot 1 \cdot 1 = a$ and $b \cdot 1 \cdot 1 \cdot 1 = b$; by Theorem 11-2-3.

▶6. $a/1 <_R b/1$ if and only if $a < b$; by E from lines **4** and **5**.

▶▶7. $a <_R b$ if and only if $a < b$; by logic from lines **3** and **6**.

8. For any $a, b \in \mathcal{J}$ we have $a <_R b$ if and only if $a < b$; by the Deduction Theorem applied to lines **1** through **7**.

EXERCISES

1. Show that if a, b, c, d are integers and either (**i**) $0 < a$ and $0 < b$ or (**ii**) $a < 0$ and $b < 0$, then $a/b <_R c/d$ if and only if $ad < bc$; but that if (**iii**) $0 < a$ and $b < 0$, or (**iv**) $a < 0$ and $0 < b$, then $a/b <_R c/d$ if and only if $bc < ad$.

2. *Show that if $<'$ is *any* ordering of $\mathcal{R}$, and if a, b, c, d are any integers of $\mathcal{J}$ such that $0 <' b$ and $0 <' d$, then $a/b <' c/d$ if and only if $ad <' bc$.

8. *Uniqueness of the Ordering* $<_R$

It is natural to ask whether there are other orderings of $\mathcal{R}$ besides the relation $<_R$. In other words, we raise the question whether there are any binary relations on R, other than $<_R$, which satisfy properties OP(**i**) through OP(**iv**) listed at the beginning of Section **7**. We have seen (Exercise 2, Chapter XI, Section 7) that there is only one ordering of $\mathcal{J}$, and hence we might suspect that there is only one ordering of $\mathcal{R}$. This is indeed the case.

THEOREM 12-8-1. *$<_R$ is the only ordering of $\mathcal{R} = \langle R, +_R, \cdot_R \rangle$.*

In order to prove this theorem it will be convenient first to prove two lemmas.

LEMMA 12-8-1.1. *If $<'$ is any ordering of $\mathcal{R}$ which is an extension of $<$ (i.e., such that for any $a, b \in \mathcal{J}$ we have $a <' b$ if and only if $a < b$), then $<' = <_R$.*

Proof

▶▶ 1. Let $<'$ be any ordering of $\mathcal{R}$ which is an extension of $<$.

▶▶ 2. Let x and y be any elements of R.

▶ 3. There are integers a, b, c, d in $\mathcal{J}$, with $b, d \neq 0$, such that $x = a/b$ and $y = c/d$; by line **2** and Theorem 12-6-5 (**ii**).

4. $x <' y$ if and only if $a/b <' c/d$; by E from lines **2** and **3**.
5. $a/b = ab/bb$ and $c/d = cd/dd$; by Theorem 12-6-4 (**Bii**).
▶ 6. $x <' y$ if and only if $ab/bb <' cd/dd$; by E from lines **4** and **5**.
7. $0 < bb$ and $0 < dd$; by line **3** and Theorem 11-7-9 (**d**).
8. $0 <' bb$ and $0 <' dd$; by lines **1** and **7** and the definition of extension of a relation.
▶ 9. $ab/bb <' cd/dd$ if and only if $ab \cdot dd <' cd \cdot bb$; by lines **1** and **8**, and Exercise 12-7-2.
▶ 10. $ab \cdot dd <' cd \cdot bb$ if and only if $ab \cdot dd < cd \cdot bb$; by line **1** and the definition of extension of a relation.
11. $ab \cdot dd < cd \cdot bb$ if and only if $a/b <_R c/d$; by Definition 12-7-1.
▶ 12. $ab \cdot dd < cd \cdot bb$ if and only if $x <_R y$; by E from lines **3** and **11**.
▶▶ 13. For any elements x and y of R we have $x <' y$ if and only if $x <_R y$; by lines **2**, **6**, **9**, **10**, and **12**.
▶▶ 14. $<' = <_R$; by line **13** and the principle of extensionality for relations (see Chapter I, Section 4).
15. The lemma follows by applying the Deduction Theorem to lines **1** through **14**.

LEMMA 12-8-1.2. *If $<'$ is* **any** *ordering of $\mathcal{R}$ then it is an extension of $<$ (i.e., for any $a, b \in \mathcal{J}$ we have $a <' b$ if and only if $a < b$).*

Proof

▶▶ 1. Let $<'$ be any ordering of $\mathcal{R}$.
▶▶ 2. Let $<''$ be the relation *on* $\mathcal{J}$ such that for all $a, b \in \mathcal{J}$ we have $a <'' b$ if and only if $a <' b$.
3. $<''$ is an ordering of $\mathcal{J}$; by line **2** and OP(**i**) through OP(**iv**).
▶▶ 4. $<'' = <$; by line **3** and Exercise 11-7-2.
▶▶ 5. $<'$ is an extension of $<$; By lines **2**, **4**, by E and the definition of extension of a relation.
6. The lemma follows on applying the Deduction Theorem to lines **1** through **5**.

The proof of Theorem 12-8-1 is now an immediate consequence of these two lemmas.

9. Density of the Rational Number System

We shall close this chapter with a discussion of an interesting property of the unique ordering $<_R$, of the rational number system $\mathcal{R}$, which is not shared by $\mathcal{J}$ and its ordering $<$.

DEFINITION 12-9-1. *A ring* $\mathcal{G} = \langle G, +_G, \cdot_G \rangle$ *with an ordering* $<_G$ *is said to be* **dense relative to the ordering** $<_G$ *if, for every pair of elements* $a, b \in G$ *such that* $a <_G b$, *there is an element* $c \in G$ *such that* $a <_G c$ *and* $c <_G b$.

We shall show that the ring of integers $\mathcal{J} = \langle J, +, \cdot \rangle$ is *not* dense relative to its unique ordering $<$. In order to do this it suffices to show that there is a single pair of integers a, b with $a < b$ but such that there is no x satisfying both $a < x$ and $x < b$. Our next theorem is, in fact, much stronger than this proposition.

THEOREM 12-9-2. *For any integer* a *(i.e., any element of* J*) there is* ***no*** *integer* x *such that both* $a < x$ *and* $x < a + 1$.

To prove this theorem we observe that if there were some integers a and x such that both $a < x$ and $x < a + 1$ then, by the additive property of x, we would have $a + (-a) < x + (-a)$ and $x + (-a) < (a + 1) + (-a)$. From this we could infer that there exists an integer z (namely $x - a$), such that $0 < z$ and $z < 1$. Now since $0 < z$, we have $z \in P$. But for all $z \in P$ we have $z = 1$ or $1 < z$, and hence *not* $z < 1$ by the Trichotomy law for $<$. From this contradiction we see that our supposition is false, and hence that the theorem is true. The details of the proof will be left as an exercise for the reader.

THEOREM 12-9-3. *The ring of rational numbers* $\mathcal{R} = \langle R, +_R, \cdot_R \rangle$ *is dense relative to* $<_R$.

To prove this theorem we observe that if x and y are any rational numbers such that $x <_R y$ then the rational number $(x +_R y)/2$ $(=m$, say), has the property that $x <_R m$ and $m <_R y$. The details of the proof are left as an exercise for the reader.

EXERCISES

1. Prove Theorem 12-9-2.
2. Prove Theorem 12-9-3.

XIII

Certain Irrational Numbers

1. Extensions of R

We have not yet finished the process of extending number systems. Here we go again! We shall see that there are still certain simple equations whose *coefficients* are in the number system we have so far developed, $\mathcal{R} = \langle R, +_R, \cdot_R \rangle$, but which have no *solution* in this system.

Before proceeding to show that the field of rational numbers does not contain all objects that we would like intuitively to call numbers, let us agree, for the sake of simplicity, to drop the subscripts "R" from the symbols "$+_R$", "$\cdot_R$" and "$<_R$". Thus, if not otherwise specified, the symbols "$+$", "$\cdot$", and "$<$" will henceforth mean "$+_R$", "$\cdot_R$", and "$<_R$" respectively. The reader will recall that in a similar manner the subscripts "J" were deleted in the last chapter without introducing ambiguity.

Now let us show that we need more numbers.

THEOREM **13-1-1.** *There is no rational number x such that $x \cdot x = 2$.*

Proof

We shall give only an informal sketch of a proof of this theorem: The form is "proof by contradiction." We leave the reader to supply detailed reasoning to justify many of the steps. In passing, we note that this theorem and its proof were due originally to the famous Greek geometer, Euclid.

1. *Suppose* there is some rational number x such that $x \cdot x = 2$.

2. Since x is rational there are integers a and b with $b \neq 0$, such that $x = a/b$. Clearly $a \neq 0$, too, since otherwise we would have $x = 0$ and hence $x \cdot x = 0$, which is contrary to line **1**.

3. $(a/b) \cdot (a/b) = (a \cdot a)/(b \cdot b)$, and so by lines **1** and **2** we get $(a \cdot a)/(b \cdot b) = 2$. It follows that $(a \cdot a) = 2 \cdot (b \cdot b)$.

4. If $a < 0$ let $c = -a$, and if $a > 0$ let $c = a$; then in any case c is an integer, $c > 0$, and $c \cdot c = a \cdot a$. Similarly, take $d = -b$ if $b < 0$ and take $d = b$ if $b > 0$. (Recall that neither $a = 0$ nor $b = 0$ by line **2**.) Then d is an integer, $d > 0$, and $d \cdot d = b \cdot b$.

5. c and d are integers, $c > 0$, $d > 0$, and $(c \cdot c) = 2 \cdot (d \cdot d)$; by lines **3** and **4**.

6. Form the set G of all those *positive* integers e such that, for some positive integer f we have $(e \cdot e) = 2 \cdot (f \cdot f)$. By line **5** the set G is not empty, since $c \in G$. Hence by Theorem 2-7-9 we can find a *smallest* number, say e_0, in G. Thus e_0 is a positive integer, and for some positive integer f_0 we have $(e_0 \cdot e_0) = 2 \cdot (f_0 \cdot f_0)$. Furthermore, if p is any positive integer such that $p < e_0$, then *there is no* positive integer q such that $(p \cdot p) = 2 \cdot (q \cdot q)$.

7. If e_0 were an odd number, say $e_0 = 2 \cdot n + 1$, then also $(e_0 \cdot e_0)$ would be an odd number, namely $(2 \cdot n + 1) \cdot (2 \cdot n + 1) = 2 \cdot 2 \cdot (n \cdot n + n) + 1$. But in fact $e_0 \cdot e_0$ is an even number, namely $2 \cdot (f_0 \cdot f_0)$, by line **6**. Hence e_0 must be an even number. That is, for some positive integer q we must have $e_0 = 2 \cdot q$.

8. $(2 \cdot q) \cdot (2 \cdot q) = 2 \cdot (f_0 \cdot f_0)$; by lines **6** and **7**. Hence $f_0 \cdot f_0 = 2 \cdot (q \cdot q)$.

9. From $(e_0 \cdot e_0) = 2 \cdot (f_0 \cdot f_0)$ and $e_0 > 0$ (line **6**) we see that we cannot have $e_0 = f_0$, for that would lead to the incorrect conclusion $1 = 2$. Furthermore we cannot have $e_0 < f_0$, for that would lead to the conclusion $e_0 \cdot e_0 < f_0 \cdot f_0$ and thence to the incorrect conclusion $e_0 \cdot e_0 < 2 \cdot (f_0 \cdot f_0)$. Hence we must have $f_0 < e_0$.

10. f_0 and q are positive integers, $(f_0 \cdot f_0) = 2 \cdot (q \cdot q)$, and $f_0 < e_0$; by lines **7**, **8**, and **9**.

11. Line **10** contradicts the final sentence of line **6**. This contradiction arises from our supposition in line **1**. Hence this supposition must be false. That is, there is *no* rational number x such that $x \cdot x = 2$.

This theorem leads us to wonder whether we can extend our number system beyond the rational numbers so as to introduce a new number x such that we do have $x \cdot x = 2$. Let us phrase the question precisely:

PROBLEM A. *Can we construct a number system* $\mathfrak{A} = \langle A, +_A, \cdot_A \rangle$, *an extension of the rational field* $\mathfrak{R} = \langle R, +, \cdot \rangle$, *in which the equation* $x \cdot_A x = 2$ *has a solution, and in which the laws which characterize fields are still satisfied?*

The reader has certainly encountered the expression "the square root of 2" during the course of his mathematical experience, so intuitively, at least, he knows that there *is* a "number" which solves $x \cdot_A x = 2$. But how do we produce it from what we have; and, furthermore, how do we imbed it in a field? The answers to these questions may not be immediately evident, but it will be seen that a field extension of $\mathfrak{R}$ can indeed be produced in which a solution of $x \cdot_A x = 2$ exists, and in which furthermore, many other equations of the form $a \cdot_A (x \cdot_A x) +_A b \cdot_A x +_A c = 0$, where a, b, c are in R, also have solutions.

Before we solve *Problem A* it might be well to recall how the square root of 2 enters into measurement problems. We know, for example, from our study of geometry, that if we have a square whose side is 1 unit in length, then the length of the diagonal d has the property that

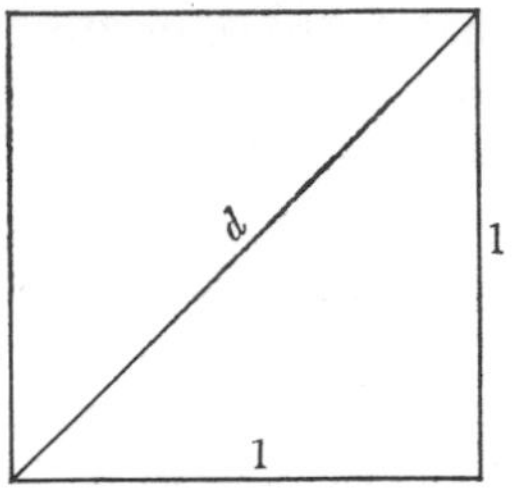

$$d \cdot d = 1 \cdot 1 + 1 \cdot 1,$$

or

$$d \cdot d = 2.$$

(This is a consequence of the famous theorem of Pythagoras which states that the sum of the squares of the lengths of the two sides of a right triangle is equal to the square of the length of the hypotenuse.)

Thus, if our number system is to have applicability to problems of measurement it is essential that we have some number whose square is 2. That is, not only for the equation solver in an ivory tower, but also for the practical man of the world, a square root of 2 is a handy number to have. Of course, the practical man is generally satisfied to have only a rough, intuitive idea of what $\sqrt{2}$ is. But we assume that the reader who has stayed with the theory this far is interested in a more precise idea of this number: He wants to know how $\sqrt{2}$ can be logically incorporated into the theory based upon our *four axioms* for the system of positive integers.

In Chapter XII we showed how an intelligent person whose mathematical experience included a knowledge of the system of integers, but not of rational numbers, might arrive at a construction of the rational number system. It would be possible to adopt a similar approach here, first giving an analysis of the problem, as we did in Chapter XII, and then proceeding with the construction of the required extension. But instead, we will revert to the method used in extending $\mathfrak{N}$ to $\mathfrak{J}$, first producing a solution of *Problem A* and then showing that it is essentially the only solution. Thus a person arriving at a solution of the problem by *any* means must arrive at essentially the one which we shall present.

There will be no harm done in letting the reader in on the intuitive idea which underlies our construction. If we can somehow construct the set of all those numbers which we customarily write in the form $a + b\sqrt{2}$, where a and b are rational, then in this set, certainly, there is the number $\sqrt{2}$ (as we see by taking $a = 0$ and $b = 1$). Furthermore, this set is closed under the operations $+$ and $\cdot$ as we see by a little high school computation: For let $a_1 + b_1\sqrt{2}$ and $a_2 + b_2\sqrt{2}$, where a_1, b_1, a_2, b_2 are rational numbers, be any numbers of the given form. Clearly $(a_1 + b_1\sqrt{2}) + (a_2 + b_2\sqrt{2}) = (a_1 + a_2) + (b_1 + b_2)\sqrt{2}$. But since a_1, b_1, a_2, b_2 are rational, the numbers $(a_1 + a_2)$ and $(b_1 + b_2)$ are also rational, and thus the sum is of the given form. Likewise, $(a_1 + b_1\sqrt{2}) \cdot (a_2 + b_2\sqrt{2}) = (a_1a_2 + 2b_1b_2) + (a_1b_2 + b_1a_2)\sqrt{2}$, and so the product is also of the given form. These observations suggest that such a set may provide a solution of the kind sought—though they are far from establishing this proposition in all detail.

Before the reader gets the idea that we have already constructed a solution to *Problem A*, however, let him be cautioned that **(i)** there is no object which we have yet identified as $\sqrt{2}$; and **(ii)** the operations $+$ and $\cdot$ are binary operations *on* R, and hence $a + b\sqrt{2}$ has no meaning at all since $\sqrt{2}$ is certainly not in R (Theorem 13-1-1). These observations show that we do not have even a partial solution of our problem. We have merely an intuitive guide to the construction of a solution.

DEFINITION 13-1-2. *Let H be the set of all ordered pairs $\langle a, b\rangle$, where $a, b \in R$. Let τ be any one-one function*[1] *with domain H such that $\tau(a, 0) = a$ for all $a \in R$, and let A be the range of τ. We define the binary operations $+_A$ and $\cdot_A$ on A as follows: For any $\langle a, b\rangle$ and $\langle c, d\rangle$ in H we set $\tau(a, b) +_A \tau(c, d) = \tau(a + c, b + d)$, and we set $\tau(a, b) \cdot_A \tau(c, d) = \tau(a \cdot c + 2 \cdot (b \cdot d), a \cdot d + b \cdot c)$. Finally, let $\mathfrak{A} = \langle A, +_A, \cdot_A\rangle$.*

This definition requires some justification. How do we know, for example, that there is such a one-one function τ as is described in the definition? To show that there is at least one such function, suppose first that there is no ordered pair $\langle a, b\rangle$ such that $a \in R$, $b \in R$, and also $\langle a, b\rangle \in R$. (Since the nature of the objects in R was never completely specified, neither this possibility nor its opposite can be ruled out.) Then we define

$$\tau(a, b) = \begin{cases} a \text{ if } b = 0 \\ \langle a, b\rangle \text{ if } b \neq 0. \end{cases}$$

Obviously, in this case, τ is one-one. But if, by chance, we *do* have $\langle a, b\rangle \in R$ for some a and b which are both in R, then we define, instead,

$$\tau(a, b) = \begin{cases} a \text{ if } b = 0 \\ \langle\langle a, b\rangle, R\rangle \text{ for } b \neq 0. \end{cases}$$

Again, on the basis of our system of set theory, it is easily shown that τ is one-one. (The reader will be asked to do this as an exercise.) Thus we obtain the existence of at least one function τ. Actually, there are others, but it is not important in what follows *which* τ we take.

That our definition of $+_A$ and $\cdot_A$ is a valid definition is evident, for if

[1] The symbol "τ" is the Greek letter tau.

$\tau(a_1, b_1) = \tau(a_2, b_2)$ and $\tau(c_1, d_1) = \tau(c_2, d_2)$ we can show easily, by using the one-one property of τ, that we must have $\tau(a_1, b_1) +_A \tau(c_1, d_1) = \tau(a_2, b_2) +_A \tau(c_2, d_2)$ and $\tau(a_1, b_1) \cdot_A \tau(c_1, d_1) = \tau(a_2, b_2) \cdot_A \tau(c_2, d_2)$.

The anxious reader who is worried about whether we have abandoned the intuitive idea discussed above can be reassured, for we will later show that $\tau(a, b)$ reduces to the form $a + b\sqrt{2}$ for all $a, b \in R$. But before we do that, let us get on with showing that $\mathcal{A}$ is a solution of our problem.

THEOREM 13-1-3. *The system* $\mathcal{A} = \langle A, +_A, \cdot_A \rangle$ *is an extension of the system of rationals* $\mathcal{R} = \langle R, +, \cdot \rangle$ *(i.e.,* **(i)** $R \subseteq A$; **(ii)** *for any* $x, y \in R$ *we have* $x +_A y = x + y$; **(iii)** *for any* $x, y \in R$, *we have* $x \cdot_A y = x \cdot y$.*)*

Proof of Part **(i)**: $R \subseteq A$

1. Let x be any element of R.

2. $x = \tau(x, 0)$; by line **1** and the definition of τ (Definition 13-1-2).

3. $x \in A$; by line **2**, E, and Definition 13-1-2.

4. If x is any element of R then we have $x \in A$; by the Deduction Theorem applied to lines **1** through **3**.

5. $R \subseteq A$; by line **4** and the definition of $\subseteq$ (Definition 9-3-1).

Proof of Part **(ii)**: For any $x, y \in R$, we have $x +_A y = x + y$.

1. Let x, y be any elements in R.

2. $x +_A y = \tau(x, 0) +_A \tau(y, 0)$; by line **1** and Definition 13-1-2.

3. $= \tau(x + y, 0)$; by the Definition of $+_A$ (Definition 13-1-2).

4. $= x + y$; by the definition of τ (Definition 13-1-2).

5. $x +_A y = x + y$; by E applied to lines **2** through **4**.

6. For any $x, y \in R$, we have $x +_A y = x + y$; by the Deduction Theorem applied to lines **1** through **5**.

Proof of Part **(iii)**: For any $x, y \in R$, we have $x \cdot_A y = x \cdot y$.
The proof of this part will be left as an exercise for the reader.

Clearly Theorem 13-1-3 follows immediately from parts **(i)** through **(iii)** and the definition of an extension of a number system.

To complete the verification that $\mathcal{A}$ is a solution to *Problem A* we must show that $\mathcal{A}$ is a field and that it contains an element x such that $x \cdot_A x = 2$. In order to minimize the references back to previous chapters we shall list here the conditions that are necessary and sufficient for any number system $\mathcal{G} = \langle G, +_G, \cdot_G \rangle$ to be a field. On referring to Definitions 12-2-2, 11-7-1, and 11-6-1, we readily see that $\mathcal{G}$ is a field if and only if the following conditions hold.

F**(i)** The operations $+_G$ and $\cdot_G$ are commutative;

F**(ii)** $+_G$ and $\cdot_G$ are associative;

F**(iii)** $\cdot_G$ is left distributive over $+_G$;

F(**iv**) For every $a, b \in G$ there is one, and only one, $x \in G$ such that $x +_G b = a$;

F(**v**) If a, b are any elements of G such that $a \neq e$, where e is the null element of the group $\langle G, +\rangle$, then there is an element $x \in G$ such that $a \cdot_G x = b$. (Recall that e is the unique element, whose existence follows from F(**i**) through F(**iv**), such that $e +_G x = x$ and $e \cdot_G x = e$ for all $x \in G$.)

THEOREM 13-1-4. *The system* $\mathfrak{A} = \langle A, +_A, \cdot_A\rangle$ *is a field.*

Proof of Part (**i**): $\mathfrak{A}$ satisfies F(**i**).

1. Let $\tau(a, b)$ and $\tau(c, d)$ be any elements in A.
2. $\tau(a, b) +_A \tau(c, d) = \tau(a + c,\ \ b + d)$; by the definition of $+_A$ (Definition 13-1-2).
3. $= \tau(c + a,\ \ d + b)$; by E and the commutative law for $+$ (Theorem 12-4-12).
4. $= \tau(c, d) +_A \tau(a, b)$; by definition of $+_A$.
5. $\tau(a, b) +_A \tau(c, d) = \tau(c, d) +_A \tau(a, b)$; by E applied to lines **2** through **4**.
6. That $+_A$ is commutative follows by applying the Deduction Theorem to lines **1** through **5**.

Verification that $\cdot_A$ is commutative will be left as an exercise for the reader.

Proof of Part (**ii**): $\mathfrak{A}$ satisfies F(**ii**).

We shall prove that $\cdot_A$ is associative and leave the proof that $+_A$ is associative to the reader.

►► **1.** Let $\tau(a, b)$, $\tau(c, d)$, and $\tau(e, f)$ be any elements in A.
2. $\tau(a, b) \cdot_A \tau(c, d) = \tau(a \cdot c + 2 \cdot (b \cdot d),\ \ a \cdot d + b \cdot c)$; by the definition of $\cdot_A$ (Definition 13-1-2).
► **3.** $[\tau(a, b) \cdot_A \tau(c, d)] \cdot_A \tau(e, f) = \tau(a \cdot c + 2 \cdot (b \cdot d),\ \ a \cdot d + b \cdot c) \cdot_A \tau(e, f)$; by E from line **2**.
► **4.** $= \tau[(a \cdot c + 2 \cdot (b \cdot d)) \cdot e + 2 \cdot (a \cdot d + b \cdot c) \cdot f,\ \ (a \cdot c + 2 \cdot (b \cdot d)) \cdot f + (a \cdot d + b \cdot c) \cdot e]$; by the definition of $\cdot_A$ (Definition 13-1-2).
5. $\tau(c, d) \cdot_A \tau(e, f) = \tau(c \cdot e + 2 \cdot (d \cdot f),\ \ c \cdot f + d \cdot e)$; by the definition of $\cdot_A$.
► **6.** $\tau(a, b) \cdot_A [\tau(c, d) \cdot_A \tau(e, f)] = \tau(a, b) \cdot_A \tau(c \cdot e + 2 \cdot (d \cdot f),\ \ c \cdot f + d \cdot e)$; by E from line **5**.
► **7.** $= \tau[a \cdot (c \cdot e + 2 \cdot (d \cdot f)) + 2 \cdot (b \cdot (c \cdot f + d \cdot e)),\ \ a \cdot (c \cdot f + d \cdot e) + b \cdot (c \cdot e + 2 \cdot (d \cdot f))]$; by the definition of $\cdot_A$ (Definition 13-1-2).
► **8.** $= \tau[(a \cdot c + 2 \cdot (b \cdot d)) \cdot e + 2 \cdot (a \cdot d$

$+ b \cdot c) \cdot f,\ (a \cdot c + 2 \cdot b \cdot d) \cdot f + (a \cdot d + b \cdot c) \cdot e]$; by the commutative and associative laws for $+$ and $\cdot$ (Theorem 12-4-12).

▶▶ **9.** $[\tau(a, b) \cdot_A \tau(c, d)] \cdot_A \tau(e, f) = \tau(a, b) \cdot_A [\tau(c, d) \cdot_A \tau(e, f)]$; by E from lines **3**, **4**, **6**, and **8**.

10. The Associative Law for $\cdot_A$ follows by applying the Deduction Theorem to lines **1** through **9**.

Proof of Part (**iii**): $\mathfrak{A}$ satisfies F(**iii**).

The proof of part (**iii**) is left as an exercise.

Proof of Part (**iv**): $\mathfrak{A}$ satisfies F(**iv**).

▶▶**1.** Let $\tau(a, b)$ and $\tau(c, d)$ be any elements in A.

2. $a, b, c, d \in R$; by line **1** and the definition of A (Definition 13-1-2).

3. $\mathfrak{R} = \langle R, +, \cdot \rangle$ is a field; by Theorem 12-4-12.

▶▶**4.** There are elements $x, y \in R$ such that $x + a = c$ and $y + b = d$; by lines **2** and **3** and F(**iv**).

5. $\tau(x, y) +_A \tau(a, b) = \tau(x + a,\ y + b)$; by the definition of $+_A$ (Definition 13-1-2).

6. $\qquad = \tau(c, d)$; by E from line **4**.

▶▶**7.** $\tau(x, y) +_A \tau(a, b) = \tau(c, d)$; by E from lines **5** and **6**.

8. If $\tau(a, b)$ and $\tau(c, d)$ are any elements of A there is an element $\tau(x, y)$ of A such that $\tau(x, y) +_A \tau(a, b) = \tau(c, d)$; by the Deduction Theorem applied to lines **1** through **7**.

To complete the proof that $\mathfrak{A}$ satisfies F(**iv**) it remains to show that there is *only one* element $\tau(x, y)$ of A such that $\tau(x, y) +_A \tau(a, b) = \tau(c, d)$. This we leave as Exercise 9 below.

Finally we wish to prove that $\mathfrak{A}$ satisfies F(**v**). First of all we observe that because $\mathfrak{A}$ satisfies F(**i**), F(**ii**), and F(**iv**), we know that $\langle A, +_A \rangle$ is a commutative group (see Definition 11-6-1). Let us identify the null element of this group. To do this we observe that for any $\tau(a, b) \in A$ we have $\tau(a, b) +_A \tau(0, 0) = \tau(a + 0,\ b + 0) = \tau(a, b)$. Thus, $\tau(0, 0)$ is the null element of the group $\langle A, +_A \rangle$. Now let $\tau(a, b)$ be any element of A which is *not* the null element of $\langle A, +_A \rangle$, and let $\tau(c, d)$ be any element of A whatever. In order to show that $\mathfrak{A}$ satisfies F(**v**) we would like to show that there exists an element $\tau(x, y) \in A$ such that $\tau(a, b) \cdot_A \tau(x, y) = \tau(c, d)$. Since $\tau(a, b) \neq \tau(0, 0)$ and since τ is one-one we can easily show that we cannot have both a and b equal to 0. And from this it follows (using Theorem 13-1-1) that $a \cdot a - 2 \cdot b \cdot b \neq 0$. Thus we have outlined proofs of the following two lemmas.

LEMMA 1. $\tau(0, 0)$ *is the null element of* $\langle A, +_A \rangle$.

LEMMA 2. *If* $\tau(a, b) \neq \tau(0, 0)$ *then* $a \cdot a - 2 \cdot (b \cdot b) \neq 0$.

Now in order to find $\tau(x, y)$ we shall go back to our intuitive guide. How can we find rational numbers x and y such that $(a + b\sqrt{2}) \cdot (x + y\sqrt{2}) = (c + d\sqrt{2})$, where a, b, c and d are given rational numbers? By high school algebra we first write $x + y\sqrt{2} = (c + d\sqrt{2})/(a + b\sqrt{2})$, and then we "rationalize the denominator," getting $x + y\sqrt{2} = [(ac - 2bd) + (ad - bc)\sqrt{2}]/(aa - 2bb)$. This suggests trying to prove, within the framework of our logical development, that if we take $x = (ac - 2bd)/(aa - 2bb)$, and $y = (ad - bc)/(aa - 2bb)$, we will find that $\tau(a, b) \cdot \tau(x, y) = \tau(c, d)$, as required. (Note that it is Lemma 2 which permits us to form the indicated ratios.)

With this much by way of suggestion the detailed proofs of Lemmas 1 and 2, and then of Part (**v**), will be left as exercises for the reader.

Thus the proof of Theorem 13-1-4 is completed.

To complete the verification that $\mathcal{A}$ is a solution of *Problem A* there remains only to show that A contains a "square root of 2."

THEOREM 13-1-5. $\tau(0, 1) \cdot_A \tau(0, 1) = 2$.

The proof of this is trivial and is left as an exercise.

DEFINITION 13-1-6. *In any number system* $\mathcal{F} = \langle F, +_F, \cdot_F \rangle$ *which is an extension of the rational number system, the numbers in* F *which are not rational are called* **irrational numbers.**

EXERCISES

1. Prove that there is no rational number x such that $x \cdot x = 3$. Can you find a general law which includes this proposition and Theorem 13-1-1 as special cases?

2. Prove Lemmas 1 and 2 and Parts (**iii**) and (**v**) of the proof of Theorem 13-1-4.

3. Prove Theorem 13-1-5.

4. Show that the function τ described after Definition 13-1-2 is one-one. Also show that any function τ satisfying the conditions of Definition 13-1-2 is a representation function on the set H for the relation $\doteq$. (See discussion following Theorem 12-4-3.)

5. Show that A contains an element y *distinct from* $\tau(0, 1)$ such that $y \cdot_A y = 2$.

6. *Using the ideas of the preceding section, construct an extension $\mathcal{B} = \langle B, +_B, \cdot_B \rangle$ of the system $\mathcal{R}$ which is a field and which contains an element x such that $x \cdot_B x = 3$.

7. *Show that a construction similar to the one used in the preceding section, but employing the number 4 in place of the number 2, yields an extension $\mathcal{C} = \langle C, +_C, \cdot_C \rangle$ of $\mathcal{R}$ which contains an element x *other than* 2 or -2 such that $x \cdot_C x = 4$, but that $\mathcal{C}$ is *not* a field. Which of the conditions F(**i**) through F(**v**) fails to hold for $\mathcal{C}$?

8. Verify that conditions F(**i**) through F(**v**) are equivalent to the definition of the field concept.

9. Show that if $a, b, c, d, x_1, y_1, x_2$, and y_2 are elements of R such that $\tau(x_1, y_1) + \tau(a, b) = \tau(c, d)$ and $\tau(x_2, y_2) + \tau(a, b) = \tau(c, d)$, then $\tau(x_1, y_1) = \tau(x_2, y_2)$.

2. *Uniqueness of the Solution of Problem A*

We see on referring to Theorems 13-1-3, 13-1-4, and 13-1-5 that we have constructed one solution of *Problem A*. Are there others? Could our hypothetical intelligent being from outer space have found a completely different solution? The next theorem tells us that the solution found in Section 1 is essentially the *only* one.

THEOREM 13-2-1. *Let* $\mathcal{V} = \langle V, +_V, \cdot_V \rangle$ *be any system which satisfies the following conditions:*

(i) $+_V$ *and* $\cdot_V$ *are commutative.*
(ii) $+_V$ *and* $\cdot_V$ *are associative.*
(iii) $\cdot_V$ *is distributive over* $+_V$.
(iv) $\mathcal{V}$ *is an extension of* $\mathcal{R}$.
(v) *There is an element* $s \in V$ *such that* $s \cdot_V s = 2$.
(vi) $0 \cdot_V s = 0$.

Then $\mathcal{V}$ *must contain a part which is "just like"* $\mathcal{R}$, *in the following sense.*

(A) *There is a one-one mapping* σ *of* H *(the set of all ordered pairs* $\langle a, b\rangle$ *for all* $a, b \in R$*) into* V *such that:*
(A.1) $\sigma(a, b) +_V \sigma(c, d) = \sigma(a + c, \quad b + d)$,
(A.2) $\sigma(a, b) \cdot_V \sigma(c, d) = \sigma(a \cdot c + 2 \cdot b \cdot d, \quad a \cdot d + b \cdot c)$.

(B) *There is an isomorphism* f *of* $\mathcal{A}$ *into* $\mathcal{V}$, *i.e., a one-one function* f *mapping* A *into* V, *such that for any elements* $\tau(a, b)$ *and* $\tau(c, d)$ *of* A *we have:*
(B.1) $f(\tau(a, b) +_A \tau(c, d)) = f(\tau(a, b)) +_V f(\tau(c, d))$,
(B.2) $f(\tau(a, b) \cdot_A \tau(c, d)) = f(\tau(a, b)) \cdot_V f(\tau(c, d))$.

Proof

We shall give only an outline of a proof of this theorem.

Suppose, then, that $\mathcal{V} = \langle V, +_V, \cdot_V \rangle$ is any number system satisfying hypotheses **(i)** through **(vi)** of Theorem 13-2-1.

For any $a, b \in R$ let $\sigma(a, b)$ be the element $(a +_V b \cdot_V s)$ of V.

Then it is easy to see, by computation, that equations **A.1** and **A.2** hold for all $a, b, c, d \in R$. Leaving the reader to check **A.1** we verify **A.2** as follows:

$\sigma(a, b) \cdot_V \sigma(c, d) = (a +_V b \cdot_V s) \cdot_V (c +_V d \cdot_V s)$; by definition of σ.
$= a \cdot_V (c +_V d \cdot_V s) +_V (b \cdot_V s) \cdot_V (c +_V d \cdot_V s)$; by **(iii)**.
$= (a \cdot_V c +_V a \cdot_V (d \cdot_V s)) +_V ((b \cdot_V s) \cdot_V c +_V (b \cdot_V s) \cdot_V (d \cdot_V s))$; by **(iii)**.
$= (a \cdot_V c +_V (b \cdot_V d) \cdot_V (s \cdot_V s)) +_V ((a \cdot_V d) \cdot_V s +_V (b \cdot_V c) \cdot_V s)$; by **(i)** and **(ii)**.
$= (a \cdot c + 2 \cdot (b \cdot d)) +_V ((a \cdot d) \cdot_V s +_V (b \cdot c) \cdot_V s)$; by **(iv)** and **(v)**.
$= (a \cdot c + 2 \cdot (b \cdot d)) +_V (a \cdot d +_V b \cdot c) \cdot_V s$; by **(iii)**.
$= \sigma(a \cdot c + 2 \cdot b \cdot d, \quad a \cdot d + b \cdot c)$; by definition of σ.

Thus, to complete the demonstration of (**A**), it remains only to show that σ is a *one-one* mapping of H into V. To do this, suppose that $\langle a, b\rangle$ and $\langle c, d\rangle$ are any elements of H such that $\sigma(a, b) = \sigma(c, d)$. That is, we suppose that $a, b, c, d \in R$ and

$$(*) \qquad a +_V b \cdot_V s = c +_V d \cdot_V s.$$

We shall show that this assumption implies that $a = c$ and $b = d$, and hence $\langle a, b\rangle = \langle c, d\rangle$, and this will establish that σ is one-one.

Let $f = b - d = b + (-d)$ and $e = c - a = c + (-a)$. (See Exercise 12-4-6.) Then we can compute as follows:

$f \cdot_V s = (0 + (b - d)) \cdot_V s$; by definition of f.
$= 0 \cdot_V s +_V (b \cdot_V s +_V -d \cdot_V s)$; by (**iii**) and (**iv**).
$= (0 +_V b \cdot_V s) +_V -d \cdot_V s$; by (**ii**) and (**vi**).
$= (-a +_V (a +_V b \cdot_V s)) +_V -d \cdot_V s$; by (**ii**) and (**iv**).
$= (-a +_V (c +_V d \cdot_V s)) +_V -d \cdot_V s$; by (*) above.
$= (c +_V -a) +_V (d \cdot_V s +_V -d \cdot_V s)$; by (**i**) and (**ii**).
$= (c - a) +_V (0 \cdot_V s)$; by (**iii**) and (**iv**).
$= e +_V 0$; by (**vi**) and definition of e.
$= e$; by (**iv**)

(In this computation we have left the reader to supply details of reasoning which involve only rules for computing in R; and we continue to do this below.)

Using the equation $f \cdot_V s = e$ just derived, we compute further:
$(f \cdot_V s) \cdot_V (f \cdot_V s) = e \cdot_V e$; by E.
$(f \cdot_V f) \cdot_V (s \cdot_V s) = e \cdot_V e$; by (**i**) and (**ii**).
$(f \cdot f) \cdot 2 = e \cdot e$; by (**iv**) and (**v**).

Now $(f \cdot f)$ and $(e \cdot e)$ are elements of R, as we see from the definitions of e and f. Hence if $f \cdot f \neq 0$ we would infer from the last equation that

$$2 = (e \cdot e)/(f \cdot f),$$

contrary to Theorem 13-1-1. It follows that we must have $f \cdot f = 0$, and hence

$$0 \cdot 2 = e \cdot e$$

and so

$$e \cdot e = 0.$$

From $e \cdot e = 0$ we easily get $e = 0$ (since $0 \cdot e = 0$ and there is *only one* $x \in R$ such that $x \cdot e = 0$); and similarly from $f \cdot f = 0$ we get $f = 0$. Referring to the definitions of e and f we see that $a - c = 0$ and $b - d = 0$, so that $a = c$ and $b = d$. This completes the proof that σ is one-one, as noted above, and hence establishes part (**A**) of our theorem.

To prove part (**B**) is now a simple matter. We define the function g by the rule that for every element $\tau(a, b)$ of A.

$$g(\tau(a, b)) = \sigma(a, b).$$

This function, mapping A into V, is easily seen to be one-one because σ is one-one (by part (**A**)). For if $g(\tau(a, b)) = g(\tau(c, d))$ then $\sigma(a, b) = \sigma(c, d)$ by definition of g, hence $a = c$ and $b = d$ by part (**A**), and hence $\tau(a, b) = \tau(c, d)$ by E.

Thus to complete the proof of part (**B**) we need only establish the equations (**B.1**) and (**B.2**) for elements $\tau(a, b)$ and $\tau(c, d)$ of A. But this is easily done by combining Definition 13-1-2 with equations (**A.1**) and (**A.2**), as we leave the reader to verify.

3. *Square Roots*

Let us begin this section with the familiar definition of "square root."

DEFINITION 13-3-1. *Let $\mathcal{G} = \langle G, +_G, \cdot_G \rangle$ be any ring. If a and x are any elements of G such that $x \cdot_G x = a$, then we call x a* **square root** *of a.*

Using this terminology, we see that *Problem A* of this chapter can be phrased as follows: Is it possible to extend $\mathcal{R}$ to a field in which there exists a square root of 2? This is the problem we have answered affirmatively in Section 1.

In fact we see from Theorem 13-1-6 that the element $\tau(0, 1)$ of A is a square root of 2. Let us introduce a symbol for this particular square root of 2.

DEFINITION 13-3-2. *We set $\sqrt{2} = \tau(0, 1)$.*

And now we are in a position to tie up our logical construction of the system $\mathcal{A}$ with the intuitive idea which underlay this construction.

THEOREM 13-3-3. *For any rational numbers a and b we have $\tau(a, b) = a +_A b \cdot_A \sqrt{2}$.*

Proof

1. Let a and b be any rational numbers.
2. $a +_A b \cdot_A \sqrt{2} = \tau(a, 0) +_A \tau(b, 0) \cdot_A \tau(0, 1)$; by E from Definitions 13-1-2 and 13-3-2.
3. $= \tau(a, 0) +_A \tau(0, b)$; by E and Definition 13-1-2 and Exercise 12-4-7.
4. $= \tau(a, b)$; by Definition 13-1-2 and Exercise 12-4-7.
5. $a +_A b \cdot_A \sqrt{2} = \tau(a, b)$; by E from lines **2** through **4**.

6. The theorem follows by applying the Deduction Theorem to lines **1** through **5.**

On the basis of this theorem and Definition 13-1-2 we see that the set A is simply the set of all numbers $(a +_A b \cdot_A \sqrt{2})$, where a and b are any rational numbers. Thus we have converted an intuitive idea into a rigorously developed mathematical concept.

DEFINITION 13-3-4. *Following the practice of modern algebraists we shall henceforth write* $\mathcal{R}(\sqrt{2})$ *for the system* $\mathfrak{A} = \langle A, +_A, \cdot_A\rangle$.

The system $\mathcal{R}(\sqrt{2})$ is generally referred to as the field obtained by "adjoining" the element $\sqrt{2}$ to $\mathcal{R}$.

EXERCISES

1. Let $\mathcal{G} = \langle G, +_G, \cdot_G\rangle$ be any field. Show that if r and s are any elements in G such that r is a square root of s, then the *only* square roots of s in G are r and $-_G r$. (As a consequence of this we see that the only square roots of 2 in A are $\sqrt{2}$ and $-_A\sqrt{2}$.)

2. *Suppose that $\mathcal{G} = \langle G, +_G, \cdot_G\rangle$ is any field which is an extension of $\mathcal{R}$ and which contains an element t such that $t \cdot_G t +_G 4 \cdot_G t +_G 2 = 0$. Show that G contains a square root of 2.

4. *Similar Extensions*

It is natural to ask whether there are other equations with rational coefficients, in addition to the equation $x \cdot_A x = 2$, which can be solved in our new system $\mathcal{R}(\sqrt{2})$ but which cannot be solved in the rational number system $\mathcal{R}$ itself. The following theorem partially answers this question.

THEOREM 13-4-1. *Let a, b, c be any rational numbers such that $a \neq 0$ and $b \cdot b - 4 \cdot (a \cdot c) = 2 \cdot (q \cdot q)$ for some rational number q. Then the numbers $x_1 = (-_A b +_A q \cdot_A \sqrt{2})/_A (2 \cdot a)$ and $x_2 = (-_A b -_A q \cdot_A \sqrt{2})/_A (2 \cdot a)$ of A are solutions of the equation $a \cdot_A (x \cdot_A x) +_A b \cdot_A x +_A c = 0$, and they are the* **only** *solutions* **in** A.

If there has been any doubt in the reader's mind that we are really "retracing elementary mathematics" it should by now be dispelled: Here we are in Chapter XIII and we are just taking up the subject of square roots. Of course everyone who has taken a high school course in algebra will recognize the "quadratic formula" which appears in Theorem 13-4-1. The proof of this theorem consists of two parts: first, it is necessary to show that x_1 and x_2 actually satisfy the given equation, and secondly that the *only* two numbers of A which satisfy the equation are x_1 and x_2.

Proof of Part (**i**): x_1 and x_2 are solutions of the equation given in the Theorem.

We shall ask the reader to give the details of the proof of this part by substituting x_1 and x_2 in the equation and showing that indeed they are solutions.

Proof of Part (**ii**): x_1 and x_2 are the *only* elements in A which are solutions of the equation given in the theorem.

An outline of a proof of this part of the theorem proceeds as follows.

1. Let a, b, c and q be any elements of R such that $a \neq 0$ and $b \cdot b - 4 \cdot (a \cdot c) = 2 \cdot (q \cdot q)$; and let $x_1 = (-_A b +_A q \cdot_A \sqrt{2})/_A (2 \cdot a)$ and $x_2 = (-_A b -_A q \cdot_A \sqrt{2})/_A (2 \cdot a)$.

2. A computation carried out with the aid of the algebraic laws for fields, which hold for R, allows us to conclude that $x_1 +_A x_2 = -(b/a)$ and $x_1 \cdot_A x_2 = (b \cdot b - 2 \cdot (q \cdot q))/_A 4 \cdot (a \cdot a)$, and when the second of these equations is combined with the given equation connecting a, b, c and q, another computation leads easily to $x_1 \cdot_A x_2 = c/a$.

3. Now let x be *any* element of A such that $a \cdot_A (x \cdot_A x) +_A b \cdot_A x +_A c = 0$.

4. A third computation shows us that $(x -_A x_1) \cdot_A (x -_A x_2) = x \cdot x -_A (x_1 +_A x_2) \cdot_A x +_A x_1 \cdot_A x_2$, and hence, by line **2**, that $(x -_A x_1) \cdot_A (x -_A x_2) = x \cdot_A x +_A -(b/a) \cdot_A x +_A (c/a)$.

5. From line **4** we obtain $a \cdot_A ((x -_A x_1) \cdot_A (x -_A x_2)) = a \cdot_A (x \cdot_A x) +_A b \cdot_A x +_A c$ and hence, by line **3**, $a \cdot_A ((x -_A x_1) \cdot_A (x -_A x_2)) = 0$.

6. Since $a \neq 0$, by line **1**, line **5** implies that $(x -_A x_1) \cdot_A (x -_A x_2 = 0$ (by Exercise 12-4-8). Then, by another application of Exercise 12-4-8, we infer that either $(x -_A x_1) = 0$ or $(x -_A x_2) = 0$. By definition of $-_A$, this in turn gives either $x = x_1$ or $x = x_2$.

7. By applying the Deduction Theorem to lines **3** through **6** we obtain the desired result that the *only* elements x of A such that $a \cdot_A (x \cdot_A x) +_A b \cdot_A x +_A c = 0$ are x_1 and x_2.

So much for some equations we *can* solve in $\mathcal{R}(\sqrt{2})$. But there remain other equations with rational coefficients which have no solution in $\mathcal{R}(\sqrt{2})$. We have already seen (Exercise 13-1-1) that there is no *rational* number x such that $x \cdot x = 3$. Since $\mathcal{R}(\sqrt{2})$ is an extension of $\mathcal{R}$ which contains many additional numbers which are not in R, we might hope that there is some number $x \in A$ such that $x \cdot_A x = 3$. Unfortunately, this is not the case. We shall leave it as an exercise for the reader to show there is no solution of $x \cdot_A x = 3$ even in the system $\mathcal{R}(\sqrt{2})$. On the other hand we know from Exercise 13-1-6 that it is possible to construct a field, $\mathcal{R}(\sqrt{3}) = \langle B, +_B, \cdot_B \rangle$, in which $x \cdot_B x = 3$ can be solved. But then we can show that there is no solution of the equation $x \cdot_B x = 2$ in *this* field.

These observations may lead us to ask whether $\mathcal{R}(\sqrt{2})$ can be extended to a field, say $\mathcal{R}(\sqrt{2})(\sqrt{3}) = \langle C, +_C, \cdot_C \rangle$, in which *both* of the equations $x \cdot_C x = 3$ and $x \cdot_C x = 2$ have solutions. The answer is that indeed this can be done. But our joy is shortlived. For in the resulting field we can show that the equation $x \cdot_C x = 5$ has no solution!

Thus it would seem that the stride we made in passing from $\mathcal{R}$ to $\mathcal{R}(\sqrt{2})$, or which we could make by undertaking similar extensions, is not as great, say, as the stride made in passing from $\mathcal{J}$ to $\mathcal{R}$. In passing from $\mathcal{J}$ to $\mathcal{R}$ we went from a system in which only certain equations of the form $a \cdot_J x = b$ have solutions, to a system in which *all* (nondegenerate) equations of the form $a \cdot_R x = b$ have solutions. But no matter how many times we make extensions of the sort suggested in Section 1 of this chapter, it can be shown that there will still remain some equations of the form $x \cdot x = k$, where $k \in R$, which are not solvable in the extended system. (It is true that in a sense we can make infinitely many such extensions and obtain a field in which *all* elements have square roots. But that brings in difficulties and complications of a new kind. And in the resulting system we find that certain rational numbers lack *cube* roots.)

The extension $\mathcal{R}(\sqrt{2})$ is one of a kind called *algebraic extensions* of R. By an algebraic extension of a field $\mathfrak{F} = \langle F, +_F, \cdot_F \rangle$ we mean a field, say $\mathcal{G} = \langle G, +_G, \cdot_G \rangle$, which is an extension of $\mathfrak{F}$ and in which every element in G satisfies a *polynomial equation* with coefficients in F. Of course, we have not introduced the concept of an arbitrary polynomial into our theory in a precise way, but the reader indubitably has an intuitive notion of this concept.

We can see from this informal description of algebraic extensions that $\mathcal{R}(\sqrt{2})$ is an algebraic extension of the field of rationals, for if $a +_A b \cdot_A \sqrt{2}$ is any element in $\mathcal{R}(\sqrt{2})$, a and b being rational numbers, it is easily verified that it satisfies the equation $1 \cdot_A (x \cdot_A x) -_A (2\, a) \cdot_A x +_A (a \cdot a - 2 \cdot b \cdot b) = 0$ whose three coefficients, 1, $2 \cdot a$, and $a \cdot a - 2 \cdot b \cdot b$, are rational.

The study of algebraic extensions of fields is an interesting part of abstract algebra, but we shall not go into it further here. Suffice it to say that no algebraic extension of the field of rational numbers contains all the numbers commonly known to us. In fact, it can be shown that no algebraic extension of $\mathcal{R}$ contains one of the most well known (and anciently known) numbers of mathematics—the number pi.

EXERCISES

1. Prove Part (i) of Theorem 13-4-1.

2.* Construct a field extension of $\mathcal{R}$ which contains square roots of both 2 and 3, by starting with a function θ which assigns some object $\theta(a, b, c, d)$ to each sequence $\langle a, b, c, d \rangle$ of four rational numbers,[1] in such a way that (i) $\theta(a, 0, 0, 0) = a$ for all $a \in R$, and (ii) whenever $\theta(a, b, c, d) = \theta(a_1, b_1, c_1, d_1)$ then $a = a_1$, $b = b_1$, $c = c_1$, and $d = d_1$. Take S to be the set of all objects $\theta(a, b, c, d)$, for all $a, b, c, d \in R$, and define operations $+_S$ and $\cdot_S$ on S so as to obtain a field $\langle S, +_S, \cdot_S \rangle$ in which the elements $\theta(0, 1, 0, 0)$ and $\theta(0, 0, 1, 0)$ are square roots of 2 and 3 respectively. Calling these elements $s(2)$ and $s(3)$ respectively, show that for all $a, b, c, d \in R$ we have $\theta(a, b, c, d) = (a +_S b \cdot_S s(2)) +_S (c \cdot_S s(3) +_S d \cdot_S (s(2) \cdot_S s(3))$.

[1] The symbol "θ" is the Greek letter theta.

3. Verify in detail that if $a +_A b \cdot_A \sqrt{2}$ is any number in $\mathcal{R}(\sqrt{2})$ then, it satisfies an equation with rational coefficients.

4.* Define a relation $<_A$ on A by specifying that for any elements $\tau(a, b)$ and $\tau(c, d)$ of A we have $\tau(a, b) <_A \tau(c, d)$ if and only if either ($a < c$ and $b < d$), or $a < c$ and $d \leq b$ and $2 \cdot (b - d) \cdot (b - d) < (c - a) \cdot (c - a)$, or $c \leq a$ and $b < d$ and $(c - a) \cdot (c - a) < 2 \cdot (b - d) \cdot (b - d)$. Show that the relation $<_A$ is an ordering of the field $\mathcal{R}(\sqrt{2})$. (See Section 12-7, Conditions **OP (i)** through **OP (iv)**.)

5.* Show that there is one and *only* one ordering of the field $\mathcal{R}(\sqrt{2})$ *other than* the relation $<_A$ defined in Exercise 4 above.

5. The Number Pi

The successive extensions of our number system which we have undertaken so far have all been motivated by a desire to obtain numbers which satisfy certain kinds of equations. The existence of such solutions to equations serve two purposes: On the one hand they facilitate *computations* and on the other hand they increase the *applicability* of the number system. For example, when $\sqrt{2}$ is introduced into the number system we can use it to determine the length of diagonals of squares.

The number π, with which we shall deal in this section, is needed in order to make numerical applications to another geometric figure—the circle. However, as we shall see below, from the algebraic viewpoint this number π does *not* arise as a solution to an equation, but serves instead to fill a "gap" in the ordered system of rational numbers.

What do we mean by a "gap" in this context? In the case of the ordered system of *integers*, we can recognize in an intuitive way that there are many gaps: In fact, if x is any integer then there is a gap between x and $x + 1$ because there is no integer *between* them, i.e., no integer y such that $x < y$ and $y < x + 1$, (cf. Theorem 12-9-2). But in the case of *rational* numbers there is no gap of this kind, for by Theorem 12-9-3 we see that whenever we have rational numbers a and b such that $a < b$, we can find another rational number *which is between them*, i.e., a rational number c such that we have both $a < c$ and $c < b$.

Nevertheless, there is a more subtle sense in which there do exist gaps in the ordered system of rational numbers. This will be made clear below when we seek to find a number which can be used to represent the area of a circle. Our consideration of this problem will not be conducted at the level of logical rigor which has characterized our earlier development of the number system, but will be formulated at an intuitive level based on our knowledge of high school geometry.

The basic problem in representing areas by numbers is this: We wish to assign a number to each plane figure which will serve as an indication of its "size." Of course this is not a precisely formulated problem since we have not explained what we mean by "size." But even this rough formulation can serve to guide our thinking on the subject, because it suggests the following principle:

Whenever we have two plane figures one of which is a part (but not the whole) of the other, then the number assigned to represent the area of the first should be less than the number assigned to the second.[1]

Let us call this the *comparison principle*, and see how we can apply it to the problem of obtaining a numerical representation for the area of a circle (of radius 1, say).

Before turning to the circle, however, it is necessary to recall the method for obtaining the numerical values of the areas of polygonal figures. The method consists in breaking the given figure into nonoverlapping triangles (which can always be done), obtaining the numerical value of the area of each triangle by the familiar formula (one half the product of the length of (any) one side by the length of the altitude from the opposite vertex), and then summing these areas of triangles to obtain the desired area of the given polygonal figure.

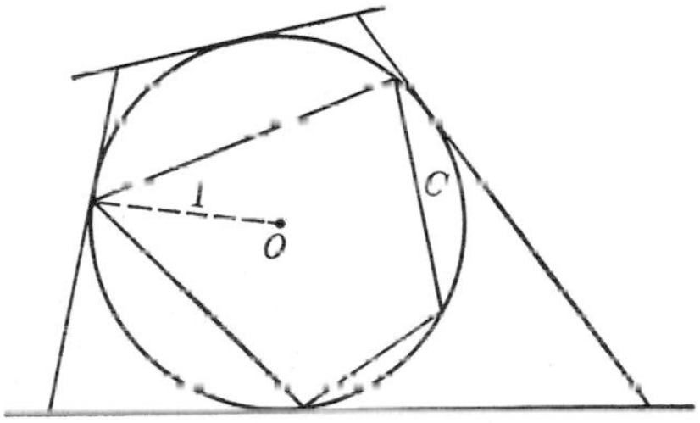

Figure 13.1

Now let us return to the case of a circle C of radius 1, and let us seek a number—which we shall call π—to represent its area. As is obvious from examples such as provided in Figure 1, when we apply the *comparison principle* to such a circle we come to the following conclusion: The numerical value of the area bounded by any polygon circumscribed about C must be greater than π, and the numerical value of the area bounded by any *inscribed* polygon must be *less* than π.

Let G be the set of all *rational numbers* which represent the area bounded by some polygon *inscribed in* the circle C, and let H be the set of all *rational numbers* which represent the area bounded by some polygon *circumscribed about* C. Evidently every number in G is less than every number in H, and from what we have said, in order to represent the area of the circle we need a number π which is *between* the sets H and G in the sense that $x < \pi$ for all $x \in G$ and $\pi < y$ for all $y \in H$. However, it can be shown that *there is no rational number with this property.* In this sense the sets H and G define a *gap* in the ordered system of rational numbers.

[1] In this proposition the term "plane figure" must not be identified with "arbitrary set of points in the plane", else the proposition would violate a basic principle of the mathematical theory of measure. Our present principle refers rather to "elementary plane figures".

As a matter of fact, not only is there no *rational* number between G and H, but there is not even any such *algebraic* number. That is, no number which satisfies a polynomial equation (with rational coefficients) can be both greater than every rational number in G and less than every rational number in H. We remark, however, that the known proofs of the non-algebraic character of π, or even of its irrationality, all require mathematical techniques which put them outside the scope of the present work. (The interested reader who wishes to pursue this matter can consult the book *Irrational Numbers*, by Ivan Niven.)

Thus, if we are to enlarge our number system $\mathcal{R}$ so as to provide a number which can be used to represent the area of a circle of radius 1, we must proceed by a method quite different from that employed in the extension of $\mathcal{R}$ to $\mathcal{R}(\sqrt{2})$. In Chapter XIV we shall present a construction which leads us in one step from the number system $\mathcal{R}$ to a system obtained from it by filling *all* gaps of the kind defined by sets such as G and H.

In the remainder of this section we wish to take up the problem of finding rational numbers in the sets G and H which are "close" to π.

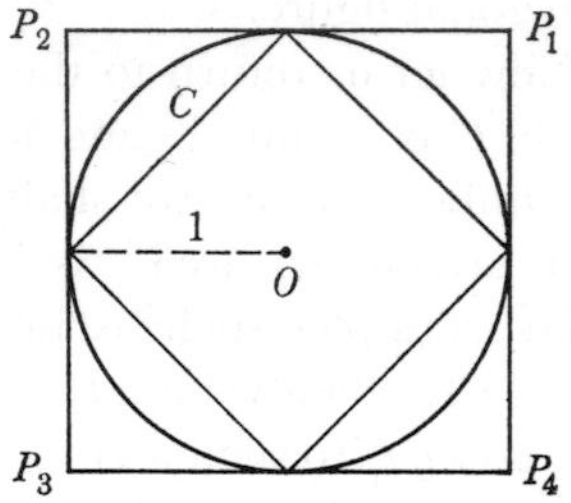

Figure 13.2

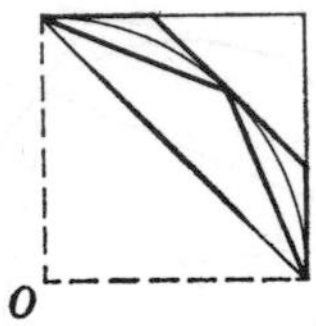

Figure 13.3

By the most elementary principles of geometry we can compute that a square circumscribed about the circle C has area 4, while the inscribed square has area 2. (See Figure 2.) Thus we have $2 \in G$, $4 \in H$, and hence $2 < \pi < 4$. This pair of inequalities gives us an approximate idea of the location of π, but of course it is a very rough approximation, and so it is natural to ask how we can obtain a better one. That is, we would like to obtain another rational number, say a, in G, which is *greater* than 2, and another rational number $b \in H$ which is *less* than 4, so that the pair of inequalities $a < \pi < b$ will give us a more accurate idea of the location of π. How can we do this?

Geometrically, we can proceed from the circumscribed square of Figure 2 to a circumscribed octagon obtained by "cutting off the corners" of the square. By the principle of comparison, the area of the octagon must be less than that of the square (but more than that of the circle). Hence if its area is represented by a *rational* number, we can use that number for the number b we are seeking. Similarly, if the inscribed octagon (whose vertices are the points where the circumscribed octagon makes contact with the circle) turns out to have an area which is represented by a rational number, *that* number can be used as the a we are seeking. In Figure 3 we show one quarter of the diagram in which these octagons are indicated (with heavy lines) in relation to the circle and squares of Figure 2.

The "natural" way to cut the corners from the circumscribed square of Figure 2 in order to form the circumscribed octagon of Figure 3 is to make the cuts symmetric (i.e., parallel to the sides of the inscribed square, and hence touching the circle at the midpoints of the four arcs determined by the original vertices of that square). In this way an *equilateral* octagon results. Unfortunately, an elementary computation shows that the area of this octagon is $8(\sqrt{2} - 1)$, which is *not* a rational number (as one easily deduces from Theorem 13-3-1), and so this method of cutting does not serve our purpose.

Below we shall describe an *asymmetric* method of cutting the corners which does give both circumscribed and inscribed octagons having rational areas, and hence will permit us to compute our desired numbers a and b. Furthermore, the same method can then be used to cut the corners from the resulting circumscribed octagon so as to obtain circumscribed and inscribed 16-gons with rational areas; and if we call these areas b' and a' respectively, then the principle of comparison will assure us that all of the inequalities

$$2 < a < a' < \pi < b' < b < 4$$

hold, so that the pair (a', b') give us a more accurate idea of the location of π than the pair (a, b). Repeating the process once more, we can cut the corners from the circumscribed 16-gon to obtain a pair of 32-gons having rational areas a'' and b'' which serve still more accurately to locate the number π. And by continuing further we can locate π to any accuracy (i.e., any number of decimal places) which we may desire.

A description of the method of "cutting corners" is contained in the following definition and theorem which underlie our method.

DEFINITION 13-5-1. *Let C be a circle of radius* 1. *By a* **corner** *we shall mean a configuration consisting of a point P outside of C, and the two segments from P which are tangent to C (at points Q and R, say). The segments PQ and PR will be called the* **sides** *of the corner. By a* **cut** *of such a corner we shall mean a segment which is tangent to C and whose endpoints lie on the sides of the corner. Finally, if θ is a number between* 0 *and* 1, *then by the* **θ-cut on the side PR** *we shall mean the cut such that the ratio $\overline{TR} : \overline{PR}$ is θ, where T is the endpoint of the cut which lies on the side PR of the corner. (See Figure* 4.)

THEOREM 13-5-2. *Consider a circle C of radius* 1, *and a corner whose sides are PQ and PR. Suppose that x is the length of these sides. (Both have the same length by elementary geometry.) Let θ be a number between* 0 *and* 1, *and let ST be the θ-cut* *on the side PR, with U the point of tangency of ST to C. Then the sides TR and TU of the corner at T have length $\theta \cdot x$, and the sides SU and SQ of the corner at S have length* $\dfrac{(1-\theta)\cdot x}{1+\theta\cdot x^2}$.

Proof

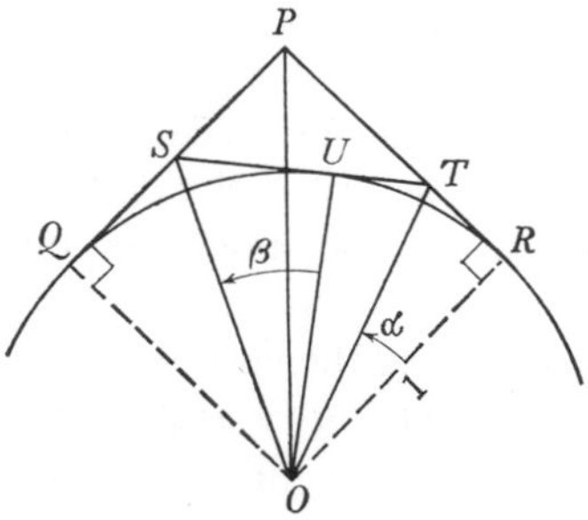

Figure 13.4

That TR (and hence, by geometry, TU) has length θx is immediate from the definition of θ-cut. To compute the length of SU (and hence of SQ), we may proceed as follows.

Let α be the measure of angle ROT (and hence of TOU), and let β be the measure of angle UOS (and hence of SOQ). It follows that angle ROQ has measure $2\alpha + 2\beta$, and since OP is the bisector of this angle we see that angle ROP has measure $\alpha + \beta$.

Now since OR has length 1, we have $\tan\alpha = \overline{TR} = \theta \cdot x$ (by considering triangle ROT), and $\tan(\alpha+\beta) = \overline{PR} = x$ (by considering triangle ROP). But also OU has length 1. Hence $\tan\beta = \overline{SU}$ (by considering triangle UOS).

Using the trigonometric formula

$$\tan(\alpha+\beta) = \frac{\tan\alpha + \tan\beta}{1 - \tan\alpha \cdot \tan\beta}$$

we infer that

$$x = \frac{\theta\cdot x + \overline{SU}}{1 - \theta\cdot x\cdot\overline{SU}},$$

and from this we easily solve for $\overline{SU}$ getting the desired result

$$\overline{SU} = \frac{(1-\theta)\cdot x}{1+\theta\cdot x^2}.$$

We see at once from theorem 13-5-2 that if the corner at P has sides whose length x is a *rational* number, and if we choose θ to be a rational number between 0 and 1, then the sides of the corners at S and T (which are formed by the θ-cut of the original corner) *will also have rational length.*

We see, also, that whereas the total length of the two sides of the original corner is $2\cdot x$, the total length of the four sides of the two new corners produced by the θ-cut is

$$2\cdot\theta\cdot x + \frac{2\cdot(1-\theta)\cdot x}{1+\theta\cdot x^2} = \frac{2\cdot x\cdot(1+\theta^2\cdot x^2)}{1+\theta\cdot x^2}.$$

Since $0 < \theta < 1$ we have $\theta^2 < \theta$ and hence

$$\frac{1 + \theta^2 \cdot x^2}{1 + \theta \cdot x^2} < 1.$$

Thus the four sides of the new corner have total length *less than* the two sides of the given corner.

These observations lead at once to the following result.

THEOREM 13-5-3. *Suppose that C is a circle of radius 1, and that D is a polygon circumscribed about C and having n vertices $P_1, \ldots, P_n$. At each vertex P_1 there is a corner of the polygon: Let us suppose that the length of the sides of this corner is x_i. Then the perimeter of D is $2x_i + 2x_2 + \cdots + 2x_n$. Now if we form a new circumscribed polygon D′, with 2n vertices, obtained from D by making a θ_i-cut at each vertex P_i (where the numbers $\theta_1, \ldots, \theta_n$ are chosen between 0 and 1), then the corner of D at P_i will be replaced by two corners of D′ whose sides are of length $\theta_i x_i$ and*

$$\frac{(1 - \theta_i) \cdot x_i}{1 + \theta_i \cdot x_i^2}$$

respectively, and the perimeter of D′ will be

$$2x_1\left(\frac{1 + \theta_1^2 \cdot x_1^2}{1 + \theta_1 \cdot x_1^2}\right) + 2x_2\left(\frac{1 + \theta_2^2 \cdot x_2^2}{1 + \theta_2 \cdot x_2^2}\right) + \cdots + 2x_n\left(\frac{1 + \theta_n^2 \cdot x_n^2}{1 + \theta_n \cdot x_n^2}\right).$$

Now by a theorem of elementary geometry the area of a polygon circumscribed about a circle is equal to one half the product of the perimeter of the polygon by the radius of the circle. (To prove this, connect each vertex of the polygon to the center of the circle, observe that the area of the polygon is the sum of the areas of the triangles thus formed, and compute the area of each triangle as one half the product of a side of the polygon by the radius of the circle.) Hence the previous theorem leads directly to the following.

THEOREM 13-5-4. *Let C be a circle with radius 1, and D a polygon circumscribed about C with n vertices $P_1, \ldots, P_n$. Suppose that the corner of D at vertex P_i has sides of length x_i. Then the area of D is $x_1 + \cdots + x_n$. Now form a new circumscribed polygon D′, with 2n vertices, obtained from D by making a θ_i-cut at each vertex P_i (where $0 < \theta_i < 1$). Then the area of D′ is*

$$x_1 \cdot \left(\frac{1 + \theta_1^2 \cdot x_1^2}{1 + \theta_1 \cdot x_1^2}\right) + \cdots + x_n \cdot \left(\frac{1 + \theta_n^2 \cdot x_n^2}{1 + \theta_n \cdot x_n^2}\right)$$

and this is less than the area of D. If $x_1, \ldots, x_n$ and $\theta_1, \ldots, \theta_n$ are all rational numbers, then both D and D′ have rational areas.

By using Theorems 13-5-3 and 13-5-4 repeatedly we can generate a succession of rational numbers of *H*, getting smaller and smaller, but each one remaining greater than π. Taking D to be the circumscribed square of Figure 2 we have $x_1 = x_2 = x_3 = x_4 = 1$ and an area of 4. Using $\theta_1 = \theta_2 = \theta_3 = \theta_4 = 1/2$, and making θ_i-cuts at each corner of D, we obtain an octagon D′, and by Theorem 13-5-3 the sides of four of its corners have length 1/2, while the sides of the other four corners are of length $(1/2)/(1 + 1/2) = 1/3$. Using the formulas of Theorem 13-5-4 we thus obtain 3 1/3 as the area of D′. Now by a second application of Theorem 13-5-4, starting with the octagon just obtained, we can form a 16-gon, D'' say, by making a θ-cut at each of the 8 vertices of D' (using $\theta = 1/2$ in each case). The four corners of D' having sides of length 1/2 will produce four corners of D'' whose sides have length 1/4, and four with sides of length $(1/4)/(1 + 1/8) = 2/9$, while the four corners of D' having sides of length 1/3 will produce four corners of D'' with sides of length 1/6 and four of length $(1/6)/(1 + 1/18) = 3/19$. Thus the area of D'' will be $1 + 8/9 + 4/6 + 12/19 = 545/171 = 3\ 32/171$. With a third application we would obtain a 32-gon D''' whose area is less than 3 32/171 but still greater than π. And we could continue for as many steps further as desired.

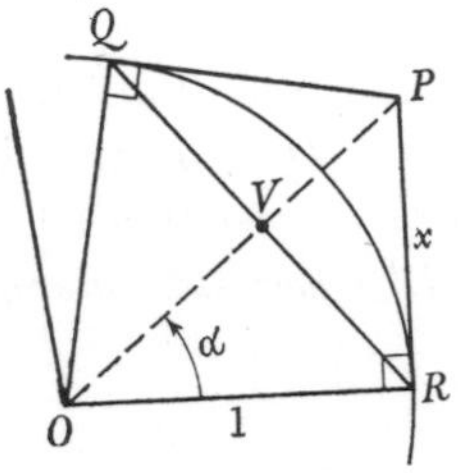

Figure 13.5

The computation of areas of *inscribed* polygons rests upon the following result.

THEOREM 13-5-5. *Let C be a circle of radius* 1 *and center O, and let P be a point outside the circle. Suppose that the sides of the corner at P meet C at points Q and R and have length x. Then the area of triangle QOR is $x/(1 + x^2)$.*

Proof

Referring to Figure 5, we have $\overline{PQ} = \overline{PR} = x$ by hypothesis. Then we see that the area of triangle $QOR = 1/2\ \overline{OV}\ \overline{QR} = \overline{OV}\ \overline{VR} = \cos\alpha \sin\alpha = \cos^2\alpha \tan\alpha = x/(1 + x^2)$.

From this result we obtain at once:

THEOREM 13-5-5. *Let C be g circle of radius* 1 *and center O, and let P be polygon with n vertices $P_1, \ldots, P_n$. Suppose that x_i is the length of the sides of the corner at P_i, for $i = 1, 2, \ldots, n$, and let E be the inscribed polygon whose n vertices are the points where the sides of D are tangent to C. Then the area of E is*

$$\frac{x_1}{1 + x_1^2} + \frac{x_2}{1 + x_2^2} + \cdots + \frac{x_n}{1 + x_n^2}\,.$$

Thus if all of the numbers $x_1, \ldots, x_n$ are rational then the area of E is rational.

Taking D and E to be the circumscribed and inscribed squares of Figure 2, respectively, this theorem gives us the previously found value 2 for the area of E. Now letting D' be the octagon considered in the computation preceding this theorem, and letting E' be the corresponding inscribed octagon, we can use Theorem 13-5-6 a second time to obtain, for the area of E', the value

$$4 \cdot \frac{(1/2)}{1 + (1/2)^2} + 4 \cdot \frac{(1/3)}{1 + (1/3)^2} = 2\frac{4}{5} \cdot$$

A third application, giving the area of the inscribed polygon E'' which corresponds to the circumscribed polygon D'' considered above, produces the result

$$4 \cdot \frac{(1/4)}{1 + (1/4)^2} + 4 \cdot \frac{(2/9)}{1 + (2/9)^2} + 4 \cdot \frac{(3/19)}{1 + (3/19)^2}$$

$$+ 4 \cdot \frac{(1/6)}{1 + (1/6)^2} = \frac{9602}{3145} = 3\frac{167}{3145}$$

Collecting our computed values for the areas of the circumscribed polygons D, D', and D'', and for the inscribed polygons E, E', and E'', we have the inequalities

$$2 < 2\frac{4}{5} < 3\frac{167}{3145} < \pi < 3\frac{32}{171} < 3\frac{1}{3} < 4.$$

Suppose that we continue the process of cutting corners to form further circumscribed polygons D''', D^{iv}, ... $D^{(k)}$, with corresponding inscribed polygons E''', E^{iv}, . . . , $E^{(k)}$. What can we say about the narrowing interval within which we are locating the number π?

If at each stage we form a new circumscribed polygon from the old one by cutting all corners, it is easy to see that we double the number of vertices. Hence $D^{(k)}$ and $E^{(k)}$ will each have 2^{k+2} vertices. If $x_1, x_2, \ldots, x_{2^{k+2}}$ are the lengths of the sides of the corners determined by the vertices of $D^{(k)}$, then by Theorems 13-5-4 and 13-5-6 we see that *the difference between the areas of* $D^{(k)}$ *and* $E^{(k)}$ is

$$[x_1 + \cdots x_{2^{k+2}}] - \left[\frac{x_1}{1 + x_1^2} + \cdots + \frac{x_{2^{k+2}}}{1 + x_{2^{k+2}}^2}\right]$$

$$= \frac{x_1^3}{1 + x_1^2} + \cdots + \frac{x_{2^{k+2}}^3}{1 + x_{2^{k+2}}^2} < x_1^3 + \cdots + x_{2^{k+2}}^3 .$$

If, in forming the consecutive polygons $D^{(1)}, D^{(2)}, \ldots, D^{(k)}$, we cut all corners by means of θ-cuts using the value $\theta = 1/2$, then it is not difficult to see that the *largest* side of any corner of D is 1, of D' is 1/2, of D'' is 1/4, and in general of $D^{(k)}$ will be $1/2^k$. Hence *the difference between the areas of* $D^{(k)}$ *and* $E^{(k)}$ *is less than*

$$x_1^3 + \cdots + x_{2^{k+2}}^3 < 2^{k+2} \cdot \left(\frac{1}{2^k}\right)^3 = \frac{4}{2^{2k}} = \frac{1}{4^{k-1}} \,.$$

We have shown that for successive polygons formed by θ-cuts with $\theta = 1/2$ we obtain a difference in area between circumscribed polygon $D^{(k)}$ and inscribed polygon $E^{(k)}$ which is less than $1/4^{k-1}$. Thus, since 4^{10} is somewhat greater than 1,000,000, we see that by computing the areas of $D^{(11)}$ and $E^{(11)}$ (through use of Theorems 13-5-4 and 13-5-6) we can locate π accurately to at least 6 decimal places.

The method described above for computing rational numbers which approximate π with increasing fidelity is based upon very elementary ideas. There are many other computational methods known, some of which permit much more rapid approximation to any given number of decimal places, but most of these are based on more advanced mathematical ideas—particularly those of the calculus. One such method, very simple to describe, is based upon the infinite alternating series

$$1 - 1/3 + 1/5 - 1/7 + \cdots$$

It can be shown by methods of the calculus that $\pi/4$ is *greater* than each of the numbers

$$\begin{array}{l} 1 - 1/3 \\ 1 - 1/3 + 1/5 - 1/7 \\ 1 - 1/3 + 1/5 - 1/7 + 1/9 - 1/11, \quad \text{etc.,} \end{array}$$

and is *less* than each of the numbers

$$\begin{array}{l} 1 \\ 1 - 1/3 + 1/5 \\ 1 - 1/3 + 1/5 - 1/7 + 1/9, \quad \text{etc.} \end{array}$$

EXERCISES

1. Compute the area of D'', taking $\theta = 1/3$.
2. Compute the areas of D''' and E''', taking $\theta = 1/2$.

XIV

Real Numbers

1. *Introductory Remarks*

We turn now to the task of extending the rational number system to the real number system. What we wish to do is to fill the "gaps" in the ordering of the rational number system which were noted in the preceding chapter—not just a few at a time, as we did in extending $\mathcal{R}$ to $\mathcal{R}(\sqrt{2})$, but all at once.

Here the reader may be handicapped by a lack of experience in dealing with the real number system. For, even when we have occasion to use nonrational numbers, we generally employ rational approximations to them in performing elementary computations. For example, in the early grades pupils often use 22/7 as a rational approximation to π in the computation of areas of circles, etc. Later on, in more sophisticated work, a student may compute with 3.1416 (which, of course, is the rational number 31,416/10,000) in place of π. The very nature of practical computation, whether we do it with pencil and paper, on a desk calculator, on a slide rule, or on a modern high speed electronic computer, leads to the systematic use of rational approximations for real numbers.

But if the reader feels certain shortcomings in his intuitive understanding of real numbers he will be comforted to know that mathematicians struggled with the idea for many centuries before coming up with a satisfactory definition of real number. The Greeks came close to a definition of this concept, but it was not until the nineteenth century that a really sound and workable definition was proposed.

2. *Dense Ordered Systems*

Before turning to a construction of the real numbers, it will be useful to undertake a preliminary investigation concerning "gaps" and certain closely related notions, which have to do only with an ordering relation and so can be studied without reference to any operations of addition or multiplication. For this purpose we introduce the following definition.

DEFINITION 14-2-1. *By a* **dense ordered system** *we mean an ordered pair* $\langle B, <_B\rangle$ *such that* B *is any nonempty set,* $<_B$ *is a binary relation on* B, *and the following conditions hold:*

(i) *For all* $x, y, z \in B$ *such that* $x <_B y$ *and* $y <_B z$ *we have* $x <_B z$ (*the* TRANSITIVE LAW *for* $<_B$);

(ii) *For all* $x, y \in B$ *either* $x <_B y$ *or* $x = y$ *or* $y <_B x$, *and no two of these can hold for any* x *and* y (*the* TRICHOTOMY LAW *for* $<_B$);

(iii) *For all* $x, y \in B$ *such that* $x <_B y$ *there is a* $z \in B$ *such that* $x <_B z$ *and* $z <_B y$ (*the* DENSITY LAW *for* $<_B$).

Of course the principal example of a dense ordered system which we have in mind has as its components the set R of all rational numbers and the relation $<_R$, defined in Chapter XII, which is the unique ordering of the *field* of rational numbers $\langle R, +_R, \cdot_R\rangle$. Other examples can easily be constructed however; for example, by considering only the set of *positive* rationals, or by considering the set $R(\sqrt{2})$ of all numbers $a + b\sqrt{2}$ for all $a, b \in R$, in each of these cases taking the usual order relation on the numbers involved.

DEFINITION 14-2-2. *Let* $B = \langle B, <_B\rangle$ *be any dense, ordered system. By a* **break** *of* B *we shall mean an ordered pair* $\langle B_1, B_2\rangle$ *such that:*

(i) B_1 *and* B_2 *are nonempty subsets of* B;

(ii) *For every* $x \in B_1$ *and every* $y \in B_2$ *we have* $x <_B y$;

(iii) *For every* $x \in B_1$ *there is a* $u \in B_1$ *such that* $x <_B u$, *and for every* $z \in B_2$ *there is a* $v \in B_2$ *such that* $v <_B z$.

Intuitively, we can express conditions (**ii**) and (**iii**) of this definition by saying that every element of B_1 is less than each element of B_2, but that B_1 has no greatest element and B_2 has no least element. In the dense ordered system $\langle R, <_R\rangle$ of rational numbers it is easy to find breaks of this kind. The reader is invited to consider, for example, the following pairs $\langle B_1', B_2'\rangle$, $\langle B_1'', B_2''\rangle$, $\langle B_1''', B_2'''\rangle$, $\langle B_1^{iv}, B_2^{iv}\rangle$, where:

B_1' is the set of all negative rationals,
B_2' is the set of all positive rationals,
B_1'' is the set of all negative rationals,
B_2'' is the set of all rationals greater than $1/2$,
B_1''' is the set of all $x \in R$ such that $x > 0$ and $x^2 <_R 2$,
B_2''' is the set of all $x \in R$ such that $x > 0$ and $2 <_R x^2$,
B_1^{iv} is the set of all $x \in R$ which are perimeters of polygons inscribed in a unit circle,
B_2^{iv} is the set of all $x \in R$ which are perimeters of polygons circumscribed about a unit circle.

DEFINITION 14-2-3. *Let* $\mathcal{B} = \langle B, <_B \rangle$ *be a dense ordered system, and let* $\langle B_1, B_2 \rangle$ *be one of its breaks. An element* $u \in B$ *is said to be* **between** B_1 *and* B_2 *if* $x <_B u$ *for every* $x \in B_1$ *and* $u <_B y$ *for every* $y \in B_2$. *The break* $\langle B_1, B_2 \rangle$ *will be called a* **gap** *of* B *if there is* ***no*** *element of* B *which is between* B_1 *and* B_2. *The system* $\mathcal{B}$ *will be called* **complete** *if it has* ***no*** *gaps.*

If we consider the four examples of breaks in the dense ordered system $\langle R, <_R \rangle$ which were considered after Definition 14-2-2, we see that in the case of $\langle B_1', B_2' \rangle$ there is just one rational number between B_1' and B_2', namely, 0; there are infinitely many rationals between B_1'' and B_2''; and there are no rationals between B_1''' and B_2''', or between B_1^{iv} and B_2^{iv}, as we have seen in the previous chapter, so that $\langle B_1''', B_2''' \rangle$ and $\langle B_1^{iv}, B_2^{iv} \rangle$ are *gaps* in $\langle R, <_R \rangle$. It follows that $\langle R, <_R \rangle$ is *not complete*, and our aim in constructing the system of real numbers will be to achieve an extension of the ordered field of rational numbers which *is* complete.

DEFINITION 14-2-4. *Let* $\langle B, <_B \rangle$ *be a dense ordered system,* $\mathcal{B}$, *let* A *be a subset of* B, *and let* u *be an element of* B. *We say that* u *is an* **upper bound** *of* A *in* $\mathcal{B}$ *if, for every* $x \in A$, *we have* $x <_B u$ *or* $x = u$. *We say that* u *is a* **least upper bound** *of* A *in* $\mathcal{B}$ *if* u *is an upper bound of* A *and if, for* ***every*** *upper bound* v *of* A, *we have* $u <_B v$ *or* $u = v$.

Of course not every subset of a dense ordered system need have an upper bound. For example, in the system $\langle R, <_R \rangle$ the set of all positive rational numbers has no upper bound.

Furthermore, even if a set possesses upper bounds, it need not have any least upper bound in the system. As examples, the sets B_1''' and B_1^{iv} considered after Definition 14-2-2 both have upper bounds, but there is no rational number which is a least upper bound for either of them.

On the other hand, if a set *does* have a least upper bound it can have only one, as the following theorem shows.

THEOREM 14-2-5. *If* $\mathcal{B} = \langle B, <_B \rangle$ *is a dense ordered system, if* $A \subseteq B$, *and if* u *and* v *are any least upper bounds of* A *in the system* $\mathcal{B}$, *then* $u = v$.

Proof

▶▶**1.** Let $\langle B, <_B \rangle$ be any dense ordered system and let A be a subset of B.

▶▶**2.** Suppose that u and v are least upper bounds of A in the system $\langle B, <_B \rangle$.

▶**3.** u and v are upper bounds of A; by line **2** and Definition 14-2-4.

▶**4.** Either $u <_B v$ or $u = v$, and also either $v <_B u$ or $v = u$; by lines **2** and **3** and Definition 14-2-4.

▶**5.** If $u \neq v$ then $(u <_B v$ and $v <_B u)$; by logic from line **4**.

▶6. *Not* both $u <_B v$ and $v <_B u$; by line **1** and Definition 14-2-1 **(ii)**.

▶▶7. $u = v$; by logic from lines **5** and **6**.

The theorem now follows by applying the Deduction Theorem to lines **1** and **2** through **7**.

Although an arbitrary subset of an ordered system need not possess a least upper bound, there is one important case in which it does. This is described in the following definition and theorem.

DEFINITION 14-2-6. *Let $\langle B, <_B \rangle$ be a dense ordered system and A a subset of B. An element u of B is called a* **maximum** *element of A if $u \in A$ and if, for every $x \in A$, we have $x <_B u$ or $x = u$.*

We can express this definition in somewhat different words by saying that u is a maximum element of A if $u \in A$ and u is an upper bound of A. (Compare Definition 14-2-4.) An upper bound of a set A, even a least upper bound, need not be a maximum of A, since it may not be an element of A; but a maximum is always an upper bound, and indeed it is a least upper bound as is shown next.

THEOREM 14-2-7. *Suppose that $\langle B, <_B \rangle$ is a dense ordered system, that A is a subset of B, and that u is a maximum element of A. Then u is a least upper bound of A.*

Proof

▶▶1. Suppose that $\langle B, <_B \rangle$ is a dense ordered set, that A is a subset of B, and that u is a maximum element of A.

2. $u \in A$; by line **1** and Definition 14-2-6.

3. For every $x \in A$ we have $x <_B u$ or $x = u$; by line **1** and Definition 14-2-6.

▶▶4. u is an upper bound of A; by line **3** and Definition 14-2-4.

5. If v is any upper bound of A then $u <_B v$ or $u = v$; by line **2** and Definition 14-2-4.

▶▶6. u is a least upper bound of A; by lines **4** and **5** and Definition 14-2-4.

The theorem is now obtained by applying the Deduction Theorem to lines **1** through **6**.

Although we have just shown that a set which has a maximum element must have a least upper bound, it is also possible for a set with no maximum element to have a least upper bound. For example, in the dense ordered system $\langle R, <_R \rangle$ the set of all negative rational numbers has no maximum element, but it has a least upper bound, namely, the number 0.

The following theorem, which will be useful in the sequel, is almost an immediate corollary of the preceding theorem.

THEOREM 14-2-8. *Suppose that* $\langle B, <_B \rangle$ *is a dense ordered system, and that* x *is any element of* B. *Then* x *is a least upper bound of the unit set* $\{x\}$.

The proof is left as an exercise.

We now return to the notion of *completeness* for a dense ordered system. Although this was defined as the *nonexistence* of gaps, we show below that it is equivalent to the *existence* of sufficiently many least upper bounds.

THEOREM 14-2-9. *A dense ordered system* $\mathcal{B} = \langle B, <_B \rangle$ *is complete if, and only if, every nonempty subset of* B *which has an upper bound in* $\mathcal{B}$ *also has a least upper bound in* $\mathcal{B}$.

Proof. We break the proof into two parts, showing first (Part I) that in a complete system every nonempty set with an upper bound has a least upper bound. The converse (Part II) is left as an exercise.

Part I

▶▶ **1.** Let $\mathcal{B} = \langle B, <_B \rangle$ be any dense ordered system which is complete.

▶▶ **2.** Suppose that A is a nonempty subset of B, and that v is an upper bound of A in the system $\mathcal{B}$.

▶▶ **3.** *Assume* that A has no least upper bound in $\mathcal{B}$.

4. A has no maximum element; by line **3** and Theorem 14-2-7.

5. For every $x \in A$ there is a $u \in A$ such that $x <_B u$; by line **4**, Definition 14-2-6, line **1**, and Definition 14-2-1 (**ii**).

▶ **6.** Let A' be the set of all upper bounds of A in the system $\mathcal{B}$.

7. A' is non-empty; by lines **6** and **2**.

8. For every $y \in A'$ there is a $w \in A'$ such that $w <_B y$; by lines **6**, **3**, and **1** and Definitions 14-2-4 and 14-2-1 (**ii**).

▶ **9.** The ordered pair $\langle A, A' \rangle$ is a *break* of the system $\langle B, <_B \rangle$; by Definition 14-2-2 and lines **2**, **5**, **7**, and **8**.

▶▶ **10.** There is an element z of B *between* A and A'; by lines **1** and **9** and Definition 14-2-3.

11. For every $x \in A$ we have $x <_B z$; by line **10** and Definition 14-2-3.

▶ **12.** z is an upper bound of A; by line **11** and Definition 14-2-4.

▶ **13.** For every $y \in A'$ we have $z <_B y$; by line **10** and Definition 14-2-3.

▶▶ **14.** z is a least upper bound of A in $\mathcal{B}$; by lines **12**, **13**, and **6** and Definition 14-2-4.

15. If A has no least upper bound in $\mathcal{B}$, then z is a least upper bound of A in $\mathcal{B}$; by the Deduction Theorem applied to lines **3** through **14**.

16. A has a least upper bound in $\mathcal{B}$; by logic applied to line **15**.

17. If $\mathcal{B} = \langle B, <_B \rangle$ is any dense ordered system which is complete, and if A is any nonempty subset of B which has an upper bound in $\mathcal{B}$, then A has a least upper bound in $\mathcal{B}$; by the Deduction Theorem applied to lines **1** and **2** through **16**.

The concepts of upper bound and least upper bound are paralleled in the following definition.

DEFINITION 14-2-10. *Let $\mathcal{B} = \langle B, <_B \rangle$ be a dense ordered system, let A be a subset of B, and let u be an element of B. We say that u is a* **lower bound** *of A in $\mathcal{B}$ if, for every $x \in A$, we have $u <_B x$ or $u = x$. We say that u is a* **greatest lower bound** *of A in $\mathcal{B}$ if u is a lower bound of A and if, for* **every** *lower bound v of A in $\mathcal{B}$ we have $v <_B u$ or $v = u$.*

In a certain intuitive sense it is clear that each of the notions of least upper bound and greatest upper bound is "one-sided," while the notion of a gap, and hence of completeness, is "symmetric." It is natural to expect, therefore, that there is a counterpart to Theorem 14-2-8 which connects completeness with the existence of sufficiently many greatest lower bounds. This is indeed the case.

THEOREM 14-2-11. *A dense ordered system $B = \langle B, <_B \rangle$ is complete if, and only if, every nonempty subset of B which has a lower bound in B also has a greatest lower bound in B.*

The proof is left to the reader.

The following is an immediate consequence of Theorems 14-2-9 and 14-2-11.

THEOREM 14-2-12. *Let $\langle B, <_B \rangle$ be any dense ordered system. If every subset of B which has an upper bound also has a least upper bound, then every subset of B which has a lower bound also has a greatest lower bound; and conversely.*

EXERCISES

1. Prove Theorem 14-2-8.

2. Prove Theorem 14-2-11.

3. Give a proof of Theorem 14-2-12 directly from Definitions 14-2-1, 14-2-4, and 14-2-10, without using Theorems 14-2-9 or 14-2-11.

4. Complete the proof of Theorem 14-2-9.

3. The Completion of Dense Ordered Systems

In this section we take up the problem of "filling" the gaps which may exist in an arbitrary dense ordered system. That is, given any such system, we wish to construct an extension of it which is complete. (Such a system is called a *completion* of the given system.) Let us begin by clarifying our notion of extension.

DEFINITION 14-3-1. *Suppose that* $\mathcal{B} = \langle B, <_B\rangle$ *and* $\mathcal{C} = \langle C, <_C\rangle$ *are two dense ordered systems. We say that* $\mathcal{C}$ *is an* **extension** *of* $\mathcal{B}$ *if* $B \subseteq C$ *and if, for all* $x, y \in B$, *we have* $x <_C y$ *if and only if* $x <_B y$.

Intuitively, we can think of C as formed by adding certain new elements to those of B; and then the new relation $<_C$ must be defined for all ordered pairs of elements of C, in such a way that for an ordered pair of *old* elements (i.e., elements of B), the new relation holds just in case the old relation $<_B$ holds.

With the concept of extension thus made precise, we can now formulate the problem to be treated in this section.

PROBLEM C. *Given an* **arbitrary** *dense ordered system, is it always possible to construct an* **extension** *of it which is* **complete?**

We shall see that the answer to this question is affirmative, and indeed that in a certain sense the complete extension of the given system is unique.

The key to our solution of *Problem C* lies in focussing attention on those sets of the given dense ordered system which have upper bounds in the system, and then for each such set to study the set of *all* of its upper bounds. Accordingly we introduce the following notation.

DEFINITION 14-3-2. *Let* $\mathcal{B} = \langle B, <_B\rangle$ *be an arbitrary dense ordered system. By* $T(\mathcal{B})$ *we shall mean the set of all those nonempty subsets* A *of* B *such that* A *has an upper bound in* $\mathcal{B}$. *And for each* $A \in T(\mathcal{B})$ *we shall define* $U(A)$ *to be the subset of* B *consisting of all those* $u \in B$ *such that* u *is an upper bound of* A.

Note: It is clear that for every $A \in T(\mathcal{B})$ the set $U(A)$ is nonempty. This follows at once from the definitions of T and U.

The basic facts about the function U which we shall use in the sequel are the following.

THEOREM 14-3-3. *Let* $\mathcal{B} = \langle B, <_B\rangle$ *be an arbitrary dense ordered system, and let* A_1 *and* A_2 *be arbitrary sets in* $T(\mathcal{B})$. *Then:*

(i) *whenever* $A_1 \subseteq A_2$ *we have* $U(A_2) \subseteq U(A_1)$;
(ii) *either* $U(A_1) \subseteq U(A_2)$ *or* $U(A_2) \subseteq U(A_1)$;
(iii) *for any* $x, y \in B$ *we have* $x <_B y$ *if, and only if,* $U(\{y\}) \subseteq U(\{x\})$ and $x \neq y$.

Proof. We shall leave the proofs of parts **(i)** and **(iii)** as exercises for the reader, and present here a proof of part **(ii)**.

▶▶ **1.** Let $\mathcal{B} = \langle B, <_B \rangle$ be any dense ordered system, and let A_1 and A_2 be any sets in $T(\mathcal{B})$.

▶▶ **2.** *Assume* that there is an element $w \in A_2$ which is an upper bound of A_1 in $\mathcal{B}$.

3. For every $x \in A_1$ we have $x <_B w$ or $x = w$; by line **2** and Definition 14-2-4.

▶ **4.** Let v be any element of $U(A_2)$.

5. For every $y \in A_2$ we have $y <_B v$ or $y = v$; by line **4** and Definitions 14-3-2 and 14-2-4.

6. $w <_B v$ or $w = v$; by lines **5** and **2**.

7. For every $x \in A_1$ we have $x <_B v$ or $x = v$; by lines **3**, **6**, **1** and Definition 14-2-1 (**i**).

▶ **8.** $v \in U(A_1)$; by line **7** and Definitions 14-3-2 and 14-2-4.

9. If v is any element of $U(A_2)$ then v is an element of $U(A_1)$; by the Deduction Theorem applied to lines **4** through **8**.

10. $U(A_2) \subseteq U(A_1)$; by line **9** and the definition of $\subseteq$ (Definition 9-3-1).

▶▶ **11.** If there is an element of A_2 which is an upper bound of A_1 in $\mathcal{B}$, then $U(A_2) \subseteq U(A_1)$; by the Deduction Theorem applied to lines **2** through **10**.

▶▶ **12.** Now *assume* that there is *no* element of A_2 which is an upper bound of A_1 in $\mathcal{B}$.

13. For every $y \in A_2$ there is an $x \in A_1$ such that $y <_B x$; by lines **12** and **1** and Definitions 14-2-4 and 14-2-1 (**ii**).

▶ **14.** Let u be any element of $U(A_1)$.

15. For every $x \in A_1$ we have $x <_B u$ or $x = u$; by line **14** and Definitions 14-3-2 and 14-2-4.

16. For every $y \in A_2$ we have $y <_B u$ or $y = u$; by lines **13**, **15**, **1** and Definition 14-2-1 (**i**).

▶ **17.** $u \in U(A_2)$; by line **16** and Definitions 14-3-2 and 14-2-4.

18. If u is any element of $U(A_1)$ then also $u \in U(A_2)$; by the Deduction Theorem applied to lines **14** through **17**.

▶▶ **19.** $U(A_1) \subseteq U(A_2)$; by line **18** and the definition of $\subseteq$ (Definition 9-3-1).

▶▶ **20.** If there is no element of A_2 which is an upper bound of A_1 in $\mathcal{B}$, then $U(A_1) \subseteq U(A_2)$; by the Deduction Theorem applied to lines **12** through **19**.

▶▶ **21.** Either $U(A_2) \subseteq U(A_1)$ or $U(A_1) \subseteq U(A_2)$; by lines **11** and **20**.

The proof is now completed by applying the Deduction Theorem to lines **1** through **21**.

In order to construct our solution to *Problem C* we require a function which closely resembles U, but which differs from it in one way. In fact, we shall need a function λ which, like U, has $T(\mathcal{B})$ as its domain, and which is such that for all A_1 and A_2 of $T(\mathcal{B})$ we have $\lambda(A_1) = \lambda(A_2)$ if and only if $U(A_1) = U(A_2)$, but for which $\lambda(A) =$ the least upper bound of A whenever A is an element of $T(\mathcal{B})$ which *has* a least upper bound. To prepare the way for showing the existence of such a function we note the following result.

THEOREM 14-3-4. *Suppose that* $\mathcal{B} = \langle B, <_B \rangle$ *is a dense ordered system, and that* A_1 *and* A_2 *are elements of* $T(\mathcal{B})$ *such that* $U(A_1) = U(A_2)$. *If* v *is a least upper bound of* A_1 *in* $\mathcal{B}$, *then also* v *is a least upper bound of* A_2 *in* $\mathcal{B}$.

The basic idea of the proof of this theorem is a very simple one indeed. In fact, if v is a least upper bound of A_1 in $\mathcal{B}$ it must, by the definition of U, be the minimum element of $U(A_1)$. Since $U(A_1) = U(A_2)$ by hypothesis, it follows that v is the minimum element of $U(A_2)$. Again appealing to the definition of U, we conclude that v is a least upper bound of A_2 in $\mathcal{B}$.

We shall leave to the reader the task of giving a more detailed proof.

THEOREM 14-3-5. *If* $\mathcal{B} = \langle B, <_B \rangle$ *is any dense ordered system, we can find a function* λ *with the following properties:*

(i) *the domain of* λ *is* $T(\mathcal{B})$;
(ii) *for all* $A_1, A_2 \in T(\mathcal{B})$ *we have* $\lambda(A_1) = \lambda(A_2)$ *if, and only if,* $U(A_1) = U(A_2)$;
(iii) *if* A *is any element of* $T(\mathcal{B})$ *which has a least upper bound, say* u, *in* $\mathcal{B}$, *then* $\lambda(A) = u$.

We shall give only an outline of a proof of this theorem.

Consider first the function ν, having $T(\mathcal{B})$ as its domain, whose value for any $A \in T(\mathcal{B})$ is given by the following rule: If A has no least upper bound in $\mathcal{B}$ we set $\nu(A) = U(A)$, while if A has a least upper bound v (necessarily unique by Theorem 14-2-5) in $\mathcal{B}$, then we set $\nu(A) = v$.

Clearly we have (i) the domain of ν is $T(\mathcal{B})$, and (iii) for any $A \in T(\mathcal{B})$ such that A has a least upper bound v in $\mathcal{B}$, $\nu(A) = v$. *If* it should happen that none of the sets $U(A)$ is itself an element of B, we could also show that (ii) $\nu(A_1) = \nu(A_2)$ if, and only if, $U(A_1) = U(A_2)$, and hence we could use ν for the required function.

However, since $\langle B, <_B \rangle$ is an arbitrary dense ordered system, we know nothing about the nature of the elements of B, and it may well happen that for some $A \in T(\mathcal{B})$ the subset $U(A)$ of B is itself an element of B. Hence we modify our definition of ν to obtain the function λ, as follows.

In fact, we take λ to be the function with domain $T(\mathcal{B})$, whose value for any $A \in T(\mathcal{B})$ is given by the following rule: If A has no least upper bound in $\mathcal{B}$ we set $\lambda(A) = \langle U(A), B\rangle$, while if A has a (necessarily unique) least upper bound, say v, in $\mathcal{B}$, we set $\lambda(A) = v$.

Again, as for the function ν, it is clear that λ has the properties **(i)** and **(iii)** of Theorem 14-3-5. Hence it remains only to indicate that it also possesses property **(ii)**.

To establish **(ii)** we first suppose that $U(A_1) = U(A_2)$ and wish to show that $\lambda(A_1) = \lambda(A_2)$. Two cases arise. If A_1 has a least upper bound v in $\mathcal{B}$, then v is also a least upper bound of A_2 in $\mathcal{B}$ by Theorem 14-3-4; and in this case, by definition of λ, we have $\lambda(A_1) = v$ and $\lambda(A_2) = v$, so that $\lambda(A_1) = \lambda(A_2)$ as required. On the other hand if A_1 has *no* least upper bound in $\mathcal{B}$ then neither has A_2 (for if it did, then by Theorem 14-3-4 A_1 would also have to have one). Hence in this case the definition of λ tells us that $\lambda(A_1) = \langle U(A_1), B\rangle$ and $\lambda(A_2) = \langle U(A_2), B\rangle$, and since $U(A_1) = U(A_2)$ we get again the desired result $\lambda(A_1) = \lambda(A_2)$.

To complete the outline of our proof of **(ii)** we suppose that $\lambda(A_1) = \lambda(A_2)$ and wish to show that $U(A_1) = U(A_2)$. We first observe that from the supposition $\lambda(A_1) = \lambda(A_2)$ we can infer that if one of the sets A_1, A_2 has a least upper bound in $\mathcal{B}$, then the other does also. For *assume* that A_1, say, has a least upper bound v in $\mathcal{B}$, while A_2 has none. Then by the definition of λ we have $\lambda(A_1) = v$ and $\lambda(A_2) = \langle U(A_1), B\rangle$, so that $v = \langle U(A_1), B\rangle$ by our supposition that $\lambda(A_1) = \lambda(A_2)$. But $v \in B$; hence by the logic of identity we get $\langle U(A_1), B\rangle \in B$. But this is impossible, as it violates a fundamental principle of set theory (see Theorem 9-11-26). Thus our *assumption* above has led to a contradiction, and must be false.

We have shown that the supposition $\lambda(A_1) = \lambda(A_2)$ admits only two cases: Either *both* A_1 and A_2 have least upper bounds in $\mathcal{B}$, or *neither* do. In the latter case we have (by definition of λ), $\lambda(A_1) = \langle U(A_1), B\rangle$ and $\lambda(A_2) = \langle U(A_2), B\rangle$, so that $\langle (UA_1), B\rangle = \langle U(A_2), B\rangle$; and by the fundamental property of ordered pairs (See Theorem 9-5-5) it follows that $U(A_1) = U(A_2)$, as required. On the other hand in the former case, if both A_1 and A_2 have least upper bounds in $\mathcal{B}$, then by definition of λ we see that $\lambda(A_1)$ is the least upper bound of A_1 and $\lambda(A_2)$ is the least upper bound of A_2—from which it follows that A_1 and A_2 have the same least upper bound in $\mathcal{B}$ [since we are assuming $\lambda(A_1) = \lambda(A_2)$]. Letting v be the least upper bound of A_1 (and of A_2) in $\mathcal{B}$, it is now an easy matter to show that $U(A_1)$ is the set of all $z \in B$ for which either $v <_B z$ or $v = z$ (and similarly that $U(A_2)$ is the set of all $z \in B$ for which $v <_B z$ or $v = z$); so that again we get $U(A_1) = U(A_2)$ as required.

This completes our proof of **(ii)**, and hence of Theorem 14-3-5.

In the proof just completed we have constructed a very special function λ. However, the details of the construction are of no further importance to us, for *any* function λ which satisfies conditions **(i)** through **(iii)** of Theorem

14-3-5 (and there are actually a great many such functions) will enable us to construct a solution to *Problem C*. The method is indicated in the following definition.

DEFINITION 14-3-6. *Let* $\mathcal{B} = \langle B, <_B \rangle$ *be any dense ordered system, and let* λ *be any function satisfying conditions* (**i**) *through* (**iii**) *of* Theorem 14-3-5. *We define* B_λ *to be the range of* λ, *i.e., the set of all objects* $\lambda(A)$ *for all* $A \in T(\mathcal{B})$. *And we define* $<_\lambda$ *to be the binary relation on* B_λ *such that, for any elements* $\lambda(A_1)$ *and* $\lambda(A_2)$ *of* B_λ, *we have* $\lambda(A_1) <_\lambda \lambda(A_2)$ *if, and only if,* $\lambda(A_1) \neq \lambda(A_2)$ *and* $U(A_2) \subseteq U(A_1)$. *Finally, we let* $\mathcal{B}_\lambda$ *be the ordered pair* $\langle B_\lambda, <_\lambda \rangle$.

Before discussing the intuitive content of this definition we note that our definition of the relation $<_\lambda$ requires some justification. For suppose that A_1, A_1', A_2, and A_2' are elements of $T(\mathcal{B})$ such that $\lambda(A_1) = \lambda(A_1')$ and $\lambda(A_2) = \lambda(A_2')$. Clearly if $\lambda(A_1) <_\lambda \lambda(A_2)$ we should want to conclude that $\lambda(A_1') <_\lambda \lambda(A_2')$. On the other hand if it happened that $\lambda(A_1) \neq \lambda(A_2)$ and

(**a**) $U(A_2) \subseteq U(A_1)$, but
(**b**) *not* $U(A_2') \subseteq U(A_1')$,

then we would have (by our definition of $<_\lambda$) that $\lambda(A_1) <_\lambda \lambda(A_2)$ but *not* to $\lambda(A_1') <_\lambda \lambda(A_2')$, and hence our definition would be unsatisfactory. Thus, to justify our definition of $<_\lambda$, we must show that (**a**) and (**b**) cannot happen simultaneously.

The required justification is actually very simple. Since $\lambda(A_1) = \lambda(A_1')$ and $\lambda(A_2) = \lambda(A_2')$, and since, by hypothesis, λ satisfies condition (**ii**) of Theorem 14-3-5, we have $U(A_1) = U(A_1')$ and $U(A_2) = U(A_2')$. It follows at once that (**a**) and (**b**) cannot hold simultaneously.

Now that Definition 14-3-6 is logically justified, what is its intuitive content? We are going to show that the ordered pair $\mathcal{B}_\lambda$ is, in fact, a dense ordered system; that B is, in fact, a subset of B_λ; and that for each $A \in T(\mathcal{B})$ the element $\lambda(A)$ of B_λ is a least upper bound of A in B_λ. These will be key points in establishing that $\mathcal{B}_\lambda$ is actually a solution to *Problem C*.

THEOREM 14-3-7. *Let* $\mathcal{B} = \langle B, <_B \rangle$ *be any dense ordered system, and let* λ *be any function satisfying conditions* (**i**) *through* (**iii**) *of* Theorem 14-3-5. *Then the system* $\mathcal{B}_\lambda = \langle B_\lambda, <_\lambda \rangle$ *is a dense ordered system which is an extension of* $\mathcal{B}$, *and which is complete. Furthermore, the system* $\mathcal{B}_\lambda$ *possesses these two properties:* (**i**) *If* $A \in T(\mathcal{B})$ *and* v *is a least upper bound of* A *in* $\mathcal{B}$, *then* v *is also the least upper bound of* A *in* $\mathcal{B}_\lambda$, *and* (**ii**) *for every* $a \in B_\lambda$ *there is an* $A \in T(\mathcal{B})$ *such that* a *is the least upper bound of* A *in* $\mathcal{B}_a$.

Clearly this theorem provides an affirmative solution to *Problem C*. We shall break the proof up by presenting a series of lemmas which together give the results stated in the theorem.

LEMMA A. *The relation $<_\lambda$ satisfies the transitive law.*

Proof

▶▶1. Suppose that $\lambda(A_1)$, $\lambda(A_2)$, and $\lambda(A_3)$ are any elements of B_λ such that $\lambda(A_1) <_\lambda \lambda(A_2)$ and $\lambda(A_2) <_\lambda \lambda(A_3)$.

▶2. $\lambda(A_1) \neq \lambda(A_2)$ and $U(A_2) \subseteq U(A_1)$, and $\lambda(A_2) \neq \lambda(A_3)$ and $U(A_3) \subseteq U(A_2)$; by line **1** and Definition 14-3-6.

▶3. $U(A_3) \subseteq U(A_1)$; by line **2** and the elements of set theory (Theorem 9-3-2).

4. If $\lambda(A_1) = \lambda(A_3)$ then $U(A_1) = U(A_3)$; since by hypothesis λ satisfies condition (**ii**) of Theorem 14-3-5.

5. If $\lambda(A_1) = \lambda(A_3)$ then $U(A_2) \subseteq U(A_3)$ and $U(A_3) \subseteq U(A_2)$; by E applied to lines **2** and **4**.

6. If $\lambda(A_1) = \lambda(A_3)$ then $U(A_2) = U(A_3)$; by line **5** and the elements of set theory (Theorem 9-3-3).

7. If $\lambda(A_1) = \lambda(A_3)$ then $\lambda(A_2) = \lambda(A_3)$; from line **6**, since by hypothesis λ satisfies condition (**ii**) of Theorem 14-3-5.

▶8. $\lambda(A_1) \neq \lambda(A_3)$; by lines **7** and **2**.

▶▶9. $\lambda(A_1) <_\lambda \lambda(A_3)$; by lines **3** and **8** and Definition 14-3-6.

The lemma is now obtained by the Deduction Theorem applied to lines **1** through **9**.

LEMMA B. *The relation $<_\lambda$ satisfies the trichotomy law.*

Proof

▶▶1. Let $\lambda(A_1)$ and $\lambda(A_2)$ be any elements of B_λ.

2. Either $U(A_1) \subseteq U(A_2)$ or $U(A_2) \subseteq U(A_1)$; by Theorem 14-3-3 (**ii**).

▶▶3. If $\lambda(A_1) \neq \lambda(A_2)$ then either $\lambda(A_1) <_\lambda \lambda(A_2)$ or $\lambda(A_2) <_\lambda \lambda(A_1)$; by line **2** and Definition 14-3-6.

▶▶4. If $\lambda(A_1) \neq \lambda(A_2)$ we cannot have *both* $\lambda(A_1) <_\lambda \lambda(A_2)$ and $\lambda(A_2) <_\lambda \lambda(A_1)$; by Definition 14-3-6 and the hypothesis that λ satisfies condition (**ii**) of Theorem 14-3-5.

▶▶5. If $\lambda(A_1) = \lambda(A_2)$ we cannot have *either* $\lambda(A_1) <_\lambda \lambda(A_2)$ or $\lambda(A_2) <_\lambda \lambda(A_1)$; by Definition 14-3-6.

The lemma is now a simple logical consequence of lines **3**, **4**, and **5**.

LEMMA C. *The relation $<_\lambda$ satisfies the density law.*

Proof

▶▶ 1. Let $\lambda(A_1)$ and $\lambda(A_2)$ be any elements of B_λ such that $\lambda(A_1) <_\lambda \lambda(A_2)$.

2. $\lambda(A_1) \neq \lambda(A_2)$ and $U(A_2) \subseteq U(A_1)$; by line **1** and Definition 14-3-6.

3. $U(A_1) \neq U(A_2)$; by line **2** and the hypothesis that λ satisfies condition (**ii**) of Theorem 14-3-5.

▶ 4. There is an element $v \in U(A_1)$ such that $v \notin U(A_2)$; by lines **2** and **3** and elements of set theory (Definition 9-3-1).

5. v is an upper bound of A_1 in $\mathcal{B}$, but v is not an upper bound of A_2 in $\mathcal{B}$; by line **4** and Definition 14-3-2.

▶ 6. There is an element $y \in A_2$ such that $v <_B y$; by line **5** and Definition 14-2-4.

▶ 7. There is an element $z \in B$ such that $v <_B z$ and $z <_B y$; by line **6**, the hypothesis that $\mathcal{B}$ is a dense ordered system, and Definition 14-2-1(**iii**).

▶ 8. Let A_3 be the unit set $\{z\}$, whose only element is z.

9. z is a least upper bound of A_3 in $\mathcal{B}$; by line **8** and Theorem 14-2-8.

10. $A_3 \in T(\mathcal{B})$; by line **9** and Definition 14-3-2.

11. Every upper bound of A_3 in $\mathcal{B}$ is also an upper bound of A_1 in $\mathcal{B}$, and every upper bound of A_2 in $\mathcal{B}$ is also an upper bound of A_3 in $\mathcal{B}$; by lines **5, 6, 7, 8,** and **9** and Definition 14-2-4.

▶ 12. $U(A_3) \subseteq U(A_1)$ and $U(A_2) \subseteq U(A_3)$; by line **11** and Definition 14-3-2.

13. $v \notin U(A_3)$; by lines **7** and **8** and Definitions 14-2-1 (**ii**) and 14-3-2.

▶ 14. $U(A_1) \neq U(A_3)$; by lines **4** and **13**.

15. $z \in U(A_3)$ but $z \notin U(A_2)$; by lines **9**, **7**, and **6** and Definitions 14-2-1(**ii**) and 14-3-2.

▶ 16. $U(A_3) \neq U(A_2)$; by line **15**.

▶▶ 17. $\lambda(A_1) <_\lambda \lambda(A_3)$ and $\lambda(A_3) <_\lambda \lambda(A_2)$; by lines **12, 14,** and **16** and Definition 14-3-6, since λ satisfies Theorem 14-3-5(**ii**) by hypothesis.

The lemma now follows by applying the Deduction Theorem to lines **1** through **17**.

LEMMA D. *$\mathcal{B}_\lambda$ is a dense ordered system.*

Proof

By lemmas A, B, and C and Definition 14-2-1.

LEMMA E. *B is a subset of B_λ.*

Proof

▶▶ 1. Let x be any element of B.

▶ 2. Let A be the unit set $\{x\}$.

3. x is a least upper bound of A; by line **2** and Theorem 14-2-8.

▶4. $A \in T(\mathcal{B})$ and $\lambda(A) = x$; by line **3**, Definition 14-3-2 and the hypothesis that λ satisfies condition (**iii**) of Theorem 14-3-5.

▶▶5. $x \in B_\lambda$; by line **4** and Definition 14-3-6.

6. If x is any element of B then $x \in B_\lambda$; by the Deduction Theorem applied to lines **1** through **5**.

7. $B \subseteq B_\lambda$; by line **6** and the definition of $\subseteq$.

LEMMA F. *For any $x, y \in B$ we have $x <_\lambda y$ if, and only if, $x <_B y$.*

Proof

▶▶1. Let x, y be any elements of B.

▶2. Let $A_1 = \{x\}$ and let $A_2 = \{y\}$.

3. x and y are least upper bounds in $\mathcal{B}$ of A_1 and A_2 respectively; by line **2** and Theorem 14-2-8.

4. $A_1, A_2 \in T(\mathcal{B})$ and $\lambda(A_1) = x$, $\lambda(A_2) = y$; by line **3**, Definition 14-3-2, and the hypothesis that λ satisfies condition (**iii**) of Theorem 14-3-5.

▶5. $x <_\lambda y$ if, and only if, $x \neq y$ and $U(A_2) \subseteq U(A_1)$; by line **4** and Definition 14-3-6.

▶6. $U(A_2) \subseteq U(A_1)$ if, and only if, $x <_B y$ or $x = y$; by Theorem 14-3-3(**iii**).

▶▶7. $x <_\lambda y$ if, and only if, $x <_B y$; by logic applied to lines **5** and **6** and Lemma B.

The lemma now follows by an application of the Deduction Theorem to lines **1** through **7**.

LEMMA G. *$\mathcal{B}_\lambda$ is an extension of $\mathcal{B}$.*

Proof

By Definitions 14-3-1 and 14-3-6, and lemmas D, E, and G.

LEMMA H. *The ordered system $\mathcal{B}_\lambda$ is complete.*

Proof

▶▶1. Let X be any nonempty subset of B_λ which has an upper bound in $\mathcal{B}_\lambda$.

▶2. There is an $A_0 \in T(\mathcal{B})$ such that $\lambda(A_0)$ is an upper bound for X in $\mathcal{B}_\lambda$; by line **1** and Definition 14-3-6.

▶▶3. Let A^* be the union of all sets $A \in T(\mathcal{B})$ such that $\lambda(A) \in X$.

4. For every $x \in B$ we have $x \in A^*$ if, and only if, there is an $A \in T(\mathcal{B})$ such that $x \in A$ and $\lambda(A) \in X$; by line **3** and definition of *union* (Definition 9-11-8).

In the remainder of the proof we shall show that A^* is in $T(\mathcal{B})$ (line **16**) so that $\lambda(A^*) \in B_\lambda$, and then we shall show that $\lambda(A^*)$ is an upper bound of X in $\mathcal{B}_\lambda$ (line **28**), and indeed a least upper bound of X in $\mathcal{B}_\lambda$ (line **45**). From the way in which X was picked (line **1**), we will then be able to get Lemma H by an application of Theorem 14-2-9.

▶ **5.** A_0 has an upper bound, say v, in $\mathcal{B}$; by line **2** and Definition 14-3-2.

▶ **6.** Let x be any element of A^*.

7. There is an $A \in T(\mathcal{B})$ such that $x \in A$ and $\lambda(A) \in X$; by lines **6** and **4**.

8. $\lambda(A) <_\lambda \lambda(A_0)$ or $\lambda(A) = \lambda(A_0)$; by lines **2** and **7** and Definitions 14-3-6 and 14-2-4.

9. $\lambda(A) = \lambda(A_0)$ or $U(A_0) \subseteq U(A)$; by line **8** and Definition 14-3-6.

10. $U(A) = U(A_0)$ or $U(A_0) \subseteq U(A)$; by line **9** and the hypothesis that λ satisfies condition **(ii)** of Theorem 14-3-5.

11. $v \in U(A_0)$; by line **5** and Definition 14-3-2.

12. $v \in U(A)$; by lines **10** and **11** and the Definition of $\subseteq$ (Definition 9-3-1).

▶ **13.** $x <_B v$ or $x = v$; by lines **7** and **12** and Definition 14-3-2.

14. If x is any element of A^* then $x <_B v$ or $x = v$; by the Deduction Theorem applied to lines **6** through **13**.

▶ **15.** v is an upper bound of A^*; by line **14** and Definition 14-2-4.

▶▶ **16.** $A^* \in T(\mathcal{B})$; by line **15** and Definition 14-3-2.

▶ **17.** Let A_1 be *any* element of $T(\mathcal{B})$ such that $\lambda(A_1) \in X$.

▶ **18.** Let u be any upper bound of A^* in $\mathcal{B}$.

19. Let y be any element of A_1.

20. $y \in A^*$; by lines **17**, **19**, and **4**.

21. $y <_B u$ or $y = u$; by lines **18** and **20** and Definition 14-2-4.

22. If y is any element of A_1 then $y <_B u$ or $y = u$; by the Deduction Theorem applied to lines **19** through **21**.

▶ **23.** u is an upper bound of A_1 in $\mathcal{B}$; by line **22** and Definition 14-2-4.

24. If u is any upper bound of A^* in $\mathcal{B}$, then u is an upper bound of A_1 in $\mathcal{B}$; by the Deduction Theorem applied to lines **18** through **23**.

25. $U(A^*) \subseteq U(A_1)$; by line **24**, Definition 14-3-2, and the definition of $\subseteq$.

▶ **26.** $\lambda(A_1) = \lambda(A^*)$ or $\lambda(A_1) <_\lambda \lambda(A^*)$; by line **25** and Definition 14-3-6.

27. If A_1 is any element of $T(\mathcal{B})$ such that $\lambda(A_1) \in X$, then $\lambda(A_1) <_\lambda \lambda(A^*)$ or $\lambda(A_1) = \lambda(A^*)$; by the Deduction Theorem applied to lines **17** through **26**.

▶▶ **28.** $\lambda(A^*)$ is an upper bound of X in $\mathcal{B}_\lambda$; by line **27** and Definitions 14-3-6 and 14-2-4.

▶▶**29.** Let $\lambda(A_2)$ be *any* upper bound of X in $\mathcal{B}_\lambda$.

▶**30.** Let w be any upper bound of A_2 in $\mathcal{B}$.

31. Let z be any element of A^*.

32. There is some $A_3 \in T(\mathcal{B})$ such that $z \in A_3$ and $\lambda(A_3) \in X$; by lines **31** and **4**.

33. $\lambda(A_3) <_\lambda \lambda(A_2)$ or $\lambda(A_3) = \lambda(A_2)$; by lines **29** and **32** and Definition 14-2-4.

34. $\lambda(A_3) = \lambda(A_2)$ or $U(A_2) \subseteq U(A_3)$; by line **33** and Definition 14-3-6.

35. If $\lambda(A_3) = \lambda(A_2)$ then $U(A_3) = U(A_2)$; by the hypothesis that λ satisfies condition (**ii**) of Theorem 14-3-5.

36. $U(A_2) \subseteq U(A_3)$; by lines **34** and **35**.

37. w is an upper bound of A_3 in $\mathcal{B}$; by lines **30** and **36** and Definition 14-3-6.

38. $z <_B w$ or $z = w$; by lines **32** and **37** and Definition 14-2-4.

39. If z is any element of A^* then $z <_B w$ or $z = w$; by the Deduction Theorem applied to lines **31** through **38**.

▶**40.** w is an upper bound of A^* in $\mathcal{B}$; by line **39** and Definition 14-2-4.

41. If w is any upper bound of A_2 in $\mathcal{B}$ then w is an upper bound of A^* in $\mathcal{B}$; by the Deduction Theorem applied to lines **30** through **40**.

▶**42.** $U(A_2) \subseteq U(A^*)$; by line **41** and Definition 14-3-2.

▶▶**43.** $\lambda(A^*) = \lambda(A_2)$ or $\lambda(A^*) <_\lambda \lambda(A_2)$; by line **42** and Definition 14-3-6.

44. If $\lambda(A_2)$ is *any* upper bound of X in $\mathcal{B}_\lambda$ then $\lambda(A^*) <_\lambda \lambda(A_2)$ or $\lambda(A^*) = \lambda(A_2)$; by the Deduction Theorem applied to lines **29** through **43**.

▶▶**45.** $\lambda(A^*)$ is a least upper bound of X in $\mathcal{B}_\lambda$; by lines **28** and **44** and Definition 14-2-4.

▶▶**46.** If X is any nonempty subset of B_λ which has an upper bound in $\mathcal{B}_\lambda$, then X has a least upper bound in $\mathcal{B}_\lambda$; by the Deduction Theorem, applied to lines **1** through **45**.

▶▶**47.** $\mathcal{B}_\lambda$ is complete; by line **46** and Theorem 14-2-9.

To complete the proof of Theorem 14-3-7 it remains to show that $\mathcal{B}_\lambda$ has the additional properties (**i**) and (**ii**) specified in that theorem. These facts follow swiftly from the following.

LEMMA I. *For every $A \in T(\mathcal{B})$ the element $\lambda(A)$ of $\mathcal{B}_\lambda$ is the least upper bound of A in $\mathcal{B}_\lambda$.*

Proof

▶▶ **1.** Let A be any element of $T(\mathcal{B})$.

▶▶ **2.** Let $a = \lambda(A)$.
▶ **3.** Let x be any element in A.
4. $\{x\} \subseteq A$; by line **3** and elementary set theory.
5. $U(A) \subseteq U(\{x\})$; by line **4** and Theorem 14-3-3 (**i**).
6. Either $\lambda(A) = \lambda(\{x\})$ or $\lambda(\{x\}) <_\lambda \lambda(A)$; by line **5** and Definition 14-3-6.
7. x is a least upper bound of $\{x\}$ in $\mathcal{B}$; by line **3** and Theorem 14-2-8.
8. $\lambda(\{x\}) = x$; by line **7** and the hypothesis that λ satisfies condition (**iii**) of Theorem 14-3-5.
▶ **9.** $x <_\lambda a$ or $x = a$; by E applied to lines **6**, **8**, and **2**.
10. If x is any element of A then $x <_\lambda a$ or $x = a$; by the Deduction Theorem applied to lines **3** through **9**.
▶▶ **11.** a is an upper bound of A in $\mathcal{B}_\lambda$; by line **10** and Definition 14-2-4.
▶ **12.** Let b be *any* upper bound of A in $\mathcal{B}_\lambda$.
13. For every $x \in A$ we have $x <_\lambda b$ or $x = b$; by line **12** and Definition 14-2-4.
14. For any $x \in A$, x is a least upper bound of $\{x\}$ in $\mathcal{B}$; by Theorem 14-2-8.
15. For any $x \in A$ we have $\lambda(\{x\}) = x$; by line **14** and the hypothesis that λ satisfies condition (**iii**) of Theorem 14-3-5.
16. There is an $A_1 \in T(\mathcal{B})$ such that $b = \lambda(A_1)$; by line **12** and Definition 14-3-6.
17. For any $x \in A$ we have $\lambda(\{x\}) <_\lambda \lambda(A_1)$ or $\lambda(\{x\}) = \lambda(A_1)$; by E applied to lines **13**, **15**, and **16**.
18. For any $x \in A$ we have $U(A_1) \subseteq U(\{x\})$; by line **17**, Definition 14-3-6, and the hypothesis that λ satisfies conditions (**i**) and (**ii**) of Theorem 14-3-5.
19. If u is any upper bound of A_1 in $\mathcal{B}$, then for any $x \in A$ we have u an upper bound of $\{x\}$ in $\mathcal{B}$; by line **18**, Definition 14-3-2, and definition of $\subseteq$.
20. If u is any upper bound of A_1 in $\mathcal{B}$, then for any $x \in A$ we have $x <_B u$ or $x = u$; by line **19** and Definition 14-2-4.
21. If u is any upper bound of A_1 in $\mathcal{B}$ then u is an upper bound of A in $\mathcal{B}$; by line **20** and Definition 14-2-4.
22. $U(A_1) \subseteq U(A)$; by line **21** and Definition 14-3-2.
▶ **23.** $a <_\lambda b$ or $a = b$; by lines **22**, **16**, and **2**, and Definition 14-3-6.
24. If b is any upper bound of A in $\mathcal{B}_\lambda$, then $a <_\lambda b$ or $a = b$; by the Deduction Theorem applied to lines **12** through **23**.
▶▶ **25.** a is a least upper bound of A in $\mathcal{B}_\lambda$; by lines **11**, **24**, and Definition 14-2-4.

26. $\lambda(A)$ is the (unique) least upper bound of A in $\mathcal{B}_\lambda$; by lines **2** and **25**, and Theorem 14-2-5.

The lemma is now obtained by applying the Deduction Theorem to lines 1 through **25**.

LEMMA J. *If $A \in T(\mathcal{B})$, and if v is a least upper bound of A in $\mathcal{B}$, then also v is the least upper bound of A in $\mathcal{B}_\lambda$.*

Proof

1. Let A be a subset in $T(\mathcal{B})$ which has a least upper bound v in $\mathcal{B}$.
2. $\lambda(A) = v$; by the hypothesis that λ satisfies condition **(iii)** of Theorem 14-3-5.
3. v is the least upper bound of A in $\mathcal{B}_\lambda$; by line **2** and Lemma I.

The lemma now follows by applying the Deduction Theorem to lines **1** through **3**.

LEMMA K. *For every element a of $\mathcal{B}_\lambda$ there is an $A \in T(\mathcal{B})$ such that a is the least upper bound of A in $\mathcal{B}_\lambda$.*

Proof

1. Let a be any element of $\mathcal{B}_\lambda$.
2. There is an $A \in T(\mathcal{B})$ such that $\lambda(A) = a$; by line **1** and Definition 14-3-6.
3. a is the least upper bound of A in $\mathcal{B}_\lambda$; by line **2** and Lemma I.

The lemma now follows by applying the Deduction Theorem to lines **1** through **3**.

Finally, Theorem 14-3-7 is obtained by combining Lemmas D, G, H, J, and K.

The basic problem of this section, *Problem C*, is the construction of an extension, which is complete, for an arbitrary dense ordered system. In Theorem 14-3-7 we started with any dense ordered system $\mathcal{B} = \langle B, <_B \rangle$ and showed how to define at least one complete extension, $\mathcal{B}_\lambda$. Are there other possible extensions of $\mathcal{B}$ which are complete? This question will be discussed in the following section.

EXERCISES

1. Prove parts **(i)** and **(iii)** of Theorem 14-3-3.
2. Prove Theorem 14-3-4 in detail.
3. Suppose that $\mathcal{B} = \langle B, <_B \rangle$ is a dense ordered system, that $A \subseteq B$, and that v is a least upper bound of A in $\mathcal{B}$. Show that for every $z \in B$ we have $z \in U(A)$ if,

and only if, $v <_B z$ or $v = z$. (This result is employed in our sketch of a proof of Theorem 14-3-5.)

4. Suppose that $\mathcal{B} = \langle B, <_B \rangle$ is a dense ordered system and that $A_1, A_2 \in T(B)$. Show that $U(A_2) \subseteq U(A_1)$ if, and only if, for every $x \in A_1$ there is a $y \in A_2$ such that $x <_B y$ or $x = y$.

4. *The Uniqueness of Completions*

In the previous section we have shown how, starting with an arbitrary dense ordered system $\mathcal{B}$, it is possible to construct a *complete* dense ordered system which is an extension of $\mathcal{B}$. Such a system is called a *completion* of $\mathcal{B}$. In the present section we wish to examine briefly the extent to which completions different from the one constructed may exist.

To begin with, it will be seen by Theorem 14-3-7, that the system constructed in Definition 14-3-6 is not merely a completion of $\mathcal{B}$, but possesses certain additional properties; namely, that **(i)** an element of B which is a least upper bound of a subset A of B *in the system* $\mathcal{B}$ continues to be a least upper bound of A *in the completion*, and **(ii)** every element of the completion is a *least* upper bound of some set of elements of B (having *an* upper bound in $\mathcal{B}$). It is natural to wonder whether *every* completion of $\mathcal{B}$ shares these additional properties.

The answer is negative. In particular, starting with the dense ordered system consisting of the rational numbers with their usual ordering, we can obtain completions which lack either property (i) or (ii) or both. Such systems have been studied by mathematicians and are called *non-Archimedean* systems.

However, every completion of a given dense ordered system $\mathcal{B}$ *contains a part* which is *also* a completion of $\mathcal{B}$, and which *does* have the additional properties **(i)** and **(ii)** of Theorem 14-3-7. This is described by the following theorem.

THEOREM 14-4-1. *Let $\mathcal{B} = \langle B, <_B \rangle$ be any dense ordered system, and let $\mathcal{C} = \langle C, <_C \rangle$ be any* **complete** *dense ordered system which is an* **extension** *of $\mathcal{B}$. Let C_1 be the subset of C consisting of all those elements z such that $z \in B$ or z is the least upper bound in $\mathcal{C}$ of an $A \in T(\mathcal{B})$ which has no* **least** *upper bound in $\mathcal{B}$. And let $<_{C_1}$ be the restriction of the relation $<_C$ to the set C_1, i.e., $<_{C_1}$ is the binary relation defined on C_1 such that for any $x, y \in C_1$ we have $x <_{C_1} y$ if and only if $x <_C y$ (whereas, unlike $<_C$, the relation $x <_{C_1} y$ never holds if either x or y is not in C_1). Then $\mathcal{C}_1 = \langle C_1, <_{C_1} \rangle$ is also a complete dense ordered system which is an extension of $\mathcal{B}$, and furthermore $\mathcal{C}_1$ has the additional properties* **(i)** *and* **(ii)** *which are possessed by $\mathcal{B}_\lambda$ according to* Theorem 14-3-7.

Proof. We shall merely sketch the outline of a proof for this theorem.

In the first place we must verify that the system $\mathcal{C}_1$ satisfies the three conditions of Definition 14-2-1 which entitle it to be called a dense ordered system. That the transitivity and trichotomy laws hold for $\mathcal{C}_1$ follows immediately from our hypotheses that these laws hold for $\mathcal{C}$, that C_1 is a subset of C, and that $<_{C_1}$ is the restriction of $<_C$ to C_1. However, in the case of the density law we must look more closely.

Suppose, then, that x and y are any elements of C_1 such that $x <_{C_1} y$. It follows at once from our hypotheses that $x, y \in C$ and $x <_C y$, and since the density law holds for $\mathcal{C}$ there must be some element $z \in C$ such that $x <_C z$ and $z <_C y$. Now *if* we knew somehow that $z \in C_1$, we could infer that $x <_{C_1} z$ and $z <_{C_1} y$ and hence establish the desired density law for $\mathcal{C}_1$. It turns out, however, that z need *not* be in C_1, and so we must approach the matter in another way.

Since $x, y \in C_1$ we see (from the definition of C_1) that each of these is either an element of B, or else is the least upper bound *in* $\mathcal{C}$ of some $A \in T(\mathcal{B})$ which has no least upper bound *in* $\mathcal{B}$. Accordingly four cases arise for consideration. If both x and y are elements of B, then we can use the density law which we know to hold for $\mathcal{B}$ to infer that there is a $z \in B$ such that $x <_B z$ and $z <_B y$. Since $\mathcal{C}$ is an extension of B we know that $z \in C$ and we have both $x <_C z$ and $z <_C y$. Finally, by definition of C_1 and $<_{C_1}$, we see that $z \in C_1$ and both $x <_{C_1} z$ and $z <_{C_1} y$ hold, so that the density law holds for the system $\mathcal{C}_1$ in this case. For a second case, suppose that $x \in B$ but $y \notin B$; hence y is the least upper bound in $\mathcal{C}$ of an $A \in T(\mathcal{B})$ which has no least upper bound in $\mathcal{B}$. If x were an upper bound of A in $\mathcal{B}$ we would have $y <_C x$ or $y = x$, contrary to our supposition that $x <_C y$ (which follows from $x <_{C_1} y$); therefore, x is *not* an upper bound of A in $\mathcal{B}$, so that we must have $x <_B z$ for some $z \in A$. It then readily follows that $z \in C_1$, $x <_{C_1} z$, and $z <_{C_1} y$, so that the density law is established for this case too. The remaining two cases are left for the reader.

Having established that $\mathcal{C}_1$ is indeed a dense ordered system, the definitions of C_1 and $<_{C_1}$, together with the hypothesis that $\mathcal{C}$ is an extension of $\mathcal{B}$, immediately guarantee that $\mathcal{C}_1$ must also be an extension of $\mathcal{B}$. Hence we turn to the question of the completeness of $\mathcal{C}_1$. To show this we use Theorem 14-2-9 and seek to show that every nonempty subset of C_1 with an upper bound in $\mathcal{C}_1$ must have a *least* upper bound in $\mathcal{C}_1$.

Suppose, then, that X is any nonempty subset of C_1 with an upper bound b in $\mathcal{C}_1$. We let A be the set of all those $y \in B$ such that $y <_{C_1} c$ or $y = c$ for some $c \in X$. A is nonempty, since each $c \in X$, being an element of C_1, is either in B or is an upper bound in $\mathcal{C}$ of some nonempty subset of B. Clearly, too, b is an upper bound of A in $\mathcal{C}_1$. If b is not itself an element of B, it is the least upper bound of some $A_1 \subseteq B$ such that A_1 has an upper bound b_1 in $\mathcal{B}$, and in this case b_1 is clearly an upper bound of A in $\mathcal{B}$. Thus in any case we see that A has an upper bound in $\mathcal{B}$, i.e., that $A \in T(\mathcal{B})$. Now if A has a *least* upper bound v, in $\mathfrak{B}$, then $v \in C_1$ and it is easy to see that v is also the least upper bound of A in $\mathfrak{C}_1$; while in the contrary case, the least upper bound d of A in $\mathfrak{C}$ is an element of C_1, and then d is easily seen to be the least upper bound of A in $\mathfrak{C}_1$ also. Finally, it remains to show that the least upper bound of A in $\mathfrak{C}_1$—let us call it w for definiteness—is also a least upper bound of X in $\mathfrak{C}_1$. Since each element of X is either an element of A, or a least upper bound in $\mathfrak{C}_1$ of some subset of A, we easily see that w is an upper bound of X in $\mathfrak{C}_1$. Then, since each upper bound of X in $\mathfrak{C}_1$ is also an upper bound of A in $\mathfrak{C}_1$, it follows that w, being the least upper bound of A in $\mathfrak{C}_1$, must also be the least upper bound of X in $\mathfrak{C}_1$.

Now that $\mathfrak{C}_1$ is known to be a completion of $\mathfrak{B}$, it remains only to show that it has the additional properties (**i**) and (**ii**). As to (**i**), if $A \in T(\mathfrak{B})$ and if v is a least upper bound of A in $\mathfrak{B}$, then $v \in C_1$ by definition of C_1, and v is clearly an upper bound of A in $\mathfrak{C}_1$ since $<_{C_1}$ is an extension of $<_B$ to the set C_1. That v is actually the *least* upper bound of A in $\mathfrak{C}_1$ can be deduced from the fact that for any upper bound b of A in $\mathfrak{C}_1$ we can find an upper bound u of A in $\mathfrak{B}$ such that $u <_{C_1} b$ or $u = b$ (as we see by considering separately the cases where $b \in B$ or where b is the least upper bound in $\mathfrak{C}$ of some $A_1 \in T(\mathfrak{B})$ which has no least upper bound in $\mathfrak{B}$).

Finally, to show (**ii**), we consider any element $a \in C_1$. If $a \in B$, then a is the least upper bound in $\mathfrak{C}_1$ of $\{a\}$. If $a \notin B$, then a is the least upper bound in $\mathfrak{C}$ of some $A \in T(\mathfrak{B})$, and we have also that a is the least upper bound in $\mathfrak{C}_1$ of A by an argument similar to that of the previous paragraph.

The theorem just proved shows that *every* completion of a given dense ordered system $\mathfrak{B}$ has a part, also a completion of $\mathfrak{B}$, which in addition possesses the two properties (**i**) and (**ii**) possessed by the special completion $\mathfrak{B}_\lambda$ of Theorem 14-3-7. It now becomes pertinent to ask how closely such a part resembles the constructed completion $\mathfrak{B}_\lambda$. This question is answered in the following two theorems.

THEOREM 14-4-2. *Let* $\mathfrak{B} = \langle B, <_B\rangle$ *be any dense ordered system, and let* $\mathfrak{C} = \langle C, <_C\rangle$ *be any* **complete** *dense ordered system which is an extension of* $\mathfrak{B}$ *possessing the following properties:* (**i**) *If* $A \subseteq B$ *and if* v *is a least upper bound of* A *in* $\mathfrak{B}$, *then* v *is also the least upper bound of* A *in* $\mathfrak{C}$, *and* (**ii**) *for every* $c \in C$ *there is an* $A \in T(\mathfrak{B})$ *such that* c *is the least upper bound in* $\mathfrak{C}$ *of* A. *Then there exists a function* λ, *possessing properties* (**i**) *through* (**iii**) *of* Theorem 14-3-5, *such that* C *is the range of* λ, *and such that for every* A_1 *and* A_2 *of* $T(\mathfrak{B})$ *we have* $\lambda(A_1) <_C \lambda(A_2)$ *if, and only if,* $\lambda(A_1) \neq \lambda(A_2)$ *and* $U(A_2) \subseteq U(A_1)$.

By comparing the statement of this theorem with Definition 14-3-6 we see that an *arbitrary* completion of $\mathfrak{B}$ which possesses properties (**i**) and (**ii**) can in fact be constructed exactly as the special completion $\mathcal{B}_\lambda$ of Theorem 14-3-7.

Proof. Again, we shall supply only the outlines for a proof of this theorem.

In fact, we define the required function λ by first specifying that its domain is $T(\mathcal{B})$, and then for each $A \in T(\mathcal{B})$ we let $\lambda(A)$ be the (unique) least upper bound of A in $\mathcal{C}$ (which must exist since $\mathcal{C}$ is a complete extension of $\mathcal{B}$). The fact that C is the range of λ (i.e., that λ maps $T(\mathcal{B})$ *onto* C) is then an immediate consequence of property (**ii**) of the hypothesis. And that λ satisfies condition (**iii**) of Theorem 14-3-5 follows immediately from property (**i**) of our hypothesis.

To complete the proof it suffices to show that (**a**) if $\lambda(A_1) <_C \lambda(A_2)$ then $U(A_1) \neq U(A_2)$ and $U(A_2) \subseteq U(A_1)$, and (**b**) if $\lambda(A_1) = \lambda(A_2)$ then $U(A_1) = U(A_2)$.

Tackling (**a**) first, we observe that if $\lambda(A_1) <_C \lambda(A_2)$ then there must be some $y \in A_2$ which is an upper bound of A_1 in $\mathcal{B}$, but which is not a least upper bound of A_1 in $\mathcal{B}$. If z is an upper bound of A_1 in $\mathcal{B}$ such that $z <_B y$ then we have $z \in U(A_1)$ but $z \notin U(A_2)$, so that $U(A_1) \neq U(A_2)$. That $U(A_2) \subseteq U(A_1)$ can be inferred from the existence of y be applying Exercise 4 following Section 3 of this chapter.

Turning to (**b**), we see from Exercise 3 of Section 3 that for any $z \in C$ we have $z \in U(A_1)$ if and only if $z \in B$ and either $\lambda(A_1) <_C z$ or $\lambda(A_1) = z$, with a similar characterization of the elements of $U(A_2)$. Hence from $\lambda(A_1) = \lambda(A_2)$ we infer, as required, that $U(A_1) = U(A_2)$.

Given a dense ordered system $\mathcal{B}$, Definition 14-3-6 (and Theorem 14-3-7) actually show a way of constructing *many* completions of $\mathcal{B}$—one for each function λ which satisfies conditions (**i**) through (**iii**) of Theorem 14-3-5. The two theorems stated thus far in the present section show that *any* completion of $\mathcal{B}$ contains a part which is one of these special completions $\mathcal{B}_\lambda$. But the question is left open to what extent the completions $\mathcal{B}_{\lambda_1}$ and $\mathcal{B}_{\lambda_2}$, for two different functions λ_1 and λ_2, resemble each other. This question is answered by the following theorem.

THEOREM 14-4-3. *Let $\mathcal{B}$ be a dense ordered system, and let λ_1 and λ_2 be any functions each satisfying conditions* (**i**) *through* (**iii**) *of* Theorem 14-3-5. *Let $\mathcal{B}_{\lambda_1}$ and $\mathcal{B}_{\lambda_2}$ be the dense ordered systems determined by these functions according to Definition* 14-3-6. *Then $\mathcal{B}_{\lambda_1}$ and $\mathcal{B}_{\lambda_2}$ are* ***isomorphic*** *systems, i.e., there is a one-one function φ, mapping $\mathcal{B}_{\lambda_1}$ onto $\mathcal{B}_{\lambda_2}$, such that for any $b, c \in \mathcal{B}_{\lambda_1}$ we have $\varphi(b) <_{\lambda_2} \varphi(c)$ if, and only if, $b <_{\lambda_1} c$.*[1]

Proof. The proof of this theorem is left to the reader as an exercise.

[1] The symbol "ϕ" is the Greek letter phi.

The net effect of the three theorems of this section may be roughly paraphrased by the assertion that "essentially" there is only one completion $\mathfrak{C}$ of a given dense ordered system $\mathfrak{B}$ which satisfies conditions **(i)** and **(ii)** of Theorem 14-4-2, and this completion is a *part* of *any* completion of $\mathfrak{B}$. It is thus natural to call this a *minimal completion* of $\mathfrak{B}$.

For future use we formalize this terminology in the following definition.

DEFINITION 14-4-4. *If $\mathfrak{B}$ is any dense ordered system we define a* **minimal completion** *of $\mathfrak{B}$ to be any dense ordered system $\mathfrak{C}$ which is a complete extension of $\mathfrak{B}$ and which satisfies the additional conditions* **(i)** *and* **(ii)** *of* Theorem 14-4-2.

EXERCISES

1. *Fill in details of the proof outlined for Theorem 14-4-1.
2. Do likewise for Theorem 14-4-2.
3. *Prove Theorem 14-4-3.
4. Suppose that $\mathfrak{B}$ and $\mathfrak{C}$ are dense ordered systems which satisfy the hypotheses of Theorem 14-4-2. Show that for every $x, y \in C$ such that $x <_C y$, there is a $z \in B$ such that $x <_C z$ and $z <_C y$.

5. *The Addition of Real Numbers*

We now wish to apply our findings about the completions of *arbitrary* dense ordered systems to the particular system $\langle R, <_R\rangle$, where R is the set of all rational numbers and $<_R$ is the unique ordering of the field $\mathfrak{R} = \langle R, +_R, \cdot_R\rangle$. In fact we shall choose one of the (essentially unique) minimal completions of $\langle R, <_R\rangle$ and call its elements the *real numbers*. Our major task will then be to extend the operations of addition and multiplication, which we have so far defined only on the rational numbers, so as to obtain operations which can act on *any* pair of real numbers.

DEFINITION 14-5-1. *Given the dense ordered system $\langle R, <_R\rangle$ of rational numbers we select another dense ordered system, to be denoted $\langle Rl, <_{Rl}\rangle$, which is a minimal completion of $\langle R, <_R\rangle$.* (*See* Definition 14-4-4.) *The elements of Rl will be called* **real numbers.**

Since, by this Definition, the system $\langle Rl, <_{Rl}\rangle$ is a completion of the system $\langle R, <_R\rangle$, every rational number is also a real number, i.e., for every $x \in R$ we also have $x \in Rl$. Furthermore, the ordering relation $<_{Rl}$ is an extension of the relation $<_R$, so that for every $x, y \in R$ we have $x <_{Rl} y$ if and only if $x <_R y$. As a practical matter, therefore, we have no further need for the symbol "$<_R$", since we can always use the symbol "$<_{Rl}$" in its place. Furthermore, since for the most part we shall have to deal only with this one ordering relation $<_{Rl}$, we shall simplify our notation by dropping the subscript altogether, and merely use the symbol "$<$" as a name for this relation. And again, as in Chapter XIII, we shall use the symbols "+" and "·" without subscript to denote the operations of addition and multiplication on the rational numbers.

One other notational convention will be useful: We shall reserve letters from the *latter* part of the alphabet to refer to *rational numbers*, i.e., to arbitrary elements of R, while using letters from the *early* part of the alphabet for *arbitrary real* numbers, i.e., for any elements of Rl. The reader must keep in mind that when we speak of some number $b \in Rl$, it *may* be a rational number of R or it may not; but a number $x \in R$ is *only* a rational.

For purposes of later reference it will be convenient at this point to employ the above notational conventions in stating the fundamental properties of the system of rational numbers which qualify it as an ordered field, and the fundamental properties of the ordered system of real numbers which qualify it as a minimal completion of the ordered system of rationals. This is done in the following three theorems.

THEOREM 14-5-2. *The rational number system* $\langle R, +, \cdot, < \rangle$ *is an ordered field. In particular:*

(i) *for all* $x, y, z \in R$ *we have* $(x + y) + z = x + (y + z)$;
(ii) *for all* $x, y \in R$ *we have* $x + y = y + x$;
(iii) *the number* 0 *is in* R *and for all* $x \in R$ *we have* $x + 0 = x$;
(iv) *for every* $x \in R$ *there is an element* $-x \in R$ *such that* $x + (-x) = 0$;
(v) *for all* $x, y, z \in R$ *such that* $x < y$ *and* $y < z$ *we have also* $x < z$;
(vi) *for every* $x, y \in R$ *we have either* $x < y$, $x = y$, *or* $y < x$, *and no two of these relations hold simultaneously;*
(vii) *if* x, y *are any elements of* R *such that* $x < y$, *and if* z *is* ***any*** *element of* R, *then we have* $x + z < y + z$;
(viii) *for all* $x, y, z \in R$ *we have* $(x \cdot y) \cdot z = x \cdot (y \cdot z)$;
(ix) *for all* $x, y \in R$ *we have* $x \cdot y = y \cdot x$;
(x) *for all* $x, y, z \in R$ *we have* $x \cdot (y + z) = x \cdot y + x \cdot z$;
(xi) *the number* 1 *is in* R *and for all* $x \in R$ *we have* $x \cdot 1 = x$;
(xii) *for every* $x \in R$, *if* $x \neq 0$ *then there is a* $y \in R$ *such that* $x \cdot y = 1$;
(xiii) *if* x, y, z *are any elements of* R *such that* $x < y$ *and* $0 < z$, *then* $x \cdot z < y \cdot z$.

No proof will be given of this theorem, as it is essentially a duplication of the principal result of Chapter XII. (See Theorems 12-4-12 and 12-7-2.) From the basic properties **(i)** through **(xiii)** given above, there follow a great many laws which hold in every ordered field, and which will be used in the sequel without giving specific reference. (Most of these laws appear either as theorems or exercises, but we shall merely use the phrase "*by the field properties of the rationals*" in citing the laws.) In particular, for every $x, y \in R$ there is a unique number $(x - y) \in R$ such that $(x - y) + y = x$, and if $y \neq 0$ there is a unique number $(x/y) \in R$ such that $(x/y) \cdot y = x$.

In addition to the *field properties* of the rational numbers there is one other property possessed by this system which distinguishes it from other ordered fields: The system of rational numbers is an extension of the ordered ring of *integers*, and for every $x \in R$ there are integers $p, q \in J$ such that $q \neq 0$ and $x = (p/q)$. In the sequel we shall use this property in the following form.

THEOREM 14-5-3. *The rational number system* $\langle R, +, \cdot, < \rangle$ *is an extension of the ordered ring* $\langle J, +_J, \cdot_J, <_J \rangle$ *of integers, and for every* $x \in R$ *such that* $x > 0$ *there exist elements* $p, q \in J$ *such that* $p > 0$, $q > 0$, *and* $x = (p/q)$.

No proof will be given for this theorem, as it follows simply from Theorems 12-7-3 and 12-6-5 by the field properties of the rationals.

THEOREM 14-5-4. *The ordered system* $\langle Rl, < \rangle$ *of real numbers is a minimal completion of the ordered system of rational numbers. In particular:*

(i) *if* a, b, c *are any elements of* Rl *such that* $a < b$ *and* $b < c$, *then* $a < c$;

(ii) *for any* $a, b \in Rl$ *we have either* $a < b$, $a = b$, *or* $b < a$, *and no two of these relations hold simultaneously;*

(iii) *for any* $a, b \in Rl$ *such that* $a < b$, *there is a* $c \in Rl$ *such that* $a < c$ *and* $c < b$,

(iv) *if* A *is any nonempty subset of* Rl *which has an upper bound in* Rl (*i.e., a number* $b \in Rl$ *such that for every* $a \in A$ *we have either* $a < b$ *or* $a = b$), *then* A *has one and only one* **least** *upper bound in* Rl (*i.e., a number* $c \in Rl$ *such that* c *is an upper bound of* A *in* Rl *and, for* **any** *upper bound* b *of* A *in* Rl, *we have either* $c < b$ *or* $c = b$).

(v) *if* A *is any nonempty subset of* Rl *which has a lower bound* (*i.e., a number* $b \in Rl$ *such that for every* $a \in A$ *we have either* $b < a$ *or* $b = a$) *then* A *has one and only one* **greatest** *lower bound in* Rl (*i.e., a number* $c \in Rl$ *such that* c *is a lower bound of* A *in* Rl *and, for* **any** *lower bound* b *of* A *in* Rl, *we have either* $b < c$ *or* $b = c$).

(vi) *for every* $x \in R$ *we have also* $x \in Rl$;

(vii) *for any* $a \in Rl$ *there is an* $x \in R$ *such that* $x < a$, *for any* $b \in Rl$ *there is a* $y \in R$ *such that* $b < y$, *and if* $a < b$ *there is an element* $z \in R$ *such that* $a < z$ *and* $z < b$;

(viii) *for any* $X \subseteq R$ *and* $x, y \in R$ *we have* x *the least upper bound of* X *in* Rl *if and only if* x *is the least upper bound of* X *in* R, *and* y *the greatest lower bound of* X *in* Rl *if and only if* y *is the greatest lower bound of* X *in* R;

(ix) *if* a *is any element of* Rl, *and if* X *is the set of all* x **in** R *such that* $x < a$, *then the least upper bound of* X **in** Rl *is* a; *while if* Y *is the set of all* y **in** R *such that* $a < y$, *then the greatest lower bound of* Y **in** Rl *is* a;

(x) *if* a *and* b *are elements of* Rl *such that for every* $x \in R$ *for which* $a < x$

we have also $b < x$, *and for every* $y \in R$ *for which* $b < y$ *we have also* $a < y$, *then* $a = b$.

Proof

We shall give only brief indications for constructing proofs of the several parts of this theorem. In these we omit explicit reference to Definitions 14-4-4 and 14-5-1.

In fact, parts (**i**) through (**iii**) follow at once from Definitions 14-2-1, 14-4-4, and 14-5-1. Parts (**iv**) and (**v**) are obtained from Theorems 14-2-9 and 14-2-11 respectively, by using Theorem 14-2-5. Part (**vi**) arises by application of Definition 14-3-1. Part (**vii**) is closely related to Exercise 4 of Section 4.

The statement of Part (**viii**) which deals with upper bounds is a simple consequence of Theorem 14-4-2(**i**) (which is applicable by Definition 14-4-4) in one direction, and of Definitions 14-2-4 and 14-3-1 in the other. The statement of Part (**viii**) dealing with lower bounds is left as an exercise.

A proof of the statement in Part (**ix**) which concerns upper bounds may be given along the following lines. If $a \in Rl$ and X is the set of all $x \in R$ such that $x < a$, we have that a is an upper bound of X in Rl by Definition 14-2-4. Now by Theorem 14-4-2(**ii**) we can find a subset Z of R such that a is the least upper bound of Z in Rl. Clearly, from the way in which X was chosen, every element of Z is either in X or is a itself, so that every upper bound of X is also an upper bound of Z; and from this we easily infer that a must be the least upper bound of X, as desired. A proof of the statement in Part (**ix**) which concerns lower bounds is left as an exercise.

Finally, to prove (**x**), suppose that a, b are any elements of Rl such that (**1**) for every $x \in R$ such that $a < x$ we have also $b < x$, and (**2**) for every $y \in R$ such that $b < y$ we have also $a < y$. By (**1**) we see that b is a lower bound of the set X of all those $x \in R$ such that $a < x$; but by Part (**ix**) above, a is the greatest lower bound of X in Rl; hence either $b < a$ or $b = a$. In the same way, using (**2**) instead of (**1**), we see that either $a < b$ or $a = b$. It follows that if we had $a \neq b$, we would have both $a < b$ and $b < a$, which is impossible by Part (**ii**) above. Hence we must have $a = b$, as asserted in Part (**x**). This concludes our sketch of a proof of Theorem 14-5-4.

Now that our notation for the ordered system of real numbers is established, and our review of its fundamental properties is completed, it is time to formulate explicitly our principal task in the present section. We recall that our operation of addition, $+$, is applicable to any two *rational* numbers. However, there are many real numbers which are not rational (since the ordered system for Rl is complete while that for R is not). We wish, therefore, to *extend* the operation $+$, so as to obtain an operation of addition which is applicable to any two real numbers.

PROBLEM $Rl(+)$. *Can we define a binary operation $+_{Rl}$ on the set Rl such that:*

(**i**) *$+_{Rl}$ is an extension of $+$, and*
(**ii**) *$+_{Rl}$ satisfies the various fundamental algebraic laws needed to qualify the system $\langle Rl, +_{Rl}, <\rangle$ as an* **ordered abelian group**?

We shall see that this problem has an affirmative solution, and that indeed there is only one operation $+_{Rl}$ which satisfies both conditions (**i**) and (**ii**). The algebraic laws mentioned in (**ii**) are, in fact, simply the counterparts of Theorem 14-5-2 (**i**) through (**vii**) for the operation $+_{Rl}$. (See Definition 11-6-5.)

To prepare the ground for a suitable definition of $+_{Rl}$ we introduce a preliminary concept through the following definition and theorem.

DEFINITION 14-5-5. *For any* $a, b \in Rl$ *we let* $S(a, b)$ *be the set of all rational numbers* $x + y$ *such that* $x, y \in R$, $a < x$, *and* $b < y$.

That is, the set $S(a, b)$ consists of any sum of a rational number greater than a and a rational number greater than b.

THEOREM 14-5-6. *For any $a, b \in Rl$, the set $S(a, b)$ is nonempty and has a lower bound in R (and hence in Rl).*

Proof

We first show that $S(a, b)$ is nonempty.

1. Let a, b be any elements of Rl.
2. There exist $x, y \in R$ such that $a < x$ and $b < y$; by line **1** and Theorem 14-5-4 (**vii**).
3. $x + y \in S(a, b)$; by lines **1** and **2** and Definition 14-5-5.
4. $S(a, b)$ is nonempty; by line **3**.

The desired result now follows by applying the Deduction Theorem to lines **1** through **4**.

And now we show that $S(a, b)$ has a lower bound in R.

▶▶**1.** Let a, b be any elements of Rl.
▶▶**2.** There exist $u, v \in R$ such that $u < a$ and $v < b$; by line **1** and Theorem 14-5-4 (**vii**).
3. $u + v \in R$; by line **2** and field properties of the rationals.
▶**4.** Let $x + y$ be any element of $S(a, b)$, where $x, y \in R$, $a < x$, and $b < y$; by Definition 14-5-5.
5. $u < x$ and $v < y$; by lines **2** and **4** and Theorem 14-5-4 (**i**).
6. $u + v < x + y$; by line **5** and the field properties of the rationals.

▶7. If $x + y$ is any element of $S(a, b)$, then $u + v < x + y$; by the Deduction Theorem applied to lines **4** through **6**.

▶▶8. $u + v$ is a lower bound for $S(a, b)$ in R; by lines **3** and **7**.

Now that we know that $S(a, b)$ has a lower bound $u + v$ in R, we infer at once from Theorem 14-5-4 (**vi**) that $u + v$ is also a lower bound for $S(a, b)$ in Rl.

DEFINITION 14-5-7. *For any $a, b \in Rl$ we define $a +_{Rl} b$ to be the greatest lower bound of $S(a, b)$ in Rl.*

This definition is justified by Theorems 14-5-6 and 14-5-4(**iv**).

Now that we have defined our addition operation, $+_{Rl}$, we wish to show that it is indeed a solution of *Problem* $Rl(+)$. We shall do this by a series of theorems, for which the following two results form a useful preliminary.

THEOREM 14-5-8. *For any $a, b, c \in Rl$ such that $a +_{Rl} b < c$, there exist rational numbers $x, y \in R$ such that $a < x$, $b < y$, and $x + y < c$.*

Proof

▶▶1. Let a, b, c be any elements of Rl such that $a +_{Rl} b < c$.

2. $a +_{Rl} b$ is the greatest lower bound of $S(a, b)$ in Rl; by Definition 14-5-7.

▶3. c is not a lower bound of $S(a, b)$ in Rl; by lines **1** and **2**.

▶4. There is an element z of $S(a, b)$ such that $z < c$; by line **3**.

▶5. $z = x + y$ for some $x, y \in R$ such that $a < x$ and $b < y$; by line **4** and Definition 14-5-5.

▶▶6. There exist $x, y \in R$ such that $a < x$, $b < y$, and $x + y < c$; by E applied to lines **4** and **5**.

The proof is completed by applying the Deduction Theorem to lines **1** through **6**.

THEOREM 14-5-9. *If a, b are any elements of Rl, and if x, y are any elements of R such that $a < x$ and $b < y$, then $a +_{Rl} b < x + y$.*

Proof

▶▶1. Let a, b be any elements of Rl.

▶▶2. Let x, y be any elements of R such that $a < x$ and $b < y$.

▶3. There exist $u, v \in R$ such that $a < u$, $u < x$, $b < v$, and $v < y$; by line **2** and Theorem 14-5-4 (**vii**).

4. $u + v < x + y$; by line **3** and field properties of the rationals (since $x, y \in R$ by line **2**).

5. $u + v \in S(a, b)$; by line **3** and Definition 14-5-5.

▶6. Either $a +_{Rl} b < u + v$ or $a +_{Rl} b = u + v$; by line **5** and Definition 14-5-7.

▶▶7. $a +_{Rl} b < x + y$; by lines **4** and **6**, and Theorem 14-5-4 (**i**).

The proof is completed by applying the Deduction Theorem to lines **1** and **2** through **7**.

THEOREM 14-5-10. *The associative law holds for* $+_{Rl}$: *For all* $a, b, c \in Rl$ *we have* $(a +_{Rl} b) +_{Rl} c = a +_{Rl} (b +_{Rl} c)$.

Proof

We shall show in detail that for any $x \in R$ such that $(a +_{Rl} b) +_{Rl} c < x$ we have also $a +_{Rl} (b +_{Rl} c) < x$. We shall leave the reader to show, by a similar argument, that for any $y \in R$ such that $a +_{Rl} (b +_{Rl} c) < y$ we have also $(a +_{Rl} b) +_{Rl} c < y$. From these two results we obtain the desired associative law by a direct application of Theorem 14-5-4(**x**).

▶▶ 1. Let a, b, c be any elements of Rl.

▶▶ 2. Let x be any element of R such that $(a +_{Rl} b) +_{Rl} c < x$.

▶ 3. There exist $u, v \in R$ such that $a +_{Rl} b < u$, $c < v$, and $u + v < x$; by line **2** and Theorem 14-5-8.

▶ 4. There exist $s, t \in R$ such that $a < s$, $b < t$, and $s + t < u$; by line **3** and Theorem 14-5-8.

5. $(s + t) + v < u + v$; by line **1** and the field properties of the rationals (since $u \in R$ by line **3**).

▶ 6. $(s + t) + v < x$; by lines **3** and **5** and the transitivity of $<$ on R (Theorem 14-5-2 (**v**)).

7. $(s + t) + v = s + (t + v)$; by the field properties of the rationals (since $s, t, v \in R$ by lines **3** and **4**).

▶ 8. $s + (t + v) < x$; by E applied to lines **6** and **7**.

9. $(t + v) \in R$ and $b +_{Rl} c < t + v$; by lines **3** and **4** and Theorem 14-5-9.

▶10. $a +_{Rl} (b +_{Rl} c) < s + (t + v)$; by lines **4** and **9** and Theorem 14-5-9.

▶▶11. $a +_{Rl} (b +_{Rl} c) < x$; by lines **10** and **8** and Theorem 14-5-4 (**i**).

12. If x is any element of R such that $(a +_{Rl} b) +_{Rl} c < x$, then also $a +_{Rl} (b +_{Rl} c) < x$; by the Deduction Theorem applied to lines **2** through **11**.

As indicated above, Theorem 14-5-10 follows easily from line **12** and its converse.

THEOREM 14-5-11. *The commutative law holds for* $+_{Rl}$: *For all* $a, b \in Rl$ *we have* $a +_{Rl} b = b +_{Rl} a$.

A proof of this Theorem may be constructed along the same lines as the proof for the previous theorem. The details are, in fact, rather simpler, and will not be given.

THEOREM 14-5-12. *For all* $a \in Rl$ *we have* $a +_{Rl} 0 = a$.

Proof

We leave as an exercise the task of showing that for any $a \in Rl$, and for any $x \in R$ such that $a +_{Rl} 0 < x$, we must have $a < x$. Below we shall show that if y is any element of R such that $a < y$, then also $a +_{Rl} 0 < y$. From these two results we get the desired equation $a +_{Rl} 0 = a$ by a direct application of Theorem 14-5-4(**x**).

▶▶**1.** Let a be any element of Rl.
▶▶**2.** Let y be any element of R such that $a < y$.
▶**3.** There is a rational number $z \in R$ such that $a < z$ and $z < y$; by line **2** and Theorem 14-5-4 (**vii**).
4. $y - z \in R$ and $0 < y - z$; by line **3** and field properties of the rationals (since $y \in R$ by line **2**).
▶**5.** $a +_{Rl} 0 < z + (y - z)$; by lines **3** and **4** and Theorem 14-5-9.
6. $z + (y - z) = y$; by field properties of the rationals (since $z, y - z \in R$ by lines **3** and **4**).
▶▶**7.** $a +_{Rl} 0 < y$; by E applied to lines **5** and **6**.
8. If y is any element of R such that $a < y$, then also $a +_{Rl} 0 < y$; by the Deduction Theorem applied to lines **2** through **7**.

The use of line **8** in proving Theorem 14-5-12 has been explained above.

The last three theorems, taken together, show that the system $\langle Rl, +_{Rl}\rangle$ is an abelian semi-group with the null element 0. (Compare Definitions 3-3-1, 3-3-2, and 4-3-1.) In order to show that this system is a group, it remains to show that for every element $x \in Rl$ we can find another element $-_{Rl}\, x \in Rl$ such that $x +_{Rl} (-_{Rl}\, x) = 0$. As a preliminary to defining the operation $-_{Rl}$ we give the following definition and theorem.

DEFINITION 14-5-13. *For any* $a \in Rl$ *we let* $M(a)$ *be the set of all those* $x \in R$ *such that* $-x < a$.

THEOREM 14-5-14. *For every* $a \in Rl$ *the set* $M(a)$ *is nonempty and has a lower bound in* $\mathfrak{R}$ *(and hence in* Rl*).*

Proof

We first show that $M(a)$ is nonempty.

▶▶**1.** Let a be any element of Rl.

▶2. There is a rational number $y \in R$ such that $y < a$; by line **1** and Theorem 14-5-4 (**vii**).

▶3. $-y \in R$, and there is a rational number $x \in R$ such that $-y < x$; by line **2** and Theorem 14-5-4 (**vii**).

4. $-x < y$; by line **3** and the field properties of the rationals.

5. $-x < a$; by lines **4** and **2** and Theorem 14-5-4 (**i**).

▶6. $x \in M(a)$; by line **5** and Definition 14-5-13 (since $x \in R$ by line **3**).

▶▶7. $M(a)$ is nonempty; by line **6**.

And we complete our proof of Theorem 14-5-14 by showing that $M(a)$ has a lower bound in $\mathfrak{R}$.

▶▶1. Let a be any element of Rl.

▶▶2. There is a rational number $z \in R$ such that $a < z$; by line **1** and Theorem 14-5-4 (**vii**).

▶3. Let x be any element of $M(a)$.

4. $x \in R$ and $-x < a$; by line **3** and Definition 14-5-13.

5. $-x < z$; by lines **4** and **2** and Theorem 14-5-4 (**i**).

▶6. $-z \in R$ and $-z < x$; by line **5** and field properties of the rationals (since $x, z \in R$ by lines **2** and **4**)

7. If x is any element of $M(a)$ then $-z < x$; by the Deduction Theorem applied to lines **3** through **6**.

▶▶8. $-z$ is a lower bound for $M(a)$ in $\mathfrak{R}$; by line **7** (since $-z \in R$ by line **6**).

Now that we know that $M(a)$ has a lower bound $-z$ in R, we infer at once from Theorem 14-5-4 (**vi**) that $-z$ is also a lower bound for $M(a)$ in Rl.

DEFINITION 14-5-15. *For every $a \in Rl$ we define $-_{Rl}\, a$ to be the greatest lower bound of the set $M(a)$ in Rl.*

This definition is justified by Theorems 14-5-14 and 14-5-4(**v**).

Having defined $-_{Rl}\, a$, we would like now to show that it has the desired property which will assure us that the system $\langle Rl, +_{Rl}\rangle$ is a group, namely the property that (for every $a \in Rl$) $a +_{Rl} (-_{Rl}\, a) = 0$. However, to prepare the way for this, we must first demonstrate an important relation between the ordering $<$ and the addition operation $+$ on the rationals. The establishment of this relation depends not only on the fact that the system of rational numbers forms an ordered field, but also on the special relation between the rationals and the system of integers which is expressed by Theorem 14-5-3.

THEOREM 14-5-16. *If a is any element of Rl, and if u is any element of R*

such that $0 < u$, *then there is a rational number* $x \in R$ *such that* $x < a$ *and* $a < x + u$.

Proof

We shall merely outline the steps for a proof of this theorem.

1. Let a be any element of Rl, and u any element of R such that $0 < u$. By Theorem 14-5-4(**vii**) there is a rational number $y \in R$ such that $y < a$.

2. If it should happen that $a < y + u$ then we simply take $x = y$ and there is nothing further to prove. If it should happen that $y + u = a$ then by Theorem 14-5-4(**vii**) again we could find an $x \in R$ such that $y < x$ and $x < a$, and by the field properties of the rationals we would get $y + u < x + u$, i.e., $a < x + u$; and again our assertion would be proved.

3. We may, therefore, restrict our further attention to the case that $y + u < a$. In this case we can show that there is a positive *integer* $p \in \mathcal{J}$, $0 < p$, such that $a < y + p \cdot u$. For by Theorem 14-5-4 (**vii**) there is some rational $z \in R$ such that $a < z$, and combining this with step **1** we see that $y < z$. By the field properties of the rationals we infer that $0 < z - y$, and since $0 < u$ (by step **1**), we get also $0 < \frac{z - y}{u}$. Since $\frac{z - y}{u}$ is a rational number, we can apply Theorem 14-5-3 and conclude that there are integers $p, q \in \mathcal{J}$ such that $0 < p$, $0 < q$, and $\frac{z - y}{u} = \frac{p}{q}$. Since $p/q \leq p$, we get $\frac{z - y}{u} \leq p$, and since $0 < u$ (by step **1**), this shows that $z - y \leq p \cdot u$, and hence $z \leq y + p \cdot u$. But z was chosen above so that $a < z$. It follows that $a < y + p \cdot u$, as asserted at the beginning of step **3**.

4. Now if we form the set G of all *those* positive integers n such that $a < y + n \cdot u$, it follows from the second sentence of step **3** that this set G is nonempty. We may, therefore, apply Theorem 2-7-9 to conclude that there is a *least* positive integer in G. Let us call this m.

5. Since $m \in G$, we have $a < y + m \cdot u$. Hence $m \neq 1$, since $y + u < a$ by step **3**. Since m is a positive integer $\neq 1$, $m - 1$ is also a positive integer. But since m is the *least* integer in G, we must have $m - 1 \notin G$. From the way in which G was formed, this means that we do *not* have $a < y + (m - 1) \cdot u$. That is, we must have either $y + (m - 1) \cdot u < a$ or $y + (m - 1) \cdot u = a$.

6. If $y + (m - 1) \cdot u < a$ then, since $a < y + m \cdot u$ (as noted at the beginning of step **5**) we can take $x = y + (m - 1) \cdot u$ and get the desired relations $x < a$ and $a < x + u$. On the other hand if $y + (m - 1) \cdot u = a$, so that a is a rational number, then we can simply take $x = a - u/2$ and again (since $0 < u$ by step **1**) we get the desired relations $x < a$ and $a < x + u$. These relations have now been shown to hold in every case, which completes the proof of our theorem.

With Theorem 14-5-16 at hand, we are ready to establish that our operation $-_{Rl}$ possesses the fundamental property we require of it.

THEOREM 14-5-17. *For every $a \in Rl$ we have $a +_{Rl} (-_{Rl}\, a) = 0$.*

Proof

We shall demonstrate the desired equality by applying Theorem 14-5-4 (**x**). In order to prepare for this application we first show that for every $x \in R$ such that $a +_{Rl} (-a) < x$, we have also $0 < x$.

▶▶ **1.** Let a be any element of Rl.
▶▶ **2.** Let x be any element of R such that $a +_{Rl} (-_{Rl}\, a) < x$.
▶ **3.** There exist rational numbers $y, z \in R$ such that $a < y$, $-_{Rl}\, a < z$, and $y + z < x$; by line **2** and Theorem 14-5-8.
4. $-_{Rl}\, a$ is the greatest lower bound of $M(a)$ in Rl; by Definition 14-5-15.
5. z is not a lower bound of $M(a)$ in Rl; by lines **3** and **4**.
6. There is an element $z_1 \in M(a)$ such that $z_1 < z$; by line **5**.
7. $z_1 \in R$ and $-z_1 < a$; by line **6** and Definition 14-5-13.
8. $-z_1 < y$; by lines **7** and **3** and Theorem 14-5-4(**i**).
9. $0 < y + z_1$; by line **8** and the field properties of the rationals (since $y, z_1 \in R$ by lines **3** and **7**).
▶**10.** $0 < y + z$; by lines **9** and **6** and field properties of the rationals (since $y, z \in R$ by line **3**).
▶▶**11.** $0 < x$; by lines **10** and **3** and Theorem 14-5-4(**i**).
12. If x is any element of R such that $a +_{Rl} (-_{Rl}\, a) < x$, then we also have $0 < x$; by the Deduction Theorem applied to lines **2** through **11**.

We shall combine the statement of line **12** with the proposition that for every $u \in R$ such that $0 < u$, we have also $a +_{Rl} (-_{Rl}\, a) < u$; this will be proved below.

▶▶**13.** Let u be any element of R such that $0 < u$.
▶**14.** There exists a rational number $r \in R$ such that $r < a$ and $a < r + u$; by lines **1** and **13** and Theorem 14-5-16.
15. There exists a rational number $r_1 \in R$ such that $r < r_1$ and $r_1 < a$; by line **14** and Theorem 14-5-4(**vii**).
16. $--r_1 < a$; by line **15** and field properties of the rationals.
17. $-r_1 \in M(a)$; by line **16** and Definition 14-5-13, since $-r_1 \in R$ by line **15**.
18. Either $-_{Rl}\, a < -r_1$ or $-_{Rl}\, a = -r_1$; by line **17** and Definition 14-5-15.
19. $-r_1 < -r$; by line **15** and field properties of the rationals.
20. $-_{Rl}\, a < -r$; by lines **18** and **19** and Theorem 14-5-4(**i**).

▶21. $a +_{Rl} (-_{Rl}\, a) < (r + u) + -r$; by Theorem 14-5-9 and lines **14** and **20**.

▶▶22. $a +_{Rl} (-_{Rl}\, a) < u$; by line **21** and field properties of the rationals (since $u, r \in R$ by lines **13** and **14**).

23. If u is any element of R such that $0 < u$, then we also have $a +_{Rl} (-_{Rl}\, a) < u$; by the Deduction Theorem applied to lines **13** through **22**.

The proof of Theorem 14-5-17 may now be completed by combining lines **12** and **23** with Theorem 14-5-4(**x**).

As indicated in remarks preceding Theorem 14-5-13, the demonstration of Theorem 14-5-17 (together with the earlier theorems 14-5-10 through 14-5-12) completes the proof that the system $\langle Rl, +_{Rl}\rangle$ is an abelian group. On the elements of this group we have the binary relation $<_{Rl}$ (which we agreed to write as $<$) which satisfies the transitivity and trichotomy laws [Theorem 14-5-4 (**i**) and (**ii**)], and hence is an ordering relation for the set Rl. In order to conclude that the system $\langle Rl, +_{Rl}, <\rangle$ is an ordered group, it remains only to show that the ordering relation $<$ is connected with the addition operation $+_{Rl}$ by the following law.

THEOREM 14-5-18. *If a, b are any elements of Rl such that $a < b$, and if c is any element of Rl whatever, then we have $a +_{Rl} c < b +_{Rl} c$.*

Proof

▶▶ **1.** Let a, b be any elements of Rl such that $a < b$.

▶▶ **2.** Let c be any element of Rl whatever.

▶ **3.** Let $x + y$ be any element of $S(b, c)$, where $x, y \in R$, $b < x$, and $c < y$; by Definition 14-5-5.

4. $a < x$; by lines **1** and **3** and the transitivity of $<$. (Theorem 14-5-4 (**i**)).

5. $a +_{Rl} c < x + y$; by lines **3** and **4** and Theorem 14-5-9.

6. If $x + y$ is any element of $S(b, c)$ then $a +_{Rl} c < x + y$; by the Deduction Theorem applied to lines **3** through **5**.

▶ **7.** $a +_{Rl} c$ is a lower bound of $S(b, c)$ in Rl; by line **6**.

▶ **8.** $b +_{Rl} c$ is the greatest lower bound of $S(b, c)$ in Rl; by Definition 14-5-7.

▶▶ **9.** Either $a +_{Rl} c < b +_{Rl} c$ or $a +_{Rl} c = b +_{Rl} c$; by lines **7** and **8**.

▶▶ **10.** *Assume* that $a +_{Rl} c = b +_{Rl} c$.

11. $(a +_{Rl} c) +_{Rl} (-_{Rl}\, c) = (b +_{Rl} c) +_{Rl} (-_{Rl}\, c)$; by E applied to line **10**.

12. $(a +_{Rl} c) +_{Rl} (-_{Rl}\, c) = a +_{Rl} (c +_{Rl} -_{Rl}\, c)$; by Theorem 14-5-10.

13. $\qquad = a +_{Rl} 0$; by Theorem 14-5-17.

14. $= a;$ by Theorem 14-5-12.
15. $(a +_{Rl} c) +_{Rl} (-_{Rl} c) = a;$ by E, lines **12** through **14**.
16. $(b +_{Rl} c) +_{Rl} (-_{Rl} c) = b;$ reasoning as in lines **12** through **15**.
▶**17.** $a = b;$ by E applied to lines **11**, **15**, and **16**.
18. If $a +_{Rl} c = b +_{Rl} c$ then $a = b$; by the Deduction Theorem applied to lines **10** through **17**.
▶**19.** *Not* $a = b;$ by line **1** and Theorem 14-5-4 (**ii**).
▶▶**20.** *Not* $a +_{Rl} c = b +_{Rl} c;$ by logic applied to lines **18** and **19**.
▶▶**21.** $a +_{Rl} c < b +_{Rl} c;$ by logic applied to lines **9** and **20**.

The statement of the theorem now follows by applying the Deduction Theorem to lines **1** and **2** through **21**.

As indicated in remarks above, we have now completed the task of showing that the system $\langle Rl, +_{Rl}, < \rangle$ is an ordered abelian group. We list this as a theorem for future reference.

THEOREM 14-5-19. *The system* $\langle Rl, +_{Rl}, < \rangle$ *is an ordered abelian group.*

Proof

By Theorems 14-5-10, 14-5-11, 14-5-12, 14-5-17, 14-5-4 (**i**) and (**ii**), and 14-5-18. (See Definition 11-6-5.)

To complete the demonstration that the operation $+_{Rl}$ is a solution to *Problem* $Rl(+)$, which was formulated after Theorem 14-5-4, it remains only to show that $+_{Rl}$ is an extension of $+$.

THEOREM 14-5-20. *For every* $x, y \in R$ *we have* $x + y = x +_{Rl} y$.

Proof

We shall demonstrate the desired equality by using Theorem 14-5-4(**x**). Accordingly, we first show that if z is any element of R such that $x +_{Rl} y < z$, then we also have $x + y < z$.

▶▶**1.** Let x, y be any elements of R.
▶▶**2.** Let z be any element of R such that $x +_{Rl} y < z$.
3. There exist rational numbers $x_1, y_1 \in R$ such that $x < x_1$, $y < y_1$, and $x_1 + y_1 < z$; by line **2** and Theorem 14-5-8.
4. $x + y < x_1 + y_1;$ by line **3** and field properties of the rationals.
▶▶**5.** $x + y < z;$ by lines **3** and **4**, and Theorem 14-5-4 (**i**).
6. If z is any element of R such that $x +_{Rl} y < z$, then also $x + y < z$; by the Deduction Theorem applied to lines **2** through **6**.

To complete our preparations for applying Theorem 14-5-4(**x**) we now show the converse of line **6**, namely, that for any $u \in R$ such that $x + y < u$ we have also $x +_{Rl} y < u$.

▶▶ **7.** Let u be any element of R such that $x + y < u$.

8. $x < \frac{u + x - y}{2}$ and $y < \frac{u + y - x}{2}$; by line **7** and field properties of the rationals.

9. $x +_{Rl} y < \frac{u + x - y}{2} + \frac{u + y - x}{2}$; by line **8** and Theorem 14-5-9, since $\frac{u + x - y}{2}$ and $\frac{u + y - x}{2}$ are elements of R, by lines **1** and **7**.

▶▶ **10.** $x +_{Rl} y < u$; by line **9** and field properties of the rationals.

11. If u is any element of R such that $x + y < u$, then also $x +_{Rl} y < u$; by the Deduction Theorem applied to lines **7** through **10**.

The proof of Theorem 14-5-20 is completed by combining lines **6** and **11** with Theorem 14-5-4(**x**).

From the last two theorems there follow certain elementary properties of the operation $-_{Rl}$ which will be useful to us in the next section.

THEOREM 14-5-21. *For every $a, b \in Rl$ the following are true:*

(**i**) $-_{Rl} -_{Rl}\, a = a$;
(**ii**) *either* $a = 0$ *or* $0 < a$ *or* $0 < -_{Rl}\, a$, *and no two of these hold simultaneously;*
(**iii**) $-_{Rl}\, (a +_{Rl} b) = (-_{Rl}\, a) +_{Rl} (-_{Rl}\, b)$;
(**iv**) *if* $x \in R$ *then* $-_{Rl}\, x = -x$.

Proof. See Exercise 4.

Theorems 14-5-19 and 14-5-20 show that the operation $+_{Rl}$ is a solution to *Problem Rl*(+). We close this section now by sketching a proof that there is no *other* operation which will serve as a solution.

THEOREM 14-5-22. *Suppose that $+'$ is any binary operation on Rl such that* (**i**) *for every $x, y \in R$ we have $x +' y = x + y$, and* (**ii**) *the system $\langle Rl, +', < \rangle$ is an ordered abelian group. Then for every $a, b \in Rl$ we must have $a +' b = a +_{Rl} b$.*

Proof

▶▶ **1.** Let $+'$ be any binary operation on Rl such that (**i**) for any $x, y \in R$ we have $x +' y = x + y$, and (**ii**) the system $\langle Rl, +', < \rangle$ is an ordered abelian group.

▶▶ **2.** Let a, b be any elements of Rl.

We shall first show that $a +' b$ is a lower bound of $S(a, b)$ in Rl.

▶ **3.** Consider any element $x + y \in S(a, b)$, where $x, y \in R$, $a < x$, and $b < y$; by Definition 14-5-5.

4. $a +' b < x +' y$; by line **3** and line **1(ii)**.
▶ 5. $a +' b < x + y$; by line **4** and line **1(i)**.
6. If $x + y$ is any element of $S(a, b)$, then $a +' b < x + y$; by the Deduction Theorem applied to lines **3** through **5**.
▶▶ 7. $a +' b$ is a lower bound of $S(a, b)$ in Rl; by line **6**.

We next show that of all lower bounds of $S(a, b)$ in Rl, the number $a +' b$ is the greatest.

▶ 8. Suppose that c is any element of Rl such that $a +' b < c$.
9. There are elements $-' a$ and $-' b$ in Rl such that $a +' (-' a) = 0$ and $b +' (-' b) = 0$; by line **1 (ii)** and line **2**.
10. $a < \dfrac{(c +' a) +' (-' b)}{2}$ and $b < \dfrac{(c +' b) +' (-' a)}{2}$; by lines **8**, **9**, and **1(ii)**.
11. There are rational numbers $u, v \in R$ such that $a < u$, $u < \dfrac{(c +' a) +' (-' b)}{2}$, $b < v$, and $v < \dfrac{(c +' b) +' (-' a)}{2}$; by line **10** and Theorem 14-5-4(**vii**).
12. $u +' v < \dfrac{(c +' a) +' (-' b)}{2} +' \dfrac{(c +' b) +' (-' a)}{2}$, by lines **11** and **1(ii)**.
13. $u +' v < c$; by lines **12**, **9** and **1(ii)**.
14. $u +' v \in S(a, b)$; by lines **11** and **1(i)** and Definition 14-5-5.
▶ 15. c is *not* a lower bound of $S(a, b)$ in Rl; by lines **13** and **14**.
16. If c is any element of Rl such that $a +' b < c$, then c is *not* a lower bound of $S(a, b)$ in Rl; by the Deduction Theorem applied to lines **8** through **15**.
▶▶ 17. $a +' b$ is the greatest lower bound of $S(a, b)$ in Rl; by lines **7** and **16**.

▶▶ 18. $a +_{Rl} b$ is the greatest lower bound of $S(a, b)$ in Rl; by Definition 14-5-7.
▶▶ 19. $a +' b = a +_{Rl} b$; by lines **17** and **18** and Theorem 14-5-4(**v**).

The theorem now follows by applying the Deduction Theorem to lines **1** and **2** through **19**.

EXERCISES

1. Prove Theorem 14-5-3.
2. Complete the proof of Theorem 14-5-4, parts (**vii**), (**viii**), and (**ix**).
3. Complete the proof of Theorem 14-5-12.
4. Prove Theorem 14-5-21 without using the definition of $-_{Rl}$, but using only Theorem 14-5-20 and those theorems listed in the proof of Theorem 14-5-19.

6. *The Multiplication of Real Numbers*

In the previous section, starting with the ordered system $\langle Rl, <\rangle$ of real numbers, we introduced an operation of addition on Rl which satisfies those basic algebraic laws characterizing ordered abelian groups. In the present section we complete the description of the real number system by introducing a suitable definition of multiplication.

Before we proceed to multiplication, however, let us agree to simplify our notation for addition. Namely, in view of Theorem 14-5-20 there is no longer any need for us to distinguish between the operations $+$ and $+_{Rl}$, since the latter can be applied whenever the former is applicable and will yield the same result in any such case. Therefore, throughout this section we shall employ the simpler symbol "$+$" to denote the operation of addition on Rl (heretofore denoted by "$+_{Rl}$"). However, we shall, of course, have to distinguish between two multiplication operations in this section. The operation $\cdot$, defined in Chapter XII, is already at hand, but can only be applied to pairs of *rational* numbers. Our object will be to define a wider operation, $\cdot_{Rl}$, which can be applied to any pair of *real* numbers. Since the rational numbers are included among the reals, the new operation can be applied to pairs of rational numbers, and in this case of course we wish the two operations to give the same result.

PROBLEM $Rl(\cdot)$ *Can we define a binary operation* $\cdot_{Rl}$ *on the set Rl such that:*

(i) $\cdot_{Rl}$ *is an extension of* $\cdot$, *and*

(ii) $\cdot_{Rl}$ *satisfies the various fundamental algebraic laws needed to qualify the system* $\langle Rl, +, \cdot_{Rl}, <\rangle$ *as an* ***ordered field****?*

We shall see that this problem has an affirmative solution, and that indeed there is only one operation $\cdot_{Rl}$ which satisfies both conditions **(i)** and **(ii)**. In view of Theorem 14-5-19, the algebraic laws needed to verify condition **(ii)** are simply the counterparts of Theorem 14-5-2, parts **(viii)** through **(xiii)**. (See Chapter XII Section 7.)

With the experience of the preceding section behind us, it is natural to seek a definition of $\cdot_{Rl}$ along lines similar to those which were successful in defining $+_{Rl}$. To this end, analogous to our introduction of the sets $S(a, b)$, we might consider the sets $P(a, b)$ of all rational numbers $x \cdot y$ for all $x, y \in R$ such that $a < x$ and $b < y$ (where a and b are any given real numbers). And we might then seek to define $a \cdot_{Rl} b$ as the greatest lower bound of $P(a, b)$ in Rl.

The trouble with this approach is that for certain $a, b \in Rl$ the set $P(a, b)$ *has no lower bound* in Rl! Indeed, it is not hard to see that if either a or b is negative (i.e., if $a < 0$ or $b < 0$), then $P(a, b)$ is the set of *all* rational numbers, and so has no lower bound in Rl.

However, as long as we confine ourselves to *nonnegative* real numbers, then $P(a, b)$ *will* have a greatest lower bound and we *can* define this to be the product of a and b. Our method of procedure, therefore, will be first to define a multiplication $\times$ *which operates only on nonnegative real numbers*, and to establish the basic algebraic laws which it obeys. Afterward, with the aid of the operation $-_{Rl}$ of the preceding section, we will be able to pass easily from $\times$ to $\cdot_{Rl}$. Since theorems involving $\times$ are very similar, both in their statements and proofs, to corresponding theorems about $+_{Rl}$ which were established in the previous section, many of the proofs will be left as exercises for the reader.

DEFINITION 14-6-1. *We define Rl^+ to be the set of all nonnegative real numbers. That is, $x \in Rl^+$ if and only if*

(i) *$x \in R$, and* **(ii)** *either $x = 0$ or $0 < x$.*

DEFINITION 14-6-2. *For any $a, b \in Rl^+$ we define $P(a, b)$ to be the set of all rational numbers $x \cdot y$ such that $x, y \in R$, $a < x$, and $b < y$.*

That is, the set $P(a, b)$ consists of any product of a rational number greater than a by a rational number greater than b.

THEOREM 14-6-3. *If a, b are any elements of Rl^+, then $P(a, b)$ has a lower bound in Rl (and indeed the number 0 is such a lower bound).*

Proof

▶▶**1.** Let a, b be any elements of Rl^+.

▶**2.** $a = 0$ or $0 < a$, and $b = 0$ or $0 < b$; by line **1** and Definition 14-6-1.

▶**3.** Let $x \cdot y$ be any element of $P(a, b)$, where $x, y \in R$, $a < x$, and $b < y$; by Definition 14-6-2.

4. $0 < x$ and $0 < y$; by lines **3** and **2**, and Theorem 14-5-4(**i**).

5. $0 < x \cdot y$; by line **4** and field properties of the rationals.

▶**6.** If $x \cdot y$ is any element of $P(a, b)$ then $0 < x \cdot y$; by the Deduction Theorem applied to lines **3** through **5**.

▶▶**7.** The number 0 is a lower bound of $P(a, b)$ in Rl; by line **6**.

The theorem is now obtained by applying the Deduction Theorem to lines **1** through **7**.

DEFINITION 14-6-4. *For any $a, b \in Rl^+$ we define $a \times b$ to be the greatest lower bound of $P(a, b)$ in Rl.*

This definition is justified by Theorem 14-6-3 and Theorem 14-5-4(**v**).

THEOREM 14-6-5. *For any* $a, b \in Rl^+$ *we have* $a \times b \in Rl^+$ *and* $a + b \in Rl^+$.

Proof

1. Let a, b be any elements of Rl^+.
2. 0 is a lower bound of $P(a, b)$ in Rl; by Theorem 14-6-3.
3. $a \times b$ is the greatest lower bound of $P(a, b)$ in Rl; by Definition 14-6-4.
4. Either $a \times b = 0$ or $0 < a \times b$; by lines **2** and **3**.
5. $a \times b \in Rl^+$; by Definition 14-6-1.

By applying the Deduction Theorem to lines **1** through **5** we obtain the first of the desired statements. The second one is an immediate consequence of Theorem 14-5-19.

In preparation for establishing the basic algebraic laws satisfied by the operation $\times$, we now list two theorems analogous to Theorems 14-5-8 and 14-5-9 (which concern the operation $+_{Rl}$).

THEOREM 14-6-6. *For any* $a, b, c \in Rl^+$ *such that* $a \times b < c$, *there exist* ***rational*** *numbers* $x, y \in Rl^+$ *such that* $a < x$, $b < y$, *and* $x \cdot y < c$.

Proof. See Exercise 2.

THEOREM 14-6-7. *If* a, b *are any elements of* Rl^+, *and if* x, y *are any elements of* R *such that* $a < x$ *and* $b < y$, *then* $a \times b < x \cdot y$.

Proof. See Exercise 3.

The next two theorems show that the system $\langle Rl^+, \times\rangle$ is a commutative semi-group.

THEOREM 14-6-8. *The associative law holds for the operation* $\times$, *i.e., for all* $a, b, c \in Rl^+$ *we have* $(a \times b) \times c = a \times (b \times c)$.

Observe that the notation "$(a \times b) \times c$" makes sense because from the hypothesis that $a, b \in Rl^+$ we can infer that $a \times b \in Rl^+$ by Theorem 14-6-5, and hence (using the hypothesis $c \in Rl^+$) we can form the product $(a \times b) \times c$. A similar remark applies to the notation "$a \times (b \times c)$".

Proof. See Exercise 4.

THEOREM 14-6-9. *The commutative law holds for the operation* $\times$, *i.e., for all* $a, b \in Rl^+$ *we have* $a \times b = b \times a$.

Proof

For variety we give a proof having a somewhat different form from that suggested for Theorem 14-5-11.

▶▶ **1.** Let a, b be any elements of Rl^+.

▶ **2.** Let $x \cdot y$ be any element of $P(a, b)$, where $x, y \epsilon R$, $a < x$, and $b < y$; by Definition 14-6-2.

3. $y \cdot x \epsilon P(b, a)$; by line **2** and Definition 14-6-2.

4. $x \cdot y = y \cdot x$; by field properties of the rationals, since $x, y \epsilon R$ by line **2**.

▶ **5.** $x \cdot y \epsilon P(b, a)$; by E applied to lines **3** and **4**.

6. If $x \cdot y$ is any element of $P(a, b)$, then also $x \cdot y \epsilon P(b, a)$; by the Deduction Theorem applied to lines **2** through **5**.

▶ **7.** $P(a, b) \subseteq P(b, a)$; by line **6** and the definition of subset ($\subseteq$).

▶ **8.** $P(b, a) \subseteq P(a, b)$; by an argument symmetric to that used in establishing line **7**.

▶▶ **9.** $P(a, b) = P(b, a)$; by lines **7** and **8** and the principle of extensionality for sets.

▶▶ **10.** $a \times b$ is the greatest lower bound of $P(a, b)$ in Rl, and $b \times a$ is the greatest lower bound of $P(b, a)$ in Rl; by Definition 14-6-4.

▶▶ **11.** $a \times b = b \times a$; by lines **9** and **10**, and Theorem 14-5-4(**v**).

By applying the Deduction Theorem to lines **1** through **11** we get the statement of Theorem 14-6-9.

The following result shows that in the commutative semi-group $\langle Rl^+, \times\rangle$ the number 1 serves as a null element.

THEOREM 14-6-10. *For every $a \epsilon Rl^+$ we have $a \times 1 = a$.*

Proof. See Exercise 5.

The following theorem gives an algebraic identity which has no counterpart in the preceding section since it involves *both* of the operations $+_{Rl}$ and $\times$. The establishment of this law allows us to say that the system $\langle Rl^+, +, \times\rangle$ is a semi-ring.

THEOREM 14-6-11. *The distributive law holds for $\times$ over $+$, i.e., for all $a, b, c \epsilon Rl^+$ we have $a \times (b + c) = (a \times b) + (a \times c)$.*

Observe that the notation "$a \times (b + c)$" is permissible because, from the hypothesis $b, c \epsilon Rl^+$ together with Theorem 14-6-5 we infer that $b + c \epsilon Rl^+$, and hence we may apply the operation $\times$ to a and $b + c$.

Proof

Preparatory to an application of Theorem 14-5-4(**x**), we shall first show that if x is any element of R such that $a \times (b + c) < x$, then we also have $(a \times b) + (a \times c) < x$.

▶▶ **1.** Let a, b, c be any elements of Rl^+.

2. $0 < a$ or $0 = a$; by line **1** and Definition 14-6-1.

▶▶ 3. Let x be any element of R such that $a \times (b + c) < x$.

▶ 4. There exist rational numbers $y, z \in R$ such that $a < y$, $b + c < z$, and $y \cdot z < x$; by line **3** and Theorem 14-6-6.

5. $0 < y$; by lines **2** and **4** and Theorem 14-5-4(**i**).

▶ 6. There exist rational numbers $u, v \in R$ such that $b < u$, $c < v$, and $u + v < z$; by line **4** and Theorem 14-5-8.

7. $y \cdot (u + v) < y \cdot z$; by lines **5** and **6** and field properties of the rationals (since $y, u, v \in R$ by lines **4** and **6**).

8. $(y \cdot u) + (y \cdot v) < (y \cdot z)$; by line **7** and field properties of the rationals.

▶ 9. $(y \cdot u) + (y \cdot v) < x$; by lines **8** and **4** and field properties of the rationals.

10. $a \times b < y \cdot u$ and $a \times c < y \cdot v$; by lines **4** and **6** and Theorem 14-6-7.

▶ 11. $(a \times b) + (a \times c) < (y \cdot u) + (y \cdot v)$; by line **10** and Theorem 14-5-19.

▶▶ 12. $(a \times b) + (a \times c) < x$; by lines **9** and **11** and Theorem 14-5-4 (**i**).

13. If x is any element of R such that $a \times (b + c) < x$, then we also have $(a \times b) + (a \times c) < x$; by the Deduction Theorem applied to lines **2** through **12**.

We shall leave to the reader the task of showing, by a similar argument, that the converse of line **13** is equally true. That is, if y is any element of R such that $(a \times b) + (a \times c) < y$, then we also have $a \times (b + c) < y$. When this is combined with line **13** by means of Theorem 14-5-4 (**x**) the statement of Theorem 14-6-11 results.

The final algebraic property we shall need to know about the operation $\times$ has to do with the existence of inverses. That is, for any $a \in Rl^+$ such that $a \neq 0$, we shall want to know that there exists another element $b \in Rl^+$ such that $a \times b = 1$. To prepare the ground for a definition of the inverse operation we introduce the following concept.

DEFINITION 14-6-12. *For every $a \in Rl^+$ we let $I(a)$ be the set of all those rational numbers $x \in Rl^+$ such that $1 < a \times x$.*

The reader will notice that the form of this definition differs somewhat from the corresponding Definition 14-5-13 which we used as a basis for introducing the operation $-_{Rl}$ in the preceding chapter. If we had paralleled that definition we would have defined $I(a)$ to be the set of all those $x \in R$ such that $1/x < a$. Actually, either of these definitions can be used, and we have only chosen the form used in Definition 14-6-12 for the sake of variety.

Similarly, Definition 14-5-13 could have been replaced by defining $M(a)$ to be the set of all $x \in R$ such that $0 < a +_{Rl} x$. (See Exercises 7, 8 below.)

THEOREM 14-6-13. *If a is any element of Rl^+ other than 0, then the set $I(a)$ is nonempty and has 0 as a lower bound in Rl.*

Proof

We first show that $I(a)$ is nonempty.

▶▶ **1.** Let a be any element of Rl^+ other than 0.
2. $0 < a$; by line **1** and Definition 14-6-1.
▶▶ **3.** There is a rational number $z \in R$ such that $0 < z$ and $z < a$; by line **2** and Theorem 14-5-4(**vii**).

Note: To complete the proof that $I(a)$ is nonempty we shall show that for this *arbitrary* rational number $z \in R$ such that $0 < z$ and $z < a$, we must have $1/z \in I(a)$. (See note following line **23** below).

▶ **4.** There is a rational number $y \in R$ such that $z < y$ and $y < a$; by line **3** and Theorem 14-5-4(**vii**).
▶▶ **5.** Let $x = 1/z$ (which exists since $z \neq 0$ by line **3**)
6. $x \in R$ and $0 < x$; by lines **5** and **3** and field properties of the rationals.
▶ **7.** Let $u \cdot v$ be any element of $P(a, x)$, where $u, v \in R$, $a < u$, and $x < v$; by Definition 14-6-2.
8. $y < u$; by lines **4** and **7** and Theorem 14-5-4(**i**).
9. $y \cdot x < u \cdot x$; by lines **8** and **6** and field properties of the rationals.
10. $0 < u$; by lines **2** and **7** and Theorem 14-5-4(**i**).
11. $u \cdot x < u \cdot v$; by lines **7** and **10** and field properties of the rationals.
▶ **12.** $y \cdot x < u \cdot v$; by lines **9** and **11** and Theorem 14-5-4(**i**).
13. If $u \cdot v$ is any element of $P(a, x)$ then $y \cdot x < u \cdot v$; by the Deduction Theorem applied to lines **7** through **12**.
▶ **14.** $y \cdot x$ is a lower bound of $P(a, x)$ in Rl; by line **13**.
▶ **15.** $a \times x$ is the greatest lower bound of $P(a, x)$ in Rl; by Definition 14-6-4.
16. Either $y \cdot x < a \times x$ or $y \cdot x = a \times x$; by lines **14** and **15**.
17. $z \cdot x < y \cdot x$; by lines **4** and **6** and field properties of the rationals.
▶ **18.** $z \cdot x < a \times x$; by lines **16** and **17** and Theorem 14-5-4(**i**).
19. $z \cdot x = 1$; by line **5** and field properties of the rationals.
▶▶ **20.** $1 < a \times x$; by E applied to lines **18** and **19**.
21. $x \in Rl^+$; by line **6** and Definition 14-6-1.

►►**22.** $x \in I(a)$; by lines **20** and **21** and Definition 14-6-12.
23. $I(a)$ is nonempty; by lines **22** and **5**.

(Note that by lines **5** and **22** we have, in fact, substantiated the note which follows line **3**.) To complete the proof of Theorem 14-6-13 it remains to show that 0 is a lower bound of $I(a)$ in Rl. But this is immediate by Definition 14-6-1, since every $x \in I(a)$ is also in Rl^+ by Definition 14-6-12.

With the aid of Theorem 14-6-13 we are ready to define an inverse for every positive real number.

DEFINITION 14-6-14. *For every $a \in Rl^+$ other than* 0 *we define* **inv**(a) *to be the greatest lower bound of $I(a)$ in Rl.*

This definition is justified by Theorems 14-6-13 and 14-5-4(**v**). We have at once the following result.

THEOREM 14-6-15. *For any $a \in Rl^+$ other than* 0, *we have* **inv**$(a) \in Rl^+$.

Proof

1. Let a be any element of Rl^+ other than 0.
2. 0 is a lower bound of $I(a)$ in Rl; by line **1** and Theorem 14-6-13.
3. **inv**(a) is the greatest lower bound of $I(a)$ in Rl; by line **1** and Definition 14-6-14.
4. Either $0 <$ **inv**(a) or $0 =$ **inv**(a); by lines **2** and **3**.
5. **inv**$(a) \in Rl^+$; by line **4** and Definition 14-6-1.

By applying the Deduction Theorem to lines **1** through **5** we obtain the desired statement of Theorem 14-6-15.

The following property of inverses will also be useful in the sequel.

THEOREM 14-6-16. *If $a \in Rl^+$, and if y is any rational number such that $0 < y$ and $y < a$, then* **inv**$(a) < 1/y$.

Proof

►►**1.** Suppose that $a \in Rl^+$, $y \in R$, $0 < y$, and $y < a$.
2. $a \in Rl^+$ and $a \neq 0$; by line **1** and Theorem 14-5-4 (**i**) and (**ii**).
►**3.** There is a rational number $z \in R$ such that $y < z$ and $z < a$; by line **1** and Theorem 14-5-4(**vii**).
4. $z \in R$, $0 < z$, and $z < a$; by lines **1** and **3** and Theorem 14-5-4(**i**).
5. $1/z \in I(a)$; by lines **2** and **4** and the Note following line **3** in the proof of Theorem 14-6-13.
6. **inv**(a) is a lower bound of $I(a)$ in Rl; by Definition 14-6-14.
►**7.** Either **inv**$(a) < 1/z$ or **inv**$(a) = 1/z$; by lines **5** and **6**.

▶**8.** $1/z < 1/y$; by line **3** and field properties of the rationals (since $0 \neq z, y$ by lines **1** and **4**).

▶▶**9.** **inv**$(a) < 1/y$; by lines **7** and **8** and Theorem 14-5-4(**i**).

An application of the Deduction Theorem to lines **1** through **9** gives the desired result.

And now we are ready to establish the principal property of inverses.

THEOREM 14-6-17. *If a is any element of* Rl^+ *other than* 0 *then we have* $a \times$ **inv**$(a) = 1$.

Proof

We first show that **1** is a lower bound for the set $P(a,$ **inv**$(a))$.

▶▶ **1.** Let a be any element of Rl^+ other than 0.

2. **inv**$(a) \in Rl^+$; by Theorem 14-6-15.

▶ **3.** Let $x \cdot y$ be any element of $P(a,$ **inv**$(a))$, where $x, y \in R$, $a < x$, and **inv**$(a) < y$; by lines **1** and **2** and Definition 14-6-2.

4. **inv**(a) is the greatest lower bound of $I(a)$; by Definition 14-6-14.

5. y is not a lower bound of $I(a)$; by lines **3** and **4**.

6. There is an element $z \in I(a)$ such that $z < y$; by line **5**.

7. $z \in R$, $z \in Rl^+$, and $1 < a \times z$; by line **6** and Definition 14-6-12.

8. $a \times z < x \cdot y$; by lines **3** and **6** and Theorem 14-6-7.

▶ **9.** $1 < x \cdot y$; by lines **7** and **8** and Theorem 14-5-4(**i**).

10. If $x \cdot y$ is any element of $P(a,$ **inv**$(a))$, then $1 < x \cdot y$; by the Deduction Theorem applied to lines **3** through **9**.

▶▶**11.** 1 is a lower bound of $P(a,$ **inv**$(a))$ in Rl; by line **10**.

And now we proceed to show that **1** is the *greatest* lower bound of $P(a,$ **inv**$(a))$ in Rl.

▶▶**12.** Let b be any element of Rl such that $1 < b$.

▶**13.** There exists a rational number $u \in R$ such that $1 < u$ and $u < b$; by line **12** and Theorem 14-5-4(**vii**).

▶**14.** There exists a rational number $w \in R$ such that $0 < w$ and $w < a$; by line **1** and Definition 14-6-1, and Theorem 14-5-4(**vii**).

15. $0 < w/u$; by lines **13** and **14** and field properties of the rationals.

▶**16.** There is a rational number $v \in R$ such that $0 < v$ and $v < w/u$; by line **15** and Theorem 14-5-4(**vii**).

17. $0 < (u - 1) \cdot v$; by lines **13** and **16** and field properties of the rationals.

▶**18.** There is a rational number $t \in R$ such that $t < a$ and $a < t + (u - 1) \cdot v$; by lines **1** and **17** and Theorem 14-5-16.

19. $u \cdot v < w$; by lines **16** and **13** and field properties of the rationals.

20. $u \cdot v < a$; by lines **19** and **14** and Theorem 14-5-4(**i**).

21. $u \cdot v < t + (u - 1) \cdot v$; by lines **20** and **18** and Theorem 14-5-4(**i**).

22. $v < t$; by line **21** and field properties of the rationals.

23. $0 < t$; by lines **16** and **22** and Theorem 14-5-4(**i**).

24. $\mathbf{inv}(a) < 1/t$; by lines **23** and **18** and Theorem 14-6-16.

▶**25.** $(t + (u - 1) \cdot v) \cdot 1/t \in P(a, \mathbf{inv}(a))$; by lines **18** and **24** and Definition 14-6-2.

26. $(u - 1) \cdot v < (u - 1) \cdot t$; by lines **22** and **13** and field properties of the rationals.

▶**27.** $(t + (u - 1) \cdot v) \cdot 1/t < u$; by lines **26** and **23** and field properties of the rationals.

▶**28.** $(t + (u - 1) \cdot v) \cdot 1/t < b$; by lines **27** and **13** and Theorem 14-5-4(**i**).

▶▶**29.** b is *not* a lower bound of $P(a, \mathbf{inv}(a))$ in Rl; by lines **25** and **28**.

30. If b is any element of Rl such that $1 < b$, then b is not a lower bound of $P(a, \mathbf{inv}(a))$ in Rl; by the Deduction Theorem applied to lines **12** through **29**.

▶▶**31.** The number 1 is the greatest lower bound of $P(a, \mathbf{inv}(a))$ in Rl; by lines **11** and **30**.

To complete the proof of Theorem 14-6-17 we have only to combine line **31** with Definition 14-6-4 and Theorem 14-5-4(**v**).

While this proof is probably no harder to *follow* than others in this chapter, it is one of the most difficult to find if one sets out to look for a proof instead of reading one in a book. The difficulty lies particularly in finding how to choose the numbers v and t which were introduced on lines **16** and **18** respectively. Since it is probably not very clear to the reader how v and t came to be selected in the given way, it is perhaps worth interrupting the formal development of the theory at this point to indicate some of the heuristic considerations which underlie this selection.

The fundamental aim of the second part of the proof (i.e., the part after line **11**), is to show that no b in Rl such that $1 < b$ can be a lower bound of $P(a, \mathbf{inv}(a))$ in Rl. By Definition 14-6-2 this can be a done by finding rational numbers $x, y \in R$ such that $a < x$, $\mathbf{inv}(a) < y$, and $x \cdot y < b$. Our first step (line **13**) is to choose a $u \in R$ so that $1 < u$ and $u < b$. Clearly if we can get $x \cdot y < u$ we will have $x \cdot y < b$; and the advantage of working with u rather than b is that u is a *rational* number, and so we can act on it with the field operations which are known to obey all of the algebraic laws for fields.

Using Theorem 14-6-16, the job of finding a suitable $y \in R$ so that $\mathbf{inv}(a) < y$ is tantamount to finding a suitable $t \in R$ so that $r < a$, and then taking $y = 1/t$. So what we are seeking is a pair of numbers $t, x \in R$ such that $t < a$, $a < x$, and $x \cdot 1/t < u$, where we know that $1 < u$. Now from our intuitive knowledge of arithmetic, we know that whenever $t < a$ and $a < x$ we will have $1 < x \cdot 1/t$, *and that the further t and x are from a the greater will be the quotient x/t.* Therefore, in order to insure that $x/t < u$ (which is our aim), we must make sure that neither x nor t is *too far* from a. But how far is too far?

At this point we should recall that Theorem 14-5-16 gives us a way of choosing rational numbers, one on each side of any given real number a, which are "close together," and hence perforce "close to a." In fact, given *any* positive rational number r, *no matter how small*, we can find a rational number $t < a$ such that $a < t + r$, according to Theorem 14-5-16. Hence it is reasonable to expect that if we can *choose r small* then we could use $t + r$ for the number x we are seeking. But again the question is, how small is "small enough"?

Well, let us see. We want $x \cdot 1/t < u$, i.e., $(t + r)/t < u$. Assuming that we can somehow arrange things so that $0 < t$, we see easily that the desired inequality is equivalent to $r < (u - 1) \cdot t$. This tells us how small we must take r—*providing* we know the numbers u and t to begin with. Now the number u was chosen in line **13**, so there is no difficulty with *that.* But unfortunately the number t is supplied to us by Theorem 14-5-16—*only after we have chosen a value for r*! We are still left with the problem of choosing r "small enough."

Since $0 < u - 1$ (by choice of u), it is clear that we will have the desired inequality $r < (u - 1) \cdot t$ if we can somehow find a number v such that $v < t$, and then take $r = (u - 1) \cdot v$. But how do we choose our v? Since we know by Theorem 14-5-16 that the number t will satisfy the condition $a < t + r$ (i.e., $a < t + (u - 1) \cdot v$, by our choice of r), we see that the desired inequality $v < t$ will occur providing we can pick v so that $v < a - (u - 1) \cdot v$. But of course by elementary field properties this will be accomplished if we pick v so that $u \cdot v < a$.

The simplest way to obtain such a number v is to choose $v < a/u$. But unfortunately a need not be a rational number, and in our theory we do not yet have a division operation for arbitrary real numbers. So we *first* pick a *rational* number w so that $0 < w$ and $w < a$ (line **14**). *Then* we choose v so that $0 < v$ and $v < w/u$ (line **16**), and this will ensure that $u \cdot v < a$. Finally (line **18**), taking $r = (u - 1) \cdot v$, we choose t so that $t < a$ and $a < t + r$. This "behind the scenes" excursion explains how the crucial steps of our proof were found.

With Theorem 14-6-17 we have completed the list of basic algebraic laws, obeyed by the operation $\times$, which we need for our purposes. However, there is still one other fact which we must establish about this operation, namely, that when it is applied to two *rational* numbers x and y, the resulting number, $x \times y$, is the same number $x \cdot y$ obtained by applying the operation $\cdot$ to x and y.

THEOREM 14-6-18. *For any $x, y \in R$ we have $x \times y = x \cdot y$.*

Proof

We leave this as an exercise. This will provide the reader with an opportunity to put into practice the type of heuristic reasoning which was outlined following the proof of Theorem 14-6-17.

Now we are ready to pass from consideration of the operation $\times$, which can act only on pairs of elements of Rl^+, to an operation $\cdot_{Rl}$ which is to be defined on an *arbitrary* pair of elements of Rl. The transition will be carried out by means of the operation $-_{Rl}$ which was defined in the previous section (Definition 14-5-15). The most basic facts we shall use about this operation are the following.

THEOREM 14-6-19. **(i)** *If a is any element of Rl which is* **not** *in Rl^+, then $-_{Rl}\, a \in Rl^+$ and $-_{Rl}\, a \neq 0$.* **(ii)** *If b is any element of Rl^+ other than 0, then $-_{Rl}\, b$ is* **not** *in Rl^+.*

Proof. This Theorem is a simple consequence of Theorem 14-5-21(**ii**) and Definition 14-6-1. We leave the details as an exercise.

DEFINITION 14-6-20. *For any $a, b \in Rl$ we define $a \cdot_{Rl} b$ to be the element of Rl obtained as follows:*

(**i**) $a \cdot_{Rl} b = a \times b$ *if* $a, b \in Rl^+$;
(**ii**) $a \cdot_{Rl} b = -_{Rl}(a \times -_{Rl}\, b)$ *if* $a \in Rl^+$ *and* $b \notin Rl^+$;
(**iii**) $a \cdot_{Rl} b = -_{Rl}(-_{Rl}\, a \times b)$ *if* $a \notin Rl^+$ *and* $b \in Rl^+$;
(**iv**) $a \cdot_{Rl} b = -_{Rl}\, a \times -_{Rl}\, b$ *if* $a \notin Rl^+$ *and* $b \notin Rl^+$.

This definition is justified, of course, by Theorem 14-6-19(**i**), which guarantees that the operation $\times$ can be applied as shown in each of the cases (**i**) through (**iv**). That these cases are exclusive and exhaustive is a matter of elementary logic.

Each of the basic algebraic laws which are satisfied by the operation $\cdot_{Rl}$ can now be obtained easily by combining the corresponding law for the operation $\times$ with Definition 14-6-20. Since this definition has the form of a definition by cases, it is natural that the proofs of the laws for $\cdot_{Rl}$ should also proceed by cases. While some of these proofs are lengthy because a large number of cases must be considered, the steps are all of a straightforward, semi-computational nature.

Actually, the reader will very quickly discover that the proofs look rather familiar. Indeed, the proofs turn out to be substantially identical to proofs of the algebraic laws which hold in the system $\mathcal{J}$ of integers, which were derived from corresponding laws in the system $\mathfrak{N}$ of natural numbers with the aid of an operation ν whose character closely resembles that of our operation $-_{Rl}$. (See Chapter XI.) For this reason almost all proofs will be omitted in the presentation below.

THEOREM 14-6-21. *For any* $a, b \in Rl$ *we have* $a \cdot_{Rl} b = b \cdot_{Rl} a$ *(the commutative law for* $\cdot_{Rl}$*).*

Proof

We give this proof in full as a sample of the proofs by cases which are needed in the following theorems.

1. Let a, b be any elements of Rl.

2. *Case I.* Suppose that $a, b \in Rl^+$.
3. $a \cdot_{Rl} b = a \times b$ and $b \cdot_{Rl} a = b \times a$; by line **2** and Definition 14-6-20 (**i**).
4. $a \times b = b \times a$; by line **2** and Theorem 14-6-9.
5. $a \cdot_{Rl} b = b \cdot_{Rl} a$; by E applied to lines **3** and **4**.

6. *Case II.* Suppose that $a \in Rl^+$ and $b \notin Rl^+$.
7. $a \cdot_{Rl} b = -_{Rl} (a \times -_{Rl} b)$ and $b \cdot_{Rl} a = -_{Rl} (-_{Rl} b \times a)$; by line **6** and Definition 14-6-20 (**ii**) and (**iii**).
8. $a \times -_{Rl} b = -_{Rl} b \times a$; by line **6**, Theorem 14-6-19(**i**), and Theorem 14-6-9.
9. $a \cdot_{Rl} b = b \cdot_{Rl} a$; by E applied to lines **7** and **8**.

10. *Case III.* Suppose that $a \notin Rl^+$ and $b \in Rl^+$.
11. $a \cdot_{Rl} b = b \cdot_{Rl} a$; by the logic of identity applied to Case II.

12. *Case IV.* Suppose that $a \notin Rl^+$ and $b \notin Rl^+$.
13. $a \cdot_{Rl} b = -_{Rl} a \times -_{Rl} b$ and $b \cdot_{Rl} a = -_{Rl} b \times -_{Rl} a$; by line **12** and Definition 14-6-20.
14. $-_{Rl} a \times -_{Rl} b = -_{Rl} b \times -_{Rl} a$; by line **12**, Theorem 14-6-19(**i**), and Theorem 14-6-9.
15. $a \cdot_{Rl} b = b \cdot_{Rl} a$; by E applied to lines **13** and **14**.

Since Cases I through IV exhaust all possibilities by elementary logic, and since in each of these cases we have shown that $a \cdot_{Rl} b = b \cdot_{Rl} a$, it follows that this equation holds for *all* $a, b \in Rl$.

THEOREM 14-6-22. *For any* $a, b, c \in Rl$ *we have* $a \cdot_{Rl} (b \cdot_{Rl} c) = (a \cdot_{Rl} b) \cdot_{Rl} c$ (*the associative law for* $\cdot_{Rl}$).

Proof

By cases, combining Theorem 14-6-8 with Definition 14-6-20. Eight cases will be needed in this proof, instead of the four cases considered in the preceding theorem, because of the fact that three variables enter into the statement of this theorem.

The most troublesome theorem to prove by cases is the distributive law for $\cdot_{Rl}$ over $+$. Some simplification can be achieved by first showing the following result.

THEOREM 14-6-23. *For all* $a, b, c \in Rl$ *we have:*

(i) $-_{Rl}\, a \cdot_{Rl} b = -_{Rl}\,(a \cdot_{Rl} b)$,
(ii) $a \cdot_{Rl} -_{Rl}\, b = -_{Rl}\,(a \cdot_{Rl} b)$, *and*
(iii) $-_{Rl}\, a \cdot_{Rl} -_{Rl}\, b = a \cdot_{Rl} b$.

Proof

Using Definition 14-6-20 and Theorem 14-5-21(**i**), we may show (**i**) by considering four cases. We can then obtain (**ii**) from (**i**) by Theorem 14-6-21. And finally we get (**iii**) by successive applications of (**i**), (**ii**), and Theorem 14-5-21(**i**). (See Exercise 11.)

THEOREM 14-6-24. *For any* $a, b, c \in Rl$ *we have* $a \cdot_{Rl} (b + c) = a \cdot_{Rl} b + a \cdot_{Rl} c$ (*the distributive law for* $\cdot_{Rl}$ *over* $+$).

Proof

If one seeks a straightforward proof by cases, using Definition 14-6-20, one is led to consider sixteen cases according as each of the numbers a, b, c, and $b + c$ is or is not in Rl^+. In order to cut down on this labor, we first observe that once all of the cases in which $a \in Rl^+$ have been established, we can complete the proof immediately by an application of Theorem 14-6-23(**i**).

Turning to the cases where $a \in Rl^+$, therefore, we see that if $b, c \in Rl^+$ then the distributive equation holds by Theorem 14-6-11, while if $b \notin Rl^+$ and $c \notin Rl^+$ then the same equation is obtained by combining Theorem 14-6-11 with Theorem 14-6-19(**i**) and Theorem 14-5-21(**iii**). Of the remaining two cases, the one in which $b \notin Rl^+$ and $c \in Rl^+$ can be reduced to the other one, in which $b \in Rl^+$ and $c \notin Rl^+$, by using the commutative law for $+$ (Theorem 14-5-11).

Thus to complete the proof it remains only to consider the case where $a, b \in Rl^+$ and $c \notin Rl^+$. In this case let $d = -_{Rl}\, c$, so that $a, b, d \in Rl^+$ by Theorem 14-6-19(**i**). We have $c = -_{Rl}\, d$, by Theorem 14-5-21(**i**), and so the equation we must show is:

$$a \cdot_{Rl} (b + -_{Rl}\, d) = a \cdot_{Rl} b + a \cdot_{Rl} -_{Rl}\, d.$$

Considering first the subcase $(b + -_{Rl}\, d) \in Rl^+$, we get

$$a \cdot_{Rl} (b + -_{Rl}\, d) + a \cdot_{Rl} d = a \cdot_{Rl} ((b + -_{Rl}\, d) +_{Rl} d),$$

by an application of the first case considered (where all elements are in Rl^+), and from this we easily get

$$a \cdot_{Rl} (b + -_{Rl}\, d) = a \cdot_{Rl} b + -_{Rl} (a \cdot_{Rl} d)$$

by the basic laws for $+$ and $-_{Rl}$; whereupon the desired equation is obtained by Theorem 14-6-23(**ii**). Finally, considering the subcase $(b + -_{Rl}\, d) \notin Rl^+$, we reduce this to the previous subcase by applying Theorems 14-6-19 and 14-5-21.

THEOREM 14-6-25. *For all $a \in Rl$ we have $a \cdot_{Rl} 1 = a$.*

Proof

By cases, combining Theorem 14-6-10 with Definition 14-6-20.

THEOREM 14-6-26. *If a is any element of Rl such that $a \neq 0$, then there is an element $b \in Rl$ such that $a \cdot_{Rl} b = 1$.*

Proof

By cases, combining Theorem 14-6-17 with Definition 14-6-20 and Theorem 14-6-23. It will be seen that if $a \notin Rl^+$ then the inverse of a is $-_{Rl}$ **inv** $(-_{Rl}\, a)$.

We have now listed all of the laws needed to establish that the system $\langle Rl, +, \cdot_{Rl}\rangle$ is a field. In order to show that the operation $\cdot_{Rl}$ is a solution to problem $Rl(\cdot)$, it remains only to establish the basic relation which holds between the operation $\cdot_{Rl}$ and the relation $<$.

THEOREM 14-6-27. *If a, b, and c are any elements of Rl such that $a < b$ and $0 < c$, then we have $a \cdot_{Rl} c < b \cdot_{Rl} c$.*

Proof

▶▶ **1.** Let a, b, and c be any elements of Rl such that $a < b$ and $0 < c$.
2. $0 < (b + -_{Rl}\, a)$; by line **1** and Theorem 14-5-19.
3. $c \in Rl^+$ and $(b + -_{Rl}\, a) \in Rl^+$; by lines **1** and **2** and Definition 14-6-1.
4. $c \cdot_{Rl} (b + -_{Rl}\, a) \in Rl^+$; by line **3**, Theorem 14-6-5, and Definition 14-6-20 (**i**).
5. $(c \cdot_{Rl} b + c \cdot_{Rl} -_{Rl}\, a) \in Rl^+$; by line **4** and Theorem 14-6-24.
▶ **6.** $c \cdot_{Rl} b + -_{Rl} (c \cdot_{Rl} a) \in Rl^+$; by line **5** and Theorem 14-6-23 (**ii**).
▶ **7.** Either $c \cdot_{Rl} b + -_{Rl} (c \cdot_{Rl} a) = 0$ or $0 < c \cdot_{Rl} b + -_{Rl} (c \cdot_{Rl} a)$; by line **6** and Definition 14-6-1.

8. Either $c \cdot_{Rl} b = c \cdot_{Rl} a$ or $c \cdot_{Rl} a < c \cdot_{Rl} b$; by line **7** and Theorem 14-5-19.

▶▶ 9. Either $b \cdot_{Rl} c = a \cdot_{Rl} c$ or $a \cdot_{Rl} c < b \cdot_{Rl} c$; by line **8** and Theorem 14-6-21.

▶▶ 10. *Assume* that $b \cdot_{Rl} c = a \cdot_{Rl} c$.

▶ 11. There is an element $d \in Rl$ such that $c \cdot_{Rl} d = 1$; by line **1** and Theorem 14-6-26.

12. $(b \cdot_{Rl} c) \cdot_{Rl} d = (a \cdot_{Rl} c) \cdot_{Rl} d$; by E applied to lines **10** and **11**.

▶ 13. $b \cdot_{Rl} (c \cdot_{Rl} d) = a \cdot_{Rl} (c \cdot_{Rl} d)$; by line **12** and Theorem 14-6-22.

14. $b \cdot_{Rl} 1 = a \cdot_{Rl} 1$; by lines **13** and **11**.

▶▶ 15. $b = a$; by line **14** and Theorem 14-6-25.

16. If $b \cdot_{Rl} c = a \cdot_{Rl} c$ then $b = a$; by the Deduction Theorem applied to lines **10** through **15**.

▶▶ 17. $b \neq a$; by line **1** and Theorem 14-5-4(**ii**).

18. $b \cdot_{Rl} c \neq a \cdot_{Rl} c$; by logic applied to lines **16** and **17**.

▶▶ 19. $a \cdot_{Rl} c < b \cdot_{Rl} c$; by logic applied to lines **9** and **18**.

Finally, we obtain our result by applying the Deduction Theorem to lines **1** through **19**.

Now we are ready to collect together our various algebraic laws involving the operations $+_{Rl}$ and $\cdot_{Rl}$.

THEOREM 14-6-28. *The system* $\langle Rl, +, \cdot_{Rl}, < \rangle$ *is an ordered field.*

Proof. By Theorems 14-5-19, 14-6-21, 14-6-22, and 14-6-24 through 14-6-27. (Compare Definitions 11-6-5 and 11-7-4.)

We must still show that the ordered field mentioned in this theorem is an extension of the ordered field of rational numbers. This is accomplished by the following theorem.

THEOREM 14-6-29. *For any rational numbers* $x, y \in R$ *we have* $x \cdot_{Rl} y = x \cdot y$.

Proof. By cases, combining Definition 14-6-20 with Theorem 14-6-18 and 14-6-23.

Putting together Theorems 14-6-28, 14-5-20, and 14-6-29 we see finally that the operation $\cdot_{Rl}$ is indeed a solution to *Problem* $Rl(\cdot)$. We have succeeded in extending the ordered field of rational numbers to another ordered field in which the ordering relation is complete, i.e., has no gaps. The new ordered field, called the system of real numbers, can therefore be used for such purposes as assigning a numerical length to the circumference of a circle. (See Chapter XIII.)

We conclude this section by sketching a proof that $\cdot_{Rl}$ is the *only* binary operation on Rl which provides a solution to *Problem* $Rl(\cdot)$.

THEOREM 14-6-30. *Suppose that* $\cdot'$ *is* ***any*** *binary operation on* Rl *such that* (**i**) $\cdot'$ *is an extension of the operation* $\cdot$ *on* R, *and* (**ii**) *the system* $\langle Rl, +, \cdot', < \rangle$ *is an ordered field. Then for every* $a, b \in Rl$ *we must have* $a \cdot' b = a \cdot_{Rl} b$.

Proof. We give only an outline of a proof of this theorem. It is convenient to divide the work by establishing the following lemma.

LEMMA. *Under hypotheses* (**i**) *and* (**ii**) *of the theorem, we have* $a \cdot' b = a \times b$ *for every* $a, b \in Rl^+$.

1. Let a, b be any elements of Rl^+. Consider any element $x \cdot y$ of $P(a, b)$, where $x, y \in R$, $a < x$, and $b < y$. By hypothesis (**ii**) we get $a \cdot' b < x \cdot' y$, and then, by hypothesis (**i**), $a \cdot' b < x \cdot y$. Thus $a \cdot' b$ is a lower bound of $P(a, b)$ in Rl.

2. Now consider any $c \in Rl$ such that $a \cdot' b < c$. We shall show below that c is *not* a lower bound of $P(a, b)$ in Rl. Combining this with the conclusion of (**1**) above, we see that $a \cdot' b$ is the greatest lower bound of $P(a, b)$ in Rl. Using this fact and Definition 14-6-4, we obtain $a \cdot' b = a \times b$, as stated in the lemma.

3. From $a \cdot' b < c$ we get first $0 < c + -_{Rl} (a \cdot' b)$, and then (since $a, b, c \in Rl^+$), $0 < \dfrac{c + -_{Rl} (a \cdot' b)}{a + b + c + 1}$, by hypothesis (**ii**). Letting $d = \dfrac{c + -_{Rl} (a \cdot' b)}{a + b + c + 1}$, we have $0 < d$.

4. From the last inequality we have $a < a + d$, $b < b + d$, and hence there must be rational numbers $u, v \in R$ such that $a < u$, $u < a + d$, $b < v$, and $v < b + d$. From these inequalities we get $u \cdot' v < (a + d) \cdot' (b + d)$ by hypothesis (**ii**), and then $u \cdot v < (a + d) \cdot' (b + d)$ by hypothesis (**i**), where $u \cdot v \in P(a, b)$.

5. Since $a, b \in Rl^+$ we get $a \cdot' b \in Rl^+$, by hypothesis (**ii**), and hence $c + -_{Rl} (a \cdot' b) < c$. It follows [from (**3**) above] that $d < c$, and so certainly $a + b + d < a + b + c + 1$.

6. Now $(a + d) \cdot' (b + d) = a \cdot' b + (a + b + d) \cdot' d$, by hypothesis (**ii**). Using the inequality of (**5**) above, we get $(a + d) \cdot' (b + d) < a \cdot' b + (a + b + c + 1) \cdot' d$, by hypothesis (**ii**), since $0 < d$ by (**3**). But by the definition of d in (**3**), $(a + b + c + 1) \cdot' d = c + -_{Rl} (a \cdot' b)$. Hence $(a + d) \cdot' (b + d) < c$.

7. Combining the last inequality with the results of (**4**) above, we see that $u \cdot v < c$ for some $u \cdot v \in P(a, b)$, so that c is *not* a lower bound of $P(a, b)$ in Rl. As indicated in (**2**) above, this completes the proof of the Lemma.

Now that the Lemma is established, Theorem 14-6-30 follows easily, by Definition 14-6-20, since we can obtain from hypothesis (**ii**) the laws $a \cdot' -_{Rl} b = -_{Rl} (a \cdot' b)$, $-_{Rl} a \cdot' b = -_{Rl} (a \cdot' b)$, and $-_{Rl} a \cdot' -_{Rl} b = a \cdot' b$, for all $a, b \in Rl$. (Compare Theorem 14-6-23.)

EXERCISES

1. Show that if either $a < 0$ or $b < 0$ then $P(a, b)$ is the set of *all* rational numbers, and hence has no lower bound in Rl.

2. Give a proof of Theorem 14-6-6 along the lines of the proof given for Theorem 14-5-8.

3. Give a proof of Theorem 14-6-7 along the lines of the proof given for Theorem 14-5-9.

4. Give a proof of Theorem 14-6-8. (Compare Theorem 14-5-10.)

5. Prove Theorem 14-6-10. (Compare Theorem 14-5-12.)

6. Complete the proof of Theorem 14-6-11.

7.* Instead of using Definition 14-6-12, define $I'(a)$ to be the set of all $x \in R$ such that $\frac{1}{x} < a$, show that for any $a \in Rl+$ other than 0, $I'(a)$ has a greatest lower bound a^* in Rl, and prove that $a \times a^* = 1$.

8.* Returning to the previous chapter, instead of using Definition 14-5-13 define $M'(a)$ to be the set of all $x \in R$ such that $0 < a +_{Rl} x$. Show that for any $a \in Rl$, $M'(a)$ has a greatest lower bound a' in Rl, and prove that $a +_{Rl} a' = 0$.

9.* Prove Theorem 14-6-18. Suggestion: Use ideas outlined immediately after the proof of Theorem 14-6-17.

10. Prove Theorem 14-6-19 in detail.

11. Prove Theorem 14-6-23 in detail.

12. Prove Theorem 14-6-26.

7. *Notation for Real Numbers*

If we wish to speak or write about any object it is desirable to have a name, or other notation, which refers to it and it alone. In the case of the natural numbers the system of decimal notation provides us with a unique notation for each number, the notation consisting of a *numeral*, or finite row of symbols called *digits*. The mathematical theory underlying this system of notation was discussed in Chapter VIII.

It is well known that by combining the decimal notation with the use of a minus sign, we can obtain a unique notation for each element of the set J (i.e., for each integer), consisting of a numeral which may or may not be preceded by the minus sign. Furthermore, there is a system of notation for the elements of the set R, in which each rational number is denoted by a *fraction* consisting of two numerals separated by a bar (or *fraction sign*), which may or may not be preceded by minus sign. This system of notation differs from those mentioned above, however, in that many different fractions refer to the same rational number; e.g., the fractions "$\frac{2}{4}$", "$\frac{1}{2}$", and "$\frac{30}{60}$" all refer to the rational number $\frac{1}{2}$. It is, of course, possible to extract from this system another system of notation, in which each rational number is denoted by a *unique* name, by means of the algorithm of dividing out common factors.

When we come to real numbers which are not rational, however, we have no such general system of notation in use. For certain special numbers, such as $\sqrt{2}$, we do have a notation, and indeed by use of the radical sign we can form a name for any real number some power of which is rational (e.g., $\sqrt[3]{\frac{2}{5}}$). *Roots* of rationals, as these numbers are called, are only a special case of *algebraic* numbers, i.e., numbers which satisfy a polynomial equation with rational coefficients. In principle there would be no difficulty in devising a systematic notation assigning a unique name to each real algebraic number, although in fact no such system is in general use.

Turning to real numbers which are not algebraic, the so-called *transcendental* real numbers, we find only a few isolated cases of regular names for such numbers: the most familiar of these are "π", denoting a number important in elementary geometry, and "e", referring to a certain number between 2 and 3 which plays a fundamental role in the theory of differential calculus. In this case, however, not only do we lack a systematic notation for each transcendental real number, but it can be demonstrated mathematically that it is impossible to devise such a system!

The explanation of this mysterious-seeming phenomenon lies in the theory of infinite cardinal numbers, which was developed within set theory by Georg Cantor. According to this theory various infinite sets can have different numbers of elements, with some infinite sets having more elements than others. And it can be shown, in particular, that the set of all real numbers (or even of all transcendental real numbers) has a larger number of elements than the set of all notations consisting of finite arrays of identifiable symbols.

Of course one can conceive of a system of notation consisting of infinite arrays of symbols. But it is important to recognize that such a system is only of theoretical interest, and cannot be used as a practical means of speaking or writing about the objects of reference of this notation—since of course no one can actually utter or write down an infinite array of symbols. We might, therefore, refer to such a theoretical system as a "pseudo-notation".

If we ask, now, whether it is possible to devise a system of *pseudo-notation* which assigns a name to each real number, then the answer is affirmative. And indeed such a system may be achieved by means of the infinite decimal expansions which are often mentioned in connection with numbers such as $\frac{1}{3}$, $\sqrt{2}$, or π.

Although the subject of infinite decimal expansions is usually discussed in high school mathematics courses, a precise account of this concept is not generally given there, as indeed it involves several concepts of which all mention is usually omitted in high school mathematics. Now that we have given a precise definition of the real number system, however, and proofs of its basic properties, we are in a position to understand fully the matter of infinite decimal expansions. In the following brief discussion, while striving to be accurate, we shall omit all proofs.

As a starting point, we may reduce our task by noting the following result.

THEOREM 14-7-1. *For every real number a there is an integer $p \in \mathcal{J}$, and a real number k such that $0 \leq k < 1$, for which we have $a = p + k$. Furthermore, for any $a \in Rl$ there is only one such pair p, k.*

Note: Here we have used the common notation "$0 \leq k < 1$" as shorthand for the statement "Either $0 < k$ or $0 = k$, and $k < 1$". We shall continue this practice where it serves to clarify our statements.

Proof

See Exercise 1.

Since we have a unique notation for each *integer*, it is clear that Theorem 14-7-1 permits us to reduce our task to that of obtaining a pseudo-notation for *those* real numbers k for which we have $0 \leq k < 1$. For later reference it will be convenient to assign a symbol to this class of numbers.

DEFINITION 14-7-2. *We shall use the symbol "K" to denote the set of all those real numbers k for which we have $0 \leq k < 1$.*

The next thing we must do is to fix clearly in mind what we mean by an infinite sequence of digits. The *digits*, it will be recalled from Chapter VIII, are simply the natural numbers 0, 1, 2, 3, 4, 5, 6, 7, 8, and 9. Following our earlier notation we shall use the symbol "T" to denote the next natural number, $9 + 1$.

Now the idea for making precise the notion of an infinite sequence of digits may be obtained by modifying, in an obvious way, the definition of a numeral—which is a *finite* sequence of digits. It will be recalled (again, see Chapter VIII), that if n is any positive integer then a *numeral of length n* was defined to be a *function*, whose domain consists of all those natural numbers p such that $p < n$, and whose value for each such p is a digit. For example the numeral "278", which has length 3, is identified under this definition with the function f, having domain 0, 1, 2, such that $f(0) = 2$, $f(1) = 7$, and $f(2) = 8$. Once this definition of *numeral* is assimilated with the intuitive concept of a finite row of digits, it will be seen that the following definition makes precise the intuitive idea of an "infinite row" of digits.

DEFINITION 14-7-3. *By an* **infinite sequence of digits** *we shall mean a function, having the set $\mathcal{N}$ of all natural numbers for its domain, whose value for each number in this domain is a digit. Such a function will also be called an* **infinite decimal.**

According to this definition, the infinite decimal usually indicated by the notation ".3333 . . ." is identified with the constant function, having $\mathcal{N}$ for its domain, whose value for every $p \in \mathcal{N}$ is 3. Again, the infinite decimal usually indicated by the notation ".1010101 . . ." is identified with the function f, having N as its domain, such that for all $p \in N$ we have $f(p) = 1$ if p is even and $f(p) = 0$ if p is odd. Parenthetically, we may note that the "triple-dot notation" used informally twice above in this paragraph is only of use in denoting a sequence of digits which follows some regular, recurring pattern, and does not at all afford a complete system of notation containing a distinct name for each infinite decimal.

Now that we have a precise definition of infinite decimal, the task before us is simply this. In the first place we wish to associate, with any given infinite decimal, an element of K (i.e., a real number k such that $0 \leq k < 1$), to be called the *value* of the decimal. Of course we wish to arrange this so that, in conformity with ordinary practice, the values of decimals such as .333 . . . and .1010101 . . . come out to be $\frac{1}{3}$ and $\frac{10}{99}$, respectively. Our second task will then be to show that *every* real number in K is the value of some infinite decimal.

As to the first task, the idea is a simple one. Suppose that we are given an infinite decimal f, and imagine that we generate the successive digits $f(0) = a_0$, $f(1) = a_1$, $f(2) = a_2$, . . . of this sequence. As we generate these digits we form the rational numbers $\frac{a_0}{T}$, $\frac{a_0a_1}{T^2}$, $\frac{a_0a_1a_2}{T^3}$, . . . , and we form the set A of all these rational numbers. Since the digit a_0 is less than T, since the two-digit number a_0a_1 is less than T^2, since the three-digit number $a_0a_1a_2$ is less than T^3, etc., we see that each of the rational numbers in the set A is less than 1. That is, the number 1 is an *upper bound* of the set A in Rl. It follows, since the ordering relation $<$ is *complete* in the set of real numbers, that there is a real number b which is the *least* upper bound of A in Rl; and of course b cannot exceed the upper bound 1, so that we will have $b \leq 1$. *It is this number b which we shall assign as the value of the infinite decimal f;* and we shall denote it $V(f)$.

Since $V(f)$ is an upper bound of A in Rl we have, in particular, $\frac{a_0}{T} \leq V(f)$; and since a_0 is a digit, we have $0 \leq a_0$. Hence we can conclude that $0 \leq V(f)$. Since we have already seen that $V(f) \leq 1$, this shows that we must have $V(f) \in K$—*unless* it should happen that $V(f) = 1$. As a matter of fact there is *only one* infinite decimal f such that $V(f) = 1$, namely, the f which has constant value 9, i.e., the decimal .999 · · ·. Following the usual practice we shall label this particular infinite decimal (and, for reasons which will presently appear, every other infinite decimal which has only the digit 9 as value from some place on), as an *improper* decimal, all others being called *proper*. We shall then be able to state that for any proper infinite decimal f we have $V(f) \in K$.

Now to put all of the above ideas in a mathematically more precise form, we begin with the following.

DEFINITION 14-7-4. *With every infinite decimal f, and every positive integer n, we associate a rational number called* **the part of f of length n**, *and denoted* n *Part* f, *as follows:*

$$n \; Part \; f = \sum_{i=0}^{n-1} \frac{f(i)}{T^{i+1}} .$$

The use of the "$\sum$-notation" for sums is explained in Chapter VI. It will be seen that the introduction of such sums is accomplished by means of a form of definition called "inductive definition". For this reason many theorems involving such sums must be proved by mathematical induction.

Of course the rational number n *Part* f is the same one which we denoted by "$\dfrac{a_0a_1 \ldots a_{n-1}}{T^n}$" in the intuitive discussion above (where $a_0 = f(0)$, $a_1 = f(1), \ldots$). Hence the following theorems and definitions will seem quite natural.

THEOREM 14-7-5. *For any infinite decimal f, and any positive integer n, we have* n *Part* $f < 1$.

The proof is left to the reader. (See Exercise 2.) Because of the inductive nature of the definition of n *Part* f, as noted above, it is necessary to give a proof of this theorem by mathematical induction. In order to carry through such a proof it will be useful to establish the following result, from which the theorem can be obtained as a simple corollary: For any infinite decimal f, and for every positive integer n, we have n *Part* $f \leq \dfrac{T^n - 1}{T^n}$.

DEFINITION 14-7-6. *For any infinite decimal f we define A_f to be the set of all rational numbers n Part f, for all positive integers n. That is, in the notation of set theory (see Chapter IX), we have*

$$A_f = \{b \in Rl \mid for \; some \; n \in P \; we \; have \; b = n \; Part \; f\}.$$

Theorem 14-7-5 shows that, for each infinite decimal f, the number 1 is an upper bound in Rl for the set A_f. This justifies the following.

DEFINITION 14-7-7. *For any infinite decimal f we define $V(f)$ to be the least upper bound in Rl of the set A_f.*

THEOREM 14-7-8. *For any infinite decimal f we have* $0 \leq V(f) \leq 1$.

The idea of the proof has been sketched informally above.

DEFINITION 14-7-9. *An infinite decimal f will be called* **improper** *if there is some natural number n such that, for every $p \in N$ satisfying $n < p$, we have $f(p) = 9$. An infinite decimal f will be called* **proper** *if it is not improper, that is, if for* **every** *$n \in N$ we can find another $p \in N$ such that $n < p$ and $f(p) \neq 9$.*

The fact that the improper decimal .999 . . . (i.e., the f such that $f(n) = 9$ for all $n \in N$) has value 1, may be easily deduced from the fact that in this case for every $n \in N$ we have n *Part* $f = \frac{T^n - 1}{T^n}$; and *this* fact we can show by induction. But the fact that .999 . . . is the *only* infinite decimal with value 1 requires us to know something about the value of *every* infinite decimal. The required information is contained in the following.

THEOREM 14-7-10. *Let f be any infinite decimal, and let q be any positive integer. Then for every $n \in P$ we have n Part $f < (q$ Part $f + \frac{1}{T^q})$.*

Proof

For $n < q$ the statement is best handled by showing, as a lemma, that for any infinite decimal g, and any $m, q \in P$ such that $m < q$, we have m *Part* $g \leq q$ *Part* g. For $n > q$ we can proceed by an induction similar to that suggested for Theorem 14-7-5. The details are left as an exercise.

By using Theorem 14-7-10 we can show the following.

THEOREM 14-7-11. *Suppose that f is an infinite decimal such that for some $p \in P$ we have $f(p) < 9$. Then $V(f) < \frac{T^p - 1}{T^p}$.*

Proof

See Exercise 5.

Now the last theorem can be combined with Theorem 14-7-8 to give the desired result:

THEOREM 14-7-12. *If f is any proper infinite decimal then $V(f) \in K$.*

Proof

See Exercise 6.

We now come to the second part of our task, namely, to show that *every* real number in K is the value of some proper infinite decimal. Indeed, we shall see that it is the value of *one and only one* such decimal. In order to do this we shall associate, with each $n \in N$ and each $k \in K$, a digit to be denoted n *Place* k. The definition will be an inductive one, first giving 0 *Place* k explicitly, and then explaining how, for any $p \in P$, the value of p *Place* k can be obtained from the values q *Place* k for $q < p$.

DEFINITION 14-7-13. *For any $k \in K$ we define:*

(i) 0 *Place* k = *the largest digit d such that* $\frac{d}{T} \leq k$.

(**ii**) *For any* $p \in P$, p *Place* k = *the largest digit* d *such that*

$$\frac{d}{T^p} \leq \left(k - \sum_{q=0}^{p-1} \frac{q \text{ Place } k}{T^{q+1}}\right).$$

Of course this definition must be justified by showing that there are largest digits of the kind mentioned in (**i**) and (**ii**), but this is a simple matter.

With the aid of this concept we are now ready to associate an infinite decimal with each real number in K.

DEFINITION 14-7-14. *For each* $k \in K$ *we let* $D(k)$ *be the infinite decimal* f *such that, for every* $n \in N$, *we have* $f(n) = n$ *Place* k.

The fundamental property of $D(k)$ is given in the following theorem.

THEOREM 14-7-15. *Let* k *be any element of* K *and let* $f = D(k)$. *Then* f *is a* **proper** *infinite decimal, and we have* $V(f) = k$.

Proof

See Exercise 8.

This theorem clearly shows that every real number in K is the value of some proper infinite decimal, but it does not imply that there is *only one* such decimal. The latter fact can be obtained easily from the following.

THEOREM 14-7-16. *Let* f *be any proper element of* K *and let* $k = V(f)$. *Then we must have* $f = D(k)$.

Proof

See Exercise 9.

The one kind of infinite decimal whose values have not yet been discussed is the improper kind. As regards the particular decimal $.999\cdots$ we have already seen that its value is 1. The values of all *other* improper decimals are described in the following result.

THEOREM 14-7-17. *Let* f *be any improper infinite decimal* **other** *than* $.999\cdots$. *Let* m *be the largest natural number such that* $f(m) \neq 9$. (*There must be such an* m *by Definition* 14-7-19.) *Let* g *be the* (*proper*) *decimal such that* (**i**) *for every* $n < m$ *we have* $g(n) = f(n)$, (**ii**) $g(m) = f(n) + 1$, *and* (**iii**) *for every* $n > m$ *we have* $g(n) = 0$. *Then* $V(f) = V(g)$.

Proof

See Exercise 10.

We close this section by a description of those infinite decimals whose value is a *rational* number. It turns out that these are precisely the infinite decimals which, from some point on, have a repetitive pattern of digits. Using mathematical terminology, we might call such a decimal *ultimately periodic*.

Suppose that, from a certain point on, a certain sequence of p digits is repeated over and over, without interruption, in a given decimal f. Then if the nth digit of f is beyond the point in question, it is clear that we must have $f(n) = f(n + p)$. This observation should help to motivate the following definition.

DEFINITION 14-7-18. *An infinite decimal f is called* **ultimately periodic** *if there exist a natural number m, and a positive integer p, such that for every natural number $n > m$ we have $f(n) = f(n + p)$. The smallest number p of this kind is called the* **period** *of f.*

Note that among the ultimately periodic decimals are those decimals f such that $f(n) = 0$ for all sufficiently great n. Such f are often called *terminating decimals.*

THEOREM 14-7-19. *Let f be any infinite decimal. Then $V(f)$ will be a rational number if, and only if, f is ultimately periodic.*

We shall not give a proof of this theorem here; it can be found in many works on college algebra.

This completes our sketch of the pseudo-notation for real numbers which consists of infinite decimals. The reader may wonder how it is that without a genuine system of notation for the real numbers we are able to speak of them at all. The answer is that, for lack of such notation, there are many individual real numbers which we can *not* single out to discuss its special characteristics. However, we do of course have a name for the *set* of *all* real numbers, and this enables us to make general statements which assert that certain properties hold for *every* real number, or for *some* real number (sometimes without specifying which). It is statements of this kind in which mathematicians are most often interested.

EXERCISES

1. Prove Theorem 14-7-1.
2. Prove Theorem 14-7-5. (See note in text following this theorem.)
3. Prove that $V(.99 \cdots) = 1$.
4.* Prove Theorem 14-7-10 in detail.
5. Prove Theorem 14-7-11.
6. Prove Theorem 14-7-12.
7. Show that $V(.333 \cdots) = \frac{1}{3}$ and $V(.101010 \cdots) = \frac{10}{99}$.
8.* Prove Theorem 14-7-15.

9. Prove Theorem 14-7-16.
10. Prove Theorem 14-7-17.

8. Real Numbers as Solutions of Equations

One feature of our construction of the real number system may have struck the reader as somewhat strange. Namely, the starting point of our construction was the ordered field of rational numbers, rather than the extension of it which was constructed in the previous chapter for the purpose of obtaining a root of the equation $x \cdot x = 2$. As a result, although we know that the ordering of the real number system has no gaps, and that therefore there is a real number which can be used to represent the area of a circle with diameter 1, we can no longer be sure that we have a real number whose square is 2.

The reason we have proceeded in this way is that, even though we did not incorporate the number $\sqrt{2}$ from the beginning of our construction, we can easily show that there *is* a real number x such that $x \cdot_{Rl} x = 2$. As a matter of fact the method of construction which we employed in passing from the system R to the system Rl could, without any change, be applied to the system $R(\sqrt{2})$ of Chapter XIII. However, the resulting system would have no advantages over Rl (in fact, it would be isomorphic to it), and the details of the proof would be slightly more cluttered.

The fact that the real number system possesses a square root of 2 is only a special case of the following result.

THEOREM 14-8-1. *If a is any real number such that $0 < a$, then there is a number $b \in Rl$ such that $b \cdot_{Rl} b = a$.*

That is, every positive real number possesses a real square root.

Proof

▶▶ **1.** Let a be any element of Rl such that $0 < a$.

▶▶ **2.** Let X be the set $\{c \in Rl \mid c \cdot_{Rl} c < a\}$, i.e., the set of all those real numbers c such that $c \cdot_{Rl} c < a$.

3. X is nonempty, since $0 \in X$; by lines **1** and **2**.

4. $0 < (a + 1) \cdot_{Rl} (a + 1)$; by line **1** and field properties of the reals (Theorem 14-6-28).

5. If $d \in Rl$ and $a + 1 < d$ then $d \notin X$, since $a < d \cdot_{Rl} d$; by lines **1** and **2** and field properties of the reals.

6. $a + 1$ is an upper bound of X in Rl; by line **5**.

▶▶ **7.** There is a real number b which is the least upper bound of X in Rl; by lines **3** and **6**, and completeness of the ordering $<$ (Theorem 14-5-4(**iv**)).

8. $0 < b$ or $0 = b$; by lines **3** and **7**.

We shall show that the number b mentioned in lines **7** and **8** has the property that $b \cdot_{Rl} b = a$, by showing that neither $b \cdot_{Rl} b < a$ nor $a < b \cdot_{Rl} b$ can hold.

▶▶ **9.** *Assume* that $b \cdot_{Rl} b < a$.

▶**10.** Let $e = \dfrac{a + -_{Rl}(b \cdot_{Rl} b)}{1 + a + 2b}$.

11. $0 < e$ and $e < a$; by lines **9**, **1**, and **8** and field properties of the reals.

12. $e < \dfrac{a + -_{Rl}(b \cdot_{Rl} b)}{e + 2b}$; by lines **10** and **11** and field properties of the reals.

13. $(b + e) \cdot_{Rl} (b + e) < a$; by lines **8**, **11**, and **12** and field properties of the reals.

▶**14.** $(b + e) \in X$; by lines **13** and **2**.

▶**15.** $b < b + e$; by line **11** and field properties of the reals.

▶▶**16.** b is not an upper bound of X in Rl; by lines **14** and **15**.

17. If $b \cdot_{Rl} b < a$ then b is not an upper bound of X in Rl; by the Deduction Theorem applied to lines **9** through **16**.

▶▶**18.** It is not the case that $b \cdot_{Rl} b < a$; by logic applied to lines **7** and **17**.

▶▶**19.** *Assume* that $a < b \cdot_{Rl} b$.

▶**20.** Let $e_1 = \dfrac{b \cdot_{Rl} b + -_{Rl} a}{2 \cdot_{Rl} b + 1}$.

21. $0 < e_1$ and $e_1 < b$; by lines **1**, **8**, **19**, and **20** and field properties of the reals.

22. $2 \cdot_{Rl} b \cdot_{Rl} e_1 < b \cdot_{Rl} b + -_{Rl} a$; by lines **20**, **21**, and **8** and field properties of the reals.

23. $a < b \cdot_{Rl} b + -_{Rl}(2 \cdot_{Rl} b \cdot_{Rl} e_1) + e_1 \cdot_{Rl} e_1$; by line **22** and field properties of the reals.

24. If d is any element of Rl such that $b + -_{Rl} e_1 < d$, then $a < d \cdot_{Rl} d$; by lines **21** and **23** and field properties of the reals.

▶**25.** $b + -_{Rl} e_1$ is an upper bound of X in Rl; by lines **2** and **24**.

▶**26.** $b + -_{Rl} e_1 < b$; by line **21** and field properties of the reals.

▶▶**27.** b is not the least upper bound of X in Rl; by lines **25** and **26**.

28. If $a < b \cdot_{Rl} b$ then b is not the least upper bound of X in Rl; by the Deduction Theorem applied to lines **19** through **27**.

▶▶**29.** It is not the case that $b \cdot_{Rl} b < a$; by logic applied to lines **7** and **28**.

▶▶**30.** There exists an element $b \in Rl$ such that $b \cdot_{Rl} b = a$; by lines **7**, **18**, and **29** and field properties of the reals.

The statement of the theorem is now obtained by applying the Deduction Theorem to lines **1** through **30**.

There is a more general theorem concerning the existence of real solutions to equations, of which Theorem 14-8-1 is a special case. Namely, it can be shown that every polynomial with real coefficients and leading coefficient 1, which is of even degree and has a constant term which is negative, has a real root. As to polynomials with real coefficients which are of odd degree, every one without exception possesses a real root. Both of these results, in turn, can be derived from the theorem that every polynomial with real coefficients, which has a negative value for some real argument and a positive value for another, must have a real root. In all of these cases a proof can be given along the lines of the proof given above for Theorem 14-8-1.

Despite the fact that there are a great many polynomial equations which have solutions in the set *Rl*, this is not true of *all* equations with real coefficients. In fact, we have the following result.

THEOREM 14-8-2. *There is no* $a \in Rl$ *such that* $a \cdot_{Rl} a + 1 = 0$.

Proof

We shall simply sketch the idea of the proof, which is very simple. Suppose then, that a is *any* real number. If $a = 0$, then clearly $a \cdot_{Rl} a + 1 = 1$, so $a \cdot_{Rl} a + 1 \neq 0$. If $a \neq 0$, then either $0 < a$ or $0 < -_{Rl}\, a$. Since the product of two positive elements in an ordered field is always positive, we see that either $0 < a \cdot_{Rl} a$ or $0 < (-_{Rl}\, a) \cdot_{Rl} (-_{Rl}\, a)$. But of course $a \cdot_{Rl} a = (-_{Rl}\, a) \cdot_{Rl} (-_{Rl}\, a)$. Hence we can state definitely that if $a \neq 0$ we have $0 < a \cdot_{Rl} a$. But the sum of two positive elements is also positive; hence $0 < a \cdot_{Rl} a + 1$, which proves the theorem.

Following our practice in earlier chapters of the book, we can now raise the problem whether it is possible to extend the field of real numbers to a larger number system, say $\langle C, +_C, \cdot_C \rangle$, which contains an element x satisfying the equation $x \cdot_C x + 1 = 0$, and which still obeys all of the fundamental algebraic laws required of fields. The answer to this equation is affirmative. By using the method of algebraic extension employed in Chapter XIII, we can extend the field *Rl* to another field $Rl(\sqrt{-1})$ just as we previously passed from R to $R(\sqrt{2})$. The resulting field is called *the field of complex numbers.*

It turns out that in the field of complex numbers not only the equation $x^2 + 1 = 0$, but *every* equation with real coefficients, and indeed every equation with *complex* coefficients, has a root. Mathematicians express this property by saying that the field of complex numbers is *algebraically closed.*

After the field of complex numbers is constructed, it is natural to seek an ordering relation on the set of all complex numbers so as to obtain an *ordered* field. But this proves to be impossible. In fact, using the same proof which was sketched for Theorem 14-8-2, we can show that *in any ordered field which is an extension of the rational number system* $\mathcal{R}$, *there is no root of the equation* $x^2 + 1$.

Thus the goal of obtaining an ordered field which is algebraically closed is impossible of realization. If we wish to limit ourselves to ordered fields, the real number system contains as many roots of equations as we can hope for. Indeed, it can be shown that *any* algebraic extension of the field of real numbers is isomorphic to the field of complex numbers—and hence cannot be ordered.

On the other hand, if we are interested in solvability of equations at the expense of abandoning an ordering of our numbers, then the field of complex numbers provides a number system which meets this requirement fully.

EXERCISES

1.* Prove in detail that if a_1, a_2, and a_3 are *any* real numbers, then there is an $x \in Rl$ such that

$$x \cdot_{Rl} x \cdot_{Rl} x + a_1 \cdot_{Rl} x \cdot_{Rl} x + a_2 \cdot_{Rl} x + a_3 = 0.$$

2.* Carry out the construction of the field of complex numbers by forming the algebraic extension $Rl(\sqrt{-1})$ along the lines used to construct $R(\sqrt{2})$ in Chapter 13.

APPENDIX I

The Construction of Induction Models[1]

In this section we consider the problem of "finding all 3-element induction models." Since there are actually infinitely many 3-element induction models on the one hand, and since models which are isomorphic are considered "essentially the same" on the other hand, the practical form of our problem is this: To find a set D of 3-element induction models such that no two models in D are isomorphic, while any 3-element induction model whatever is isomorphic to one of the models of D. As we shall see, such a set D may be found containing just 3 models. We may thus say that there are just 3 essentially different 3-element induction models. It will be seen that the method employed here can be used to find all k-element induction models for any given positive integer k.

Let $1, a, b$ be any three distinct objects—just what these are is immaterial. Let $P = \{1, a, b\}$; i.e., let P be the set whose only elements are 1, a, and b. We wish first to find all of the distinct binary operations $+$ on P such that $\mathfrak{M} = \langle P, 1, + \rangle$ is an induction model. Since any binary operation can be described by a 3×3 table each of whose entries is either "1", "a", or "b", and since any two distinct such tables correspond to distinct operations, it is clear that altogether there exist 3^9 or 19,683 distinct binary operations on P. Of course, not all operations will yield induction models, and some of those which are induction models will be isomorphic to others. We shall describe in detail in succeeding paragraphs how to construct all those binary operations $+$ for which $\mathfrak{M} = \langle P, 1, + \rangle$ is an induction model.

Let us begin by considering the element produced by the binary operation $+$ acting on the ordered pair $\langle 1, 1 \rangle$; i.e., we consider the element $1 + 1$. Ostensibly in defining $+$ we have three choices for $1 + 1$. However, if $\mathfrak{M}$ is to be an induction model we must have $1 \neq 1 + 1$. For, if $1 + 1 = 1$, then we may take G to be the set $\{1\}$ whose only element is 1. We then easily verify that G is a set which satisfies the hypotheses (**i**) and (**ii**) of Axiom P4 but fails to satisfy the conclusion, $G = P$. In other words, with the choice $1 + 1 = 1$ the model $\langle P, 1, + \rangle$ would fail to satisfy Axiom P4 and so could not be an induction model. Thus we are restricted to the cases

[1]See Chapter III.

$1 + 1 = a$ or $1 + 1 = b$. We shall consider first the case $1 + 1 = a$ and return to the case $1 + 1 = b$ after we have completed the construction of the operation $+$ for this case. At this stage we may consider that we have constructed one-ninth of the complete table for the operation $+$:

+	1	a	b
1	a		
a			
b			

.

Let us continue by selecting $a + 1$. If we choose $a + 1 = 1$, or $a + 1 = a$, then the set $G = \{1, a\}$ is a set which satisfies the hypotheses (**i**) and (**ii**) of Axiom P4 but fails to satisfy the conclusion $G = P$. Hence with such a choice the model $\langle P, 1, +\rangle$ would fail to be an induction model. We are thus compelled to choose $a + 1 = b$. Adding this to our table we obtain:

+	1	a	b
1	a		
a	b		
b			

.

Now we observe that *no matter how* the remainder of the table of values of $+$ is completed the model $\mathfrak{M}$ *will satisfy Axiom* P4. For let G be any subset of P such that (***i***) $1 \in G$, and (***ii***) whenever $x \in G$ then also $x + 1 \in G$. Since $1 \in G$ by (***i***), we have $1 + 1 \in G$ by (***ii***); i.e., $a \in G$ according to the table. And now that we have established that $a \in G$, we have $a + 1 \in G$ by (***ii***), so that $b \in G$ according to the table. Thus $G = \{1, a, b\} = P$ and Axiom P4 is verified. In *completing* the table of values of $+$ we may therefore concentrate on the need *to satisfy Axiom* P3.

It would be natural next to choose a value for $b + 1$. However, let us postpone this choice, entering the symbol "z" in our table to indicate that one of the elements, b or 1 or a, will be selected later. Thus our table now reads:

+	1	a	b
1	a		
a	b		
b	z		

where $z = a$ or $z = b$ or $z = 1$.

In completing the table our aim will be to obtain a model $\mathfrak{M} = \langle P, 1, +\rangle$ which satisfies Axiom P3: For all $x, y \in P$, $x + (y + 1) = (x + y) + 1$. Since there are only the three elements 1, a, and b in P, we see that Axiom P3 may be expressed equivalently as follows:

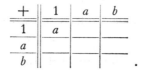

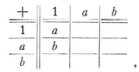

1. For all $x \in P$, $x + (1 + 1) = (x + 1) + 1$,
and
2. For all $x \in P$, $x + (a + 1) = (x + a) + 1$,
and
3. For all $x \in P$, $x + (b + 1) = (x + b) + 1$.

And from the part of the table we have already constructed, this in turn is equivalent to:

1′. For all $x \in P$, $x + a = (x + 1) + 1$,
and
2′. For all $x \in P$, $x + b = (x + a) + 1$,
and
3′. For all $x \in P$, $x + z = (x + b) + 1$.

Now, continuing with the construction of the table for + we see that condition **1′** requires us to choose:

$$\begin{aligned} 1 + a &= (1 + 1) + 1 \\ &= a + 1 \\ &= b, \\ a + a &= (a + 1) + 1 \\ &= b + 1 \\ &= z, \qquad \text{and} \\ b + a &= (b + 1) + 1 \\ &= z + 1. \end{aligned}$$

And thus, on adding to our table, we get:

+	1	a	b
1	a	b	
a	b	z	
b	z	$z + 1$	

which will satisfy Axiom P1 *and the part* **1′** *of Axiom P3* (no matter how we choose z—whether a, b, or 1).

To construct the final column, we use condition **2′** above (and the part of the table already constructed) to get:

$$\begin{aligned} 1 + b &= (1 + a) + 1 \\ &= b + 1 \\ &= z, \\ a + b &= (a + a) + 1 \\ &= z + 1, \qquad \text{and} \\ b + b &= (b + a) + 1 \\ &= (z + 1) + 1 \\ &= z + a; \end{aligned}$$

by condition **1′**, which we know is satisfied already.

And now our table is complete:

$+$	1	a	b
1	a	b	z
a	b	z	$z + 1$
b	z	$z + 1$	$z + a$

Of course it still remains to choose z as one of the elements 1, a, or b. But we have seen that no matter how this choice is made our model $\langle P, 1, +\rangle$ will satisfy Axiom P4 and the parts **1′** and **2′** of Axiom P3. Thus to determine for which choice (if any) of z we obtain an induction model, it remains only to determine *which choice of z will give a table satisfying the last part,* **3′**, *of* Axiom P3. It will be left to the reader (See Exercise 1 below) to show that actually **3′** will be verified for *any* choice of z—whether 1, a, or b. This may be done most easily by noting that the operation $+$ is commutative, *independent of the choice of z*. The fact that $x + y = y + x$ for all $x, y \in P$ is indicated by the *symmetry* of the table above: each column of the table is identical with the corresponding row.

For the three choices of z: $z = 1$, $z = a$, $z = b$, we get three binary operations, $+_1$, $+_2$, $+_3$, described in the tables below:

$+_1$	1	a	b
1	a	b	1
a	b	1	a
b	1	a	b

$+_2$	1	a	b
1	a	b	a
a	b	a	b
b	a	b	a

$+_3$	1	a	b
1	a	b	b
a	b	b	b
b	b	b	b

By our construction we have verified that each of these operations $+_i$ (where $i = 1$ or $i = 2$ or $i = 3$) leads to an induction model $\mathfrak{M}_i = \langle P, 1, +_i\rangle$, and that these are *the only such operations $+$ for the case that* $1 + 1 = a$.

To complete the description of all induction models $\langle P, 1, +\rangle$ it remains to consider the case of those binary operations $+$ on P for which $1 + 1 = b$. It turns out that this can most easily be done by first examining the question of isomorphism between models.

Suppose f is an isomorphism between two models, $\mathfrak{M} = \langle P, 1, +\rangle$ and $\mathfrak{M}' = \langle P, 1, +'\rangle$, where $+$ and $+'$ are binary operations on P. Since f must map P onto P, and since $f1 = 1$, there are only two possibilities: Either f is the identity function f_1 on P ($f_1 1 = 1$, $f_1 a = a$, $f_1 b = b$), or f is the function f_2 such that $f_2 1 = 1$, $f_2 a = b$, $f_2 b = a$. Now if the identity function f_1 is an isomorphism between $\mathfrak{M}$ and $\mathfrak{M}'$ we have, for all $x, y \in P$, $x + y = f_1(x + y) = (f_1 x) +' (f_1 y) = x +' y$, so that $+ = +'$ and hence $\mathfrak{M} = \mathfrak{M}'$. Therefore the only isomorphism that can connect two *distinct* models $\mathfrak{M}$ and $\mathfrak{M}'$ is the function f_2. Since $f_2^{-1} = f_2$ (as we easily see by noting that $f_2(f_2 x) = x$ for all $x \in P$), it follows that no model $\langle P, 1, +\rangle$ is isomorphic to more than one other model $\langle P, 1, +'\rangle$. (See Exercise 3-2-8).

In fact, if we start with any model $\mathfrak{M} = \langle P, 1, +\rangle$ we can always construct another model $\mathfrak{M}' = \langle P, 1, +'\rangle$ such that f_2 is an isomorphism between $\mathfrak{M}$ and $\mathfrak{M}'$, as follows. Simply take the table of values for $+$ and interchange "a" and "b" throughout—both in the margins and in the body of the table. (See Exercise 3-2-9.) Using this method we obtain, from the models $\mathfrak{M}_1$, $\mathfrak{M}_2$, $\mathfrak{M}_3$ above, three distinct models $\mathfrak{M}_1'$, $\mathfrak{M}_2'$, $\mathfrak{M}_3'$ such that $\mathfrak{M}_i'$ is isomorphic to $\mathfrak{M}_i$, for each $i = 1, 2, 3$, and hence (by Theorem 3-2-3) is an induction model, and such that $1 +_i' 1 = b$, for each $i = 1, 2, 3$. Furthermore, if $\mathfrak{M}' = \langle P, 1, +' \rangle$ is *any* induction model in which $1 +' 1 = b$ then $\mathfrak{M}'$ is one of these $\mathfrak{M}_i'$. For by applying the above transformation to the table of values of $+'$ we obtain a model $\mathfrak{M} = \langle P, 1, + \rangle$ isomorphic to $\mathfrak{M}'$, in which $1 + 1 = a$; as shown in detail above, $\mathfrak{M}$ must be one of the $\mathfrak{M}_i$, $i = 1, 2, 3$; and hence $\mathfrak{M}'$ must be one of the $\mathfrak{M}_i'$ (since $\mathfrak{M}$ cannot be isomorphic to two distinct models each different from $\mathfrak{M}$).

We have thus determined that of the 19,683 models $\langle P, 1, + \rangle$, exactly 6 are induction models: $\mathfrak{M}_1$, $\mathfrak{M}_2$, $\mathfrak{M}_3$, $\mathfrak{M}_1'$, $\mathfrak{M}_2'$, and $\mathfrak{M}_3'$.

Now let D be the set of three models: $\mathfrak{M}_1$, $\mathfrak{M}_2$, and $\mathfrak{M}_3$. Since each element in D is isomorphic to one of the models $\mathfrak{M}_i'$ which is not in D, and since no model $\langle P, 1, + \rangle$ can be isomorphic to two distinct models different from itself, it follows at once that no two of the models in D are isomorphic.

Thus to complete the solution of the problem set at the beginning of the section it remains only to show that any 3-element induction model whatever must be isomorphic to one of the $\mathfrak{M}_i$. Suppose, then, that $\mathfrak{M}_0 = \langle P_0, 1_0, +_0 \rangle$ is any induction model, where P_0 contains exactly three distinct elements. Now $1_0 +_0 1_0 \neq 1_0$, else $\mathfrak{M}_0$ would fail to satisfy Axiom P4. Let $c = 1_0 +_0 1_0$, and let d be the third element of P_0. Let g map P onto P_0 as follows: $g(1) = 1_0$, $g(a) = c$, $g(b) = d$. Let $+$ be the binary operation on P such that for all $x, y \in P$, $x + y = g^{-1}[g(x) +_0 g(y)]$. Clearly the model $\mathfrak{M} = \langle P, 1, + \rangle$ is isomorphic to $\mathfrak{M}_0$ (under the isomorphism g), and so (by Theorem 3-2-3) $\mathfrak{M}$ is an induction model. But $1 + 1 = g^{-1}(1_0 +_0 1_0) = g^{-1}(c) = a$, so that (as shown above) $\mathfrak{M}$ must be one of the $\mathfrak{M}_i$, $i = 1, 2, 3$. That is, the arbitrary induction model $\mathfrak{M}_0$ is isomorphic to one of the models in D.

APPENDIX II

Justification of the Definition of Multiplication

We give here the proof of Theorem 4-1-1 which was omitted from the text.

THEOREM 4-1-1. *There is one and only one binary operation f on P such that*

(i) $f\langle x, 1\rangle = x$ for all $x \in P$, and
(ii) $f\langle x, y + 1\rangle = f\langle x, y\rangle + x$ for all $x, y \in P$.

In our proof of this theorem it will be convenient to have the following lemma:

LEMMA 4-1-1.1 *If z is any element of P, there is a unique unary operation h on P such that*

(a) $h(1) = z$, and
(b) $h(x + 1) = h(x) + z$ for all $x \in P$.

Part I. We first show that for each $z \in P$ there is at least one such operation h.

Proof of Part I

1. Let G be the subset of P containing all those $z \in P$ for which there exist a unary operation h satisfying (a) $h(1) = z$ and (b) $h(x + 1) = h(x) + z$ for all $x \in P$.

2. Let g be the identity operation on P, i.e., for *all* $x \in P$, $g(x) = x$.
3. $g(1) = 1$; by line 2.
4. Let x be any element of P.
5. $g(x + 1) = x + 1$; by line 2 applied to $x + 1$.
6. $g(x) + 1 = x + 1$; by E from line 2.
7. $g(x + 1) = g(x) + 1$; by E from lines 5 and 6.
8. For all $x \in P$, $g(x + 1) = g(x) + 1$; by lines 4 and 7.
9. There is a unary operation h on P such that (a) $h(1) = 1$ and (b) $h(x + 1) = h(x) + 1$ for all $x \in P$; by lines 2, 3, and 8. (Namely, we take h to be g.)

10. $1 \in G$; by lines **1** and **9**.

11. Let z be any element of G.
12. There is a unary operation h on P such that (**a**) $h(1) = z$ and (**b**) $h(x + 1) = h(x) + z$ for all $x \in P$; by lines **1** and **11**.
13. Let j be the unary operation on P such that for each $x \in P$, $j(x) = h(x) + x$.
14. $j(1) = h(1) + 1$; by line **13**.
15. $h(1) + 1 = z + 1$; by E from line **12**(**a**).
16. $j(1) = z + 1$; by E from lines **14** and **15**.
17. Let x be any element of P.
18. $j(x) = h(x) + x$; by line **13**.
19. $j(x + 1) = h(x + 1) + (x + 1)$; by line **13**.
20. $h(x + 1) = h(x) + z$; by line **12**(**b**).
21. $h(x + 1) + (x + 1) = (h(x) + z) + (x + 1)$; by E from line **20**.
22. $= (h(x) + x) + (z + 1)$; by the associative and commutative laws for addition.
23. $= j(x) + (z + 1)$; by E from line **18**.
24. $h(x + 1) + (x + 1) = j(x) + (z + 1)$; by E from lines **21** through **23**.
25. $j(x + 1) = j(x) + (z + 1)$; by E from lines **19** and **24**.
26. For all $x \in P$, $j(x + 1) = j(x) + (z + 1)$; by lines **17** and **25**.
27. There is a unary operation h on P such that (**a**) $h(1) = z + 1$ and (**b**) $h(x + 1) = h(x) + (z + 1)$ for all $x \in P$; by lines **13, 16,** and **26**. (Namely, we take h to be j).
28. $z + 1 \in P$; from lines **1** and **27**.
29. For any $z \in G$, we have also $z + 1 \in G$; by lines **11** through **28** and the Deduction Theorem of logic.

30. $G = P$; by lines **10** and **29** and Axiom P4.
31. For each $z \in P$, there is a unary operation h on P such that (**a**) $h(1) = z$ and (**b**) $h(x + 1) = h(x) + z$ for all $x \in P$; by lines **1** and **30**.

Part II. Now we show that for a given $z \in P$ there is at most one such unary operation h.

Proof of Part II

1. Let z be *any* element of P and suppose h and g are any unary operations on P such that
(**a**) $h(1) = z$ (**a′**) $g(1) = z$,
(**b**) $h(x + 1) = h(x) + z$ for all $x \in P$, (**b′**) $g(x + 1) = g(x) + z$ for all $x \in P$.
2. Let G be the subset of P containing all those $x \in P$ for which $h(x) = g(x)$.

3. $h(1) = g(1)$; by E from lines **1(a)** and **1(a')**.
4. $1 \in G$; by lines **2** and **3**.

5. Let x be any element of G.
6. $h(x) = g(x)$; by lines **2** and **5**.
7. $h(x) + z = g(x) + z$; by E from line **6**.
8. $h(x + 1) = g(x + 1)$; by E from lines **1(b)**, **1(b')**, and **7**.
9. $x + 1 \in G$; by lines **2** and **8**.
10. For all $x \in G$ we have also $x + 1 \in G$; by lines **5** through **9** and the Deduction Theorem of logic.

11. $G = P$; by lines **4** and **10** and Axiom P4.
12. For all $x \in P$, $h(x) = g(x)$; by lines **2** and **11**.
13. $h = g$; from lines **1** and **12** and the Principle of Extensionality for functions. (See Chapter I.)
14. If z is any element of P, and if h and g are any unary operations on P such that
(**a**) $h(1) = z$, (**a'**) $g(1) = z$,
(**b**) $h(x + 1) = h(x) + z$ for all $x \in P$, (**b'**) $g(x + 1) = g(x) + z$ for all $x \in P$,
then $h = g$; by lines **1** through **13** and the Deduction Theorem of logic.
15. For each $z \in P$, there is at most one unary operation h on P such that (**a**) $h(1) = z$ and (**b**) $h(x + 1) = h(x) + z$ for all $x \in P$; by line **14**.

16. For each $z \in P$, there is exactly one unary operation on P such that (**a**) $h(1) = z$ and (**b**) $h(x + 1) = h(x) + z$ for all $x \in P$; by line **31** of Part I and line **15** of Part II.

This completes the proof of Lemma 4-1-1.1. We now proceed with a proof of Theorem 4-1-1.

Proof

1. For each $z \in P$ let h_z be the unique unary operation on P such that (**a**) $h_z(1) = z$, and (**b**) $h_z(x + 1) = h_z(x) + z$ for all $x \in P$; by Lemma 4-1-1.1.
2. Let f be the binary operation on P such that for all $y, z \in P$, $f\langle z, y\rangle = h_z(y)$.

3. Let z and y be any elements of P.
4. $f\langle z, 1\rangle = h_z(1)$; by line **2**.
5. $f\langle z, 1\rangle = z$; by lines **4** and **1(a)**.
6. $f\langle z, y + 1\rangle = h_z(y + 1)$; by line **2**.
7. $= h_z(y) + z$; by line **1(b)**.
8. $= f\langle z, y\rangle + z$; by line **2**.

9. $f\langle z, y+1\rangle = f\langle z, y\rangle + z$; by E from lines **6** through **8**.

10. For all $z, y \in P$, **(i)** $f\langle z, 1\rangle = z$ and **(ii)** $f\langle z, y+1\rangle = f\langle z, y\rangle + z$; by lines **3**, **5**, and **9** and the Deduction Theorem.

11. Let g be *any* binary operation on P such that **(i)** $g\langle z, 1\rangle = z$ for all $z \in P$, and **(ii)** $g\langle z, y+1\rangle = g\langle z, y\rangle + z$ for all $z, y \in P$.

12. For each $z \in P$, let g_z be the unary operation on P such that $g_z(y) = g\langle z, y\rangle$ for all $y \in P$.

13. Let z be any element of P.

14. $g_z(1) = g\langle z, 1\rangle$; by line **12**.

15. $g_z(1) = z$; by lines **14** and **11(i)**.

16. Let y be any element of P.

17. $g_z(y+1) = g\langle z, y+1\rangle$; by line **12**.

18. $= g\langle z, y\rangle + z$; by line **11(ii)**.

19. $= g_z(y) + z$; by E from line **12**.

20. $g_z(y+1) = g_z(y) + z$; by E from lines **17** through **19**.

21. For all $y \in P$, $g_z(y+1) = g_z(y) + z$; by lines **16** and **20**.

22. For each $z \in P$, $g_z = h_z$; by lines **1(a)**, **1(b)**, **15**, and **21** and Lemma 4-1-1.1.

23. Let z, y be any elements of P.

24. $f\langle z, y\rangle = h_z(y)$; by line **2**.

25. $= g_z(y)$; by line **22**.

26. $= g\langle z, y\rangle$; by line **12**.

27. $f\langle z, y\rangle = g\langle z, y\rangle$; by lines **24** through **26**, by E.

28. For all $z, y \in P$, $f\langle z, y\rangle = g\langle z, y\rangle$; from lines **23** and **27**.

29. $f = g$; by lines **2**, **11**, **28** and the Principle of Extensionality for functions.

30. If g is any binary operation on P such that **(i)** $g\langle z, 1\rangle = z$ for all $z \in P$, and **(ii)** $g\langle z, y+1\rangle = g\langle z, y\rangle + z$ for all $z, y \in P$, then $g = f$; by lines **11** through **29** and the Deduction Theorem.

31. There is one and only one binary operation f on P such that **(i)** $f\langle x, 1\rangle = x$ for all $x \in P$, and **(ii)** $f\langle x, y+1\rangle = f\langle x, y\rangle + x$ for all $x, y \in P$; by lines **2**, **10**, and **30**.

APPENDIX III

Extensions of the System $\mathfrak{N}$

We give here the proof of Theorem 11-3-2 which was omitted from the text.

THEOREM 11-3-2. *Let* $\mathfrak{Q} = \langle Q, +_Q, \cdot_Q \rangle$ *be any number system such that*

(i) $\mathfrak{Q}$ *is an extension of* $\mathfrak{N}$;
(ii) $\mathfrak{Q}$ *contains an element* m *such that* $m +_Q 1 = 0$;
(iii) *the associative and commutative laws for* $+_Q$ *and* $\cdot_Q$ *hold;*
(iv) *the left and right distributive laws hold for* $\cdot_Q$ *over* $+_Q$; *and*
(v) *the left and right cancellation laws hold for* $+_Q$.

Then there is an isomorphism of the system $\mathfrak{J}$ *into* $\mathfrak{Q}$. *That is, there exists a one-one mapping* h *of* $\mathcal{J}$ *into* Q *such that*

$$h(x +_J y) = h(x) +_Q h(y)$$
$$h(x \cdot_J y) = h(x) \cdot_Q h(y)$$

for all $x, y \in \mathcal{J}$. *Furthermore, for any* $x \in \mathcal{N}$ *we have* $h(x) = x$.

Proof

1. Taking $\mu(x) = m \cdot_Q x$ for all $x \in P$, as in the proof of Theorem 11-3-1, we let h be the mapping of $\mathcal{J}$ into Q such that, for any $x \in \mathcal{J}$,
$h(x) = x$ if $x \in \mathcal{N}$ and
$h(x) = \mu(\nu^{-1}(x))$ if $x \in P^-$.
Since ν is a one-one mapping of P onto P^-, ν^{-1} is a one-one mapping of P^- onto P; hence for any $x \in P^-$, $\mu(\nu^{-1}(x))$ is a unique element of Q. Because $\mathcal{J} = \mathcal{N} \cup P^-$ and $\mathcal{N} \cap P^- = \varnothing$, we see that h is defined for all elements of $\mathcal{J}$.
2. Let x be any element of P.
3. $\nu^{-1}(\nu(x)) = x$; by definition of ν^{-1}.
4. $h(\nu(x)) = \mu(\nu^{-1}(\nu(x)))$; by definition of h, line 1.
5. $= \mu(x)$; by line 3 and E.
6. For any $x \in P$, $h(\nu(x)) = \mu(x)$; from lines 2 through 5 by the Deduction Theorem.

7. Let x, y be any elements of $\mathcal{J}$.

8. *Case I.* Suppose x and y are both in P.

9. $h(x +_J y) = x +_J y$; by lines **1** and **8**.

10. $= x +_Q y$; by line **8** since $\mathcal{Q}$ is an extension of $\mathfrak{N}$ (hypothesis (**i**)).

11. $= h(x) +_Q h(y)$; by lines **1** and **8** and E.

12. $h(x +_J y) = h(x) +_Q h(y)$; by lines **9** through **11**.

13. *Case II.* Suppose $x \in P$ and $y \in P^-$.

14. $\nu(\nu^{-1}(y)) = y$; by definition of ν^{-1}.

15. $x +_J y = x +_J \nu(\nu^{-1}(y))$; by line **14** and E.

16. $= \begin{cases} x - \nu^{-1}(y) & \text{if } \nu^{-1}(y) < x, \\ \nu(\nu^{-1}(y) - x) & \text{if } x < \nu^{-1}(y), \\ 0 & \text{if } x = \nu^{-1}(y); \end{cases}$ Definition 11-2-1.

17. $x +_J y = \begin{cases} x - \nu^{-1}(y) & \text{if } \nu^{-1}(y) < x, \\ \nu(\nu^{-1}(y) - x) & \text{if } x < \nu^{-1}(y), \\ 0 & \text{if } x = \nu^{-1}(y); \end{cases}$ lines **15** and **16** by E.

18. $h(x +_J y) = \begin{cases} x - \nu^{-1}(y) \text{ if } \nu^{-1}(y) < x; & \text{by definition of } h \text{ on } N \text{ (line 1) and line 17}, \\ \mu(\nu^{-1}(y) - x) \text{ if } x < \nu^{-1}(y); & \text{by lines 6 and 17}, \\ 0 \text{ if } x = \nu^{-1}(y); & \text{by definition of } h \text{ on } N \text{ (line 1) and line 17}. \end{cases}$

19. $= x +_Q \mu(\nu^{-1}(y))$; by Theorem 11-3-1 (**iii**).

20. $= h(x) +_Q h(y)$; by definition of h (line **1**) and E.

21. $h(x +_J y) = h(x) +_Q h(y)$; lines **18** through **20** by E.

22. *Case III.* Suppose $x \in P^-$ and $y \in P$. Since $+_J$ is commutative, by Theorem 11-2-3, we have $x +_J y = y +_J x$. Hence by lines **13** through **21** we obtain $h(y +_J x) = h(y) +_Q h(x)$. Similarly, since $+_Q$ is commutative by hypothesis (**iii**), we have $h(y) +_Q h(x) = h(x) +_Q h(y)$. Therefore $h(x +_J y) = h(x) +_Q h(y)$.

23. *Case IV.* Suppose either x or y is 0. Without loss of generality we may assume that $x = 0$ and y is any element in $\mathcal{J}$.

24. $x +_J y = y$; by line **23** and Definition 11-2-1.

25. $h(x +_J y) = h(y)$; from line **24** by E.

26. $= x +_Q h(y)$; by line **23** and Lemma 11-3-1.1.

27. $= h(x) +_Q h(y)$; since $h(x) = x$ by line **23** and the definition of h on 0 (line **1**).

28. $h(x +_J y) = h(x) +_Q h(y)$; by lines **25** through **27** by E.

29. *Case V.* Suppose x and y are both elements of P^-.

30. $x +_J y = \nu(\nu^{-1}(x)) +_J \nu(\nu^{-1}(y))$; by definition of ν and E.

31. $= \nu(\nu^{-1}(x) +_J \nu^{-1}(y))$; by Definition 11-2-1.
32. $= \nu(\nu^{-1}(x) + \nu^{-1}(y))$; since $\mathcal{J}$ is an extension of $\mathcal{P}$ (Theorem 11-2-2).
33. $x +_J y = \nu(\nu^{-1}(x) + \nu^{-1}(y))$; from lines **30** through **32** by E.
34. $h(x +_J y) = \mu(\nu^{-1}(x)) + \nu^{-1}(y))$; from lines **33** and **6** by E.
35. $= \mu(\nu^{-1}(x)) +_Q \mu(\nu^{-1}(y))$; by Theorem 11-3-1 (**iii**).
36. $= h(x) +_Q h(y)$; by line **1**.
37. $h(x +_J y) = h(x) +_Q h(y)$; from lines **34** through **36** by E.
38. For all $x, y \in \mathcal{J}$, $h(x +_J y) = h(x) +_Q h(y)$; by lines **7**, **12**, **21**, **22**, **28**, and **37**.

So far in our proof of Theorem 11-3-2 we have shown that $h(x +_J y) = h(x) +_Q h(y)$ for all $x, y \in \mathcal{J}$, and by definition of h (line **1**) we have $h(x) = x$ for all $x \in \mathcal{N}$. Thus it remains only to show that $h(x \cdot_J y) = h(x) \cdot_Q h(y)$ for all $x, y \in \mathcal{J}$. This can also be proved by cases, in a manner entirely similar to that used above. We omit the details.

Index

Ideal (margin annotation)

Filter (margin annotation)